NEW YORK

Algebra 1

COMMON CORE

Richard J. Andres, Ph.D.
Retired Mathematics Teacher and SAT Instructor
Jericho High School
Jericho, New York

Joyce Bernstein, Ed.D.
Secondary Supervisor for Mathematics
East Williston Union Free School District
Old Westbury, New York

AMSCO

AMSCO SCHOOL PUBLICATIONS, INC.,
a division of Perfection Learning®

Dedication

Special thanks to Peg and Marc for their encouragement, patience, and understanding.

Reviewers

Kristine Cody
Teacher of Mathematics, Special Education
LyncX Academy
Rochester City School District
Rochester, NY

Raymond Scacalossi Jr.
Math Coordinator K-12
Manhasset Schools
Manhasset Union Free School District
Manhasset, NY

Please visit our Web sites at:
www.amscopub.com and *www.perfectionlearning.com*

When ordering this book, please specify:

Softcover: ISBN 978-0-7891-8913-4 or **94114**
Hardcover: ISBN 978-1-62974-528-2 or **9411406**
eBook: ISBN 978-1-62974-861-0 or **94114D**

7 8 9 10 11 12 EBM 20 19 18 17 16

Printed in the United States of America

Contents

Key to the icons:
The computer icon indicates Digital Activities that can be found at **www.amscomath.com.**
The globe icon indicates where Real-World Model Problems are found in the text.

Chapter 2: Writing and Solving Linear Equations and Inequalities 44

Chapter 3: Graphing Linear Equations and Functions 88

Getting Started

About This Book

New York Algebra 1 is written to help students understand and explore the concepts of algebra as well as prepare them for the *Algebra 1 (Common Core)* Regents Examination. All instruction, model problems, and practice items were developed to support the Common Core Learning Standards (CCLS) and the modules and lessons on Engage^{NY}. Each chapter opens with lesson-by-lesson alignment with the standards. The eight Mathematical Practice Standards are embedded throughout in selected Model Problems, extensive practice problem sets, and the comprehensive Chapter and Cumulative Reviews. Correlations of the lessons in *New York Algebra 1* to Engage^{NY} lessons are available in the teacher manual.

In *New York Algebra 1*, students will explore many types of functions including linear, quadratic, exponential, square root, cube root, piecewise, step, and absolute value. In addition, they will create, compare, and graph functions, and learn how various transformations affect these functions. Students will also gain experience using descriptive statistics (categorical and quantitative data) to model a context and draw meaningful conclusions.

Each chapter incorporates multiple PARCC performance tasks that measure the ability of students to think critically and apply their knowledge in real-world situations. In addition, teachers have access to a full range of digital simulations, electronic whiteboard lessons, videos, interactive problems, and applications to stimulate conceptual understanding.

Careful and consistent use of this text and the supporting materials will both prepare students for the *Algebra 1 (Common Core)* Regents Examination and ensure they are becoming college and career ready.

Eight Standards for Mathematical Practice

The mathematical practices are a common thread for students to think about and understand math as they progress from Kindergarten through high school. Students should use the mathematical practices as a method to break down concepts and solve problems, including representing problems logically, justifying conclusions, applying mathematics to practical situations, explaining the mathematics accurately to other students, or deviating from a known procedure to find a shortcut.

MP 1 Make sense of problems and persevere in solving them.

Attack new problems by analyzing what students already know. Students should understand that many different strategies can work. Ask leading questions to direct the discussion. Take time to think.

- explain the meaning of the problem
- analyze given information, constraints, and relationships
- plan a solution route
- try simpler forms of the initial problem
- use concrete objects to help conceptualize
- monitor progress and change course, if needed
- continually ask, "Does this make sense?"

MP 2 Reason abstractly and quantitatively.

Represent problems with symbols and/or pictures.

- make sense of quantities and their relationships
- decontextualize—represent a situation symbolically and contextualize—consider what given symbols represent
- create a clear representation of the problem
- consider the units involved
- attend to the meaning of numbers and variables, not just how to compute them
- use properties of operations and objects

MP 3 Construct viable arguments and critique the reasoning of others.

Ask questions, defend answers, and/or make speculations using correct math vocabulary.

- use assumptions, definitions, and previously established results
- make conjectures and build a valid progression of statements
- use counterexamples
- justify conclusions and communicate them to others
- determine whether the arguments of others seem right

MP 4 Model with mathematics.

Show the relevance of math by solving real-world problems. Look for opportunities to use math for current situations in and outside of school in all subject areas.

- apply mathematics to solve everyday problems
- analyze and chart relationships using diagrams, two-way tables, graphs, flowcharts, and formulas to draw conclusions
- apply knowledge to simplify a complicated situation
- interpret results and consider whether answers make sense

MP 5 Use appropriate tools strategically.

Provide an assortment of tools for students and let them decide which ones to use.

- choose appropriately from existing tools (pencil and paper, concrete models, ruler, protractor, calculator, spreadsheet, dynamic geometry software, etc.) when solving mathematical problems
- detect possible errors by using estimation or other mathematical knowledge
- use technology to explore and compare predictions and deepen understanding of concepts

MP 6 Attend to precision.

Use precise and detailed language in math. Instead of saying "I don't get it," students should be able to elaborate on where they lost the connection. Students should specify units in their answers and correctly label diagrams.

- speak and write precisely using correct mathematical language
- state the meaning of symbols and use them properly
- specify units of measure and label axes appropriately
- calculate precisely and efficiently
- express answers with the proper degree of accuracy

MP 7 Look for and make use of structure.

See patterns and the significance of given information and objects. Use these to solve more complex problems.

- see the big picture

- discern a pattern or structure
- recognize the significance of given aspects
- apply strategies to similar problems
- step back for an overview and shift perspective
- see complicated things as being composed of several objects

MP 8 **Look for and express regularity in repeated reasoning.**

Understand why a process works so students can apply it to new situations.

- notice repeated calculations and look for both general methods and shortcuts
- maintain oversight of the process while paying attention to the details
- evaluate the reasonableness of intermediate results
- create generalizations founded on observations

Test-Taking Strategies

General Strategies

- *Become familiar with the directions and format of the test ahead of time.* There will be both multiple-choice and extended response questions where you must show the steps you used to solve a problem, including formulas, diagrams, graphs, charts, and so on, where appropriate.
- *Pace yourself.* Do not race to answer every question immediately. On the other hand, do not linger over any question too long. Keep in mind that you will need more time to complete the extended response questions than to complete the multiple-choice questions.
- *Speed comes from practice.* The more you practice, the faster you will become and the more comfortable you will be with the material. Practice as often as you can.

Specific Strategies

- *Always scan the answer choices* before beginning to work on a multiple-choice question. This will help you to focus on the kind of answer that is required. Are you looking for fractions, decimals, percents, integers, squares, cubes, and so on? Eliminate choices that clearly do not answer the question asked.
- *Do not assume that your answer is correct just because it appears among the choices.* The wrong choices are usually there because they represent common student errors. After you find an answer, always reread the problem to make sure you have chosen the answer to the question that is asked, not the question you have in your mind.
- *Sub-in.* To sub-in means to substitute. You can sub-in friendly numbers for the variables to find a pattern and determine the solution to the problem.
- *Backfill.* If a problem is simple enough and you want to avoid doing the more complex algebra, or if a problem presents a phrase such as $x = ?$, then just fill in the answer choices that are given in the problem until you find the one that works.
- *Do the math.* This is the ultimate strategy. Don't go wild searching in your mind for tricks, gimmicks, or math magic to solve every problem. Most of the time the best way to get the right answer is to do the math and solve the problem.

Chapter 1 Review: The Elements of Algebra

Chapter Focus

This chapter lays the groundwork for the study of algebra, presenting basic terms and symbols that you will use throughout the course. Real numbers, exponents, radicals, and inequalities will be examined as well as modeling and evaluating algebraic expressions.

Chapter Content

Lessons

Chapter Vocabulary

accuracy	**distributive property**	**power**
additive identity	**evaluate**	**precision**
additive inverse	**exponent**	**principal square root**
algebraic equation	**factor**	**properties of arithmetic operations**
algebraic expression	**formula**	**radical sign**
algebraic inequality	**greatest possible error**	**radicand**
associative property	**grouping symbols**	**rational number**
base	**index**	**reciprocal property**
closed	**integer**	**scientific notation**
coefficient	**interval of measure**	**significant digits**
commutative property	**irrational number**	**square**
constant	**multiplicative inverse**	**square root**
cube root	**order of operations**	**term**
	perfect square	**zero product property**

LESSON 1.1

1.1 Writing and Translating Algebraic Expressions

A **term** is an algebraic expression written with numbers, variables, or both, and using multiplication, division, or both. A term that has no variables is often called a **constant**. 5, x, cd, $6mx$, $\frac{4x^2y}{-3m^3}$ are all terms. Of these, 5 is a constant.

The **coefficient** of a term is the numerical part of the term. If no coefficient is written, then it is understood to be 1. The coefficient of $6mx$ is 6, the coefficient of $\frac{4x^2y}{-3m^3}$ is $-\frac{4}{3}$, and the coefficient of cd is 1.

For any given term, other terms that divide evenly into that given term are called **factors**. The numbers 4 and 5 are factors of 20. The number 2 and x are factors of $2x$.

One can think of a term as including the addition or subtraction sign in front of the coefficient. For example, in $3 - x$, the two terms are 3 and $-x$. The coefficient of x is -1.

Writing Algebraic Expressions

Algebraic expressions contain arithmetic numbers, variables, and symbols for the operations (operators): $b + 2a$, $5x - 7y$, $4m^2$, and $\frac{r}{\pi}$ are algebraic expressions.

Algebraic equations are statements containing two algebraic expressions joined with a sign of equality: $6b = 30$, $5x + 6 = 41$, and $8x - 7 = x + 15$ are algebraic equations.

Algebraic inequalities contain two algebraic expressions joined with a sign of inequality: $n + 2 > 13$, $4x - 3 < 9$, and $9a + 4 \geq 3a - 8$ are algebraic inequalities.

> **The language of algebra is symbolic. When an algebra problem is presented in words, part of the job of solving the problem is to rewrite the information using algebraic expressions.**

Key Words	Symbol	English and Algebra Translations
Signs of Operations		
sum, add, increase, more than, plus, increased by, greater, exceeded by, and	$+$	f increased by 10 $f + 10$ the sum of x and 9 $x + 9$
difference, subtract, take away, minus, decrease, fewer, less, less than, decreased by, diminished by	$-$	4 less y $4 - y$ 32 fewer CDs than Abdul's $A - 32$
multiply, of, product, times	$\times$	the product of 4 and t $4 \times t$ or $4t$ One-half of the pumpkin weighs 3 pounds. $\frac{1}{2}p = 3$
divide, quotient, into, for, per, divided by	$\div$	500 divided into 4 parts $500 \div 4$ Sue cut a 24-inch board into 8 pieces. $24 \div 8$
Sign of Equality		
equals, is equivalent to, is the result of, is	$=$	Twice a number plus 4 is 14. $2n + 4 = 14$
Signs of Inequality		
is greater than, is more, has more	$>$	x is greater than 5. $x > 5$
is less than, is fewer, has fewer	$<$	Pauline and Fredrica together have fewer books than Vicki. $P + F < V$
is greater than or equal to, is at least, has at least	$\geq$	The program was at least 4 hours long. $p \geq 4$
is less than or equal to, is at most, has at most	$\leq$	The bank is at most 1.5 miles away. $b \leq 1.5$
is not equal to, is not the same as, cannot equal, does not equal	$\neq$	Today is not the third of the month. $d \neq 3$

MODEL PROBLEMS

1. The difference between the square of the hypotenuse (h) and the square of the altitude (a) of a triangle.

SOLUTION $h^2 - a^2$

2. The square root of the sum of the squares of the altitude (a) and the base (b).

SOLUTION $\sqrt{a^2 + b^2}$

3. Translate the following equation into words: $5n + 4 = 8n - 12$

SOLUTION Five times the number n increased by four is equivalent to eight times the same number n decreased by twelve.

PRACTICE

Exercises 1–10: Express the following statements by means of operators, variables, and numbers.

1. Seven less than twice a certain number n.

2. One-eighth π times the cube of the diameter (d).

3. The difference between the square root of x and π squared.

4. 6 divided by the sum of 4 times x and 5 times k.

5. Ten times the number n decreased by 13 is equal to the square of the same number n increased by 3.

6. The sum of x and y decreased by their product.

7. The product of a and b divided by an expression that is 3 times their difference.

8. The square of r increased by a quantity that is fifty times the cube of k.

9. Twice π divided by the cube of the sum of x and 2.

10. Three times the difference of a and m divided by twice their sum.

Translating English into the Language of Algebra

Points to Remember

- Before you translate a problem situation into an algebraic expression, be sure you understand what the situation means.
- Define each variable you create with an equals sign.
- When there are two or more unknown quantities, you may need to represent only one of them with a letter variable. Try to express the other unknown quantities in terms of that letter, if possible.
- Often, translation assumes that you know certain relationships about money, measurement, or time. If a relationship is not clear to you, you should try making a chart or table of the situation before translating it into an algebraic expression.
- Proper units must be used.

MODEL PROBLEMS

1. If whole milk costs 25 cents more per quart than buttermilk, express the cost of a quart of whole milk in terms of the cost of buttermilk.

SOLUTION If b is the cost of buttermilk, then the cost of whole milk = $(b + 25)$ cents.

2. **MP 2, 4** The length of a room is 5 feet less than twice its width.

Draw a diagram of the room that includes the expressions for length and width.

SOLUTION

If w represents the width, then the length of the room = $(2w - 5)$ feet.

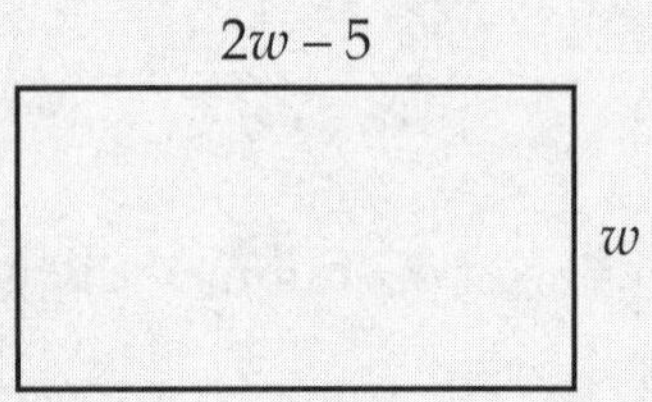

PRACTICE

Exercises 1–12: Answer each question by providing a suitable algebraic expression and equation. Label answers with the proper units.

1. Each of the 13 stripes of a flag is w inches wide. Express the width of the entire flag.

2. Frank owns x books and Sara owns one more than twice as many. What algebraic expression represents the number of Sara's books?

3. The altitude of a triangle in inches is 3 less than the number of inches in its base. Use b to represent the base.

a Represent the length of the base.

b Represent the length of the altitude.

c Draw a diagram of the triangle, labeling the altitude and base with the expressions created in **a** and **b**.

4. A notebook costs 98 cents more than a pencil. Represent the cost of half a dozen pencils and 3 notebooks.

5. Bill is twice as old as Joyce and Sam is 5 years older than Bill. If Joyce is n years old,

a Represent the age of Bill.

b Represent the age of Sam.

6. John purchased an 8-hour calling card. He used m minutes. Write an algebraic expression to represent the number of minutes he has remaining.

7. Pete drives from New York to Boston for the weekend. If the average speed for the trip is 52 miles per hour, and he travels for h hours, write an algebraic expression to represent the distance traveled.

8. George has 525 songs on his mobile device and downloads 3 new songs a week. Represent the total number of songs he has after w weeks.

Practice Problems continue . . .

9. Evelyn sells used cars. Her base salary is \$800 a week and she receives a 12% commission on each sale. Represent Evelyn's total salary for the week if she had d dollars of sales.

10. MP 2, 4 A small brick patio is made up of squares each k inches on a side. If the patio has 9 bricks on one side and twelve on the other, write an expression that represents the perimeter and area. Include a diagram.

11. MP 2, 4 The distance from first base to third base on a baseball diamond is 1.4 times the distance from home plate to third base, which is k feet. Represent the distance from first base to third base. Include a diagram.

12. MP 2, 4 During its second year of operation a company produced 4000 units of affordable housing.

a The production of 4000 housing units in its second year represents an increase of x units compared to its first year. Write an expression for the number of units produced during the first year.

b Express the company's production during its first two years of operation.

c The company earns a profit of p dollars for every unit produced. Express the total profit made in the first two years.

LESSON 1.2

1.2 Translating and Writing Formulas

A mathematical rule expressing the relationship of two or more quantities by means of real numbers, variables, and operators is a special kind of equation called a **formula**. Typically, formulas apply to real-world situations and allow us to determine the volume of a sphere, the distance an object travels, interest earned on investments, and many other things.

$A = lw$, $d = rt$, $C = 2\pi r$, $A = \pi r^2$, and $p = mv$ are all examples of formulas.

MODEL PROBLEMS

Model Problems 1–2: Translate each of the following statements into formulas.

1. The central angle (a) of a regular polygon equals 360° divided by the number of sides (n):

SOLUTION $a = \dfrac{360°}{n}$

2. The surface area of a cylinder (A) is equal to the product of twice π times the radius (r) times the sum of the radius (r) and the height (h):

SOLUTION $A = 2\pi r(r + h)$

Model Problems 3–4: Translate each of the following formulas into statements.

3. $a = \sqrt{h^2 - b^2}$, where a = altitude of a right triangle, h = hypotenuse, and b = base.

SOLUTION The altitude of a right triangle equals the square root of the difference between the hypotenuse squared and the base squared.

Model Problems continue . . .

Model Problems *continued*

4. $p = b + 2e$, where p = perimeter of an isosceles triangle, b = length of base, and e = the length of each equal side.

SOLUTION The perimeter of an isosceles triangle equals the sum of the base and twice the length of one of the equal sides.

PRACTICE

Exercises 1–6: Translate each of the following statements into formulas.

1. The average (A) of three numbers a, b, and c equals the sum of the three numbers divided by three.

2. The capital (C) of any business is the difference between the business assets (A) and the liabilities (L).

3. The rate of commission (r) is equal to the commission (c) divided by the sales (s).

4. The temperature reading on the Fahrenheit scale (F) is found by taking nine-fifths of the reading on the Centigrade scale and increasing that quantity by 32.

5. The distance (d) a free-falling body drops is equal to one-half the product of the acceleration due to gravity (g) and the square of the time falling (t).

6. Centripetal force (F) equals the product of the weight of the body (w) and the square of the velocity (v) divided by the product of the acceleration due to gravity (g) and the radius of the circle (r).

Exercises 7–12: Translate each of the following formulas into statements.

7. $r = \frac{d}{t}$, where r = the average rate of speed, d = distance traveled, and t = time spent traveling.

8. $V = \pi r^2 h$, where V = volume of a circular cylinder, r = radius of the base, and h = height of the cylinder.

9. $V = \frac{4}{3}\pi r^3$, where V = volume of a sphere and r = radius of the sphere.

10. $H = \frac{nd^2}{2.5}$, where H = horsepower rating of a gasoline engine, n = the number of cylinders, and d is the diameter of each cylinder in inches.

11. $A = \pi r(r + l)$, where A = surface area of a cone, r = radius of the base of the cone, and l = slant height of the cone.

12. $T = \frac{2\pi(r + h)}{v}$, where T = the time in hours for a satellite to complete a circular orbit, r = radius of the earth (in miles), h = approximate height of the satellite above the earth (in miles), and v = velocity of the satellite (in miles per hour).

13. **MP 1, 2, 6, 7** A jeweler orders white and yellow gold. Last month, he ordered x ounces of white gold and twice as much yellow gold. White gold costs w dollars per ounce and yellow gold costs y dollars per ounce.

a Write an algebraic expression to express the cost of last month's gold order.

b What would $3x$ represent?

c If he paid the same price for white and yellow gold, write an expression for the total spent.

LESSON 1.3

1.3 Simple Algebraic Inequalities

If we use the words "at least," "at most," "less than" or "more than," then we are talking about inequalities.

Algebraic inequalities contain two algebraic expressions joined with one of these signs of inequality: $<$, $>$, $\leq$, $\geq$, or $\neq$. Examples of algebraic inequalities are $n + 2 > 13$, $4x - 3 < 9$, and $9a + 4 \geq 3a - 8$.

To help translate key phrases, consider this table of key words and symbols.

Key Words	Symbol	English and Algebra Translations
is greater than, is more, has more	$>$	x is greater than 5. $x > 5$
is less than, is fewer, has fewer	$<$	Pauline and Allison together have fewer books than Vicki. $P + A < V$
is greater than or equal to, is at least, has at least	$\geq$	The program was at least 4 hours long. $P \geq 4$
is less than or equal to, is at most, has at most	$\leq$	The bank is at most 2.5 miles away. $b \leq 2.5$
is not equal to, is not the same as, cannot equal, does not equal	$\neq$	Today is not the third day of the month. $d \neq 3$

MODEL PROBLEMS

1. **MP 2** The base of a triangle is 4 inches longer than the altitude. If the sum of the lengths of the base and the altitude is *at least* 25 inches, what is the possible length of the base? Write an inequality to model the situation.

SOLUTION

$a + (a + 4) \geq 25$

2. **MP 4, 6** Juan plans to leave a 15% tip at the restaurant. The sales tax is 6%. He has \$30 to spend. Write an inequality that expresses the most he could spend on the lunch itself before adding in the tip and taxes. Simplify but do not solve.

SOLUTION

Taxes and tips are calculated on the initial cost, C, of the lunch. C + 15% of C + 6% of $C \leq \$30$ or $C + 0.15C + 0.06C \leq 30$.

Answer: $1.21C \leq 30$

PRACTICE

MP 2 Exercises 1–10: Write an inequality to model the situation.

1. Nancy is 6 years older than Luke.

a The sum of Luke's age and Nancy's age is less than 30 years.

b Three times Luke's age is greater than twice Nancy's age.

2. The square of a number is greater than one-tenth of the number.

3. Maria (M) is at least 10 years older than Jackie (J).

4. A number is greater than twice the result of decreasing the number by 12.

5. Twice a number is less than or equal to the sum of the number and 15.

6. Twenty-seven decreased by the product of a and b is less than x.

7. Five-sixths of the product of x, y, and the square of z is greater than 31.

8. One-eighth of a number is at most 5.024.

9. Twenty-five is at least one-third of a number.

10. Three-fourths of a number is at most -12.

11. For what integer values of x is it true that $3 \leq x < 7$?

12. If the replacement set (the domain) for x is $\{-2, -1, 0, 1, 2\}$, write the solution set for $-2x < 0$.

13. If the domain for x is $\{-2, -1, 0, 1, 2\}$, what is the solution set (or range) of answers for $3x - 1 > 3$?

14. **MP 2** The length of a rectangular garden is twice the width. If the perimeter is smaller than or equal to 900 feet, what is the greatest possible width of the garden?

a Write an inequality for the situation.

b Translate the inequality into words.

15. **MP 2** A cinnamon roll has 30 fewer calories than twice the number of calories in a slice of white bread. Together they contain at least 210 calories. What is the smallest possible number of calories of white bread alone?

a Write an inequality for the situation.

b Translate the inequality into words.

16. **MP 2, 4, 6** The most that Samantha can spend on a Father's Day gift is \$75. She has to calculate the maximum cost C of her gift if the tax is 8%.

a Write an inequality for the situation.

b Translate the inequality into words.

17. **MP 2, 3, 4** Meghan plans to leave a 15% tip at the restaurant, and she can only spend \$60. If C represents the cost of the meal without the tip,

a Write a suitable inequality as a model of the situation.

b Which of the following costs of her meal would fall within her budget? {\$50, \$52, \$54, \$55} Justify your answer.

c Meghan has a calculator and multiplies the price of the meal by 1.15 to find her total price. She says this is faster than just finding the tip and then adding that number to the meal price. Will this method always work? Explain.

LESSON 1.4

1.4 Evaluating Algebraic Expressions and Formulas

Substituting numbers for variables to find a value for an expression is called **evaluating** the expression.

For example, say we are trying to find the number of soda cans in three six-packs. Let $6x$ represent the number of soda cans in a certain number, x, of six-packs. We need to know the number of cans in three six-packs, so we can say that $x = 3$ and then substitute 3 in the expression, getting $6 \bullet 3$ or 18 soda cans.

After substituting the value, we must simplify using the **order of operations.**

(1) Simplify any expression within **grouping symbols:** parentheses ( ), brackets [ ], braces { }, and $\frac{a}{b}$ as indicated by fraction bars. When grouping symbols appear within other grouping symbols, work from the inside out.

(2) Evaluate by simplifying powers and roots.

(3) Multiply and divide in order from left to right.

(4) Add and subtract in order from left to right.

To remember the correct order of operations, use the catchword PEMDAS:

Parentheses, **E**xponents (and roots), **M**ultiply and **D**ivide, **A**dd and **S**ubtract.

MODEL PROBLEMS

1. Simplify $7(5^2 - 2 \bullet 11) \div 3 + 8$.

SOLUTION

Simplify in parentheses using exponent and multiplication.	$= 7(25 - 22) \div 3 + 8$
Simplify in parentheses using subtraction.	$= 7(3) \div 3 + 8$
Multiply and divide from left to right.	$= 7 + 8$
Add.	$= 15$

2. Evaluate $5(x^3 + y) \div \sqrt{25} - y$ if $x = 3$ and $y = -2$.

SOLUTION

Given.	$5(x^3 + y) \div \sqrt{25} - y$
Substitute 3 for x and –2 for y.	$= 5[(3)^3 + (-2)] \div \sqrt{25} - (-2)$
Simplify in parentheses using exponent and then addition.	$= 5(25) \div \sqrt{25} + 2$
Simplify root.	$= 5(25) \div 5 + 2$
Multiply and divide from left to right.	$= 25 + 2$
Add.	$= 27$

Model Problems continue . . .

Model Problems *continued*

3. MP 2 The following table reveals the total salary and bonus, but not the fixed salary:

Bonus (b)	\$50	\$120	\$180	\$230
Total Salary (S)	\$340	\$410	\$470	\$520

a Express the relationship between the quantities in words.

b Write as a formula.

c Find the total salary when the bonus is \$260, \$310, \$450, or \$500. Create a table to organize the information.

SOLUTION

a Total salary equals the fixed salary plus the bonus. Subtracting the bonus (\$50) from the total salary (\$340), or 340 −50, equals the fixed salary, or \$290.

b Formula: $S = \$290 + b$.

c

Bonus (b)	\$260	\$310	\$450	\$500
Total Salary (S)	\$550	\$600	\$740	\$790

4. Which of these values will make the algebraic fraction $\frac{2x+3}{2x-3}$ undefined?

A. 2 B. 3 C. $\frac{2}{3}$ D. $\frac{3}{2}$

When the denominator is equal to 0, the fraction is undefined.

SOLUTION

Substitute each of the value choices for x in the denominator to see which one makes the denominator equal zero.

A. $2(2) - 3 = 1$

B. $2(3) - 3 = 3$

C. $2\left(\frac{2}{3}\right) - 3 = \frac{4}{3} - 3 = \frac{4}{3} - \frac{9}{3} = -\frac{5}{3}$

D. $2\left(\frac{3}{2}\right) - 3 = 3 - 3 = 0$

Answer: D.

Model Problems continue . . .

Model Problems *continued*

5. If d is an odd integer and e is an even integer, which of the following is an odd integer?

A. $2d + e$ B. $2d + 2e$ C. $de + d$ D. $3e + 3d + 1$

Integers are whole numbers and their opposites.

SOLUTION

Select an odd number, say 3, for d and an even number, say 2, for e and substitute.

A. $2d + e = 2(3) + 2 = 8$

B. $2d + 2e = 2(3) + 2(2) = 10$

C. $de + d = 3(2) + 3 = 9$ (an odd number)

D. $3e + 3d + 1 = 3(2) + 3(3) + 1 = 16$

ALTERNATE SOLUTION

An even number can be represented by $2x$. An odd number can be represented by $2y + 1$. We let $d = 2y + 1$ and $e = 2x$, where x and y are integers.

A. Even, $2d + e = 2(2y + 1) + 2x = 4y + 2x + 2 = 2(2y + x + 1)$, two times any integer value will be even.

B. Even, $2d + 2e$ can be rewritten as $2(d + e)$, two times any integer value will be even.

C. Odd, $de + d = (2y + 1)(2x) + 2y + 1 = 4xy + 2x + 2y + 1 = 2(2xy + x + y) + 1$, $2(2xy + x + y)$ is even since it is 2 times some integer value, then we add 1, which results in an odd number.

D. Even, $3e + 3d + 1 = 3(2x) + 3(2y + 1) + 1 = 6x + 6y + 3 + 1 = 6x + 6y + 4 = 2(3x + 3y + 2)$, two times any integer value will be even.

Answer: C.

PRACTICE

Exercises 1–2: Which choice demonstrates the correct way to evaluate the given statement?

1. $6 + 4 \bullet 8 - 3$

A. $(6 + 4) \bullet (8 - 3)$

B. $[6 + (4 \bullet 8)] - 3$

C. $[(6 + 4) \bullet 8] - 3$

D. $6 + [4 \bullet (8 - 3)]$

2. $2^3 + 16 \div 4 + 4$

A. $[2^3 + 16] \div (4 + 4)$

B. $[(2^3 + 16) \div 4] + 4$

C. $2^3 + [16 \div (4 + 4)]$

D. $[2^3 + (16 \div 4)] + 4$

Exercises 3–8: Evaluate each expression.

3. $(2 \bullet 3^2) \div (3\sqrt{4})$

4. $15 - 10 \div 5 \bullet 2 + 4$

5. $x[7 - 2(y)]$; $x = -5, y = -3$

6. $b^2(d - b) + 5\sqrt{4}$; $b = 3, d = 2$

7. $\dfrac{1 + 33 \div g + 12 \times g}{g \times g - g \div g + 4}$; $g = 3$

8. $12 \bullet 4 - [h + j(8 + c) + 7] \div j - 1$; $h = 5, c = 2, j = 3$

Exercises 9–12: Choose the correct answer.

9. If $x + 3$ is an even integer, which of the following is <u>not</u> an even integer?

A. $2x + 2$ C. $x - 3$

B. $2x + 3$ D. $3x - 1$

10. If e is an even integer and d is an odd integer, which of the following is an even integer?

A. $2d^2 + 3e$ C. $3e^2 + d$

B. $de + d^2$ D. $d^2 + 3e$

Practice Problems continue . . .

11. If $a \neq b$, and a and b are prime numbers greater than 2, which of the following expressions must represent an odd integer?

A. $a + b - 2$ C. $ab + 1$

B. $ab - 1$ D. $ab + 2$

12. Which of the fractional expressions has a value greater than 1 if k is an integer greater than 1?

A. $\frac{k}{1 + k}$ C. $\frac{k + 1}{k}$

B. $\frac{1}{1 - k}$ D. $\frac{k}{1 - k}$

Exercises 13–15: Evaluate each algebraic expression.

13. If $m = -3$, then what is the value of $-2m^3$?

14. If $a = \frac{1}{2}$ and $b = -\frac{3}{4}$, then what is the value of $a^3 + b^3$?

15. If $x = 3$ and $y = -3$, what is the value of $x^3 + y^3$?

16. **MP 7** If $r = s$, rewrite the following expression using only r:
$r(r + s) - s(r - s)$

17. If the domain of v is $\{-4, -2, 0, 2, 4\}$, what is the solution set for the inequality
$3v + 3 < 15$?

Exercises 18–21: Let $x = 3$ and $y = 4$. Fill in each blank in the four statements below with "less than," "equal to," or "greater than."

18. The value of $\frac{x}{y - 1}$ is ____________ the value of $\frac{x}{y}$.

19. The value of $\frac{x - 2}{y - 1}$ is ____________ the value of $\frac{x}{y}$.

20. The value of $\frac{x^2 - 3}{2y}$ is ____________ the value of $\frac{x}{y}$.

21. The value of $\frac{x^2}{y^2}$ is ____________ the value of $\frac{x}{y}$.

MP 2, 4 Exercises 22–23: Given a table of related values:

a Express the relationship between the quantities in words.
b Write the formula.
c Find the missing numbers.

22. Number of non-overlapping triangles in a polygon formed by drawing diagonals from a single vertex:

Number of sides (s)	4	5	6	7	9	12	13	16
Number of triangles (t)	2	3	4					

23. Text message costs:

Number of texts (t)	3	4	5	6	9	10	14	20
Cost (c)	\$.50	\$.65	\$.80					

24. **MP 1, 2** One cubic foot of seawater weighs 64 pounds.

a What is the weight of 5 cubic feet of seawater?
b What is the weight of 12 cubic feet of seawater?
c Write a word rule expressing the weight in pounds (w) of a given number (n) of cubic feet of seawater.
d Write a formula expressing that relationship.

1.5 Algebraic Properties

Algebraic Operations

The four basic arithmetic operations are addition (+), subtraction (−), multiplication (×), and division (÷).

Multiplication can be indicated in several ways:

$a \times b \quad a \bullet b \quad (a)(b) \quad a(b) \quad ab$

Division can be indicated as:

$a \div b \quad \frac{a}{b} \quad b\overline{)a} \quad a/b$

Properties of Operations

The following table summarizes important **properties of arithmetic operations**.

Property	Meaning	Examples
Commutative property of addition or multiplication	The order of the numbers does NOT affect the sum or the product.	$5 + 8 = 8 + 5 = 13$ $\frac{2}{3} + \frac{1}{4} = \frac{1}{4} + \frac{2}{3} = \frac{11}{12}$ $7 \bullet 4 = 4 \bullet 7 = 28$ $3(11) = 11(3) = 33$
Associative property of addition or multiplication	The way the numbers are paired does NOT affect the sum or the product.	$(1 + 2) + 3 = 1 + (2 + 3) = 6$ $\left(\frac{1}{2} \times \frac{1}{3}\right)\frac{1}{5} = \frac{1}{2}\left(\frac{1}{3} \times \frac{1}{5}\right) = \frac{1}{30}$ $(1 \times 3)(4) = 1(3 \times 4) = 12$
Distributive property	Multiplication can be distributed over addition or subtraction.	$2 \times (3 + 5) = (2 \times 3) + (2 \times 5) = 16$ $7 \times (4 - 1) = (7 \times 4) - (7 \times 1) = 21$
Additive identity	When zero is added to or subtracted from any number, the number remains unchanged.	$18 + 0 = 18$ $18 - 0 = 18$ $0 + 25 = 25$ $25 - 0 = 25$
Additive inverse	The sum of a number and its additive inverse (also called its *opposite*) is zero.	4 and −4 are additive inverses: $4 + (-4) = 0$ $\frac{3}{4}$ and $-\frac{3}{4}$ are additive inverses: $\frac{3}{4} + \left(-\frac{3}{4}\right) = 0$
Multiplicative identity	Any number multiplied by 1 remains unchanged.	$1 \times 15 = 15$ $-7 \times 1 = -7$

continued on next page . . .

Property	Meaning	Examples
Multiplicative inverse or reciprocal property	The product of any number and its multiplicative inverse (its reciprocal) is 1.	5 and $\frac{1}{5}$ are multiplicative inverses: $5 \times \frac{1}{5} = 1$
Zero product property	The product of zero and any number is zero.	$-8 \times 0 = 0$ $\pi \times 0 = 0$

A number and its reciprocal are either both positive or both negative. For example:

$$6 \times \frac{1}{6} = 1 \qquad \frac{3}{5} \times \frac{5}{3} = 1 \qquad \left(-\frac{1}{6}\right)(-6) = 1 \qquad \left(-\frac{3}{5}\right)\left(-\frac{5}{3}\right) = 1$$

Zero has *no* reciprocal, because $\frac{n}{0}$ is undefined.

MODEL PROBLEMS

For $-\frac{2}{3}$, name the following:

SOLUTION

1. Additive inverse — $\frac{2}{3}$, because $-\frac{2}{3} + \frac{2}{3} = 0$
2. Multiplicative identity — 1, because 1 is the multiplicative identity for any number
3. Reciprocal — $-\frac{3}{2}$ or $-1\frac{1}{2}$, because $\left(-\frac{2}{3}\right)\left(-\frac{3}{2}\right) = 1$
4. Additive identity — 0, because 0 is the additive identity for any number
5. Multiplicative inverse — $-\frac{3}{2}$, because the multiplicative inverse is the reciprocal, found above

PRACTICE

1. The additive inverse of -8 is

A. $-\frac{1}{8}$
B. 0
C. $\frac{1}{8}$
D. 8

2. The reciprocal of $\frac{1}{5}$ is

A. -5
B. $-\frac{1}{5}$
C. $\frac{1}{25}$
D. 5

3. Which statement illustrates the zero product property? Note that not all statements are true.

A. $\frac{0}{n} \bullet \frac{n}{0} = 1$
B. $n^0 = 0$
C. $0n = 0$
D. $0 - n = -n$

4. Which statement illustrates the distributive property?

A. $a(b + c) = ab + ac$
B. $a + b + c = c + b + a$
C. If $ab = c$, then $a = \frac{c}{b}$.
D. $1 \bullet abc = abc$

Practice Problems continue . . .

5. A binary operation is so called because it

A. yields exactly two answers
B. is performed on two members of a set
C. is performed on members of two different sets
D. is a two-step operation

6. *Opposite* means the same as

A. additive inverse
B. additive identity
C. reciprocal
D. zero product

Exercises 7–17: Identify the property illustrated by each statement.

commutative **associative**
distributive **additive identity**
additive inverse **multiplicative identity**
multiplicative inverse

7. $-6(10) = 10(-6)$

8. $1(64) = 64$

9. $r + t = t + r$

10. $s + 0 = s$

11. $6 + (10 + 8) = (6 + 10) + 8$

12. $b(a \times c) = (b \times a) \times c$

13. $f \times g = g \times f$

14. $x(y + z) = (x \times y) + (x \times z)$

15. $-d + d = 0$

16. $v(c - x) = (v \times c) - (v \times x)$

17. $\frac{p}{q} \bullet \frac{q}{p} = 1$

18. The number 1 is its own multiplicative inverse. Name another number with this property.

19. Which integer has *no* multiplicative inverse?

20. Which number is its own additive inverse?

Closure

If we perform an operation on any number in a set with itself or with any other member of the set and the result is always still in that set, then the set is **closed** under that operation.

For example:

- For any integers a and b, the sum $a + b$ is an integer.
- For any integers a and b, the difference $a - b$ is an integer.
- For any integers a and b, the product ab is an integer.
- Therefore, the integers are closed under addition, subtraction, and multiplication.

However, a set is *not closed* under an operation if the result is *not always* in the set.

For example:

- For all integers a and b, the quotient $a \div b$ is *not* always an integer.

  For instance, when $a = 5$ and $b = 2$, the quotient $5 \div 2 = 2\frac{1}{2}$, which is *not* an integer.
- Therefore, the integers are *not* closed under division.

> The integers are closed only for addition, subtraction, and multiplication.

MODEL PROBLEM

The set $A = \{-1, 0, 1\}$ is closed under which operation?

A. addition

B. subtraction

C. multiplication

D. none of the above

SOLUTION

Test each option:

A. Since $1 + 1 = 2$ and 2 is not in set A, this set is *not* closed under addition.

B. Since $1 - (-1) = 1 + 1 = 2$, the set is *not* closed under subtraction.

C. Since the product of any number in this set with itself or any other member is only $-1, 0,$ or 1, the set is closed under multiplication.

Braces { } indicate a set.

D. Since the set is closed under multiplication, this option is obviously false.

Answer: C.

PRACTICE

1. The set {0, 1} is closed under

A. multiplication
B. division
C. addition
D. all of the above

2. Which set is closed under division?

A. {natural numbers}
B. {whole numbers}
C. {rational numbers}
D. none of the above

3. The set {rational numbers} is not closed under

A. multiplication
B. subtraction
C. extraction of square root
D. squaring

4. How many of these sets are closed under the given operation?

$\{0, 2, 4, 6, \ldots\}$ under addition
$\{0, 1, 2, \ldots\}$ under subtraction
$\{0, 1, 2\}$ under multiplication
$\{0, 1\}$ under extraction of square root

A. exactly one
B. exactly two
C. exactly three
D. all four

Practice Problems continue . . .

MP 2 Exercises 5–10: Match each set with the operation or operations under which it is closed. An answer may be used more than once or not at all.

Set	Closed Under . . .
5. $\{0\}$	(a) Addition
	(b) Squaring
6. $\{2, 4, 16, 256, \ldots\}$	(c) Addition, multiplication, and squaring
7. $\{\ldots, -3, -2, -1\}$	(d) Addition, subtraction, multiplication, and squaring
8. $\{\ldots, -21, -14, -7, 0, 7, 14, 21, \ldots\}$	(e) Multiplication, division, and squaring
9. $\left\{\frac{1}{3}, \frac{1}{9}, \frac{1}{27}, \frac{1}{81}, \ldots\right\}$	(f) Multiplication and squaring
10. $\left\{\ldots, \frac{1}{8}, \frac{1}{4}, \frac{1}{2}, 1, 2, 4, 8, \ldots\right\}$	

LESSON 1.6

1.6 Exponents

A number that can be expressed by means of a base and an **exponent** is called a **power**. A power is a term or a factor of a term that can be written as the product of equal factors. The **base** is one of the equal factors. The exponent is the number of times the base is used as a factor.

$\text{Base}^{\text{Exponent}}$

We say that the exponent *raises the base to a power*. For example:

$4^3 = (4)(4)(4)$	base = 4	exponent = 3	power = $4^3 = 64$	four to the third power, or four cubed
$10w^2$	base = w	exponent = 2	power = w^2	ten times w **squared**, or ten times w to the second power
$6j$	base = j	exponent = 1	power = j^1 or j	6 times j to the first power

We've shown examples of positive exponents, but an exponent may also be negative or zero:

$x^1 = x$

$x^0 = 1, x \neq 0$

$x^{-n} = \frac{1}{x^n}$

$1^n = 1$

- A *negative* exponent can be written as a unit fraction with a positive exponent in the denominator:

$$10^{-2} = \frac{1}{10^2} = \frac{1}{100} \qquad m^{-n} = \frac{1}{m^n}$$

- The exponent *zero* has a special meaning. Any number to the zero power equals 1:

$$10^0 = 1 \qquad 4^0 = 1 \qquad 1{,}000{,}000{,}000{,}000^0 = 1 \qquad m^0 = 1$$

MODEL PROBLEMS

1. Name the coefficient, base, and exponent of each of the following:

		SOLUTION
a	$5x^3$	coefficient = 5, base = x, exponent = 3
b	$-a^6$	coefficient = -1, base = a, exponent = 6
c	$2\pi r$	coefficient = 2π, base = r, exponent = 1
d	$(2x + 3y)^4$	coefficient = 1, base = $(2x + 3y)$, exponent = 4

2. Write each of the following using exponents.

		SOLUTION
a	$7aammm$	$7a^2m^3$
b	$8(a - b)(a - b)$	$8(a - b)^2$

PRACTICE

1. Name the factors of $4mn$.
2. Name the factors of $8m^2$.
3. Name the numerical coefficient of x: $\frac{x + 2}{3}$
4. Name the numerical coefficient of x: $6 - 4x$
5. Name the base, exponent, and power: $9(a + b)^3$
6. Name the base, exponent, and power: $\frac{-3m^2}{4}$
7. Write using exponents: $2g\pi g\pi$
8. Write using exponents: $5(x + y)(x + y)(x + y)$
9. Name the coefficient, the base, and the exponent: $7(bx)^2$
10. MP 7
    a Name the coefficient, the base, and the exponent: $-b^4$
    b Name the coefficient, base, and exponent of $(-b)^4$.
    c Are the expressions in part **a** and **b** equivalent?

Exponents and Operations

Rules for Operations on Terms with Exponents

Operation	Rule	Examples
Addition and subtraction $x^n + x^m = x^n + x^m$ $x^n - x^m = x^n - x^m$	Like bases with unlike exponents *cannot* be added or subtracted unless they can be evaluated first.	$2^2 + 2^3 = 4 + 8 = 12$ $3^3 - 3^2 = 27 - 9 = 18$ $a^2 + a^3 = a^2 + a^3$ $a^3 - a^2 = a^3 - a^2$
Multiplication $x^n \bullet x^m = x^{n+m}$	To multiply powers of like bases, add the exponents.	$3^4 \times 3^5 = 3^9$ $a^2 \bullet a^3 = a^{2+3} = a^5$ $a^{-4} \bullet a^5 = a^{-4+5} = a^1 = a$
Division $\frac{x^n}{x^m} = x^{n-m}, x \neq 0$	To divide powers of like bases, subtract the exponent of the divisor from the exponent of the dividend.	$\frac{4^7}{4^5} = 4^{7-5} = 4^2$ $\frac{a^5}{a^2} = a^{5-2} = a^3$ $\frac{a^3}{a^8} = a^{3-8} = a^{-5} = \frac{1}{a^5}$
Raising a power to a power $(x^m)^n = x^{mn}$	To raise a term with an exponent to some power, multiply the exponents.	$(5^2)^3 = 5^{2\times 3} = 5^6$ $(a^4)^3 = a^{4\bullet 3} = a^{12}$
Raising a fraction to a power $\left(\frac{x}{y}\right)^n = \frac{x^n}{y^n}$	To raise a fraction to a power, raise the numerator and the denominator to that power.	$\left(\frac{3}{5}\right)^2 = \frac{3^2}{5^2} = \frac{9}{25}$ $\left(\frac{a}{b}\right)^7 = \frac{a^7}{b^7}$
Raising a product to a power $(xy)^n = x^ny^n$	To raise a product to a power, raise each factor to that power.	$(5 \bullet 2)^3 = 5^3 \bullet 2^3 = 1{,}000$ $(4a)^2 = 4^2 \bullet a^2 = 16a^2$ $(ab)^5 = a^5b^5$

Here are some useful points to remember about working with negative bases:

- $-x^n$ means $-(x^n)$. For example: $-3^2 = -(3^2) = -9$ and $-3x^2 = -3(x^2)$
- $(-x)^n$ means $(-x)(-x)(-x)$. For example: $(-3)^2 = (-3)(-3) = 9$
- When a negative base is raised to an *even* power, the result becomes positive.

  For example: $(-2)^4 = (-2)(-2)(-2)(-2) = +16$
- When a negative base is raised to an *odd* power, the result remains negative.

  For example: $(-2)^3 = (-2)(-2)(-2) = -8$

MODEL PROBLEMS

MP 7 Model Problems 1–6: Perform each operation.

	SOLUTION
1. $5^6 \bullet 5^{-3} =$	$5^{6+(-3)} = 5^{6-3} = 5^3 = 125$
2. $p^0 + p^1 + p^5 + p^5 + 1^p =$	$1 + p^1 + p^5 + p^5 + 1 = p + 2p^5 + 2$
3. $4^3 \div 4^5 =$	$4^{3-5} = 4^{-2} = \frac{1}{4^2} = \frac{1}{16}$
4. $(10^4)^{-1} =$	$10^{(4)(-1)} = 10^{-4} = \frac{1}{10^4} = \frac{1}{10{,}000}$
5. $\left(\frac{3p}{2q}\right)^2 =$	$\frac{3p \bullet 3p}{2q \bullet 2q} = \frac{9p^2}{4q^2}$ or $\frac{3^2p^2}{2^2q^2} = \frac{9p^2}{4q^2}$
6. $(4p)^3 =$	$4^3 \bullet p^3 = 64p^3$

PRACTICE

1. What is the product of 75^3 and 75^7?

A. 75^{10}
B. 75^{21}
C. 150^{10}
D. 150^{21}

2. Which expression is equal to 10,000?

A. 100^3
B. $(5^4)(2^4)$
C. $(10^2)(50^2)$
D. $(2)(250^2)$

3. Which expression is *not* equal to the other three?

A. $x^2 \bullet x^4$
B. $(x^2)^4$
C. $x^{-2} \bullet x^8$
D. $\frac{x^{10}}{x^4}$

4. Which expression is *not* equal to the other three?

A. 2^6
B. $32(2)^0$
C. $2^5 + 2^5$
D. $(-2)^6$

5. Which statement is *false*?

A. $4^0 = 6^0$
B. $3^4 = 9^2$
C. $3 \bullet 2^0 = 1$
D. $(4^2)^3 = (4^3)^2$

6. If $5^k \times 5^3 = 5^6$, what is the value of k?

A. 2
B. 3
C. 9
D. 18

Exercises 7–13: Find each value.

7. $4^3 - 4^2$

8. $4^{-3} + 4^{-2}$

9. $4^3 \bullet 4^2$

10. $4^3 \div 4^2$

11. $3^0 + 6^0$

12. $2^{-1} - 3^{-1}$

13. $(-6)^2$

Exercises 14–18: Simplify.

14. $x^5 \bullet x^{-3}$

15. $(x^3y^3)^3$

16. $(4x^3)(3x)^2$

17. $\frac{x^2}{x^6}$

Practice Problems continue . . .

18. $\left(\dfrac{x^2}{y}\right)^2$

19. MP 3 Explain why

a $x^2 \bullet x^3 \neq (x^2)^3$

b $-4^2 \neq (-4)^2$

20. Find the value of x that makes each statement true:

a $(3^3)^{5x} = 3^{30}$

b $5^{28} = 5^{3x} \bullet 5^7$

c $6^4 \bullet 6^x = 6^{24}$

MP 7 Exercises 21–28: Simplify each and assume that in any given fraction no denominators equal zero. Leave all results with positive exponents.

21. $(5 - 3)^2 \bullet 2^{-3} + (5 + 2)^0$

22. $(10 - 7)^3 \bullet 3^{-3} + (9 + 3)^2$

23. $\dfrac{36x^{-7}}{9x^{-5}}$

24. $\dfrac{-6x^5a^2}{2x^2a^3}$

25. $\dfrac{(x^2w^{-1})^3}{(x^3w^2)^2}$

26. $\dfrac{(-8a^2b^2)^2}{(4a^3b)^3}$

27. $\dfrac{2x^{-2}y^{-3}}{3a^{-4}}$

28. $\dfrac{-2a^{-1}b^0x^{-4}}{-10a^{-7}b^{-3}x}$

29. MP 7 Solve for n: $4^n \bullet 4^3 = 4^{13}$

30. MP 7 Solve for x: $3^{x-1} \bullet 3^3 = 3^5$

31. MP 2 Using exponents, represent the sum of the surface areas of 5 square folding tables if the side of one table is $2x^2$.

32. MP 2, 4, 5 The population of a certain town in 2004 was estimated to be 45,000. It was determined that the annual rate of increase was 3.4%. The equation that models the growth of the town's population is $A = 45{,}000(1 + r)^t$. If A is the number of people living in the town t years after 2004, and r is the rate of increase, use your calculator, substitute carefully, and determine the approximate population (to the nearest whole number) for the year 2014.

Lesson 1.7

1.7 Roots and Radicals

Square Roots

To find the **square root** of a number means to find one of two equal factors of a number. The square root of n is written as $\sqrt{n}$ or radical n, where n is called the **radicand** and the symbol $\sqrt{\ }$ is called the **radical sign**. Every positive number has two different square roots. They are positive and negative numbers with the same absolute value. The positive value is called the **principal square root**. For example, while $\sqrt{9}$ is both +3 and −3, the principal square root of 9 is 3.

$$\sqrt{b} = x \text{ if and only if } x \geq 0 \text{ and } x^2 = b.$$

Unless stated otherwise, it is the principal square root that is the intended solution.

A number by which a square root is multiplied is called the *coefficient*. Thus, the product of 4 and $\sqrt{5}$ is written $4\sqrt{5}$ where the number 4 is the coefficient and the number 5 is the radicand.

A number that is the square of a rational number is called a **perfect square**. Consider the following examples:

$11^2 = 121$ $\sqrt{121} = 11$ 121 is a perfect square

$16^2 = 256$ $\sqrt{256} = 16$ 256 is a perfect square

$\left(\frac{2}{3}\right)^2 = \frac{4}{9}$ $\sqrt{\frac{4}{9}} = \frac{2}{3}$ $\frac{4}{9}$ is a perfect square

Rational numbers are the set composed of integers, fractions, terminating decimals, and repeating decimals. **Irrational numbers** are decimal numbers that neither repeat nor terminate.

Points to Remember

- The square root of every perfect square is a rational number.
- The square root of every number that is not a perfect square is irrational.
- For every non-negative real number n: $(\sqrt{n})^2 = \sqrt{n^2} = n$
- The square root of a negative number does not exist in the set of real numbers.

Cube Roots and Other Roots

The nth root of a number is one of n equal factors of the number. The symbol $\sqrt[n]{b}$ means the nth root of b. In this math notation, b is the *radicand* and n is called the **index**.

When $n = 3$, we refer to the root as the **cube root**.

$\sqrt[3]{27} = 3$ $3 \times 3 \times 3 = 27$

$\sqrt[4]{\frac{1}{16}} = \frac{1}{2}$ $\frac{1}{2} \times \frac{1}{2} \times \frac{1}{2} \times \frac{1}{2} = \frac{1}{16}$

$\sqrt[5]{32} = 2$ $2 \times 2 \times 2 \times 2 \times 2 = 32$

Points to Remember

- Finding the nth root of a number is the inverse operation of raising a number to the power n. In general, the nth root of b is x (written as $\sqrt[n]{b} = x$) if and only if $x^n = b$.
- When no index appears, the index is 2 and the operation is square root.
- If the *index n is even,* the operation is closed in the set of real numbers for all non-negative real numbers only. When we multiply an even number of identical values together, the product is always non-negative.
- If the *index n is odd,* the operation is closed regardless of the sign of the radicand. For example, $\sqrt[3]{8} = 2$ and $\sqrt[3]{-8} = -2$. In other words, with an odd index, the root always has the same sign as the radicand.

We highlight one important pattern in the relationship between radicals and fractional exponents:

We know that $(\sqrt{x})^2 = x$ and $\left(x^{\frac{1}{2}}\right)^2 = x^{\frac{1}{2}} \bullet x^{\frac{1}{2}} = x^1 = x$.

Therefore, since $(\sqrt{x})^2 = x$ and $\left(x^{\frac{1}{2}}\right)^2 = x$, then $\sqrt{x} = x^{\frac{1}{2}}$.

MODEL PROBLEMS

MP 7 Model Problems 1–5: Show how the expressions are equivalent.

1. $(\sqrt{21})^2 = 21$

SOLUTION $(\sqrt{21})^2 = \sqrt{21} \bullet \sqrt{21} = \sqrt{21 \bullet 21} = 21$

2. $16^{\frac{1}{2}} = 4$

SOLUTION $16^{\frac{1}{2}} = \sqrt{16} = \sqrt{4 \bullet 4} = 4$

3. $8^{\frac{2}{3}} = 4$

SOLUTION $8^{\frac{2}{3}} = \left(\sqrt[3]{8}\right)^2 = \left(\sqrt[3]{2 \bullet 2 \bullet 2}\right)^2 = (2)^2 = 4$

4. $5^3 = 125$

SOLUTION $5 \bullet 5 \bullet 5 = 5^3 = 125$

5. Solve for $x^2 = 49$.

SOLUTION

If $x^2 = 49$, then $x = \pm\sqrt{49}$. Thus, $x = 7$ or $x = -7$.
Answer: $\{7, -7\}$

6. Find the principal square root of $16n^2$.

SOLUTION

$\sqrt{16n^2} = 4n$, which represents the product of the square roots of two factors that are perfect squares, $\sqrt{16} \times \sqrt{n^2} = \sqrt{4 \bullet 4} \bullet \sqrt{n \bullet n} = 4n$
Answer: $4n$

7. **MP 3** Give an example of multiplying two irrational numbers and getting another irrational number.
SOLUTION

One example of an answer: $\sqrt{3} \bullet \sqrt{5} = \sqrt{15}$

8. **MP 3** Give an example of multiplying two irrational numbers and getting a rational number.

SOLUTION

One example of an answer: $\sqrt{3} \bullet \sqrt{3} = \sqrt{9} = 3$

PRACTICE

Exercises 1–15: Evaluate each expression based upon the principal square root.

1. $\pm\sqrt{144}$
2. $\pm\sqrt{1}$
3. $\sqrt{\frac{9}{16}}$
4. $\sqrt{169}$
5. $-\sqrt{0.09}$
6. $\sqrt{0.0081}$
7. $\pm\sqrt{\frac{25}{49}}$
8. $-\sqrt{\frac{1}{81}}$
9. $\sqrt[3]{729}$
10. $\sqrt[3]{\frac{27}{64}}$
11. $-\sqrt[3]{-343}$
12. $(\sqrt{20})^2$
13. $\left(\sqrt{\frac{1}{3}}\right)^2$
14. $\sqrt{\left(\frac{5}{6}\right)^2}$
15. $\sqrt[3]{5^3}$

Exercises 16–22: Find the principal square root of each monomial. Assume all variables represent positive numbers.

16. $9m^2$
17. $\frac{9}{16}x^2$
18. $25d^4$
19. $0.81a^2b^2$
20. $1.21k^2$
21. $4x^4y^6$
22. $0.49x^2y^8z^{12}$

Exercises 23–25: Solve for *x*, considering all possible roots.

23. $x^2 = 64$
24. $x^2 = 169$
25. $x^2 = \frac{25}{36}$

Exercises 26–28: Simplify.

26. $9^{\frac{3}{2}}$
27. $125^{\frac{2}{3}}$
28. $16^{\frac{3}{4}}$
29. Simplify and then identify each of the following as rational or irrational.
    - **a** $\sqrt{2 \bullet 8}$
    - **b** $\sqrt[3]{4 \bullet 2}$
    - **c** $\sqrt{11 \bullet 3}$
    - **d** $\sqrt[3]{5 \bullet 25}$
    - **e** $\sqrt[3]{8 \bullet 3}$
    - **f** $\pi \bullet \frac{1}{\pi}$
    - **g** $(\sqrt{\pi})^2$
    - **h** $\sqrt[3]{3 \bullet 9}$
30. **MP 7** If $0 < k < 1$, which of the following, $>$, $<$, or $=$, should replace the blank in k ___ k^2?

Simplifying Square Root Radicals

Most often, radical expressions will not contain perfect square monomials and we will be asked to simplify the radical. A radical is simplified when the integer remaining in the radical has no perfect square factor other than 1. The final expression has no radical in the denominator.

> In general, if a and b are non-negative integers or non-negative-valued variables:
>
> $$\sqrt{a \bullet b} = \sqrt{a} \bullet \sqrt{b}$$
>
> $$\sqrt{\frac{a}{b}} = \frac{\sqrt{a}}{\sqrt{b}}$$

MODEL PROBLEMS

MP 7 Model Problems 1–3: Simplify the following expressions.

1. Simplify $\sqrt{32}$.

SOLUTION

Factor using 16, the greatest perfect square factor of 32.

$\sqrt{32} = \sqrt{16 \bullet 2} = \sqrt{16} \bullet \sqrt{2} = 4\sqrt{2}$

Note that if we factored using 4, which is also a perfect square factor of 32, the process would require an additional step.

$\sqrt{32} = \sqrt{4 \bullet 8} = \sqrt{4} \bullet \sqrt{8} = 2\sqrt{8}$. Since 8 has a perfect square factor, the process is repeated, simplifying $2\sqrt{8}$.

$2\sqrt{8} = 2\sqrt{4 \bullet 2} = 2\sqrt{4} \bullet \sqrt{2} = 2 \bullet 2\sqrt{2} = 4\sqrt{2}$

Answer: $4\sqrt{2}$

2. Simplify $\sqrt{50x^3y^2}$.

SOLUTION

Simplify using $25x^2y^2$, the greatest square factor of $50x^3y^2$.

$\sqrt{50x^3y^2} = \sqrt{25x^2y^2 \bullet 2x} = \sqrt{25x^2y^2} \bullet \sqrt{2x} = 5xy\sqrt{2x}$

Answer: $5xy\sqrt{2x}$

3. Simplify $\sqrt{\frac{2}{3}}$.

SOLUTION

Remember that the denominator must not contain a radical. Multiply the numerator and denominator by the radical in the denominator you want to eliminate.

$\sqrt{\frac{2}{3}} = \frac{\sqrt{2}}{\sqrt{3}}$

Multiply the numerator and denominator by $\sqrt{3}$, which is the same as multiplying by 1.

$\frac{\sqrt{2}}{\sqrt{3}} \bullet \frac{\sqrt{3}}{\sqrt{3}} = \frac{\sqrt{2} \bullet \sqrt{3}}{\sqrt{3} \bullet \sqrt{3}} = \frac{\sqrt{2 \bullet 3}}{\sqrt{3 \bullet 3}} = \frac{\sqrt{6}}{\sqrt{9}} = \frac{\sqrt{6}}{3}$

Since the radicand in the numerator has no perfect square factors other than 1 and the denominator has no radical, the expression is simplified.

Answer: $\frac{\sqrt{6}}{3}$

PRACTICE

1. The principal square root of 64 is

A. 8
B. -8
C. 8 and -8
D. not a real number

2. Simplify: $\sqrt{1{,}176}$

A. 42
B. $7\sqrt{24}$
C. $14\sqrt{3}$
D. $14\sqrt{6}$

3. Simplify: $\dfrac{3^2}{\sqrt{80}}$

A. $\dfrac{\sqrt{80}}{3^{-2}}$
B. $\dfrac{4}{9}\sqrt{5}$
C. $\dfrac{5}{4}\sqrt{5}$
D. $\dfrac{9}{20}\sqrt{5}$

4. $\dfrac{7}{\sqrt{45}} =$

A. $\dfrac{7}{9}$
B. $\dfrac{3}{7}$
C. $\dfrac{7\sqrt{3}}{9}$
D. $\dfrac{7\sqrt{5}}{15}$

MP 7 Exercises 5–20: Simplify based upon the principal square root.

5. $\sqrt{25}$

6. $\sqrt{864}$

7. $\sqrt{162}$

8. $\dfrac{7}{\sqrt{11}}$

9. $\dfrac{6}{\sqrt{18}}$

10. $\dfrac{19}{\sqrt{19}}$

11. $\dfrac{1}{2}\sqrt{32}$

12. $\dfrac{4}{5}\sqrt{50}$

13. $\sqrt{\dfrac{1}{4}}$

14. $\sqrt{\dfrac{2}{5}}$

15. $\sqrt{\dfrac{4}{7}}$

16. $6\sqrt{\dfrac{5}{6}}$

17. $\sqrt{24x^2y}$

18. $\sqrt{72a^2b^4c^3}$

19. $\sqrt{\dfrac{4}{5xy}}$

20. $\dfrac{2}{3}\sqrt{\dfrac{2c^2d}{3a^2b}}$

Operations with Radicals

Rules for Adding and Subtracting Square Root Radicals

- *Like radicals* have the same index and the same radicand. Only like radicals can be added or subtracted.
- If the indices are different, the radicals cannot be added or subtracted.
- If the radicands are different, try to simplify by factoring to see if the radicands are then the same.
- Finally, add or subtract the coefficients.

MODEL PROBLEMS

1. Add: $5\sqrt{7} + 2\sqrt{112}$

SOLUTION

Simplify $2\sqrt{112}$. $\quad 2\sqrt{112} = 2\sqrt{16 \times 7} = 2 \times 4\sqrt{7} = 8\sqrt{7}$

Add the coefficients. $\quad 5\sqrt{7} + 8\sqrt{7} = 13\sqrt{7}$

2. Subtract: $3\sqrt{48} - \sqrt{27}$

SOLUTION

Simplify $3\sqrt{48}$. $\quad 3\sqrt{48} = 3\sqrt{16 \times 3} = 12\sqrt{3}$

Simplify $\sqrt{27}$. $\quad \sqrt{27} = \sqrt{9 \times 3} = 3\sqrt{3}$

Subtract the coefficients. $\quad 12\sqrt{3} - 3\sqrt{3} = 9\sqrt{3}$

Rules for Multiplying Square Roots

- The radicands do *not* need to be the same.
- Write the factors under one radical sign.
- Multiply.
- If possible, simplify the product.

MODEL PROBLEMS

Multiply.

SOLUTION

1. $\sqrt{3} \bullet \sqrt{6} =$ $\quad\sqrt{3 \bullet 6} = \sqrt{18} = \sqrt{9} \bullet \sqrt{2} = 3\sqrt{2}$

2. $\sqrt{10} \bullet \sqrt{15} =$ $\quad\sqrt{10 \bullet 15} = \sqrt{150} = \sqrt{25 \bullet 6} = 5\sqrt{6}$

Rules for Dividing Square Roots

- The radicands do *not* need to be the same.
- Write the divisor and the dividend as a fraction under one radical sign.
- Simplify the denominator and numerator by factoring.
- If the denominator of the answer contains a radical, rationalize.

MODEL PROBLEM

Divide: $\dfrac{\sqrt{10}}{\sqrt{15}}$

SOLUTION

Rewrite under one radical: $\dfrac{\sqrt{10}}{\sqrt{15}} = \sqrt{\dfrac{10}{15}}$

Simplify: $\sqrt{\dfrac{10}{15}} = \sqrt{\dfrac{2 \times 5}{3 \times 5}} = \sqrt{\dfrac{2}{3}}$

Rationalize: $\sqrt{\dfrac{2}{3}} = \dfrac{\sqrt{2}}{\sqrt{3}} \bullet \dfrac{\sqrt{3}}{\sqrt{3}} = \sqrt{\dfrac{6}{9}} = \dfrac{\sqrt{6}}{3}$

PRACTICE

1. $3\sqrt{48} + 11\sqrt{75} =$

A. $33\sqrt{48}$ C. $72\sqrt{5}$

B. $67\sqrt{3}$ D. $81\sqrt{2}$

2. $\sqrt{14} \div \sqrt{6} =$

A. $\dfrac{2}{3}$ C. $\dfrac{3}{\sqrt{21}}$

B. $\dfrac{21}{\sqrt{3}}$ D. $\dfrac{\sqrt{21}}{3}$

3. $\sqrt{54} - \sqrt{96} =$

A. $-\sqrt{6}$ C. $\sqrt{6}$

B. $2\sqrt{3}$ D. $7\sqrt{6}$

4. $3\sqrt{125} + 6\sqrt{80} =$

A. $-29\sqrt{5}$ C. $39\sqrt{5}$

B. $-9\sqrt{5}$ D. 145

Practice Problems continue . . .

5. $\sqrt{8}(\sqrt{13} - \sqrt{117}) =$

A. $-4\sqrt{26}$
B. $4\sqrt{2}$
C. $2\sqrt{13}$
D. $2\sqrt{26}$

6. In simplest form, $5\sqrt{12} + 7\sqrt{108} =$

A. $12\sqrt{120}$
B. $52\sqrt{6}$
C. $52\sqrt{3}$
D. $20\sqrt{3}$

MP 7 Exercises 7–11: Perform the indicated operations. Give your answers in simplified radical form and identify each as rational or irrational.

7. $4\sqrt{3} - 3\sqrt{3} + 3\sqrt{2}$

8. $3\sqrt{8} - 4\sqrt{3} + \sqrt{18}$

9. $\sqrt{4} + \sqrt{50} - \sqrt{32}$

10. $\sqrt{0.5} \bullet \sqrt{32}$

11. $3\sqrt{7} \bullet 7\sqrt{6}$

MP 7 Exercises 12–20: Name a value of x that makes the expression rational, and another value of x that makes it irrational.

12. $8\sqrt{12x} + \sqrt{27x}$

13. $3\sqrt{6x^2} - 4\sqrt{24x^2} + 2\sqrt{x^2}$

14. $\sqrt{m^2n} \bullet \sqrt{mn^2}$

15. $2\sqrt{5x} \bullet 4\sqrt{3x}$

16. $\sqrt{2x^3} \bullet 4\sqrt{10x}$

17. $\sqrt{2} \bullet \sqrt{0.02x}$

18. $\dfrac{\sqrt{x^7}}{\sqrt{x^3}}$

19. $\sqrt{\dfrac{x}{4}}$

20. $\dfrac{\sqrt{8x^3}}{\sqrt{2x}}$

LESSON 1.8

1.8 Scientific Notation, Significant Digits, Precision, and Accuracy

Scientific Notation

In working with very large or very small numbers, it is often easier to write the numbers in scientific notation. **Scientific notation** is the product of two factors: (a decimal greater than or equal to 1 but less than 10) × (an integer power of 10), or $a \times 10^n$. An example of scientific notation is 8.3×10^4.

To raise a number to a given power use the ^ key on a graphing calculator.
$7^3 \rightarrow 7$ ^ $3 = 343$

Powers of 10

10^4	10,000
10^3	1,000
10^2	100
10^1	10
10^0	1
10^{-1}	0.1
10^{-2}	0.01
10^{-3}	0.001
10^{-4}	0.0001

- For *positive* powers of 10, the number of zeros following the 1 is the same as the exponent of 10. 10^3 has 3 zeros and equals 1,000.
- For *negative* powers of 10, the number of decimal places is the same as the absolute value of the exponent. 10^{-3} has 3 decimal places and equals 0.001.

To Write a Standard Number Greater Than 10 in Scientific Notation

- Move the decimal point to make the number a decimal between 1 and 10.
- Count how many places you moved the decimal point to the left.
- Write the number of places the decimal moved as the exponent.

MODEL PROBLEMS

1. Write 21,400 in scientific notation.

SOLUTION

21,400. =	2.14 ×	10^4
↑	↑	↑
Move the decimal point **4** places to the **left**.	number between 1 and 10	**4**th power of 10

Answer: 2.14×10^4

2. Write this product in scientific notation: $(2.7 \times 10^4) \times (5 \times 10^7)$

SOLUTION

Use the commutative property to rearrange the numbers and the associative property to group the numbers and powers together.	$(2.7 \times 5) \times (10^4 \times 10^7)$
Multiply the elements in the two groupings.	13.5×10^{11}
Rewrite in scientific notation.	$1.35 \times 10 \times 10^{11} = 1.35 \times 10^{12}$

To Write a Standard Number Between 0 and 1 in Scientific Notation

- Move the decimal point to make the number a decimal between 1 and 10.
- Count how many places you moved the decimal point to the right.
- Write the negative of the number of places the decimal moved as the exponent.

MODEL PROBLEM

Write 0.0000034 in scientific notation.

SOLUTION

0.0000034 =	3.4 ×	10^{-6}
↑	↑	↑
Move the decimal point **6** places to the **right**.	number between 1 and 10	negative **6**th power of 10

Answer: 3.4×10^{-6}

In scientific notation, if a number is greater than or equal to 10, the exponent of the power of 10 is positive. If a number is greater than or equal to 1 but less than 10, the exponent of the power of 10 is zero. If a number is between 0 and 1, the exponent of the power of 10 is negative.

To Multiply by a Power of 10

> To change a number in scientific notation to standard form, multiply.

- To multiply a decimal by a positive power of 10, move the decimal point one place to the right for each power of 10.

  $5.68 \times 10 = 56.8$

  $5.68 \times 10^2 = 568$

  $5.68 \times 10^3 = 5680$ ← add zero as a placeholder

- To multiply a decimal by a negative power of 10, move the decimal point one place to the left for each power of 10.

  $87.25 \times 10^{-1} = 8.725$

  $87.25 \times 10^{-2} = 0.8725$

  $87.25 \times 10^{-3} = 0.08725$ ← add zero as a placeholder

MODEL PROBLEM

Between what two integers does 3.445×10^2 lie?

A. 3 and 4
B. 33 and 34
C. 34 and 35
D. 344 and 345

SOLUTION

Convert the number from scientific notation into standard form.

$3.445 \times 10^2 = 344.5$

344.5 lies between 344 and 345.

Answer: D.

PRACTICE

1. Find the expression with the smallest value.
A. 5^0
B. 1^5
C. 0^{10}
D. 10^{-1}

2. Express 5.46×10^0 in standard form.

A. 546
B. 54.6
C. 5.46
D. 0.546

3. Express 9.19×10^{-5} in standard form.

A. 0.0000919
B. 0.00000919
C. 0.00919
D. 919,000

4. In scientific notation 3,450,000 is equal to

A. 34.5×10^5
B. 345×10^4
C. 3.45×10^6
D. 3450×10^3

Practice Problems continue . . .

5. Which of the following represents a number between 0.01 and 0.001?

A. 3.7×10^0
B. 3.7×10^{-1}
C. 3.7×10^{-2}
D. 3.7×10^{-3}

6. Between what two integers does 4.23×10^{-5} lie?

A. 1 and 2
B. 0 and 1
C. -4 and -5
D. -5 and -6

Exercises 7–11: Write in standard decimal form.

7. 3.76×10^5

8. 4.5×10^{-3}

9. 3.9×10^{-2}

10. 7.0×10^6

11. 6.88×10^{-1}

Exercises 12–21: Write in scientific notation.

12. 198,000,000

13. 0.006

14. 56,200

15. 0.0008722

16. $\frac{2}{125}$

17. 7,255,000,000,000

18. 8,040,000,000

19. 0.00019

20. 0.000000002

21. 30.232×10^6

MP 2 Exercises 22–26: Express the measurement in scientific notation.

22. The distance from the sun to Pluto is about six billion kilometers.

23. The sun is approximately 93 million miles from Earth.

24. The width of a virus is 0.0000001 meter.

25. A diode in a microchip measures 0.00025 centimeter thick.

26. The wavelength of a long X-ray is 0.000001 cm.

MP 7 Exercises 27–35: Simplify and express each product or division in scientific notation.

27. $(5.9 \times 10^4) \times (3.7 \times 10^5)$

28. $(8.1 \times 10^{13}) \times (4.8 \times 10^{16})$

29. $(4.3 \times 10^{-3}) \times (1.6 \times 10^8)$

30. $(3.2 \times 10^{-3}) \times (2.2 \times 10^{-4})$

31. $(4.8 \times 10^{12}) \div (3.2 \times 10^6)$

32. $(5.6 \times 10^{15}) \div (2.5 \times 10^5)$

33. $63{,}000{,}000 \times 3{,}700{,}000$

34. $0.000025 \times 0.000000005$

35. $300{,}000{,}000 \div 250{,}000$

Significant Digits

When a measurement is written in scientific notation, such as 3.41×10^3, the digits in the first factor (3.41) are always considered **significant digits**.

- Digits other than zero are significant. 1 through 9 are significant.
- Zero is significant if it is between 1 through 9.
- The final zeros to the right of the decimal point are significant.

Examples	Number of Significant Digits
12,000	2
3052	4
0.00321	3
9.80	3

MODEL PROBLEMS

1. Identify the number of significant digits in each given number.

SOLUTION

Number	Number of Significant Digits	Answer Underlined
0.0609	3	0.0<u>609</u>
7.005	4	<u>7.005</u>
7.80	3	<u>7.80</u>
7,800	2	<u>7,8</u>00
67,000	2	<u>67</u>,000

2. **a** Round the number 0.002608 to 3 significant digits.
b Write the result in scientific notation.

SOLUTION

a 0.00261
b 2.61×10^{-3}

In calculations with significant digits, there are two important rules to keep in mind:

Addition and Subtraction	For sums or differences, round your answer to the same place as the last significant digit of *the least precise measurement*.
Multiplication and Division	For products or quotients, the answer must have the same number of significant digits as the measurement with the fewest significant digits.

MODEL PROBLEM

If a rectangular window is measured and the length is found to be 62.4 inches and the width is 41 inches, what is the *perimeter* and the *area* of that window?

SOLUTION

The perimeter is $2(62.4) + 2(41) = 206.8$ inches. Since the least precise measurement is 41 inches, the least significant digit is in the units place. Thus, the perimeter sum = 207 in.

The area is the product of $62.4 \text{ in} \times 41 \text{ in} = 2558.4 \text{ in}^2$. The measurement with the fewest significant digits is 41 in. It has 2 significant digits. Thus, the area = 2600 in^2.

PRACTICE

Exercises 1–10: Find the number of significant digits.

1. 57,306
2. 448,000
3. 0.1204
4. 0.003103
5. 0.7000
6. 6.01×10^3
7. 30,003,000
8. 0.00061
9. 305.03
10. 0.0812×10^{-2}

Exercises 11–15: Round each number to three significant digits, and then write the result in scientific notation.

11. 0.04109
12. 350,800
13. 56,770
14. 7.066
15. 12,345,000,000

16. An artist measures his canvas and finds its dimensions to be 17 inches by 24.8 inches. Using the concept of significant digits, what is the perimeter and the area of the canvas?
17. Paul measures a rectangular window in his bedroom and finds it has a height of 48.25 inches and a width of 31 inches. Using correct significant digits, find the perimeter and area.
18. Jack measures his outdoor deck and finds its dimensions are 15.25 feet by 20.8 feet. Using correct significant digits, find the perimeter and area.
19. The plot of land to build a beach house on is 110 ft by 55.75 ft. Using correct significant digits, find the perimeter and area of the land.

Units of Measure

The **greatest possible error** of any measurement is defined as equal to $\frac{1}{2}$ of the unit of measure, and one-half of 1 inch is 0.5 inches.

If you are told that the length of a pen is 6 inches, to the nearest inch, then the greatest possible error in this measurement is 0.5 inches and the actual length lies somewhere between 5.5 and 6.5 inches. The real **interval of measure** is 6.0 ± 0.5.

The smaller the unit of measure, the smaller the greatest possible error and the more precise the measurement.

Accuracy and Precision

The **accuracy** of a measurement is a technical term used by scientists and engineers and refers, in general, to the fact that the greater the number of significant digits in a measurement, the *more accurate* the measurement is.

For example, while the length of a table is said to be 35 inches and the speed of light is approximately 186,000 miles per second, using scientific notation we can represent 35 as 3.5×10 and 186,000 as 1.86×10^5. Hence, the measure of the speed of light is a more accurate measure because there are three significant digits.

Precision refers to the level of exactness that a given measuring tool can deliver. For instance, consider the actual length and width of a room to be 12 feet 4 inches by 9 feet 3 in. If you're buying a wall-to-wall rug, you do not want to take measurements to the nearest foot because a rug 12 feet by 9 feet will not be wall to wall.

MODEL PROBLEMS

Model Problems 1–4: In each of the following, a measurement is given. Use that measure to find the unit of measure, the greatest possible error, and the interval of measure.

1. The given measure is 2.4 feet.

SOLUTION

Since the place of the digit furthest to the right indicates the unit of measure, 2.4 feet means the unit of measure is 0.1 foot. The greatest possible error is one-half of 0.1 or 0.05, and the interval of measure, m, is 2.4 ± 0.05.

2. The given measure is 2.53 meters.

SOLUTION

Thus, the unit of measure must be 0.01 meters, and the greatest possible error is one-half of 0.01 or 0.005. The interval of measure, m, is 2.53 ± 0.005.

3. On his golfing vacation, George flew 2.318×10^3 miles or 2,318 miles.

SOLUTION

Since the unit of measure is 1 mile, the greatest possible error is 0.5, and the interval of measure, m, is $2{,}318 \pm 0.5$ miles.

4. **MP 1** If the speed limit on a certain road is listed at 35 mph and the police radar scan estimates that the car is traveling at 1584 feet in 30 seconds, was the car speeding and will the driver get a ticket?

SOLUTION

$$\frac{1584 \text{ ft}}{30 \text{ sec}} \bullet \frac{60 \text{ sec}}{1 \text{min}} \bullet \frac{60 \text{ min}}{1 \text{ hr}} \bullet \frac{1 \text{ mile}}{5280 \text{ ft}} = 36 \text{ mph}$$

Answer: The greatest possible error of the police radar scanner is ± 0.5 mph. The car was traveling at 36 mph, which falls above 35 ± 0.5 mph. Yes, the driver will receive a speeding ticket.

PRACTICE

1. If the *precision* of a tool for measuring is listed as 0.01 cm, what is the greatest possible error for this measure?

A. 0.1 cm B. 0.5 cm C. 0.02 cm D. 0.005 cm

2. If the *precision* of a measurement is 0.5 gallons, what is the greatest possible error for this measurement?

A. 1.05 gal B. 0.5 gal C. 0.25 gal D. 0.05 gal

Practice Problems continue . . .

3. If the *greatest possible error* of a measurement is $\frac{1}{16}$ in, what is the actual precision of this measurement?

A. $\frac{1}{4}$ in B. $\frac{1}{8}$ in C. $\frac{1}{16}$ in D. $\frac{1}{32}$ in

4. If the measure of a certain diamond is listed as 9.83 g, the actual interval of measure is between

A. 9.73 g and 9.93 g C. 9.825 g and 9.835 g

B. 9.78 g and 9.88 g D. 9.82 g and 9.84 g

5. If a car manufacturer specifies that the length of a steel bolt must be 2.0 ± 0.05 cm, which of the following lengths would be rejected?

A. 1.94 cm B. 1.97 cm C. 2.0 cm D. 2.04 cm

MP 6 Exercises 6–15: For each of the following, find the unit of measure, the greatest possible error, and the interval of measure. Copy the table and complete it.

Measurement	Unit of Measure	Greatest Possible Error	Interval of Measure
3.7 lb	0.1 lb	0.05 lb	3.7 ± 0.05 lb
6. 549 ft			
7. 9.4 in			
8. 56.32 gal			
9. 9.104 sec			
10. 3.125 ft			
11. 0.005 oz			
12. 507 tons			
13. .0006 cm			
14. 880 yd			
15. 3.6×10^{-3} g			

16. **MP 2, 4** Claire and Martin are trying to determine the length of a slug. Claire has a measuring stick whose markings are 1 cm apart, and Martin has a measuring stick whose markings are 0.1 cm apart.

a Draw diagrams of Claire's and Martin's rulers.

b Explain who can make the more precise measurement.

CHAPTER 1 REVIEW

1. When 8 is subtracted from 3 times a number, the result is 19. Which of the following equations represents this statement?

A. $8 - 3x = 19$

B. $3x - 8 = 19$

C. $3(x - 8) = 19$

D. $3(8 - x) = 19$

2. Jonas has 20 coins, all nickels and dimes. The total value is \$1.25. If n represents the number of nickels, which algebraic equation represents this situation?

A. $20n = 125$

B. $5n = 1.25$

C. $5n + 10(20 - n) = 125$

D. $5n + 10n - 20 = 125$

3. Eight years ago, Clyde was 7 years old. Which equation is true if C represents Clyde's age now?

A. $8 + C = 7$

B. $7 + C = 8$

C. $8 - 7 = C$

D. $C - 8 = 7$

4. Which of the following represents the total cost of x shirts bought at a cost of $(x + 5)$ dollars each?

A. $(x + 5)$ dollars

B. $x + (x + 5)$ dollars

C. $x(x + 5)$ dollars

D. $x^2 + 5$ dollars

5. For all x, $5 - 2(x + 1) =$

A. $3 - 2x$

B. $4 - 2x$

C. $2x - 3$

D. $-2x - 3$

6. $(k^4)^{15}$ is equivalent to

A. k^{11}

B. k^{19}

C. k^{60}

D. $15k^4$

7. A batch of holiday cookies requires 3 cups of flour. How many cups of flour are needed to bake m batches of cookies?

A. $m + 3$

B. $m - 3$

C. $\frac{m}{3}$

D. $3m$

8. y represents the tens digit. x represents the units digit. The two-digit number is best represented by

A. $y + x$

B. yx

C. $10x + y$

D. $10y + x$

9. George is 15 years old. He is one-third as old as his father. Which equation is true if f represents the father's age?

A. $3f = 15$

B. $f + 3 = 15$

C. $\frac{1}{3}f = 15$

D. $f - 3 = 15$

10. Joyce was y years old 5 years ago. How old will she be 14 years from now?

A. $y + 19$

B. $5(y + 14)$

C. $y + 9$

D. $y + 14$

11. The centripetal force, F, acting on a revolving object equals the mass, m, multiplied by the square of its velocity, v, divided by the radius, r, of its circular path.

This formula can be written as

A. $F = m + \left(\frac{v}{r}\right)^2$

B. $F = \frac{(mv)^2}{r}$

C. $F = \frac{m + v^2}{r}$

D. $F = \frac{mv^2}{r}$

Chapter Review continues . . .

12. Which formula would we use to find the cost (D) of two quarts of milk and three packages of cream cheese, if a quart of milk costs (m) dollars and a package of cream cheese costs (c) dollars?

A. $D = m + c$

B. $D = 3m + 2c$

C. $D = 2m + 3c$

D. $D = 2m \bullet 3c$

13. Nancy sells three times as many magazine subscriptions as Janet. If Nancy and Janet need to sell *at least* 92 subscriptions in all, which inequality could be used to determine how many subscriptions, x, Janet needs to sell?

A. $3x \geq 92$

B. $3x + x \geq 92$

C. $3x - x \geq 92$

D. $x \geq 46$

14. Including a sales tax of 6%, Aaron paid a total of \$93.55 for a pair of sneakers. Find the price, P, before the taxes. Which of the following equations would *not* represent an algebraic model of this situation?

A. $P + .06P = \$93.55$

B. $P = \$93.55 - .06P$

C. $\$93.55 - P = .06P$

D. $P - \$93.55 = .06P$

15. If the greatest possible error of a measurement is $\frac{1}{32}$ in, what is the actual precision of this measurement?

A. $\frac{1}{4}$ in C. $\frac{1}{16}$ in

B. $\frac{1}{8}$ in D. $\frac{1}{32}$ in

MP 2 Exercises 16–23: Represent (or model) each situation with an algebraic equation. Choose and identify your own variables where necessary. Do not solve.

16. Todd's weight, T, is 16 pounds more than three times his son's weight, w.

17. A number squared, increased by 15, is the same as the square of 1 more than the number.

18. Twice Jacqueline's age (J) is the same as her father's age, (F).

19. The quotient of p divided by r, decreased by the product of p and r, is 5.

20. In 20 years, Tracy's age (T) will be 5 years greater than twice her current age.

21. Jack worked 6 hours on Friday and $x + 2$ hours on Saturday at a constant rate of pay per hour (p). He earned \$92.

22. If b baseball cards were divided equally among 3 people, each person would receive 25 cards less than if the b baseball cards were divided equally between 2 people.

23. The product of $3x - 2$ and $4x + 3$, minus double the square of $(2x + 5)$, is 0.

24. A large soda container holds 6.5 gallons of soda. How many ounces of soda does this container hold? Solve and show the changing of units. (Note: 1 quart = 32 ounces and 1 gallon = 4 quarts.)

25. **MP 1, 2, 4** Study the given figure, and write:

a A word rule expressing the area of a flat washer if the inner radius of the hole is r and the outer radius is R.

b A formula representing the rule.

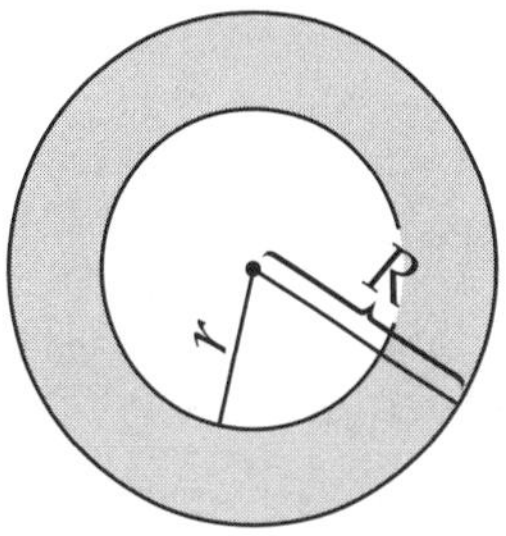

Chapter Review continues . . .

26. MP 1, 2, 4, 6 Janine has \$12.50 in pennies (p), dimes (d), and half-dollars (h) in her pickle jar. She has 5 times as many dimes as half-dollars and 5 times as many pennies as dimes.

a If Janine has h half-dollars, write algebraic expressions for the numbers of dimes and pennies that she has.

b Using these expressions, write an equation showing that the total value of all Janine's coins is \$12.50.

27. Using the order of operations, simplify the following:

a $3 \times 4 + 8 \div 2 - 6 \div 2$

b $10 - 4[3 - 2(15 \div 3)]$

c $5(2^3 + 4) \div \sqrt{36} - 4$

28. $S = \dfrac{rm - a}{r - 1}$, evaluate S when $r = 3$, $m = -5$, and $a = 5$.

29. For each of the following, name the coefficient, the base, and the exponent.

a $4k^2$

b $-(gh)^3$

c $(x + y)^{\mathrm{m}}$

30. For each of the following, simplify and write the answers in simplest radical form.

a $\sqrt{8ab^3c^8}$

b $3\sqrt{20m} + 2\sqrt{45m}$

c $4\sqrt{12} - 3\sqrt{2} + \sqrt{3} + \sqrt{18}$

d $3\sqrt{12x^3} + 2\sqrt{27x^3}$

e $\dfrac{2\sqrt{x^6}}{3\sqrt{x^3}}$

f $\dfrac{\sqrt{3b} \bullet \sqrt{2b}}{\sqrt{8b^3}}$

31. Using the domain $\{-1, 0, 1\}$, find the solution set of the equation $x + 1 = 1$.

32. Using the domain $\{-2, -1, 0, 1, 2, \}$, find the solution set of the inequality $x + 1 > 0$.

33. Using the replacement set $\{-1, 0, 1\}$, find the solution set for the inequality $2x - 1 < -1$.

34. Find the solution set for the inequality $8n + 1 \leq 6$, if the domain is $\left\{\frac{1}{2}, \frac{3}{4}, 1, \frac{5}{4}\right\}$.

35. Identify the number of significant digits in each of the following:

a 458

b 45,920

c 0.0067

d 1600

36. If an herb garden measures 6.505 yards by 10.4 yards, what is the most *accurate* answer for the perimeter and for the area of the garden?

37. Simplify each of the following:

a $27^{\frac{2}{3}}$

b $144^{\frac{3}{2}}$

c $125^{\frac{4}{3}}$

38. Simplify each of the following:

a $(-2)^{-2}$

b $(-5)^2(5)^{-3}$

c $-2^0 - 2^0 + (5a)^0$

d $(x^{-3})^2(x^{-2})^3$

39. MP 2 Simplify each and assume that no denominators equal zero. Negative exponents should not be used in your final answer.

a $\dfrac{x^0}{5}$

b $\dfrac{a^7x^{-4}}{a^4x^{-7}}$

c $\dfrac{a^4b^2c^0}{a^{-3}b^{-1}}$

d $\dfrac{6a^5b^7c^3}{8a^2b^{10}c^3}$

40. MP 7 Find the value of n. $3^{3n-3} \bullet 3^6 = 3^{18}$

Chapter Review continues . . .

41. MP 3, 6 If $x < 0$ and $a > b$, which of the following algebraic expressions is greater: $x(b - a)$ or $x(a - b)$? Justify your answer.

42. MP 7 Calculate the maximum possible value of $14 - (a + b)^2$ if a and b are both integers. Is there a minimum value? Explain your reasoning.

43. MP 7 What are all the values of x that make the inequality true? $5x > x^2$

44. MP 2, 4 Jimmy throws a ball. His dog takes off after the ball at the exact time that the ball is released. The ball travels x feet and stops as soon as it hits the soft sand y seconds later. The dog reaches the ball 2 seconds later. How fast was the dog running? Express your answer as an algebraic expression in ft/sec.

45. MP 3, 7 Miranda and Tony were asked to solve the problem $(3.12 \times 10^3) + (5 \times 10^2)$ and write their answer in scientific notation. Their methods for solving are shown.

Miranda's method:

$(3.12 \times 10^3) + (5 \times 10^2)$
$(31.2 \times 10^2) + (5 \times 10^2)$
36.2×10^2
3.62×10^3

Tony's method:

$(3.12 \times 10^3) + (5 \times 10^2)$
$(3.12 \times 10^3) + (0.5 \times 10^3)$
3.62×10^3

Who is correct? Which method is more efficient?

Chapter 2

Writing and Solving Linear Equations and Inequalities

Chapter Focus

This chapter explores the idea of an equation, namely, that two algebraic expressions are equal. We will use basic operations to solve equations and inequalities, and apply that knowledge to the solving of word problems.

Chapter Content

Chapter Vocabulary

addition property of equality	distributive property of multiplication over subtraction	multiplication property of inequality
addition property of inequality	division property of equality	multiplicative identity
associative property of addition	division property of inequality	properties of equality
associative property of multiplication	equation	proportion
commutative property of addition	identity	rate
commutative property of multiplication	inequality	ratio
comparison property of numbers	isolating the variable	root
compound inequality	least common denominator	solution
conditional equation	like terms	substitution principle
contradiction	linear	subtraction property of equality
cross multiplication	literal equation	subtraction property of inequality
distributive property of multiplication over addition	multiplication property of equality	transitive property of equality
		transitive property of inequality

LESSON 2.1

2.1 Solving Linear Equations

> An **equation** is an open sentence that states that two algebraic expressions are equal.

The equation is **linear** if the variables on either side of the equal sign have an exponent value or degree of one.

Examples of linear equations:

$3x + 4 = 17, \frac{1}{2}x = 6, x - 5 = 11, 3n = 21, 3x = 2x - 13$, and $6y - 1 = y + 3$.

> The value of the variable that makes the equation true is called the **solution**, or **root**. For instance, in $3n = 21$, the *solution*, or *root*, is 7 since $3 \times 7 = 21$.

The process of finding the solutions for a variable requires *keeping the equation in balance.*

- To keep the equation in balance, any change made to one side of the equal sign must also be made on the other side.
- When the variable is finally left alone on one side, you have solved the equation.
- Once we have a solution, we must test it, or check it out. Checking an answer takes two steps:

  (1) The solution must be substituted for the variable in the *original equation.*

  (2) Each side of the equation must be evaluated. If the two sides are the same, then the solution is correct.

For the most part, the solution process involves using the Properties of Equality and performing opposite, or inverse, operations to *unwrap* the value of the variable. This is called **isolating the variable.**

There are three general categories of equations:

- A **conditional equation** is an equation that is true for only some values of the variable or variables. $8x = 16$ is a conditional equation because it is true only when $x = 2$. In this type of equation, we call x an "unknown."
- **Identities** are true for all defined values of the variable. For instance, $4x + 2x = 6x$ is an identity, since any number replacing the x will make the equation true. If, in the process of solving an equation, the variables are eliminated and we end up with a true statement such as $0 = 0$ or $7 = 7$, the solution set is the set of all real numbers.
- However, if we end up with an equation having no variables (as in solving $1 + x = x$) so that a false statement results, such as $1 = 0$ or $5 = 2$, then no value of x will make it true, and the solution set is the empty set, or $\varnothing$. This kind of equation is called a **contradiction**.

Solving Equations by Adding and Subtracting

Knowledge of certain **Properties of Equality** is essential to solving equations. These properties can be used to justify the steps taken to solve an equation. For equations of the form $x + a = b$, consider these properties:

Addition Property of Equality	For all a, b, and c, if $a = b$, then $a + c = b + c$.
Subtraction Property of Equality	For all a, b, and c, if $a = b$, then $a - c = b - c$.
Additive Inverse	$a + (-a) = (-a) + a = 0$
Additive Identity	For any number a, $a + 0 = 0 + a = a$.
Associative Property of Addition	$(a + b) + c = a + (b + c)$
Commutative Property of Addition	$a + b = b + a$
Transitive Property of Equality	For all a, b, and c, if $a = b$, and $b = c$, then $a = c$.
Substitution Principle	For all a and b, if $a = b$, then a and b may be substituted for each other.

MODEL PROBLEMS

1. Solve the equation $x - 7 = 2$.

SOLUTION

Write the equation.	$x - 7 = 2$	Given
Add the opposite of −7 to both sides.	$+7 = +7$	Addition Property of Equality
Arrange in columns and add.	$x = 9$	Simplify

Answer: $x = 9$

Check. $x - 7 = 2$

$9 - 7 = 2$ ✓

> To undo the addition or subtraction of a number, add its opposite to both sides of the equation.

2. If $x - \frac{7}{10} = \frac{1}{2}$, solve for x.

SOLUTION

Write the equation.	$x - \frac{7}{10} = \frac{1}{2}$	Given
Add the opposite of $-\frac{7}{10}$ to both sides.	$x - \frac{7}{10} + \frac{7}{10} = \frac{1}{2} + \frac{7}{10}$	Addition Property of Equality
Simplify.	$x = \frac{5}{10} + \frac{7}{10}$	Simplify
Convert the fraction.	$x = \frac{12}{10} = \frac{6}{5} = 1.2$	Convert the fraction to a decimal

Answer: $x = 1.2$

Check. $x - \frac{7}{10} = \frac{1}{2} \Rightarrow \frac{12}{10} - \frac{7}{10} = \frac{5}{10} = \frac{1}{2}$ ✓

PRACTICE

1. If $9 = x + 2$, then $x =$

A. −7　　C. 11

B. 7　　D. 18

2. If $x + 4\frac{3}{4} = 7$, then $x =$

A. $11\frac{3}{4}$　　C. $2\frac{3}{4}$

B. $3\frac{3}{4}$　　D. $2\frac{1}{4}$

3. If $x - 2.5 = -6$, then $x =$

A. −8.5　　C. 3.5

B. −3.5　　D. 8.5

4. If $x - \$1.25 = \$4.90$, then $x =$

A. \$3.65

B. \$3.92

C. \$6.13

D. \$6.15

5. To solve $1.4 = x + 8.2$, what number should you add to both sides of the equation?

MP 6 Exercises 6–18: Solve for the unknown. Identify the Property of Equality needed to solve each step.

6. $x + 5\frac{1}{2} = 3$

7. $x - 1.6 = -3.8$

Practice Problems continue . . .

8. $2 = k + 0.4$

9. $x - \frac{1}{8} = 2\frac{3}{8}$

10. $x + 2.4 = -9$

11. $23 + m = -15$

12. $-12 = 7 - x$

13. $-\frac{3}{8} + w = \frac{7}{8}$

14. $-\frac{3}{4} - x = \frac{1}{2}$

15. $-4.1 + x = -6.1$

16. $4.2 = x + 7.3$

17. $-8 = -9 - n$

18. $-1.34 + y = 0.98$

MP 1 Exercises 19–23: Define a variable. Write an equation. Solve the problem.

19. Thirty-two minus a number is 24. Find the number.

20. A number increased by 7 is equal to 43. Find the number.

21. A number decreased by 59 is −87. Find the number.

22. The sum of a number and −53 is 89. Find the number.

23. The difference between a number and −32 is 53. Find the number.

Solving Equations by Multiplying and Dividing

For equations of the form $ax = b$, consider these properties:

Multiplication Property of Equality	For all a, b, if $a = b$, then $a \bullet c = b \bullet c$.
Division Property of Equality	For all a, b, if $a = b$, and $c \neq 0$, then $\frac{a}{c} = \frac{b}{c}$.
Multiplicative Inverse or Reciprocal Property	If $c \neq 0$, then $c\left(\frac{1}{c}\right) = \left(\frac{1}{c}\right)c = 1$.
Multiplicative Identity	For any number a, $1 \bullet a = a \bullet 1 = a$.
Associative Property of Multiplication	$(a \bullet b)\, c = a\,(b \bullet c)$
Commutative Property of Multiplication	$a \bullet b = b \bullet a$
Distributive Property of Multiplication Over Addition	For all a, b, and c, $a(b + c) = ab + ac$ and $ab + ac = a(b + c)$.
Distributive Property of Multiplication Over Subtraction	For all a, b, and c, $a(b - c) = ab - ac$, or $ab - ac = a(b - c)$.

In the Division and Inverse Properties, we note that $c \neq 0$ because division by zero is undefined.

MODEL PROBLEMS

1. Solve $12x = 36$ for x.

SOLUTION

Write the equation.	$12x = 36$	Given
Divide both sides by 12.	$\frac{12x}{12} = \frac{36}{12}$	Division Property of Equality
Simplify.	$x = 3$	Simplify

Answer: $x = 3$

Check. $12x = 36$

$12(3) = 36$ ✓

> To undo multiplication by a number, do the opposite. That is, divide by that number or multiply by its reciprocal. Remember that the process of multiplying by the reciprocal is the same as dividing by the number.

2. Solve the equation $\frac{x}{4} = -5$ for x.

SOLUTION

Write the equation.	$\frac{x}{4} = -5$	Given
The opposite of division by 4 is multiplication by 4.	$(4)\frac{x}{4} = (4)(-5)$	Multiplication Property of Equality
Simplify each side.	$x = -20$	Simplify

> A term containing a fractional coefficient may be written as a fraction. $\frac{1}{4}x = \frac{x}{4}$

Answer: $x = -20$

Check. $\frac{x}{4} = -5$

$\frac{-20}{4} = -5$ ✓

3. Solve $0.01x = 7$ for x.

SOLUTION

Write the equation.	$0.01x = 7$	Given
Rewrite the equation.	$\frac{1}{100}x = 7$	Convert the decimal to a fraction
Multiply both sides by 100.	$(100)\frac{1}{100}x = 7(100)$	Multiplication Property of Equality
Simplify.	$x = 700$	Simplify

Answer: $x = 700$

Check. $0.01x = 7$

$0.01(700) = 7$ ✓

Model Problems continue . . .

Model Problems *continued*

4. **MP 6** In the given solution, state the property being used.

SOLUTION

$(a + 8) - 5 = 17$	Given
$a + (8 - 5) = 17$	Associative Property of Addition
$a + 3 = 17$	Simplify
$a + 3 - 3 = 17 - 3$	Subtraction Property of Equality
$a + 0 = 17 - 3$	Additive Inverse
$a = 17 - 3$	Additive Identity
$a = 14$	Simplify

5. **MP 6** Simplify $2(4x + 1) - 8x$, and name the property that justifies each step.

SOLUTION

$2(4x + 1) - 8x$	Given
$(8x + 2) - 8x$	Distributive Property
$(2 + 8x) - 8x$	Commutative Property of Addition
$2 + (8x - 8x)$	Associative Property of Addition
$2 + 0$	Additive Inverse
2	Additive Identity

PRACTICE

1. A piece of imported cheese costs $4.77. If the piece weighs $\frac{9}{10}$ of a pound, solve the equation $\$4.77 = \frac{9}{10}x$ to find how much the cheese costs per pound.

A. $3.87

B. $4.29

C. $5.30

D. $5.67

Exercises 2–15: Solve for the unknown and check.

2. $\frac{3}{4}a = \frac{4}{3}$

3. $0.03 = 30x$

4. $\frac{-3m}{5} = -15$

5. $\frac{a}{5} = -6$

6. $0.7m = -1.4$

7. $\frac{3}{4}x = -27$

Practice Problems continue . . .

8. $-12x = -60$

9. $18 = -2x$

10. $0.06m = 12$

11. $6x = 3$

12. $\frac{1}{4}x = 3$

13. $3 = \frac{1}{9}x$

14. $\frac{2}{3}x = 8$

15. $-0.02x = 6.4$

MP 6 Exercises 16–22: In the following chain of equalities, name the property that justifies each step.

Equation	Reason
$2(3x - 4) = 8x - 11$	Given
$6x - 8 = 8x - 11$	**16.**
$6x - 8 + 11 = 8x - 11 + 11$	**17.**
$6x + 3 = 8x + 0$	**18.**
$6x - 6x + 3 = 8x - 6x$	**19.**
$3 = 2x$	**20.**
$\frac{3}{2} = \frac{2x}{2}$	**21.**
$\frac{3}{2} = x$	**22.**

Solving Multi-Step Equations

To solve equations of the form $ax + b = c$, one needs to undo the additions and subtractions before undoing the multiplication and division.

When working backwards, or *unwrapping* an equation, one follows PEMDAS in reverse order.

MODEL PROBLEMS

1. Solve $-6x + 4 = 34$ for x and check.

SOLUTION

Write the equation.	$-6x + 4 = 34$	Given
Add the opposite of 4 to each side.	$-4 = -4$	Subtraction Property of Equality
	$-6x = 30$	Simplify
Divide each side by -6.	$\frac{-6x}{-6} = \frac{30}{-6}$	Division Property of Equality
Simplify.	$x = -5$	Simplify

Answer: $x = -5$

Check.

$$-6x + 4 = 34$$
$$-6(-5) + 4 = 34$$
$$30 + 4 = 34$$
$$34 = 34 \checkmark$$

Model Problems continue . . .

Model Problems *continued*

2. Solve for x and check. $\frac{2x}{3} + 7 = 5$

SOLUTION

Add −7 to both sides.	$\frac{2x}{3} + 7 - 7 = 5 - 7$	Subtraction Property of Equality
Simplify.	$\frac{2x}{3} = -2$	Additive Inverse
Multiply both sides by the reciprocal.	$\left(\frac{3}{2}\right) \bullet \frac{2x}{3} = -2 \bullet \left(\frac{3}{2}\right)$	Multiplication Property of Equality
Cancel.	$x = (-1) \bullet 3$	Multiplicative Inverse
Simplify.	$x = -3$	Simplify

Answer: $x = -3$

Check. $\frac{2x}{3} + 7 = 5$

$\frac{2(-3)}{3} + 7 = 5$

$\frac{-6}{3} + 7 = 5$

$-2 + 7 = 5$ or $5 = 5$ ✓

PRACTICE

1. Solve: $7x + 5 = 33$

A. $x = 4$

B. $x = 5\frac{1}{5}$

C. $x = 5\frac{3}{7}$

D. $x = 8$

2. Which choice is the solution to $8 = 3x - 4$?

A. $x = 1\frac{1}{3}$

B. $x = 4$

C. $x = 12$

D. $x = 36$

3. If $v = V + gt$, what is the value of t when $v = 116$, $V = 20$, and $g = 32$?

A. 3,732　　C. 64

B. 96　　D. 3

4. Which choice is *not* a step you would take to solve the equation $4 - \frac{x}{2} = 0$?

A. Add −4 to both sides of the equation.

B. Divide both sides by −2.

C. Multiply each term by −2.

D. Subtract 4 from both sides.

5. To solve $10 - 2x = 18$, what number should you add to both sides of the equation for the first step? For the second step, what number should you divide by?

6. If the two angles shown form a right angle, write and solve an equation to find x and the measure of both angles.

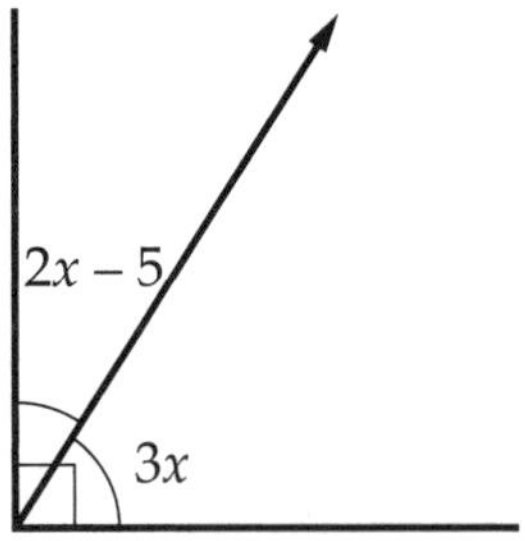

Practice Problems continue . . .

Exercises 7–16: Solve for the unknown and check.

7. $5y - 7 = 15$

8. $4 - 2x = 14$

9. $\frac{1}{4}m + 5 = -3$

10. $\frac{3}{4}c - 8 = 4$

11. $5x + 6 = 81$

12. $-6x + 1 = 31$

13. $d + 0.02d = 510$

14. $4x + x - 2x = 24$

15. $2(x - 4) = -28$

16. $3(x + 8) = -9$

17. **MP 2** James earns \$2.20 less than twice Greg's hourly wage. If James earns \$16.50 per hour, what is Greg's hourly wage?

18. **MP 2** A farmer bought a pig weighing 30 pounds. He expects it to gain 13 pounds a month, and he plans on selling the pig when it weighs approximately 212 pounds. How many months will it be before he can sell the animal?

19. **MP 2** At the year's end, a share of Ardex Industries was worth \$49.50. This was \$9 less than three times its value at the beginning of the year. What was the price of one share of Ardex stock at the beginning of the year?

20. **MP 2** Thirty-five more boys than $\frac{2}{3}$ the number of girls participate in intramural sports at a local high school. If the number of boys participating is 115, how many girls participate?

Solving Equations with Variables on Both Sides

To solve equations with variables on both sides, such as $6x - 3 = 2x + 21$, requires a bit more creativity. We use both addition and subtraction properties to move the terms from side to side in order to combine **like terms**. The objective is to get the unknown terms on one side and the known terms on the other side.

> Any constants are like terms, as are any terms where the variables are exactly the same. For example, $3x$ and $5x$ are like terms.

For example:

Solve for x.	$6x - 3 = 2x + 21$
Use the subtraction property to move the x terms to the same side	$6x - 2x - 3 = 2x - 2x + 21$
Use the addition property to move the known terms to the right side	$6x - 2x - 3 + 3 = 2x - 2x + 21 + 3$
Combine like terms.	$4x = 24$
Use the division property of equality.	$\frac{4x}{4} = \frac{24}{4}$
Simplify.	$x = 6$

MODEL PROBLEMS

1. Solve for x: $7x - 8 = 10 + 4x$

SOLUTION

Write the equation.	$7x - 8 = 10 + 4x$	Given
Add 8 to each side.	$+ 8 = + 8$	Addition Property of Equality
	$7x = 18 + 4x$	Simplify
Subtract $4x$ from each side.	$-4x = -4x$	Subtraction Property of Equality
	$3x = 18$	Simplify
Divide both sides by 3.	$x = 6$	Division Property of Equality and Simplify

Answer: $x = 6$

2. **MP 6** Solve for x: $6 + 4(2 - x) = 3x$, stating relevant properties.

SOLUTION

$6 + 4(2 - x) = 3x$	Given
$6 + 8 - 4x = 3x$	Distributive Property
$14 - 4x = 3x$	Simplify
$14 - 4x + 4x = 3x + 4x$	Addition Property of Equality
$14 = 7x$	Additive Inverse and Simplify
$\frac{14}{7} = \frac{7x}{7}$	Division Property of Equality
$2 = x$	Simplify and Multiplicative Inverse

3. Frank is 3 times as old as Ken. Frank is also 15 years older than Eileen, while Ken is 1 year younger than Eileen. What are the ages of Frank, Ken, and Eileen?

SOLUTION

Let x = Ken's age.

Frank is 3 times older than Ken, so $3x$ = Frank's age.

Eileen is 15 years younger than Frank. So $3x - 15$ = Eileen's age.

Ken is a year younger, so $x + 1$ = Eileen's age as well.

Now, set both statements of Eileen's age equal to each other and solve for x.

$3x - 15 = x + 1$	Given
$3x - 15 + 15 = x + 1 + 15$	Addition Property of Equality
$3x = x + 16$	Simplify
$3x - x = x - x + 16$	Subtraction Property of Equality
$2x = 16$	Simplify
$x = 8$	Division Property of Equality and Multiplicative Inverse

Answer: Ken's age $= x = 8$. Frank's age $= 3x = 24$. Eileen's age $= x + 1 = 9$.

Model Problems continue . . .

Model Problems *continued*

4. Solve for x: $9x + 3(4 + 2x) = 15(x + 1) - 3$

SOLUTION

$9x + 3(4 + 2x) = 15(x + 1) - 3$	Given
$9x + 12 + 6x = 15x + 15 - 3$	Distributive Property
$15x + 12 = 15x + 12$	Simplify
$15x - 15x + 12 = 15x - 15x + 12$	Subtraction Property of Equality
$12 = 12$	Additive Inverse

This is an *identity*. Any replacement for x makes the equation true. The solution set is {all real numbers}.

PRACTICE

1. If $6x - 4 = 20 - 2x$, then $x =$

A. 6 C. 3
B. 4 D. 2

2. If $5x - 2 = 28 - x$, then $x =$

A. 6 C. 4
B. 5 D. 3

3. If $8x - 4 + 7 = 6x + x + 9$, then $x =$

A. 6 C. 2
B. 4 D. 0

4. At a school fund-raising drive, \$350 was collected for washing sedans, coupes, and sport-utility vehicles. The cost of a wash for any type of vehicle was \$2. Twice as many coupes were washed as sedans. Four times as many sport-utility vehicles were washed as sedans. How many coupes were washed?

A. 175 C. 50
B. 100 D. 25

Exercises 5–20: Solve for the unknown and check.

5. $\frac{5}{6}x - \frac{1}{6}x = 10$

6. $\frac{7}{8}x - \frac{1}{8}x = 9$

7. $5x = 15 + 2x$

8. $4x + 6 = 6x$

9. $a - 0.04a = 240$

10. $3x + 10 = 8x$

11. $6x + 3x - 4 = 32$

12. $5x + 2 = 8x - 7$

13. $3x + 5x - x = 56$

14. $9x - 12 = 7x - 6$

15. $5a + 3 = 15 + 2a$

16. $3a - a = a + 8$

17. $7x - 8 - 2x = 64 - 3x$

18. $7x + 6 = 8 - x - 2$

19. $11 - \frac{1}{2}(4x - 6) = x + 2$

20. $2x - 4(x + 2) = 5(x + 4)$

Practice Problems continue . . .

21. If the difference between twice a number and the number itself is equal to the number, what is the number?

22. John, who is 42 years old, has a nephew age 9. In how many years will the age of his nephew be one-fourth John's age? Solve algebraically.

23. In ΔABC, the measure of $\angle A$ is 40° greater than $\angle B$. If the measure of $\angle B$ is 5° less than one-half the measure of $\angle A$, what are the degree measures of angles A, B, and C? The sum of the three internal angles of a triangle is equal to 180°.

24. **MP 1, 2** A cup of coffee contains 30 more milligrams of caffeine than a cup of tea and 90 more milligrams of caffeine than a can of soda. If one cup of tea and four cans of soda contain the same amount of caffeine as one cup of coffee, how many milligrams of caffeine are there in one cup of coffee?

Solving Equations Using the Least Common Denominator

To solve equations that contain fractions, multiply each term in the equation by the **least common denominator** (LCD).

MODEL PROBLEMS

1. Solve and check: $\dfrac{4a+3}{3} - \dfrac{7a-1}{4} = 5$

SOLUTION

Write the equation. $\dfrac{4a+3}{3} - \dfrac{7a-1}{4} = 5$

Multiply each term by the LCD, 12. $12\left(\dfrac{4a+3}{3}\right) - 12\left(\dfrac{7a-1}{4}\right) = 12 \bullet 5$

Simplify. $\overset{4}{\cancel{12}}\left(\dfrac{4a+3}{\cancel{3}}\right) - \overset{3}{\cancel{12}}\left(\dfrac{7a-1}{\cancel{4}}\right) = 12 \bullet 5$

Multiply. $16a + 12 - 21a + 3 = 60$

Simplify. $-5a + 15 = 60$

Subtract 15 from both sides. $-15 = -15$

$-5a = 45$

Divide by -5. $a = -9$

Answer: $a = -9$

Check. $\dfrac{4a+3}{3} - \dfrac{7a-1}{4} = 5$

$\dfrac{4(-9)+3}{3} - \dfrac{7(-9)-1}{4} = \dfrac{-33}{3} - \dfrac{-64}{4} = -11 + 16 = 5$ ✓

Model Problems continue . . .

Model Problems *continued*

2. Solve $\frac{2}{3x} + \frac{1}{4} = \frac{11}{6x} - \frac{1}{3}$ for x and check.

SOLUTION

Write the equation.

$$\frac{2}{3x} + \frac{1}{4} = \frac{11}{6x} - \frac{1}{3}$$

Multiply every term by the LCD, $12x$.

$$\overset{4}{\cancel{12x}} \bullet \frac{2}{\cancel{3x}} + \overset{3}{\cancel{12}}x \bullet \frac{1}{\cancel{4}} = \overset{2}{\cancel{12x}} \bullet \frac{11}{\cancel{6x}} - \overset{4}{\cancel{12}}x \bullet \frac{1}{\cancel{3}}$$

Simplify.

$$4 \bullet 2 + 3x \bullet 1 = 2 \bullet 11 - 4x \bullet 1$$

$$8 + 3x = 22 - 4x$$

Add -8 to each side.

$$\begin{array}{r} -8 \quad = -8 \\ \hline 3x = 14 - 4x \end{array}$$

Add $4x$ to each side.

$$\begin{array}{r} +4x = \quad +4x \\ \hline 7x = 14 \end{array}$$

Divide each side by 7.

$$\frac{7x}{7} = \frac{14}{7}$$

Simplify.

$$x = 2$$

Answer: $x = 2$

Check.

$$\frac{2}{3x} + \frac{1}{4} = \frac{11}{6x} - \frac{1}{3}$$

$$\frac{2}{3(2)} + \frac{1}{4} = \frac{11}{6(2)} - \frac{1}{3}$$

$$\frac{2}{6} + \frac{1}{4} = \frac{11}{12} - \frac{1}{3}$$

$$\frac{4}{12} + \frac{3}{12} = \frac{11}{12} - \frac{4}{12}$$

$$\frac{7}{12} = \frac{7}{12} \checkmark$$

PRACTICE

1. Solve $5x - (x + 3) = 7 + 2(x + 2)$ for x.

   A. 3 C. 6

   B. 4 D. 7

2. Solve $3x + 2(50 - x) = 110$ for x.

   A. 5 C. 15

   B. 10 D. 105

3. $\frac{x-5}{10} = \frac{x+4}{4}$

   A. -40 C. 10

   B. -10 D. 40

4. $\frac{5}{10x} + \frac{1}{3} = \frac{3}{5x} + \frac{2}{5}$

   A. $-\frac{3}{2}$

   B. $-\frac{2}{3}$

   C. $\frac{2}{3}$

   D. $\frac{3}{2}$

5. A cash register has 5 times as many quarters as nickels, 2 fewer dimes than nickels, and 30 pennies. All together, the cash register contains $8.50 in change. How many nickels are in the cash register?

   A. 4 nickels C. 6 nickels

   B. 5 nickels D. 30 nickels

MP 6 Exercises 6–17: Solve for the unknown. Assume that no denominator is equal to zero. Identify the Property of Equality used in each step of your process.

6. $2x(3x + 1) = 3x(2x + 1) - 2$

7. $(a - 1) - (a + 2) - (a - 3) = a$

8. $\frac{x}{5} = \frac{x-3}{2}$

9. $\frac{x+2}{4} = \frac{x}{2}$

10. $\frac{4x+5}{6} = \frac{7}{2}$

11. $\frac{x-3}{2} = \frac{x+4}{6}$

12. $\frac{8}{3x} = \frac{4}{4x-5}$

13. $\frac{2x-3}{4} - \frac{x-2}{3} = 2$

14. $\frac{x}{3} - \frac{3x}{4} = 5 - \frac{5x}{6}$

15. $\frac{9}{x} + \frac{3}{x} = 4$

16. $\frac{17}{2x} - \frac{5}{2x} = 12$

17. $1 + \frac{1}{2n} + \frac{2}{3n} = \frac{13}{6n}$

18. Of four consecutive even numbers, 4 times the smallest minus twice the largest is 4. Find the smallest number.

19. The sum of five consecutive integers equals 5.5 times the middle integer. Find the integers.

20. **MP 1, 2, 5, 6** Two airplanes start at 9:30 A.M. from the same airport and travel in opposite directions at 315 miles per hour and 345 miles per hour, respectively. At what time will they be 2310 miles apart?

21. **MP 1, 2, 5, 6** How fast would a car have to go to overtake a bus in 5 hours if the bus averaged 40 mph and left 3 hours before the car?

22. **MP 1, 2, 5, 6** Ceci has $2.55 in nickels and dimes. If she has 9 more dimes than nickels, how many of each coin does she have?

23. It is given that one number is 6 more than another. If three times the sum of the two numbers is equal to 22 more than the larger number, what are the two numbers?

24. Find three consecutive even integers such that 2 times the second equals the sum of the first and third.

LESSON 2.2

2.2 Solving for a Variable in Literal Equations

An equation with more than one variable is called a **literal equation.** Many *formulas* are literal equations because they contain more than one variable. For example, Albert Einstein's $E = mc^2$ states that energy (E) equals the product of mass (m) and the speed of light (c) squared. Other formulas are:

(1) $A = \pi r^2$ is the formula for the area of a circle.

(2) $d = rt$ for distance equals rate $\times$ time.

(3) $F = \frac{9}{5}C + 32°$, which relates temperatures in degrees Fahrenheit and degrees Celsius.

Literal equations can be solved using the same methods as any other equation.

MODEL PROBLEMS

1. Solve for x in the literal equation $a(x + b) = w$.

SOLUTION

Write the equation.	$a(x + b) = w$	Given
Divide both sides by a.	$x + b = \frac{w}{a}$	Division Property of Equality
Subtract b from both sides.	$x = \frac{w}{a} - b$	Subtraction Property of Equality

$a \neq 0$, since division by 0 is undefined.

2. Solve for R in $I = \frac{E}{R}$.

SOLUTION

Write the equation.	$I = \frac{E}{R}$
Multiply both sides by R to eliminate the fraction.	$R \bullet I = \frac{E}{R} \bullet R$
	$RI = E$
Divide both sides by I.	$\frac{RI}{I} = \frac{E}{I}$
	$R = \frac{E}{I}$

3. Solve the equation $a + c = b - a$ for a.

SOLUTION

Write the equation.	$a + c = b - a$
Combine the a terms.	$+a \quad = \quad +a$
	$2a + c = b$
Isolate a.	$-c = \quad -c$
	$2a = b - c$
	$\frac{2a}{2} = \frac{b - c}{2}$
	$a = \frac{b - c}{2}$

Model Problems continue . . .

4. **MP 7** Solve the equation $m(n + r) = s$ for n. Show two methods to solve for n.

METHOD 1

Write the equation.	$m(n + r) = s$
Use the distributive property.	$mn + mr = s$
Add $-mr$ to both sides.	$-mr = \quad -mr$
	$mn = s - mr$
Divide both sides by m.	$\frac{mn}{m} = \frac{s - mr}{m}$
Simplify.	$n = \frac{s - mr}{m}$

METHOD 2

Write the equation.	$m(n + r) = s$
Divide by m.	$\frac{m(n + r)}{m} = \frac{s}{m}$
Simplify.	$n + r = \frac{s}{m}$
Subtract r from both sides.	$n + r - r = \frac{s}{m} - r$
Simplify.	$n = \frac{s}{m} - r$

Answer: $n = \frac{s - mr}{m}$ or $\frac{s}{m} - r$

5. Solve for p in $A = p + prt$.

SOLUTION

Write the equation.	$A = p + prt$
Undistribute the p.	$A = p(1 + rt)$
Divide both sides by $(1 + rt)$.	$\frac{A}{(1 + rt)} = \frac{p(1 + rt)}{(1 + rt)}$
Simplify.	$\frac{A}{(1 + rt)} = p$

Answer: $p = \frac{A}{1 + rt}$

6. The area of a rectangle is 48 square inches. If the length l of the rectangle is 8 inches, find the width w to the nearest inch. The formula for the area of a rectangle is $A = lw$.

SOLUTION

Given.	$A = lw$
Substitute 48 for A and 8 for l.	$48 = 8w$
Divide both sides by 8.	$\frac{48}{8} = \frac{8w}{8}$
	$w = 6$ inches

Check. $A = lw$

$48 = (8)(6)$

$48 = 48$ ✓

PRACTICE

1. Solve the volume formula $V = lwh$ for h.

A. $h = Vlw$
B. $h = V - lw$
C. $h = V + lw$
D. $h = \frac{V}{lw}$

2. Solve $c = ax + b$ for x.

A. $x = \frac{c - b}{a}$
B. $x = ca - b$
C. $x = \frac{cb}{a}$
D. $x = a(c - b)$

3. Solve for x in the equation $\frac{ax}{b} = \frac{bx}{a}$. Assume that $a \neq b$ and that neither a nor b equals zero.

A. $x = \frac{a^2}{b^2}$
B. $x = 0$
C. x can equal any real number as the equation is an identity.
D. x has no answer as the equation is a contradiction.

Practice Problems continue . . .

4. Solve the equation $p(q + r) = 1$ for q.

A. $q = 1 - p - r$
B. $q = \dfrac{1}{p + r}$
C. $q = \dfrac{1 - pr}{p}$
D. $q = \dfrac{1 - p}{r}$

Exercises 5–13: Solve for x.

5. $ax = 7$

6. $mx = g$

7. $2a + x = 6$

8. $ax + n = m$

9. $nx = 4j - 5x$

10. $R = \dfrac{a(x + b)}{3}$

11. $5x - 8a = 3x + 7a$

12. $\dfrac{1}{x} - \dfrac{1}{a} = \dfrac{1}{b}$

13. $\dfrac{ax}{c} - b = \dfrac{c}{b}$

Exercises 14–19: Solve for the indicated variable.

14. $B = \dfrac{P}{R}$ for R

15. $S = \dfrac{\pi r^2 A}{90}$ for A

16. $S = c + g$ for g

17. $R = \dfrac{gs}{g + s}$ for g

18. $fz - gz = h$ for z

19. $2k = ak + 7$ for k

20. The formula for the total amount of money owed on a long-term loan is $A = p + prt$.

a Solve for t (time in years).

b Find t when p (principal) = \$7,400, A (total amount) is \$9,176, and r (rate) is 8%.

21. **MP 2** The length of a rectangle is 4 centimeters longer than the width. The perimeter of the rectangle is 72 centimeters. Find the length and width of the rectangle.

22. **MP 2** The length of each side of a square is 2 inches less than the length of the side of an equilateral triangle. The perimeters of the two shapes are the same. Find the lengths of the sides of each figure.

23. **MP 2** When Lillian emptied her wallet, she had 14 coins, all quarters, dimes, and nickels. She had twice as many dimes as quarters and twice as many nickels as dimes. All together, the value of the coins was \$1.30. How many quarters did she have? How many dimes? How many nickels?

24. **MP 2, 4, 6** Barbara babysat for 8 hours. Copy the table below and fill in the spaces using the answers to **a** through **c**.

	Hours	Salary per Hour	Salary Earned
Before Midnight			
After Midnight			

a If x is the total number of hours Barbara worked before midnight, express, in terms of x, the number of hours she worked after midnight.

b Barbara earns \$8.00 an hour before midnight. Express, in terms of x, her earnings before midnight.

c Barbara earns \$10.50 an hour after midnight. Express, in terms of x, her earnings after midnight.

d Last Saturday Barbara earned \$74. How many hours did she work before midnight? How many hours did she work after midnight? Explain your reasoning. Identify the properties you used to arrive at your answer.

25. **MP 2, 6, 7, 8** Cereal is sold in rectangular solid-shaped boxes. The formula for the volume of a rectangular solid is $V = lwh$, where V is the volume, l is the length of the base, w is the width of the base, and h is the height.

a Solve the formula for the width of the base.

b Create two other formulas that are equivalent to the formula you found in part **a**. In each step to create the equivalent formula, identify the property that makes it true.

LESSON 2.3

2.3 Ratios, Rates, and Proportions

Ratios and Rates

A **ratio** is a comparison of two numbers by division. Ratios can be written in several ways. For example, if your school has 4 freshmen to every 3 sophomores, the ratio can be written as 4 to 3, 4 : 3, or $\frac{4}{3}$.

The fraction form of a ratio is the most useful.

A *continued ratio*, or compound ratio, has more than two ratios in a definite order.

- For example, if the ratio a to b to c is 2 : 3 : 5, then $\frac{a}{b} = \frac{2}{3}$, $\frac{b}{c} = \frac{3}{5}$, and $\frac{a}{c} = \frac{2}{5}$.

A ratio can compare quantities that measure similar properties, such as time. In this case, the unit of measure must be the same.

- For example, in a ratio of time (h) spent doing homework to time (t) spent watching television, h and t should both be in minutes or both be in hours.

A **rate** is a ratio. Rates often compare measurements of different quantities, such as miles per hour.

Slope, or rise over run, is a rate.

A *unit rate* is a rate written with a denominator of 1. If a given rate has some other denominator, we can find the unit rate by simplifying.

- For example, $\frac{125 \text{ miles}}{2 \text{ hours}} = \frac{125}{2} = 62.5$ miles per hour or $\frac{62.5}{1}$ miles per one hour

A *unit price* is a rate of cost, or price, per 1 unit of measure, such as \$2.50 per pound.

- For example, to find the unit price of some gasoline, divide the total cost by the number of units, as in \$33.20 for 8 gallons of gas or $\frac{\$33.20}{8 \text{ gal}} = \frac{\$4.15}{1 \text{ gal}} = \$4.15$ per gallon.

MODEL PROBLEMS

1. Carol's favorite radio station plays 6 new hit songs and 4 oldies every hour. Write a comparison using three ratio notations.

SOLUTION

This problem does not specify order of terms, so we can write the ratio of hits to oldies or oldies to hits.

Words	6 hits to 4 oldies	4 oldies to 6 hits
Colon	6 hits : 4 oldies	4 oldies : 6 hits
Division	$\frac{6 \text{ hits}}{4 \text{ oldies}} = \frac{3 \text{ hits}}{2 \text{ oldies}}$	$\frac{4 \text{ oldies}}{6 \text{ hits}} = \frac{2 \text{ oldies}}{3 \text{ hits}}$

Model Problems continue . . .

Model Problems *continued*

2. Write a ratio comparing 8 hours to 3 days.

SOLUTION

To make the unit of measure the same, we can convert days to hours or hours to days. (Note that this problem specifies order of terms.)

Converting 3 Days to Hours	Converting 8 Hours to Days
Step 1. There are 24 hours in a day, so multiply: $3 \times 24 \text{ hours} = 72 \text{ hours}$	Step 1. In this case we divide by 24: $8 \text{ hours} \div 24 = \frac{8}{24} \text{ day} = \frac{1}{3} \text{ day}$
Step 2. Set up the ratio: $\frac{8 \text{ hours}}{3 \text{ days}} = \frac{8 \text{ hours}}{72 \text{ hours}} = \frac{1}{9}$	Step 2. Write the ratio and simplify: $\frac{1}{3} \text{ day to } 3 \text{ days} = \frac{1}{3} \div 3 = \frac{1}{3} \bullet \frac{1}{3} = \frac{1}{9}$

3. Which costs less per ounce: 12 ounces of Oatsies for \$2.79 or 17.2 ounces of Kornsies for \$3.33?

SOLUTION

Find the unit price—the rate per 1 ounce—of each cereal and see which is less:

$$\text{unit price of Oatsies} = \frac{\text{total cost}}{\text{number of units}} = \frac{\$2.79}{12} = \$0.2325\text{, rounded to } \$0.23 \text{ per ounce}$$

$$\text{unit price of Kornsies} = \frac{\text{total cost}}{\text{number of units}} = \frac{\$3.33}{17.2} = \$0.1936\text{, rounded to } \$0.19 \text{ per ounce}$$

Answer: Kornsies cost less.

4. **MP 2, 6** Nathan attends college in Australia. He bicycles from his apartment, which is 12 km from the college. Hint: 1 mile = 1.6 km.

a If it takes him x minutes, what is his average speed in miles per hour?

b If it takes him 40 minutes, what is his average speed in miles per hour?

SOLUTION

a $$\frac{12 \text{ km}}{x \text{ min}} \bullet \frac{1 \text{ mile}}{1.6 \text{ km}} \bullet \frac{60 \text{ min}}{1 \text{ hr}} = \frac{450 \text{ miles}}{x \text{ hr}}$$

b $$\frac{12 \text{ km}}{40 \text{ min}} \bullet \frac{1 \text{ mile}}{1.6 \text{ km}} \bullet \frac{60 \text{ min}}{1 \text{ hr}} = 11.25 \text{ miles/hr}$$

5. **MP 2, 6** Maria can read about 160 words per minute. She has an assignment to read a book that is 300 pages long.

a If a typical book has about x words per page, how many minutes should she set aside for this reading?

b If a typical book has about 360 words per page, how many hours and minutes should she set aside for this reading?

SOLUTION

a $$\frac{300 \text{ pages}}{1} \bullet \frac{x \text{ words}}{1 \text{ page}} \bullet \frac{1 \text{ min}}{160 \text{ words}} = 1.875x \text{ minutes}$$

b $$\frac{300 \text{ pages}}{1} \bullet \frac{360 \text{ words}}{1 \text{ page}} \bullet \frac{1 \text{ min}}{160 \text{ words}} = 675 \text{ minutes, or 11 hours and 15 minutes}$$

PRACTICE

1. John F. Kennedy High School is collecting waste metal and paper for recycling. Five classes bring in the following amounts. Which two classes brought in the same ratio of bags of metal to bags of paper?

	Number of Bags	
Class	Metal	Paper
Ms. Ginty's	4	6
Ms. Greenberg's	7	3
Mr. Rondone's	2	3
Mr. Scott's	3	2
Mr. Stanley's	4	3

A. Mr. Scott's and Mr. Rondone's

B. Ms. Ginty's and Mr. Stanley's

C. Mr. Scott's and Mr. Stanley's

D. Ms. Ginty's and Mr. Rondone's

2. A candy dish contains p peppermints, s spearmints, and b butterscotch candies. Write an expression for the ratio of spearmints to total number of candies.

A. $s : (p + s + b)$

B. $s : (p + b)$

C. $(p + s + b) : 3$

D. $s : b$

3. On each floor of a building, the ratio of offices to windows to doors is 25 : 55 : 33. What is the ratio of doors to windows?

A. 11 to 5 C. 3 to 5

B. 11 to 10 D. 5 to 3

4. Write a ratio comparing 4 feet to 2 yards.

A. 4 : 2 C. 12 : 2

B. 4 : 6 D. 12 : 6

5. Every working day, Angela commutes 35 minutes each way. If she works 7 hours, what is the ratio of her total travel time to her time at work?

A. $\frac{5}{1}$ C. $\frac{10}{1}$

B. $\frac{1}{6}$ D. $\frac{1}{12}$

6. A school has 500 books for every 25 students. Express this as a unit rate.

A. 20 books per student

B. 20 students per book

C. 500 books per student

D. 1 student per 25 books

7. Write two other notations for "7 to 10."

8. A soccer team played 32 games, won 20, and tied none. Find the ratio and simplify:

a games won to games lost
b games won to total number of games

9. A baseball team played 5 games and scored a different number of runs in each game: 3, 4, 1, 0, 5. How many runs per game does the team score?

10. A secretary types a 500-word document in 12 minutes. How many words per minute can he type?

11. Arriving in Freedonia, you cash a $100 traveler's check and get 912.35 freedons (the local currency). What is the exchange rate for:

a dollars to freedons
b freedons to dollars

12. Cindy watched a music channel for an hour and a half and counted 5 commercial breaks. She then watched a movie on network TV for 3 hours and counted 13 commercial breaks. Which channel had a higher rate of commercial breaks per hour, and what was its rate?

13. Write as a ratio in simplest form: 750 milliliters to 2 liters.

14. **MP 2, 3, 6** Which costs *more* per ounce: 13.5 ounces of Wheatsies for $3.09 or 20 ounces for $3.99? Explain how you arrived at your answer.

15. **MP 2, 3, 6** Which costs *less* per cup: 3 cups of yogurt for $2 or 5 cups for $3? Explain how you arrived at your answer.

Proportions

A **proportion** is a statement that two ratios are equal, or proportional. Proportions may be written in several ways. For example:

$\frac{4}{5} = \frac{8}{10}$ Four-fifths is proportional to eight-tenths.

$4 : 5 = 8 : 10$ Four is to five as eight is to ten.

Two ratios in fraction form are equal if and only if their *cross products* are equal:

$$\frac{4}{5} \times \frac{8}{10}$$

$4 \bullet 10 = 40$ and $5 \bullet 8 = 40$

Since cross products are equal, we can use **cross multiplication** to find the missing value in a proportion.

As with ratios, it is often most useful to express proportions as fractions when calculations are necessary. A proportion in fraction form has four terms: a numerator and a denominator for each of two fractions. Proportion problems often involve finding one missing term, or value, when the other three terms are known.

MODEL PROBLEMS

1. Solve $\frac{4x}{9} = \frac{2(x + 4)}{3}$.

SOLUTION

Write the equation.

$$\frac{4x}{9} = \frac{2(x + 4)}{3}$$

Cross multiply.

$$4x \bullet 3 = 9 \bullet [2(x + 4)]$$

Use the distributive property.

$$12x = 18x + 72$$

Subtract $18x$ from both sides.

$$12x - 18x = 18x + 72 - 18x$$

Simplify.

$$-6x = 72$$

Divide both sides by -6.

$$\frac{-6x}{-6} = \frac{72}{-6}$$

Simplify.

$$x = -12$$

Answer: $x = -12$

2. **MP 7** A builder uses 20 bricks to cover 3 square feet of wall. How many square feet can be covered with 2,090 bricks?

SOLUTION

Set up a proportion, being sure to write each ratio in the same way. We use the rate of bricks to square feet.

$$\frac{20 \text{ bricks}}{3 \text{ square feet}} = \frac{2{,}090 \text{ bricks}}{x \text{ square feet}}$$

or $\frac{20}{3} = \frac{2{,}090}{x}$ where x = square feet to be covered with 2,090 bricks

Cross multiply. $20 \bullet x = 3 \bullet 2{,}090$

Divide. $x = \frac{6{,}270}{20} = 313.5$

Answer: 2,090 bricks will cover 313.5 square feet.

ALTERNATE SOLUTION

There is more than one way to set up a proportion. Here, our proportion could also be:

$$\frac{20}{2{,}090} = \frac{3}{x} \text{ or } \frac{3}{20} = \frac{x}{2{,}090} \text{ or } \frac{2{,}090}{20} = \frac{x}{3}$$

Model Problems continue . . .

3. If $\frac{5a - x}{5a} = \frac{-1}{5}$, find the ratio of $a : x$.

SOLUTION

Cross multiply.	$5(5a - x) = (-1)(5a)$
Simplify using the order of operations.	$25a - 5x = -5a$
Add 5a to both sides of the equation.	$25a - 5x + 5a = -5a + 5a$
Simplify.	$30a - 5x = 0$
Add 5x to both sides of the equation.	$30a - 5x + 5x = 0 + 5x$
Simplify.	$30a = 5x$
Divide both sides by x.	$\frac{30a}{x} = \frac{5x}{x}$
Simplify.	$\frac{30a}{x} = 5$
Divide both sides by 30.	$\frac{a}{x} = \frac{5}{30}$
Simplify to find the ratio.	$\frac{a}{x} = \frac{1}{6}$

4. The numerator of a fraction is 6 less than the denominator of the fraction. The value of the fraction is $\frac{2}{3}$. Find the original fraction.

SOLUTION

Let x = the denominator of the original fraction. Let $x - 6$ = the numerator of the original fraction.

Then $\frac{x-6}{x} = \frac{2}{3}$.

Cross multiply.

$$\begin{aligned} 3(x - 6) &= 2x \\ 3x - 3(6) &= 2x \\ 3x - 18 &= 2x \\ -2x \quad &= -2x \\ \hline x - 18 &= 0 \\ +18 &= +18 \\ \hline x &= 18 \text{ (denominator)} \\ x - 6 &= 12 \text{ (numerator)} \end{aligned}$$

Therefore, the fraction is $\frac{12}{18}$. The check for this problem is to make sure $\frac{12}{18} = \frac{2}{3}$.

Answer: $\frac{12}{18}$

Model Problems continue . . .

Model Problems *continued*

5. **MP 2, 4** A merchant sells a digital clock at a profit that is $\frac{2}{7}$ of his cost.

a What is the ratio of his profit (P) to his selling price (SP)?

b If his selling price is \$45, what is his profit?

c What was his initial cost?

SOLUTION

Let P = profit, SP = selling price, and C = cost.

a Since $P = \frac{2}{7}C$, then $\frac{P}{C} = \frac{2}{7}$ so that $P = 2x$ and $C = 7x$.
The selling price is the sum of the cost and profit.

$SP = C + P$ or $7x + 2x = 9x$

The ratio $P : SP = 2x : 9x$ or $2 : 9$

b Given that $SP = \$45$, then $SP = 9x = 45$ and $x = 5$.

If $x = 5$, Profit $= 2x$ or \$10

c $SP - P = \text{Cost}$; $\$45 - \$10 = \$35$

PRACTICE

1. $\frac{6}{p} = \frac{36}{24}$. Solve for p.

A. $p = 1\frac{1}{2}$

B. $p = 4$

C. $p = 9$

D. $p = 144$

2. $3 : x = 2 : 3$. Solve for x.

A. $\frac{2}{3}$

B. 2

C. 3

D. $\frac{9}{2}$

3. In one county in New York state, the ratio of Eagle Scouts to Boy Scouts is 1 : 4. If the number of Boy Scouts is 2,400, what is the number of Eagle Scouts?

A. 38,400

B. 9,600

C. 2,400

D. 600

4. Which proportion is equivalent to $y : 7 = 5 : 3$?

A. $y : 3 = 5 : 7$

B. $y : 3 = 7 : 5$

C. $5 : y = 3 : 7$

D. $5 : y = 7 : 3$

5. According to the directions on the box, $1\frac{1}{3}$ cups of pancake mix and 1 cup water will make enough pancakes for 2 people. How many cups of mix are needed to make pancakes for 5 people?

A. $1\frac{7}{8}$

B. $2\frac{2}{3}$

C. $3\frac{1}{3}$

D. $3\frac{1}{2}$

6. At a book sale, 6 books cost \$13. At that rate, how many books could you buy for \$32.50?

A. 15

B. 17

C. 19

D. 23

Practice Problems continue . . .

7. MP 3, 6 $\frac{100\text{ fleas}}{16\text{ dogs}} = \frac{25\text{ dogs}}{4\text{ fleas}}$

a Explain what is wrong with this proportion.

b Rewrite it correctly.

8. The wingspan of a jet plane is 22.5 m. If a model of the plane is built to a scale of 1 cm = 3 m, what is the wingspan of the model?

9. The ratio of boys to girls in a school band is 4 : 3. There are 21 girls in the band. How many members does the band have?

10. In 2 weeks, a family drinks 3 gallons of milk. How many gallons will this family drink in 9 weeks?

11. If $\frac{2}{3}$ of a bucket is filled in 1 minute, how much *more* time will it take to fill the whole bucket?

12. You are making a cookie recipe that calls for 2 cups of flour and 4 eggs. You have $6\frac{1}{2}$ cups of flour, and you want to use it all up. How many eggs will you use?

13. A theater has 1,500 seats. One night, 9 out of every 10 seats were filled. How many people attended that night?

14. The tax bill for a house with an assessed value of $75,620 is $847. At the same rate, find the tax (to the nearest dollar) for a house with an assessed value of $110,000.

15. On a bus, 2 adults can ride for the same price as 3 children. If 1 adult ticket costs $48, what is the price of a child's ticket?

16. The denominator of a fraction exceeds the numerator by 4. If 2 is subtracted from the numerator of the original fraction and the denominator is left unchanged, the resulting fraction is equal to $\frac{1}{2}$. Find the original fraction.

17. In each of the following, find the ratio of $a : x$

a $5a = x$

b $4a + 2x = 0$

c $3x - 2a = 0$

d $\frac{4a + 3x}{3x} = 7$

e $\frac{3x + 2a}{2a} = \frac{4}{3}$

18. The lengths of the sides of a quadrilateral are in the ratio of 2 : 4 : 5 : 9. If the perimeter of the quadrilateral is 620 cm, what are the lengths of the sides?

19. MP 4 The shadow lengths were all measured at the same time of day.

a Complete the table.

Object	Length of Shadow (ft)	Height (ft)
Basketball Player	2	7
Maple Tree	8	
Flagpole		20
Tomato Plant Stakes	1.5	

b Write the equation used to complete the table.

20. Two numbers are in the ratio of 5 to 7.5. If the smaller number is 164, what is the other number?

21. If an investment profit of $120,000 is to be divided among three investors in the ratio of 3 : 5 : 7, how much did each investor receive?

22. Solve for the indicated variable:

a Solve for x. $\frac{12}{x + 2} = \frac{4}{x - 2}$

b Solve for x. $\frac{x + 3}{x - 1} = 9$

c Solve for t. $P = \frac{A}{1 + rt}$

Practice Problems continue . . .

23. Victoria is building a scale model of her mint, first-of-its-kind, 1967 Lion using a ratio of 24 inches to one inch. If the length of the actual car is 15.8 ft, what will be the length in inches of her scale model?

24. If the volume of a cube of sugar is 1 cubic inch, what is the total surface area of the sugar cube?

25. If the volume of a cube is 216 cubic inches, what is the surface area of the cube?

26. If the ratio of the areas of the faces of two cubes is 25 : 81, what is the ratio of their volumes?

27. If the ratio of tin to silver in 78 pounds of a certain alloy is 12 : 1, how much silver is in the alloy?

LESSON 2.4

2.4 Modeling with Linear Equations

To solve word problems with modeling, read the problem carefully and assign variables to quantities in a meaningful manner (p for perimeter, d for distance, t for time, etc.). Then use the wording of the problem to write an algebraic expression and equation. Complete the process by solving the equation.

MODEL PROBLEMS

1. The sum of two numbers is 20. Four times the larger is 1 less than five times the smaller.

What are the numbers?

SOLUTION

Let x = one number (say the larger), and $20 - x$ = the other number.

$4x = 5(20 - x) - 1$

$4x = 100 - 5x - 1$

$9x = 99$

$x = 11$ and $20 - x = 9$

Answer: 9, 11

Model Problems continue . . .

2. **MP 4** The train stations in New York and Boston are 220 miles apart. A train left New York for Boston at 8:00 A.M. traveling at 65 mph. An hour later, an express train left Boston for New York traveling at 90 mph. Draw a diagram of the situation. At what time did they pass each other?

SOLUTION

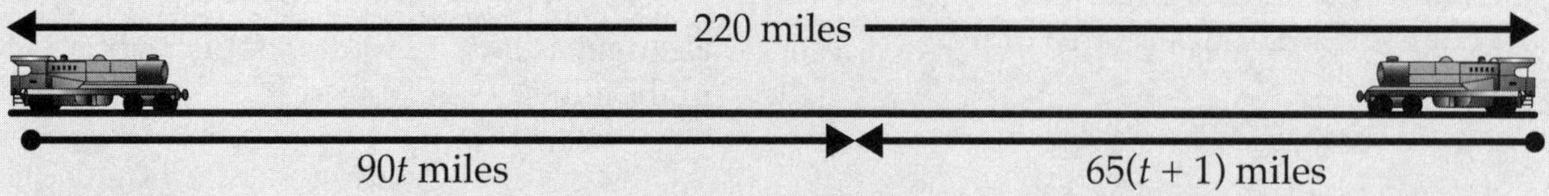

When the trains meet, the total distance traveled is the same as the distance between cities, 220 miles. Let t represent the time the express train was traveling and $t + 1$ represent the travel time of the other train.

Use $d = rt$.	$90t + 65(t + 1) = 220$
Distribute.	$90t + 65t + 65 = 220$
Combine like terms.	$155t + 65 = 220$
Add -65 to both sides.	$-65 \quad -65$
	$155t = 155$
Solve.	$t = 1$

Answer: The trains passed after the express train had been traveling for one hour, which was at 10:00 A.M.

Check. $90t + 65(t + 1) = 220 \rightarrow 90(1) + 65(1 + 1) = 90 + 130 = 220$ ✓

PRACTICE

1. Divide a 21-inch-long piece of duct tape into two parts in the ratio of 3 : 4.
2. If two numbers are in the ratio 5 to 3 and the sum of the numbers is -24, what is the smaller number?
3. What is the ratio of profit to selling price if the cost is \$8 and the selling price is \$12?
4. If the cost to a computer store for a PC is \$1800, and the store wants to make a profit that is $\frac{1}{10}$ of the selling price, for how much should the store sell the computer?
5. Kim drives 378 miles and uses 18 gallons of gasoline. At that rate, how many miles can she go on 24 gallons of gas?
6. Marcello travels 172 miles in 4 hours. At that rate, how long will it take him to travel 387 miles?
7. Two similar cylinders have volumes of 27 cubic centimeters and 8 cubic centimeters. If the height of the larger cylinder is 9 centimeters, what is the height of the smaller cylinder?

Practice Problems continue . . .

8. A pentagonal drawing (figure *ABCDE*) of a museum is shown in relation to the similar shape and indicated dimensions of the actual museum (figure *FGHJK*). Using the given measurements, find the length of side *HJ* of the museum.

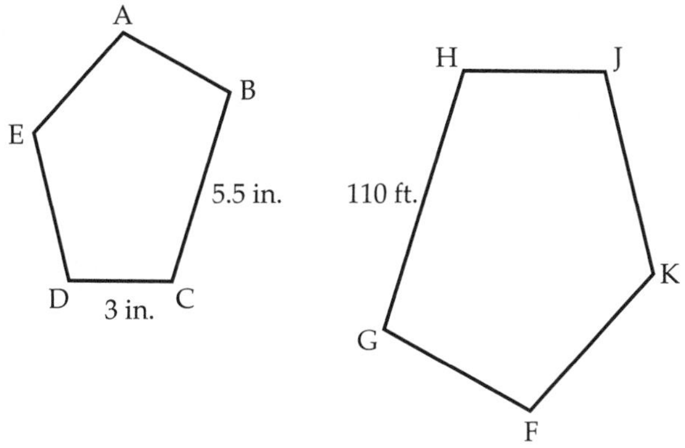

9. For Mother's Day, Jim bought 3 hydrangea plants. For Father's Day, he bought two ties. If a tie costs $5 more than a plant and he spent a total of $94.75 on both the ties and hydrangeas, how much was the cost of a tie? What was the cost of a hydrangea plant?

10. The difference between twice a number and $\frac{2}{3}$ of the number is 68. What is the number?

11. The perimeters of two gardens are equal. The measures of those gardens are shown below. One is a rectangle and the other is an isosceles triangle. Find the perimeters of the gardens.

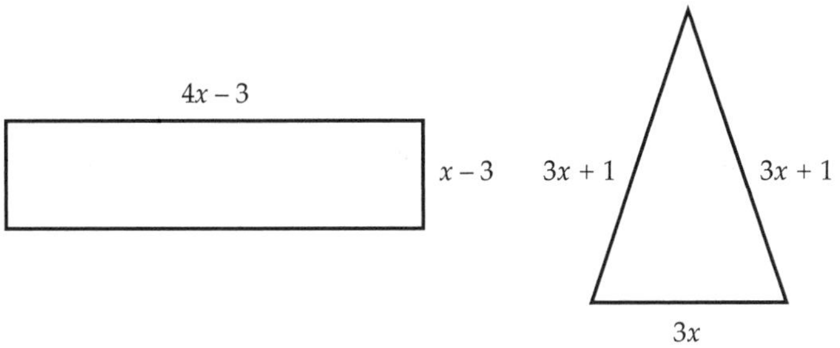

12. Jason consumes 1500 calories and needs to put on weight, so he plans on increasing his caloric intake by 150 calories a day. His sister, Lisa, needs to lose weight and decrease her present intake of 3500 calories by 100 calories a day. After how many days will they be consuming the same number of calories?

13. Moving Company A charges a flat fee of $1200 plus $18 an hour. Company B charges $900 plus $23 an hour. After how many hours would the price be the same regardless of which company was chosen?

14. The length of each side of a square is 3 inches less than the length of a side of an equilateral triangle. If the perimeters of the two figures are the same, what is the measure of the sides of each figure?

15. At a summertime poolside snack bar, 200 ice cream cones were sold in one day. Double scoops sold for $1.25 each, and single scoops sold for $1 each. If the proceeds from the sale of cones were $221.75, how many of each kind of cone were sold? In all, how many scoops of ice cream were sold?

16. Twice the sum of half a number and 3 times the number is 27 more than 2.5 times the number. Find the number.

17. If the degree measures of the three angles of ΔABC have the ratio 4 : 4 : 7, what are the measures of the angles? The sum of the three internal angles of a triangle is equal to 180°.

18. The lengths of the sides of a triangle are in the ratio of 3 : 3 : 5. If the perimeter of the triangle is 44 cm, what are the lengths of the sides?

Practice Problems continue . . .

19. The train stations of New York City and Burlington, Vermont, are approximately 295 miles apart. One train leaves New York for Burlington at 9 A.M. at an average speed of 70 mph. A second train leaves Burlington for New York 2 hours later and travels at 85 mph. At what time did they pass each other?

20. The given rectangle is 6 in. wide. A rectangular strip 4 in. long (as shown) is cut off from the end of the rectangle. The area of the remaining rectangle is now 75% of the original area. What were the dimensions of the original rectangle?

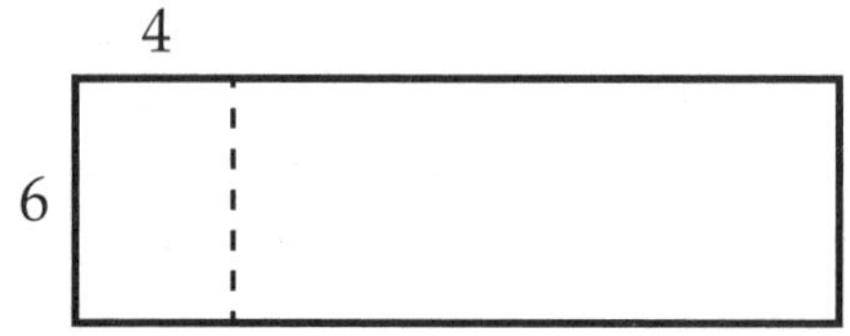

21. In Egypt, the Suez Canal was opened 45 years before the Panama Canal. Up until 1959, the Suez Canal had been operating twice as long as the Panama Canal. In what year was the Suez Canal opened? In what year was the Panama Canal opened?

22. If the Statue of Liberty were 325 feet taller, it would be just as tall as the Gateway Arch in St. Louis. The height of the Statue of Liberty is 10 feet less than half the height of the Gateway Arch. How tall is each one of these structures?

23. Thomas Jefferson was born 11 years after George Washington. In 1772, Washington's age was 5 years more than 7 times the age of Jefferson in the year 1748. What was the age of each man in 1748, 1776 (Declaration of Independence), and 1787 (Constitutional Convention)?

24. **MP 2, 4** The given figure is that of a tennis court. Here are some facts:

(1) the doubles court and the singles court have the same length,

(2) the width of the doubles court is 9 feet greater than that of the singles court,

(3) the length of the singles court is 6 feet greater than twice the width of the doubles court, and

(4) the width of the singles court is one foot greater than one-third the length of the doubles court.

Find the dimensions of the singles court and the doubles court.

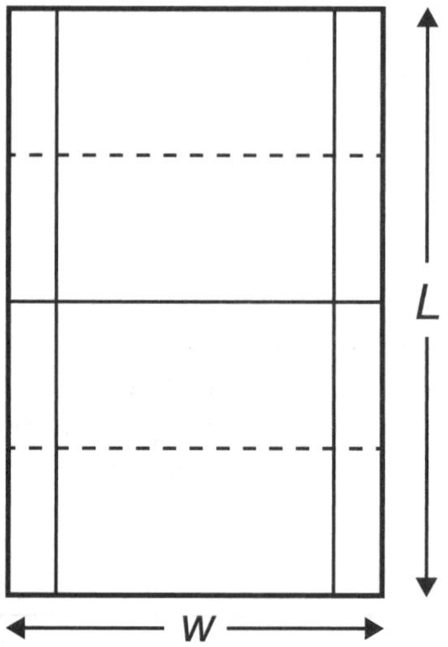

LESSON 2.5

2.5 Solving Inequalities

An **inequality** consists of two or more expressions joined by a sign of inequality. The signs of inequality are $<$ (less than), $>$ (greater than), $\leq$ (less than or equal to), $\geq$ (greater than or equal to), and $\neq$ (not equal to).

A *linear inequality in one variable* is an inequality of the first degree that contains only one variable.

Examples of linear inequalities in one variable are $x - 2 > 2x$ and $5x + 2 \neq 4$.

Unless a restriction is stated, the domain of any inequality is the real number line. The solution set is the set of all numbers in the domain that make the inequality true. This set can be represented on a number line.

An open circle marking a value on the number line indicates that the number is *not* included in the solution set.

$x < 4$

A closed circle marking a value on the number line indicates that the number *is* included in the solution set.

$x \geq -2$

A **compound inequality** is formed by joining two inequalities with *and* or *or*, using the symbol $\wedge$ for *and*, and the symbol $\vee$ for *or*.

- $(x < 5)$ *and* $(x \geq -2)$ can be written as $(x < 5) \wedge (x \geq -2)$, as well as $-2 \leq x < 5$. This compound inequality containing *and* is true *only if both inequalities are true*. The graph of this compound inequality is the *intersection* of the graphs of the two inequalities.

$(x < 5)$ means

$(x \geq -2)$ means

The overlap, or *intersection*, of the two sets represented by $(x < 5) \wedge (x \geq -2)$ is

An easy way to remember the symbol $\wedge$ for *and* is that it looks like an A without the crossbar.

- $(x > 4)$ or $(x \leq 0)$ can be written as $(x > 4) \vee (x \leq 0)$. There is no shorter notation. This compound inequality containing the word *or* is true *if one or more of the inequalities is true*. The graph of this compound inequality is the *union* of the graphs of the two inequalities.

$(x > 4)$ means

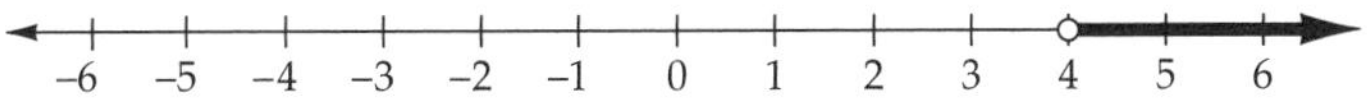

$(x \leq 0)$ means

The *union* of the two sets represented by $(x > 4) \vee (x \leq 0)$ is

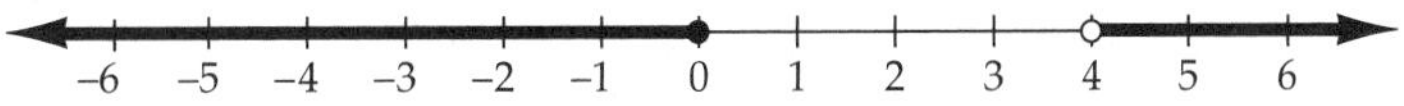

Properties of Inequalities

In each case below, assume that a, b, and c are real numbers.

Property	Description	Examples
Comparison or order property of numbers	For all numbers a and b, exactly one of the following statements is true: $a < b$, $a = b$, or $a > b$.	For numbers 2 and 3, only $2 < 3$ is true.
Addition property of inequality	If $a > b$, then $a + c > b + c$.	$4 > 1$, so $4 + 2 > 1 + 2$ $6 > 3$
	If $a < b$, then $a + c < b + c$.	$-3 < 1$, so $-3 + 5 < 1 + 5$ $2 < 6$
Subtraction property of inequality	If $a > b$, then $a - c > b - c$.	$2 > -5$, so $2 - 4 > -5 - 4$ $-2 > -9$
	If $a < b$, then $a - c < b - c$.	$0 < 3$, so $0 - 4 < 3 - 4$ $-4 < -1$
Multiplication property of inequality	If $a > b$ and c is positive ($c > 0$), then $ca > cb$.	$3 > 1$, so $2 \bullet 3 > 2 \bullet 1$ $6 > 2$
	If $a < b$ and c is positive ($c > 0$), then $ca < cb$.	$5 < 6$, so $3 \times 5 < 3 \times 6$ $15 < 18$
	If $a > b$ and c is negative ($c < 0$), then $ca < cb$.	$9 > 4$, so $-1 \times 9 < -1 \times 4$ $-9 < -4$
	If $a < b$ and c is negative ($c < 0$), then $ca > cb$.	$3 < 8$, so $-3 \times 3 > -3 \times 8$ $-9 > -24$
Division property of inequality	If c is positive ($c > 0$) and $a > b$, then $\frac{a}{c} > \frac{b}{c}$.	$12 > 6$, so $\frac{12}{3} > \frac{6}{3}$ $4 > 2$
	If c is positive ($c > 0$) and $a < b$, then $\frac{a}{c} < \frac{b}{c}$.	$4 < 8$, so $\frac{4}{2} < \frac{8}{2}$ $2 < 4$
	If c is negative ($c < 0$) and $a > b$, then $\frac{a}{c} < \frac{b}{c}$.	$3 > 2$, so $\frac{3}{-1} < \frac{2}{-1}$ $-3 < -2$
	If c is negative ($c < 0$) and $a < b$, then $\frac{a}{c} > \frac{b}{c}$.	$3 < 6$, so $\frac{3}{-3} > \frac{6}{-3}$ $-1 > -2$
Transitive property of inequality	For all numbers a, b, and c: If $a < b$ and $b < c$, then $a < c$ and similarly, if $a > b$ and $b > c$, then $a > c$.	If $4 < 5$ and $5 < 7$, then $4 < 7$ Also, if $3 > 1$ and $1 > -5$, then $3 > -5$

To Solve a Linear Inequality

- Follow the same steps that apply to solving equations, with one very important exception: *When you multiply or divide by a negative number, you must change the direction of the inequality.*
- To check the answer for an inequality, substitute a number from the graph of the solution set.

MODEL PROBLEMS

1. Solve and graph $x + 3 \geq 6$.

SOLUTION

$$x + 3 \geq 6$$
$$x + 3 - 3 \geq 6 - 3$$
$$x \geq 3$$

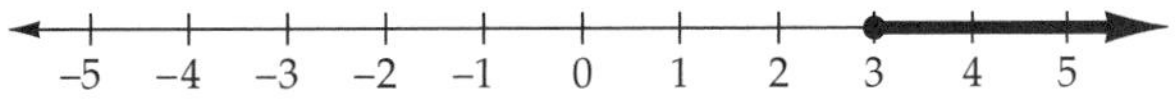

2. Solve and graph $1 - 4x < 13$.

SOLUTION

$$1 - 4x < 13$$
$$1 - 1 - 4x < 13 - 1$$
$$-4x < 12$$
$$\frac{-4x}{-4} > \frac{12}{-4}$$ *Note the change in the inequality!*
$$x > -3$$

3. Solve the inequality $\frac{2x}{5} - \frac{x}{2} > \frac{9}{10}$, and graph the solution set.

SOLUTION

The LCD of 5, 2, and 10 is 10.

$$10\left(\frac{2x}{5} - \frac{x}{2}\right) > 10\left(\frac{9}{10}\right)$$
$$4x - 5x > 9$$
$$-x > 9$$
$$(-1)(-x) < (-1)9$$ *Note the change in the inequality!*
$$x < -9$$

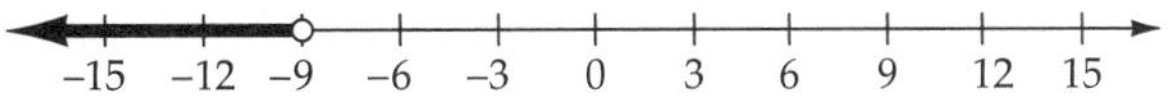

4. Graph the following:

SOLUTIONS

a $x \neq 1$

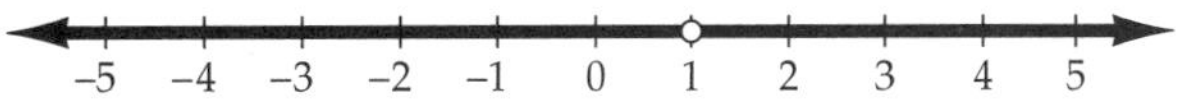

All real numbers except 1 are included in the solution set.

b $(x \leq -1)$ or $(x > 4)$

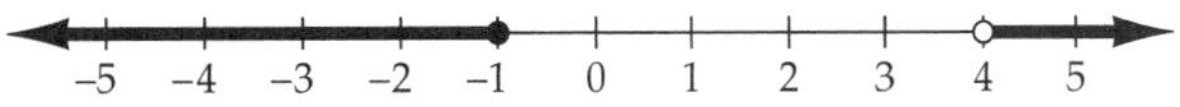

The word *or* means that the solution set is all the values that satisfy at least one of the inequalities.

c $(x > 2)$ and $(x \leq 5)$

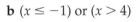

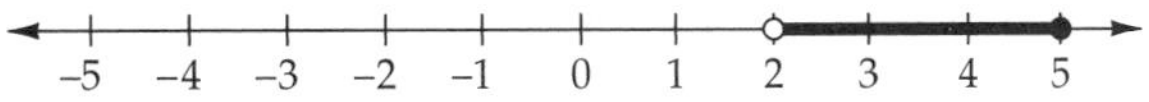

The word *and* means that the solution set is all the values that satisfy both inequalities.

Model Problems continue . . .

Model Problems *continued*

5. Solve and graph the following:

a $(2 \leq y + 5) \wedge (y + 5 < 9)$

b $(3 + x \leq -2) \vee (5 + x \geq 5)$

SOLUTIONS

a $2 \leq y + 5$ and $y + 5 < 9$

$2 - 5 \leq y$ and $y < 9 - 5$

$-3 \leq y$ and $y < 4$

b $3 + x \leq -2$ or $5 + x \geq 5$

$x \leq -2 - 3$ or $x \geq 5 - 5$

$x \leq -5$ or $x \geq 0$

6. Write a compound inequality for the solution set graphed below.

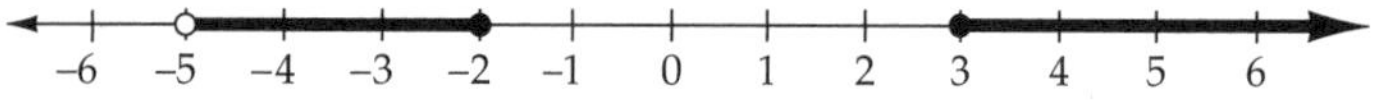

> **This is an example of a compound inequality that contains another compound inequality.**

SOLUTION

The graph to the left is an *and* inequality, while the graph to the right is part of an *or* inequality. Therefore, the statement is $(-5 < x \leq -2)$ or $(x \geq 3)$

Answer: $(-5 < x \leq -2) \vee (x \geq 3)$

PRACTICE

1. Which of the following is a member of the solution set of $-6 < x \leq -1$?

A. -7 C. -1

B. -6 D. 3

2. Which inequality is represented by this graph?

A. $4 \leq x < -3$ C. $-3 < x \leq 4$

B. $-3 \leq x \leq 4$ D. $-3 \leq x < 4$

3. Which graph represents the solution set of $2x > 6$?

A. 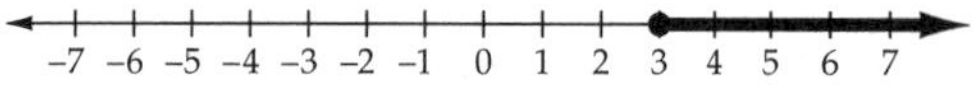

B. 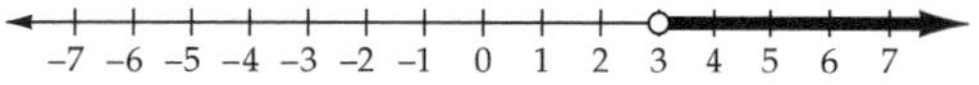

C. 

D. 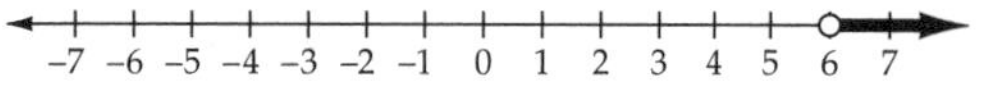

4. Which graph shows the solution to $(x < 3)$ and $(x > -1)$?

A. 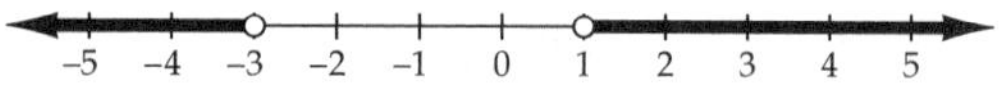

B. 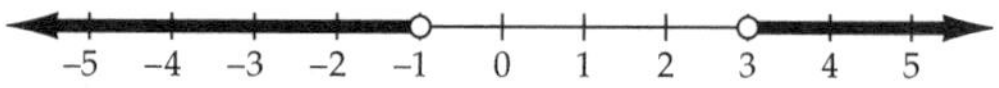

C. 

D. 

5. Which of the following inequalities represents the graph below?

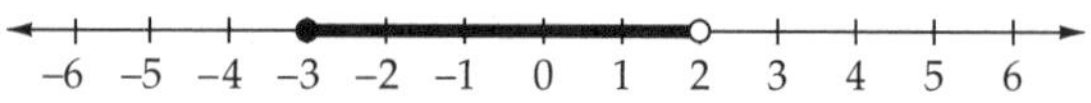

A. $-3 > x > 3$

B. $-3 \leq x < 2$

C. $-3 < x \leq 2$

D. $3 \leq x < -2$

Practice Problems continue . . .

6. Find the solution set for $\frac{1}{2}x + 4 \geq 4$ if the domain or replacement set for x is $\{-2, 0, 2, 3\}$.

A. $\{-2, 0\}$ C. $\{2, 3\}$
B. $\{0\}$ D. $\{0, 2, 3\}$

7. The solution set of $-5(x - 4) + 3x > -16$ is

A. $x > 18$

B. $x > -6$

C. $x < 6$

D. $x < 18$

8. Choose a variable and write an inequality that could be used to solve each problem. Then solve the problem.

a A number decreased by -5 is at least 10.
b The sum of a number and -4 is no smaller than 18.
c Twice a number is greater than three times the number added to 10.
d Five times a number is at most 40.
e The sum of five times a number and 8 is less than three times that number.
f A number increased by 3 is at most 7.
g A number increased by -7 is at least 11.
h The opposite of 7 times a number is less than 140.
i If the area of a square with side s is at least 64 square feet, what could be the possible values of s?
j The product of 3 and a number is no more than the sum of 8 and three times the number.

Exercises 9–27: Solve each inequality and graph the solution set.

9. $x - 3 > 1$

10. $4j + 1 \geq 25$

11. $1.5 - 3x \neq -4.5$

12. $21 - 5x \leq 36$

13. $4x + 3 > 3x - 7$

14. $6x - 7 \geq 2x + 25$

15. $3(x + 2) + 11 > 20$

16. $-5(x - 7) < 15$

17. $2(n + 9) \leq 3n + 15$

18. $20(1 - 0.5x) < 0.5(4 - 8x)$

19. $-6(x - 5) \leq -2(5x - 1)$

20. $-4(3x + 5) \geq -5(2x - 2)$

21. $3(n - 1) + 4(n + 1) \geq 22$

22. $3(y - 1) - 4 \leq 2 - 4(2 - y)$

23. $\frac{2}{x + 5} \geq \frac{1}{2x + 3}$

24. $\frac{3}{x - 4} \leq \frac{2}{3x + 2}$

25. $\frac{1}{2}x + \frac{1}{3}x \neq 5$

26. $-2 \leq x < 3$

27. $-4 < x - 2 \leq 3$

Exercises 28–38: Solve each compound inequality. State your answer and graph the solution.

28. a $-4 < 3x - 7 < 2$
b $5(x + 2) \leq 4(x + 1)$ and $11 + x < 0$

29. a $-5 < 2x + 1 \leq 9$

b $\frac{x}{2} + 3 > -2$ or $4 - x > 4$

30. a $-20 < -6x + 4 \leq 10$
b $x - 1 < -4$ or $x - 4 \geq 0$

31. $(c \geq -1)$ or $(c < -4)$

32. $(2x > 8) \vee (-3x > -6)$

33. $(x + 3 \geq 7) \wedge (3x < 15)$

34. $(x < -2) \vee (x > 4)$

35. $-3 < x + 2 < 7$

36. $(2y + 4 > 0)$ and $(y < 1)$

37. $2 + x \leq 2$ and $2 + x \geq 4$

38. $(9 - 4j > 17)$ or $(2j + 1 > 1)$

Practice Problems continue . . .

39. If the replacement set for x is $\{-4, -3, -2, -1, 0, 1, 2, 3, 4\}$, what is the solution set for $-2x > 6$?

40. If the domain for x is $\{-2, -1, 0, 1, 2, 3, 4\}$, what is the solution set (or range) of answers for $3x - 1 > 5$?

41. What are the integer values in the solution set of $3 \leq x < 7$?

42. Find the whole number that makes the following sentence true when substituted for x: $(3x > 6)$ and $(x < 4)$.

Exercises 43–49: Write the compound inequality for each solution set graphed below.

43. 

44. 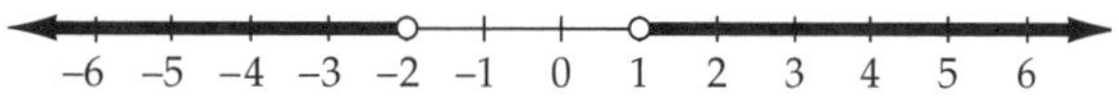

45. 

46. 

47. 

48. 

49. 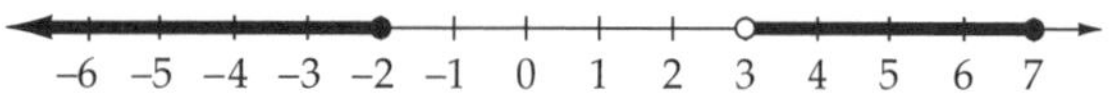

50. **MP 2, 6** If x, $x + 1$, and $x + 2$ are three consecutive integers, write the inequality given in the three sentences below. Then solve each inequality. Identify the properties used to solve the problem.

a The sum of two consecutive integers is less than or equal to 9.

b The sum of three consecutive integers is greater than 20.

c The sum of three consecutive integers is less than -6.

LESSON 2.6

2.6 Modeling with Inequalities

We use the same process that we used with modeling equalities to model inequalities. Remember to read the problem carefully, assign variables to quantities, create an inequality based on the word problem, and then solve the inequality.

MODEL PROBLEMS

1. The members of a school booster club are creating buttons for sale at basketball games. The machine to make the buttons costs \$45. The material needed to make each button costs 20 cents. The buttons will be sold for \$1 each. How many buttons must be sold to make a profit of at least \$100?

SOLUTION

Let number of buttons sold $= b$.

Then the income from sales $= \$1.00(b)$, or simply b dollars.

The expense of making buttons $= 0.20b$ dollars.

The total expenses $= 45 + 0.2b$ dollars.

Profit is equal to the income from sales minus the expenses. Profit is at least \$100. $\quad b - (45 + 0.2b) \geq 100$

Distribute -1 over the parentheses. $\quad b - 45 - 0.2b \geq 100$

Combine like terms. $\quad 0.8b - 45 \geq 100$

Add 45 to both sides. $\quad 0.8b \geq 145$

Divide both sides by 0.8. $\quad b \geq \frac{145}{0.8}$

$b \geq 181.25$

Replace 181.25 with the nearest greater whole number, since they cannot sell pieces of buttons. $\quad b \geq 182$

Answer: They must sell at least 182 buttons to make a profit of at least \$100.

2. If the two congruent sides of an isosceles triangle are 3.5 and the measure of the perimeter is an integer,

a What are the possible integer lengths of the base?

b What are the least and greatest possible perimeters of the triangle?

SOLUTION

The third side of any triangle is less than the sum of the other two sides and greater than the difference of those two sides: Difference < Third side < Sum.

a Difference $3.5 - 3.5 = 0$; sum $= 3.5 + 3.5 = 7$; $0 <$ base of triangle < 7;
Possible integer base lengths $= \{1, 2, 3, 4, 5, 6\}$

b Perimeter: smallest 8, largest 13.

3. The relationship between Celsius and Fahrenheit temperature scales is given by the formula $C = \frac{5}{9}(F - 32)$ where C is in degrees Celsius and F is in degrees Fahrenheit.

What interval on the Celsius scale corresponds to the temperature range $59° \leq F \leq 95°$?

SOLUTION

Substitute 59 and 95 for F in the given formula.

$C = \frac{5}{9}(59 - 32) = 15$ and $C = \frac{5}{9}(95 - 32) = 35$

Answer: $15° \leq C \leq 35°$

PRACTICE

1. Twice the sum of a number and 9 is no more than 3 times the same number increased by 15. Solve the inequality and graph the solution set.

2. Using algebra, find the smallest three consecutive integers whose sum is greater than 20.

3. The product of two numbers is no greater than 90. If one of the numbers is -10, what is the other number? Write an inequality that can be used to find the other number, and identify the smallest integer for which it is true.

4. The sum of any two sides of a triangle must be greater than the length of its third side. If two sides of a triangle are 3.3 and 5.7 and the perimeter must have an integer length,

   a What are the possible lengths of the 3rd side?

   b What are the least and greatest perimeters?

5. In triangle ABC, $AB = 2x + 1$, $AC = 5x$, and $BC = 50$.

   a What are the possible values for x, if we know that the sum of any two sides is greater than the length of the third side?

   b What are the smallest possible integer lengths for sides AB and AC?

6. In a given rectangle, the length is $4x - 5$ and the width is $x + 7$. If the perimeter is at most 44 feet, write an inequality that models that condition. Solve the inequality and state the largest dimensions of the figure.

7. If the length of a rectangular planting field is 10 km and the width is $x + 1$ km, for what values of x would the area of the planting field be greater than the perimeter?

8. The base of a triangle is 4 in. longer than the altitude. The sum of the base and the altitude is at least 25 in.

   a What is the least possible integer length of the base?

   b Using your answer to part **a**, what is the smallest possible area of the triangle?

9. Otto's loose change glass jar contains twice as many nickels as pennies and two-thirds as many dimes as nickels. If the total value is at least $3.65, what is the smallest possible number of coins in his collection? How many of each are there?

10. The members of a school booster club are creating armbands for sale at football games. The machine to make the armbands costs $185. The material needed to make each armband costs 25 cents apiece. The armbands will be sold for $2.50 each. How many armbands must be sold to make a profit of at least $200?

11. Two cars leave Equinox Country Club at the same time. One travels east at an average of 55 mph and the other west at 45 mph. After how many hours and minutes will the two cars be at least 360 miles apart?

12. Tony knows that his score on the Statewide Math Exam in June will count as two grades. He presently has four quarterly grades that average out to 88. What possible grades can he get on his State final to achieve an A average, which is 90 or better? The maximum possible grade is 100.

13. MP 2, 4 William currently has a backyard, square, blue-slate patio. He is redesigning his patio and making it into a larger rectangle with a length that is 5 feet shorter than three times its width. Side x, one of the original sides of the square, is an integer. William decides that the perimeter should be no less than 80 feet.

    a Write an inequality to model this situation and solve it.

    b What could be the smallest dimensions of the original square?

    c Using your answer to part **b**, determine the least area in square feet of his new patio.

14. Andrea sells cell phones in Sydney, but never on Sunday. She is paid $3,500 a month plus 20% of her monthly sales. She needs to earn at least $4,800 a month to pay for her rent, food, fun, and other life essentials. To afford her lifestyle, what amount of sales will Andrea need to achieve?

Practice Problems continue . . .

15. Usain is racing against his cousin, Korday, and he gives him a head start of 21 feet. If Korday runs at 6 feet/sec and Usain chases him at 9 feet/second, for how long will Korday remain ahead?

16. If the temperature range in Phoenix, Arizona, for a certain year is given as $5° \leq F \leq 104°$, where F is in degrees Fahrenheit, what interval on the Celsius scale corresponds to that temperature range?

17. What interval on the Fahrenheit scale corresponds to the temperature range in San Diego of $5° \leq C \leq 35°$, where C is in degrees Celsius?

18. Dry air moving upward expands and cools at a rate of approximately 1° Celsius for each 100 m rise above ground up to about 12 km.

a If the ground temperature registers 20°C, write a formula for the temperature T at height h (in meters).

b What range of temperatures in Celsius can be expected if a plane takes off and reaches a height of 6 km?

19. If the temperature at the base of the Empire State Building at 34th Street is 40° Fahrenheit and the temperature falls by approximately 1.80° for each 100 m in height h,

a Write a formula for the temperature T at any height h (in meters).

b Use the formula to determine the temperature on the outdoor viewing balcony, which is 350 meters above the street.

20. A manufacturer makes a line of woolen Alpaca rugs that measure 4 ft wide and have varying lengths n in feet. The floor area covered by these rugs ranges from 18 ft^2 to 29 ft^2. Write and then solve a compound inequality to find the range of the lengths of the rugs.

CHAPTER 2 REVIEW

1. A ride in a taxi costs $3.50 plus $0.35 for every fourth of a mile traveled. If Sam travels x miles, then which of the following algebraic expressions represents the cost of the trip?

A. $3.50 + 1.40x$

B. $3.50 + 0.35x$

C. 3.85x$

D. $0.35 + 3.50x$

2. Mr. Schmidtmann took 55 minutes to drive into the city and back. He took 5 minutes less for the return trip than for the drive into the city. How long did his return trip take?

A. 20 minutes

B. 25 minutes

C. 30 minutes

D. 35 minutes

3. Which inequality is equivalent to $5x - 5 > 15$?

A. $x > 4$

B. $x < 4$

C. $x > \frac{1}{4}$

D. $x < \frac{1}{4}$

4. Which inequality is equivalent to $4 - 4x > 16$?

A. $x > -3$

B. $x > 3$

C. $x < -3$

D. $x < 3$

Chapter Review continues . . .

Exercises 5–15: Solve for the unknown.

5. $\frac{7}{12}x = 3\frac{1}{2}$

6. $\frac{5}{8}n = 55$

7. $7 = 3x - 8$

8. $3x - 4 = 14$

9. $x + 0.02x = 510$

10. $\frac{2}{3}m + 7 = 27$

11. $5(x + 2) = 6 + 3(2x - 1)$

12. $\frac{3x - 5}{2} + \frac{5x + 1}{4} = 2x$

13. $\frac{x}{2} + \frac{x}{3} - \frac{x}{4} = 21$

14. $5m - 8 + 4m = 5 - (3m + 13)$

15. $20 - (8 + x) - (x - 1) = 39$

Exercises 16–23: Evaluate.

16. If $l = 25$, $n = 8$, $d = 3$, and $l = a + (n - 1)d$, find the value of a.

17. If $A = p + prt$, and $A = 77$, $p = 70$, and $r = 0.02$, what is the value of t?

18. Using the formula $C = \frac{5}{9}(F - 32)$, find the value of C if $F = 14$.

19. If $A = p + prt$, and $A = 250$, $r = 0.05$, and $t = 5$, what is the value of p?

20. The sum of the angles of any triangle is 180°. In $\triangle ABC$, $\angle A$ is twice $\angle C$, and $\angle B$ is 10° more than $\angle A$. What is the degree measure of each angle?

21. The volume, V, of a right circular cone is 7,700 cu in. If $V = \frac{1}{3}\pi r^2 h$, the radius is 35, and $\pi = \frac{22}{7}$, then what is the value of the height, h?

22. The formula for the volume of a sphere is $V = \frac{4}{3}\pi r^3$. If r is the radius of the sphere, what is the volume of a sphere, *to the nearest hundredth*, with a diameter of 6?

23. If the replacement set (the domain) for x is $\{-3, -2, -1, 0, 1, 2, 3\}$, write the solution set for $-3x < 0$.

Exercises 24–34: In each literal equation, solve for x.

24. $a + x = 2$

25. $mx = 1$

26. $ax - m = 2m - 10$

27. $6ab + 3ax = 3ac$

28. $ax = am - at$

29. $7dx - 2d = 3dx + 6d$

30. $\frac{ax}{x} = b$

31. $5(x + a) = -2(2x + 3a)$

32. $\frac{a - x}{d} = b$

33. $\frac{5 + a}{2}x = m$

34. $ab(d + x) = x$

Exercises 35–37: Solve for x and graph the solution set.

35. $6 - 4x > 8 + 5x$

36. $0.5(3 - 8x) < 10(1 - 0.5x)$

37. $\frac{x}{2} - \frac{x}{6} \leq \frac{7}{3}$

Chapter Review continues . . .

38. Replace each ? with one <, >, or =.

a $4^2 ? 2^4$

b $5^2 ? 2^5$

c $2^{-3} ? 3^{-2}$

d $1^8 ? 1^{-3}$

e $3^7 ? 3 \bullet 3^6$

f $2x ? 2(x + 1)$

g $7(m + 3) ? 7m + 3$

h $|-1| ? -3$

i $3 + (-4) ? 6 + (-10)$

j $-9 ? 7 + (-16)$

k $|1 + (-1)| ? |1| + |-1|$

l $|-4 + (-7)| ? |-4| + |-7|$

m $(-2)^2 ? -(2)^2$

39. Solve each inequality. Graph the solution set on a number line.

a $x + 6 > 10$

b $\frac{x}{3} \leq 1$

c $\frac{x}{2} \geq -1$

d $2 > -3 + x$

40. For the following compound inequalities, solve and graph the solution set. Where necessary, simplify first and then solve.

a $x \geq -3$ and $x < 4$

b $(x \geq -1) \vee (x < -4)$

c $-1 < x + 2 < 5$

d $(2a + 7 \leq 1) \wedge (a + 12 > 2 - a)$

e $(-5 + x \leq -4) \vee (x \leq 4)$

f $(x \leq 1) \wedge (x > 3)$

41. In the figure below, if rectangle *ABCD* has the given dimensions, write the algebraic expression for

a the perimeter

b the area

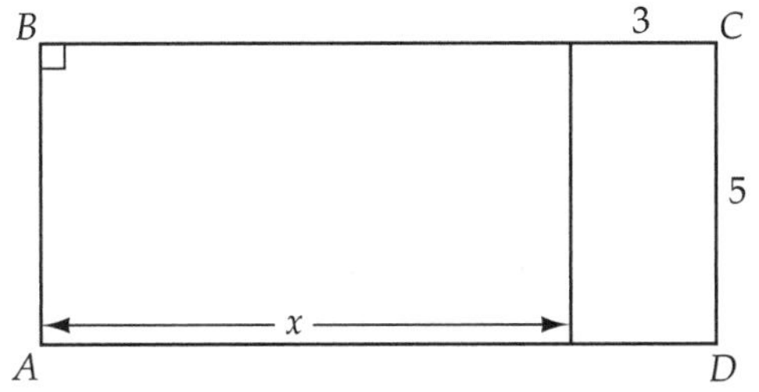

42. The number of girls on a committee was supposed to be more than three times the number of boys. If 15 girls are on the committee, how many possible values are there for the number of boys?

43. A sugar donut has 110 more calories than twice the number of calories in a slice of brown bread. Together they contain at least 194 calories. What is the smallest possible number of calories in the slice of bread?

44. If the area of the rectangle in the figure below is at least 55 square inches, what are the possible values of x? Write an inequality that can be used to solve this problem. Solve the inequality.

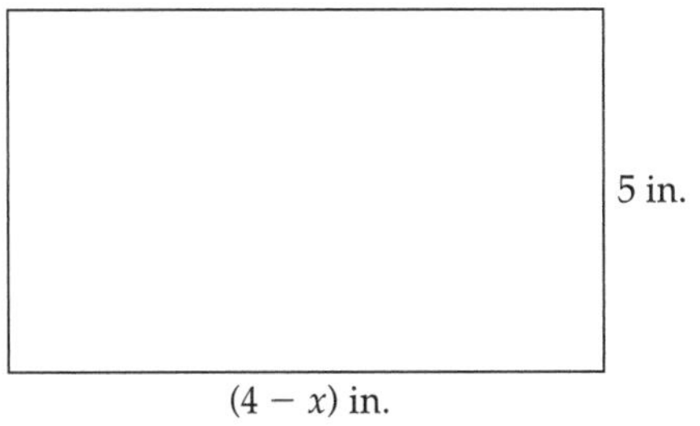

45. The sophomore class is planning to sell school mascot puppets to help cover the cost of a class trip. A local supplier will charge $76.25 for the design and $2.25 for each puppet ordered. The class plans to sell the puppets for $5. How many puppets must be sold to earn at least $2,000?

Chapter Review continues . . .

46. One option for a tennis club's yearly membership costs $650 with no monthly charge. Another option is a monthly membership that costs $150 as a one-time fee plus $50 a month. Write and solve an inequality for how many months it is less expensive to have a monthly membership.

47. Funline Amusement Park charges $12.50 for admission and $2.25 for each ride. If Samantha has $80 to spend and she spends $8.00 for food, what is the maximum number of rides she can go on? Write an inequality and solve it.

48. The length in yards of a rectangular planting field is twice the width. If the perimeter is at most 1800 yards, find the greatest possible width of the field.

49. **MP 1, 2, 4** Keeping in mind the temperature relationship of Celsius and Fahrenheit, $C = \frac{5}{9}(F - 32)$, what interval on the Celsius scale corresponds to the temperature range in a New York year of $-10° \le F \le 100°$, where F is in degrees Fahrenheit? Use reasonable estimates to find the best choice of the answers given.

A. $-40° \le C \le 70°$

B. $-20° \le C \le 35°$

C. $-5° \le C \le 50°$

D. $0° \le C \le 65°$

50. **MP 2, 4** If two congruent sides of an isosceles triangle are each 4.5 and the length of the perimeter is a prime number,

a What are the possible lengths of the 3rd side?

b Using your answers to part **a**, what are the possible perimeters?

c If the perimeter had to be a perfect square, what could be the possible lengths of the 3rd side? What would the perimeter be?

51. **MP 1, 2, 4** You want to get in shape for soccer by lifting weights. One gym charges a $30 monthly fee and $2 for each aerobics class. Another charges $20 a month but $5 per aerobics class. Write an inequality for when the $30 plan is cheaper. How many classes would you have to take for the $30 plan to be cheaper?

52. **MP 2, 6, 7** Look for patterns to identify all the linear equations that have the same solution as $5 = ax - 4$.

A. $5 - 4 = ax$

B. $5 + 4 = a(x - 1) + a$

C. $5 + 4 = (a + 2)x - 2x$

D. $5 + ax = 4$

E. $5 - 3 = ax - 7$

Cumulative Review for Chapters 1–2

1. If a, b, and c are real numbers, the commutative property of addition states that

   A. $(a + b) + c = c + (a + b)$

   B. $a(b + c) = ab + ac$

   C. $a(bc) = (ab)c$

   D. $(a + b) + c = a + (b + c)$

2. Which expression equals zero if $x = 3$ and $y = -3$?

   A. $x^2 - y^2$ C. xy

   B. $x^2 + y^2$ D. $x - y$

3. Which expression has two values that must be restricted from the domain when evaluating the given expression?

   A. $(x + 3)(x - 3)$

   B. $\frac{mt}{x - 1} \bullet \frac{P}{SP} = \frac{P}{21{,}000} = \frac{1}{10}$

   C. $\frac{5}{x} + \frac{5}{x - 1}$

   D. $\frac{6}{x^2 + 9}$

4. On a map, the scale of 1 inch represents 50 miles. If two cities are 275 miles apart, how many inches apart are they on the map?

   A. 13.75 inches

   B. 5.5 inches

   C. 3.25 inches

   D. 2.25 inches

5. A first-class letter in 2013 costs \$0.46 for the first ounce and \$0.20 for every additional ounce. The cost is $C = 0.46 + 0.20(z - 1)$, where z is the weight of the letter in ounces. Solve for z.

   A. $z = \frac{C - 0.46}{0.20}$ C. $z = C - 0.66$

   B. $z = \frac{C - 0.26}{0.20}$ D. $z = \frac{C - 0.46}{0.20} + 1$

6. Santos can spend at most \$115 on track shoes, including a 7% state tax. Which inequality represents this situation?

   A. $S + 0.07S > \$115$

   B. $S + 0.07S \geq \$115$

   C. $S + 0.07S < \$115$

   D. $S + 0.07S \leq \$115$

7. Which of these compound inequalities has no solution?

   A. $x + 1 > 5$ or $x + 3 < 2$

   B. $x + 1 < 5$ or $x + 3 > 2$

   C. $x + 1 > 5$ and $x + 3 < 2$

   D. $x + 1 > 5$ and $x + 3 > 2$

8. If $ax - mt = a$, which expression represents x?

   A. $\frac{a + mt}{a}$ C. $\frac{a}{a - mt}$

   B. $\frac{a}{a + mt}$ D. $\frac{a - mt}{a}$

9. For what value of x is it true that $x^3 < x < \frac{1}{x} < x^2$?

   A. -2 C. $-\frac{1}{2}$

   B. -1 D. $\frac{1}{2}$

10. For the following questions, state your answer and explain your reasoning:

a The center of a line segment is at 5. If the line segment has a length of 12, what is the sum of the endpoints of the line segment?

b The center of a line segment is at -3. If the line segment has a length of 18, what is the sum of the endpoints of the line segment?

c The center of a line segment is at 4. If the line segment has a length of 40, what is the sum of the endpoints of the line segment? Do you see a pattern? Explain.

d The center of a line segment is at x. If the line segment has a length of $2y$, what is the sum of the endpoints of the line segment? Show your steps algebraically.

11. If $a = 2$, what is the value of $2^a - a^3$?

12. Find the value of $x - (a - b)$ when $x = -3$, $a = 4$, and $b = -5$.

13. Find the value of $4^{-1} + 4^0 + 4^1 + 4^2$.

14. The table given shows the pay received per hour for a given amount of time working. Find the rate of change.

Time (in hours)	2	5	7
Pay (in dollars)	30	75	105

15. a If $x + 3 = x$, what is the solution set?

b If $x = x$, what is the solution set?

16. Solve for x in each of the following equations. Identify which two equations have the same solution set:

a $3x - 4 = 17$

b $3(x + 3) - 4 = 17$

c $3(2x - 3) - 4 = 17$

d $6(x + 3) - 8 = 34$

17. If the scale on a map of Southeastern United States is 1 inch = 25 miles, then the distance of 345 miles from West Palm Beach, Florida, to Savannah, Georgia, is how many inches on the map?

18. The ratio of the heights of two similar cylinders is 2 : 3. If the smaller cylinder has a volume of 28 cubic inches, what is the volume of the larger one?

19. Solve for x: $\frac{6}{x - 1} = \frac{5}{x + 2}$

20. The dimensions of a rectangular planting field are 42 yards by $3x$ yards, and the area is at least 6930 square yards.

a Write the algebraic sentence that corresponds to these facts.

b Solve for the minimal dimensions of the field.

21. MP 2 If the altitudes of two similar triangles, ΔABC and ΔFGH, are given as 12 inches and 3 inches, respectively, the area of ΔABC is how many times larger than the area of ΔFGH?

22. MP 2, 4 A man wills $36,000 to his 3 sons. He specifies that the first and second sons are to receive sums in the ratio of 4 : 3 and that the first and third sons are to receive sums in the ratio of 2 : 1. How much does each son get?

23. MP 1 Solve for a: $\frac{2}{3}(9a - 4) = a + 3\left(a + \frac{2}{3}\right)$

24. **MP 2, 3, 4, 6** Jeff and Jermaine go to an indoor ice-skating rink. Jeff has to rent skates at \$3.50 a pair, while Jermaine has brought her own skates. Every hour of skating costs \$2.00 per person. Jeff can spend at most \$10, while Jermaine can spend at most \$9.

a Write inequalities for Jeff and for Jermaine that describe how many hours Jeff and Jermaine can each skate.

b Solve the inequalities.

c Determine how much longer Jermaine can skate than Jeff.

d If they combine their money, how many hours could they skate together?

25. **MP 2, 4** Frank earns 5 times as much in his regular job as a farm consultant than he does as a poet. His total income is *at least* \$35,000 more than that of his sister, Donna, who earns only half as much as Frank does in his regular job.

Write equations and/or inequalities that will help to answer the following questions. Identify clearly all variables.

a What is the least amount Frank earns in his regular job?

b What does he make as a poet?

c What is the least amount that Donna makes?

26. **MP 3, 6** Solve for a. Show your work and state the property used for each step.

$ax - mt = a$

27. **MP 2, 4** A salesman sells a used car at a profit that is $\frac{1}{9}$ of the initial cost to the dealership.

a What is the ratio of his profit (P) to his selling price (SP)?

b If his selling price is \$21,000, what is his profit?

c What was the cost (C) to the dealership?

28. **MP 2** Let x and d be two numbers.

a If $x = 24 + d$, then which is greater, x or d, or it cannot be determined? Explain how you could be certain your choice is correct.

b If $x = 24 - d$, then which is greater, x or d, or it cannot be determined?

29. **MP 1, 7, 8** Determine which of the following equations have the same solution set by recognizing properties, rather than solving.

a $5(2x - 3) + 10 = 6$

b $3x - 9 = 15 + 6x$

c $10x - 5 = 6$

d $6x + 20 = 5(x - 4)$

e $0.5x - 2 = 0.6x + 2$

f $x - 3 = 2x + 5$

30. **MP 1, 3** Solve the inequality using two different methods. Record each step and the property used. Which method was easiest? Why?

$$-\frac{x}{2} + 3 \geq \frac{x}{4} - 3$$

31. **MP 1, 3, 8** Solve for x. Record your steps.

a $\frac{2 + x}{x - 3} = -4$

b $\frac{2 + x}{x - 3} = y$

32. **MP 1, 2, 7** Three students each solved a literal equation. Their answers are shown below. Two students are correct. Which two?

Jill: $\frac{xy - x}{5 - a}$

Ivan: $\frac{x(1 - y)}{a - 5}$

Marcus: $\frac{xy}{5} + \frac{x}{a}$

Chapter 3 Graphing Linear Equations and Functions

Chapter Focus

In this chapter, you will study open sentences in two variables and find their solution sets. You will examine the characteristics of linear functions that can be written in the form $f(x) = mx + b$. We can also state it as a linear equation, $y = mx + b$. Linear functions (and equations) have a constant rate of change. You will learn to write and solve linear functions, compare linear functions, and learn how to transform the graphs of linear functions in the coordinate plane. Lastly, you will apply linear functions and graphic solutions to real-world situations.

Chapter Content

Chapter Vocabulary

constant function	**independent axis**	**range**
constant of variation	**independent variable**	**rate of change**
dependent axis	**intercept**	**slope**
dependent variable	**linear function**	**slope-intercept form**
direct variation	**parallel**	***x*-intercept**
domain	**perpendicular**	***y*-intercept**
identity function	**point-slope form**	

LESSON 3.1

3.1 Graphing Linear Equations

> The standard form of a linear equation in two variables is $Ax + By = C$ where A, B, and C are integers and A and B are *not both* equal to 0.

For example, $2x + y = 4$, $x - 3y = 8$, $3y = 1$, and $-x + 4y = -5$ are linear equations in standard form $Ax + By = C$.

The *graph of a linear equation* is the graph of its solution set, which is always a straight line. Of course, a first-degree equation in two variables, such as $x + y = 10$, has an infinite number of pairs of values of x and y that satisfy it.

- Every coordinate pair (x, y) that satisfies a given equation is a point that lies on the graph, and every point that lies on the graph has coordinates, or a number pair, (x, y), that satisfies the equation.

To Graph a Linear Equation Using Standard Form

- Solve the equation for y in terms of x.
- Find at least three points in the solution set by picking three convenient values for x and computing the corresponding values of y. (Although two points determine a straight line, we use a third point as a check.)
- Graph the three points determined by the ordered pairs (x, y).
- Draw a line through the three points. (If the three points are not in a straight line, there has been a mistake.)

> **A graphing calculator can easily find points in the solution set and display them.**

MODEL PROBLEMS

1. Graph $x - y + 4 = 0$.

SOLUTION

Solve the equation for y: $y = x + 4$

Make a table using three values of x:

x	y
0	4
1	5
2	6

Plot these points and draw the line through them.

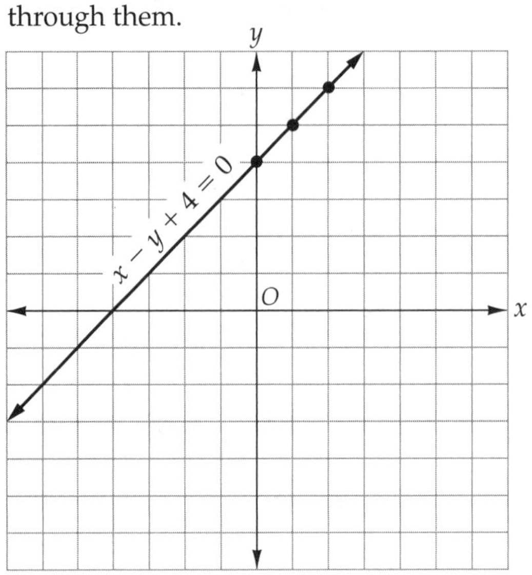

2. Explain why the point (2, 3) does or does not lie on the line $y = 4x - 3$.

SOLUTION

Substitute the coordinates of the point in the equation of the line.

$$y = 4x - 3$$
$$(3) = 4(2) - 3$$
$$3 = 8 - 3$$
$$3 \neq 5$$

Answer: Since the coordinates of the point are not a solution of the equation, the point does not lie on the line.

The graph of any linear equation in standard form eventually crosses one or both of the x- and y-axes. The point at which the graph intersects an axis is called the **intercept.**

- The y-value of the point at which the line intersects the y-axis is called the ***y*-intercept** of the line. Since the x-value of any point on the y-axis is 0, we can easily find the y-intercept.
- Similarly, the x-value of the point at which the line intersects the x-axis is called the ***x*-intercept** of the line. The y-value of any point on the x-axis is 0.

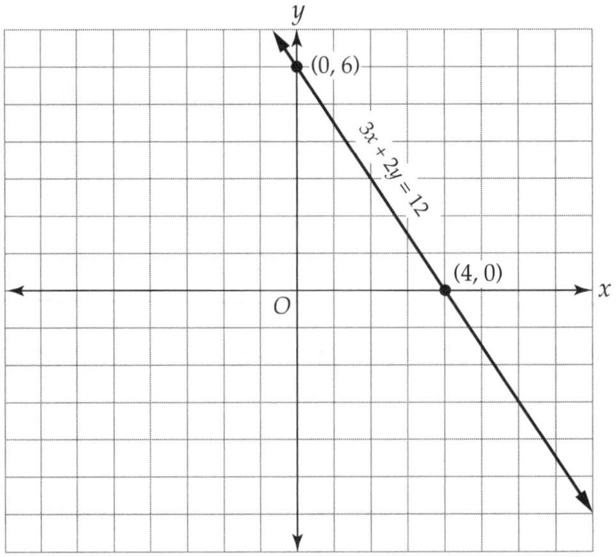

To Find the y-intercept of a Linear Equation

- Substitute 0 for x.
- Solve for y.

To Find the x-intercept of a Linear Equation

- Substitute 0 for y.
- Solve for x.

MODEL PROBLEM

Find the x- and y-intercepts of $x - y + 4 = 0$.

SOLUTION

To find the x-intercept, replace y with 0.	$x - 0 + 4 = 0$
Solve for x.	$x = -4$
To find the y-intercept, replace x with 0.	$0 - y + 4 = 0$
Solve for y.	$y = 4$

Answer: The x-intercept is -4 and the coordinates are $(-4, 0)$. The y-intercept is 4 and the coordinates are $(0, 4)$.

PRACTICE

1. The x-coordinate for an ordered pair in the solution set of $x + 2y = 11$ is 3. Find the y-coordinate.

A. 3
B. 4
C. 5
D. 9

2. Which point lies on the graph of $y = x + 3$?

A. $(-3, 0)$
B. $(1, 3)$
C. $(3, 9)$
D. $(5, 9)$

3. Which line passes through the point $(2, -1)$?

A. $2y - x = 0$
B. $2x - y = 0$
C. $3x - 2y = 8$
D. $3x + 2y = 8$

4. Which line has a y-intercept of 2?

A. $2 = x$
B. $4 = x + y$
C. $5 = x + 2y$
D. $6 = x + 3y$

5. If the y-coordinate is -1 in the equation $4x - y = 9$, what is the x-coordinate?

6. If the x-coordinate is -2 in the equation $2x + 3y = -10$, what is the y-coordinate?

7. What is the y-coordinate of every point on the x-axis?

8. What is the x-coordinate of every point on the y-axis?

9. Write each of the following verbal sentences as an equation.

a The y-coordinate is five less than the x-coordinate.

b The y-coordinate is three less than twice the x-coordinate.

c The y-coordinate is seven less than three times the x-coordinate.

Practice Problems continue . . .

10. MP 6, 7 Determine whether or not each equation is a linear equation. Justify your reasoning.

a $4x - 3y = 16$

b $y = x^2 + 8$

c $\frac{1}{2}x = y + 5$

d $xy = 20$

e $2y - 4x = 0$

f $3y - 2x - 6 = 0$

11. Find the coordinates of the point where the graph of each equation crosses

(1) the x-axis

(2) the y-axis

a $2x + 3y = 18$

b $5x - 2y - 30 = 0$

c $5y = 9x$

d $3x - 6y = 12$

e $2x = 12 - 4y$

f $y - x = 0$

Exercises 12–14: Which of the three given points, if any, lie on the given line?

12. $x + y = 7$ $(2, 5), (-2, -5), (-3, 10)$

13. $2x = y + 1$ $(-1, -3), (0, 1), (2, 3)$

14. $2x - y = 8$ $(4, 0), (1, -7), (-2, -12)$

Exercises 15–18: Find the unknown coordinate of the point on the given line.

15. $x + y = 5$ $(x, 4)$

16. $x - 2y = 8$ $(6, y)$

17. $3y - 1 = x$ $(-3, y)$

18. $3x + 7 = 5y$ $(x, 5)$

Exercises 19–22: State whether the given line passes through the given point. Show your work.

19. $2y + x = 7$ $(1, 3)$

20. $4x + y = 10$ $(2, -2)$

21. $2y = 3x - 5$ $(-1, -4)$

22. $y = -2x + 4$ $(3, 10)$

Exercises 23–29: Use each equation to create a table of ordered pairs. Graph the line using the ordered pairs in the table. State the y-intercept and the x-intercept.

23. $2x - y = 2$

24. $x - 2y = -6$

25. $2x + y = 0$

26. $3y = 6x - 6$

27. $y = 2x + 3$

28. $x + y = 12$

29. $4x = 12 - 2y$

30. Find the value of c so that the point $(3, 2)$ will be on the line $2x - y = c$.

31. Find the value of m so that the line $y = mx - 5$ will pass through the point $(-2, 3)$.

32. Find the value of c so that the line $2x + 3y = c$ will pass through the origin.

33. Without plotting, find a point on the graph of $y = 7x - 15$ whose y-coordinate is twice its x-coordinate.

34. Without plotting, find a point on the graph of $x + y = 21$ whose y-coordinate is three more than its x-coordinate.

Graphing a Line Parallel to an Axis

The graph of a first-degree equation in only one variable is either the x-axis, the y-axis, or a line **parallel** to one of the axes. Actually, we can think of these equations as linear equations in two variables by writing them in the form $y = 0x + n$ or $x = 0y + n$, where n is any real number.

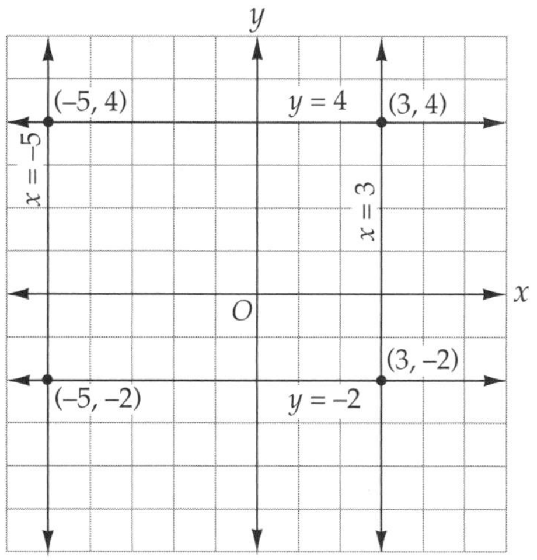

- The graph of $y = 0$ is the x-axis, and the graph of $x = 0$ is the y-axis.
- The graphs of $y = 4$ and $y = -2$ are lines *parallel* to the x-axis, so that $(x, 4)$ is the ordered pair of any point on the line $y = 4$ and $(x, -2)$ is the ordered pair of any point on the line $y = -2$. For $y = 4$, $(-6, 4)$, $(0, 4)$, $(3, 4)$, $(9, 4)$, and $(89, 4)$ are some of the infinite pairs of points in the solution set.
- The graphs of $x = 3$ and $x = -5$ are lines *parallel* to the y-axis, so that $(3, y)$ and $(-5, y)$ are the ordered pairs, respectively, of any point on the lines $x = 3$ and $x = -5$. For $x = 3$, $(3, -7)$, $(3, 0)$, $(3, 8)$, and $(3, 19)$ are some of the infinite pairs of points in the solution set.

Points to Remember

- The equation of a horizontal line is $y = b$, where b is a constant and where the *y-intercept* is b.
- The equation of a vertical line is $x = a$, where a is a constant and where the *x-intercept* is a.
- The *intersection* (x, y) of lines parallel to the axes are constants of the two linear equations. In the graph above, the ordered pair $(3, 4)$ indicates the intersection of the two lines $x = 3$ and $y = 4$. Similarly, $(-5, -2)$ is the ordered pair found at the intersection of $x = -5$ and $y = -2$.

A function whose graph is a horizontal line, as in $y = b$, is called a **constant function**. The linear equation $x = a$ is constant, but it is not a function since the first element x has an infinite set of y-values in the range.

PRACTICE

1. The equation of the y-axis is

A. $x = 0$ C. $y = 0$
B. $x = y$ D. $y = y$

2. Which equation describes the line in this graph?

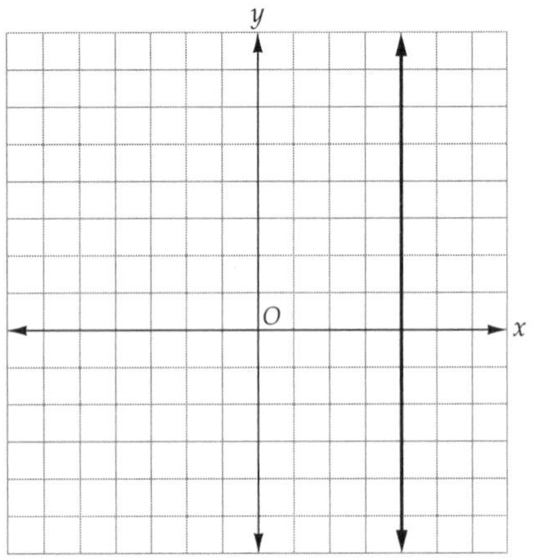

A. $x = 4$ C. $y = 4$
B. $x = 6$ D. $y = 6$

3. What is the x-intercept of $x = 7$?

A. 0
B. 1
C. 7
D. $x = 7$ has no x-intercept

4. Which equation has a graph that is parallel to the x-axis?

A. $x = 0$ C. $x = 25 + y$
B. $x = 25$ D. $x = 25 + y + x$

Exercises 5–12: Use the given description to write the equation of each of the lines.

5. The line parallel to the y-axis and 5 units to the right of it

6. The line parallel to the x-axis and 4.5 units above it

7. The line parallel to the y-axis and 5 units to the left of it

8. The line parallel to the x-axis and 3 units below it

9. The line parallel to the line $y = 5$ and 4 units above it

10. The line parallel to the line $x = 23$ and 2 units to the left of it

11. The line containing all the points whose x-values are 15

12. The line containing all the points whose y-values are -7

13. Describe fully the graph of a line whose equation is

a $y = 3$
b $x = -2$
c $x = 5$
d $y = -4.5$
e $x = 0$
f $x = 3.5$
g $y = 0$
h $y = x$

MP 3, 7 Exercises 14–16: Is the line containing points A and B vertical or horizontal? Write an equation of the line. Determine another point on the line and justify your answer.

14. $A(-2, 5)$ and $B(-2, 8)$

15. $A(-3, -6)$ and $B(10, -6)$

16. $A(3, 8)$ and $B(3, 0)$

Exercises 17–22: Graph each pair of equations and state the ordered pair (x, y) of the intersection.

17. $y = 2$ and $x = 3$

18. $x = -3$ and $y = -1$

19. $y = 0$ and $x = -1$

20. $x = 5$ and $y = -8$

21. the y-axis and $y = -8$

22. $x = -4$ and the x-axis

Exercises 23–26: Given the ordered pair (x, y) of an intersection of two lines parallel to the axes, state the equations of those two lines.

23. $(-3, 5)$

24. $(0, -11)$

25. $(2, -7)$

26. $(-5.5, 10)$

3.2 Direct Variation

A teacher hands out a 25-question quiz with a note that each correct answer is worth 4 points. A table can be created to show the relation between the number of correct answers (x) and points earned (y).

x	1	2	3	...	25
y	4	8	12	...	100

> The sum or difference of any two pairs in the table will create a new pair of values in the table. For example, if 2 bagels cost $6 and 3 bagels cost $9, then 5 bagels will cost $15.

Notice that in comparing the values of x and the corresponding values of y, the ratios, $\frac{y}{x}$, are all equivalent: $\frac{y}{x} = \frac{4}{1} = \frac{8}{2} = \frac{12}{3} = 4$. This relationship between the variables y and x is a **direct variation.** We say that y varies directly as x or that y is directly proportional to x. This constant ratio of $\frac{y}{x}$ is called the **constant of variation**, or k.

> We can write direct variation as an equation $y = kx$, where k is the constant of variation.

The ratio of any set of (x_1, y_1) values is equal to the ratio of any other corresponding set of (x_2, y_2) values in the table. Thus, setting the two equivalent ratios equal to each other yields a proportion: $\frac{y_1}{x_1} = \frac{y_2}{x_2}$.

It is necessary to indicate the order in which the variables are being compared. The constant of variation of y with respect to x is $\frac{y}{x} = \frac{4}{1}$, since y equals $4x$. The constant of variation of x with respect to y is $\frac{x}{y} = \frac{1}{4}$, since x equals $\frac{1}{4}y$. Note that the two constants are reciprocals.

Points to Remember

- For positive k, if x increases, y increases.
- For negative k, if x decreases, y decreases.
- If x is multiplied by a number, then y is multiplied by the same number.
- If x is divided by a number, then y is divided by the same number.

MODEL PROBLEMS

1. If x varies directly as y and $x = 1.5$ when $y = 3.75$,

a Find the constant of variation for x in terms of y.
b Find the constant of variation for y in terms of x.

SOLUTION

a Constant of variation $= \frac{x}{y} = \frac{1.5}{3.75} = 0.4 = \frac{2}{5}$

b Constant of variation $= \frac{y}{x} = \frac{3.75}{1.5} = 2.5 = \frac{5}{2}$

Model Problems continue . . .

Model Problems *continued*

2. **MP 7** The cost (C) of ground beef varies directly with the weight (W) of the package. Find the cost of 5 pounds of ground beef if 2 pounds costs \$3.90.

SOLUTION

The constant of variation is $= \frac{\text{cost}}{\text{weight}} = \frac{3.90}{2}$.

> **The constant of variation is useful because it captures the value of 1 unit. In this example, it describes the cost of 1 pound.**

Use the constant of variation. $k = \frac{3.90}{2}$

$C = kW$

$C = \frac{3.90}{2} \bullet 5$

Evaluate. $C = 1.95(5)$

$C = \$9.75$

Answer: Five pounds of ground beef costs \$9.75.

3. **MP 2, 4** Express each of the following relations as an equation using k as the constant of variation.

SOLUTION

a The cost (c) of a railroad ticket varies directly as the distance in miles (m) of the trip.

$\frac{c}{m} = k$ and $c = km$

b The distance (d) of a train ride varies directly with the time (t) if the train is going at a constant speed.

$\frac{d}{t} = k$ and $d = kt$

c The dollars earned (d) varies directly with the number of hours worked (h) at a job that pays by the hour.

$\frac{d}{h} = k$ and $d = kh$

PRACTICE

1. Two quantities, A and h, vary directly. When $A = 18.75$, $h = 7.25$. Find the value of h rounded to the nearest hundredth when $A = 8.75$.

A. 3.38 C. 2.14
B. 2.59 D. 1.21

2. A car travels 4 miles in 5 minutes. If the car continues at this constant speed, what distance will the car cover in 33 minutes?

A. 6.6 miles C. 26.4 miles
B. 8.25 miles D. 41.25 miles

3. Paul set up a car wash to raise money for a school fund-raiser. He found that he needed 5 buckets of water for every 2 cars. If 35 cars were washed, how many buckets of water were used?

A. 14 buckets
B. 62.5 buckets
C. 75 buckets
D. 87.5 buckets

4. Andrea is making cookies from a recipe that calls for $2\frac{1}{2}$ cups of flour for a yield of 2 dozen cookies. How much flour will she need to make 5 dozen cookies?

A. $5\frac{1}{5}$ cups

B. $5\frac{1}{2}$ cups

C. 6 cups

D. $6\frac{1}{4}$ cups

Exercises 5–9: The table shows a relationship between two variables.

a Check the proportionality of the variables to see if the variation is direct.

b If the variation is direct, find the constant of variation and express the relationship between the variables as a formula.

5.

x	2	3	4	5	6
y	4	8	12	16	20

6.

r	0.5	1	1.5	2	2.5
d	2	4	6	8	10

7.

s	2	3	4	5	6
a	4	9	16	25	36

8.

h	6.0	6.2	6.4	6.6	6.8
w	10	11	12	13	14

9.

x	0	1	2	3	4
y	2	3	4	5	6

10. MP 2, 4, 8 In the following table, one variable varies directly as the other.

a Find the missing numbers.

b Write the formula that relates the variables.

h	1	2		7
d	5		25	35

11. MP 2, 4, 8 In the following table, one variable varies directly as the other.

a Find the missing numbers.

b Write the formula that relates the variables.

d	4	8		22
s	6		15	33

12. Two quantities, x and y, vary directly. When $x = 4$, $y = 10$. Find the value of y when $x = 6$.

13. If x varies directly as y when $x_1 = 13$, $x_2 = 3$, and $y_1 = 7$, then what is the value of y_2?

14. If x varies directly with y and $x = 6$ when $y = 10$, what is the value of x when $y = 25$?

15. MP 2

a Bruce earns w dollars per hour. If he worked h hours, express in terms of w and h how much money he made.

b Bruce makes $10 more an hour than Doug. If Doug makes d dollars an hour, define w in terms of d.

c Using your answer from part **b**, express in terms of d and h how much money Bruce made.

Graphing Direct Variation

There are several special cases of the **linear function,** $y = mx + b$ or $f(x) = mx + b$.

- **Constant function.** If $m = 0$, then we have the *constant function*, $y = 0x + b$ or $y = b$, which is graphed as a horizontal line, such as $y = 4$ in the figure on the right.
- **Identity function.** If $m = 1$ and $b = 0$, then we have the *identity function*, $y = 1x + 0$ or $y = x$, as graphed in the figure on the right.
- **Direct variation function.** If m is a nonzero constant and $b = 0$, then we have the function, $y = mx$, which is called a *direct variation*, and where m is called the *constant of variation*. In direct variation, rather than using m, we use the letter k as the symbol for the *constant of variation* in the generic equation for direct variation.

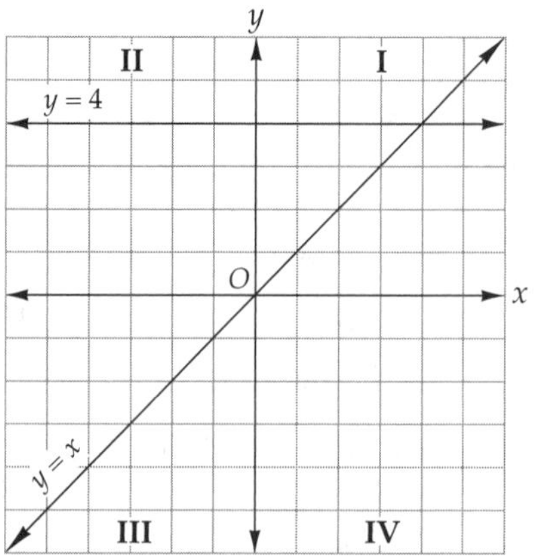

MODEL PROBLEMS

1. Determine whether the given table expresses a direct variation. Find the constant of variation and write the equation. Then graph the equation.

x	-6	-3	3	6	9
y	-4	-2	2	4	6

SOLUTION

In each case, the constant of variation, $\frac{y}{x}$, from $\frac{-4}{-6}$ to $\frac{6}{9}$, is $\frac{2}{3}$. Thus, the equation for $y = kx$ is $y = \frac{2}{3}x$ or $f(x) = \frac{2}{3}x$. All the given values lie on the graph of $y = \frac{2}{3}x$ and illustrate the direct variation.

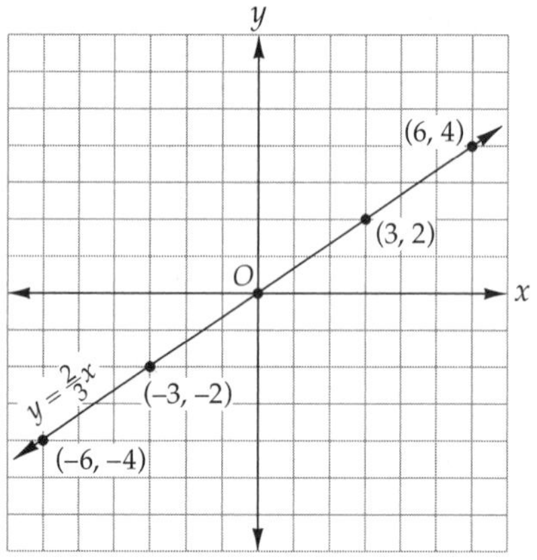

Model Problems continue . . .

Model Problems *continued*

2. In the graph below, a straight line passes through the indicated points.

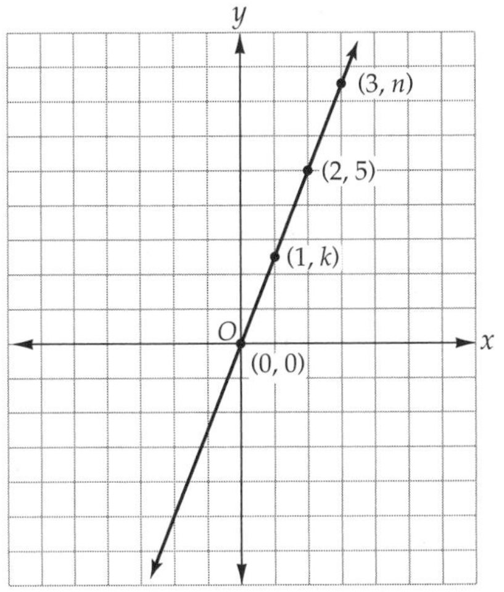

a Is this the graph of a direct variation?
b If it is, what is the constant of variation?
c What is the equation of the line?
d What is the value of n?

SOLUTION

a Since the graph of this linear equation passes through the origin, this is a direct variation.

b The constant of variation, $k = \frac{y}{x} = \frac{5}{2} = 2.5 = \frac{2.5}{1}$. Because this is direct variation, the graph passes through (1, 2.5).

c The equation of the line is $y = \frac{5}{2}x$ or $f(x) = \frac{5}{2}x$.

d Substitute $x = 3$ and $y = n$ and then solve for n. Thus, $n = \frac{5}{2} \bullet 3 = \frac{15}{2}$ or 7.5.

PRACTICE

1. MP 7 Determine which of the following equations expresses direct variation. State the constant of variation.

a $y = 3x - 1$
b $r = 4h$
c $C = 2\pi r$
d $y = 3x^2$
e $\frac{3y}{x} = -9$
f $\frac{x}{y} = -7$
g $-2y = 8$
h $\frac{y}{x} = \frac{3}{7}$
i $-5y = -20x$

Exercises 2–6: Determine whether the given table expresses a direct variation. If it does, find the constant of variation. Write the equation in the form $y = kx$ and graph the equation using the given table of values.

2.

x	2	4	5	6	8
y	−8	−16	−20	−24	−32

3.

x	−2	4	3	−1	5
y	−6	12	9	−3	15

4.

x	2	4	6	8	10
y	4	6	10	16	24

5.

x	5	10	15	20	25
y	1	2	3	4	5

6.

x	−4	0	8	12	20
y	5	0	−10	−15	−25

Exercises 7–14: Create tables from the values given. Then fill in the table and answer the question using the constant of variation.

7. If the ABC Company paid a total dividend of \$44 on 400 shares of its stock, how much of a dividend did it pay on 225 shares of stock?

Practice Problems continue . . .

8. Gas consumption is directly proportional to the distance traveled. If 21 gallons are used on a trip of 378 miles, then how far will the car travel on 7 gallons of gas?

9. If 7 cubic centimeters of blood contain 0.8 gram of hemoglobin, how many grams of hemoglobin can we expect to find in 9.8 cubic centimeters of blood?

10. If gasoline is used in an amount that varies directly as the time traveled, and if 3 gallons of gas are consumed in 1 hour and 15 minutes, how long (in hours and minutes) will 8 gallons of gas last?

11. If 24 square feet of a fabric weighs 50 ounces, what is the weight of a rectangular piece that is 12 feet long and 8 feet wide?

12. The distance from a lightning bolt is directly proportional to the time elapsed between seeing the lightning bolt and hearing the thunder. Thus, if you hear the thunder 7 seconds after you see the lightning bolt, then you are 1.5 miles away from the bolt. How far away is the bolt if you hear the thunder 2 seconds after you see the bolt?

13. A number, a, varies directly as the square of another number, m. If $a = 14$ when $m = 3$, what is the value of a when $m = 12$?

14. **MP 2, 4** The distance necessary to stop a car varies directly as the *square* of its speed. If a car traveling 60 mph needs 144 feet to stop, what distance is required to stop a car going only 40 miles an hour? Give the answer in feet as well as in yards.

15. The amount of work done in a given time varies directly as the number of men employed.

a Express this as a ratio.

b If 18 men in 10 days can dig a 90-foot drainage ditch for water, how many men will be needed to dig a ditch 120 feet long in the same amount of time?

c Draw the graph of a linear equation showing the relationship between the number of men and the number of feet dug in 10 days.

16. An automatic box machine can fabricate 180 pizza boxes in 3 hours. How many 8-hour days would it take the machine to produce 3000 pizza boxes?

17. The weight of a uniform steel beam is directly proportional to its length. If a length of 3 feet weighs approximately 35 pounds, find the approximate weight (to the nearest tenth of a pound) of a length of 8.5 feet.

18. According to a certain recipe on a box of corn muffin mix, the number n of corn muffins you can make is a function of the number c of cups of the mix you use. If 2 cups make 14 muffins, and a full box of corn muffin mix contains 9 cups of mix, how many muffins can you make when you use the full box?

19. The number of inches s of snow that falls steadily varies directly with the length of time t of a given storm. In the first 3 hours of the storm 4.5 inches of snow fell.

a Write a direct variation equation that relates s and t.

b How many inches of snow fell in 7 hours?

20. The number n of tablespoons of sugar needed in a large commercial coffee urn varies directly with the number of gallons of water w in the urn. The store owner adds 40 tablespoons of sugar to a 5-gallon urn.

a Write a direct variation equation to represent this relationship.

b How many tablespoons of sugar should be added to a smaller 3.5-gallon urn?

3.3 The Slope of a Line

The **slope** of a line is the ratio of the difference in y-values to the difference in x-values between any two points on the line. Slope is usually symbolized by the letter m. The formula for the slope of the line connecting points (x_1, y_1) and (x_2, y_2) is:

$$m = \frac{\Delta y}{\Delta x} = \frac{y_2 - y_1}{x_2 - x_1}$$

m = slope, or **rate of change**

Δy = difference in y-values, or vertical change

Δx = difference in x-values, or horizontal change

> **Mathematicians use the Greek letter Δ (delta) as a symbol for difference.**

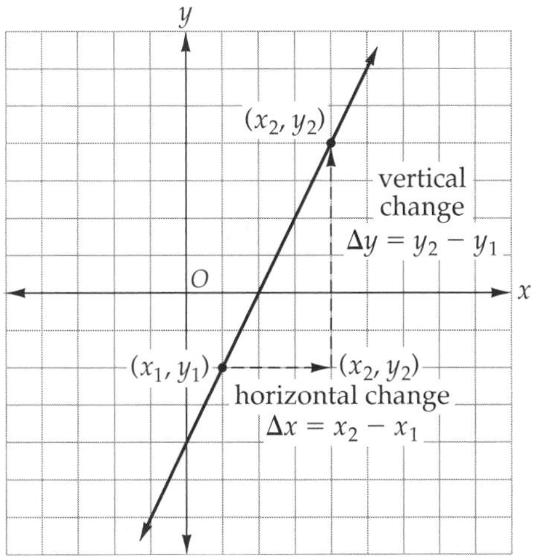

We calculate the slope for the line graphed to the left. We use the points given, (1, –2) and (4, 4), so that

$$m = \frac{4 - (-2)}{4 - 1} = \frac{6}{3} = \frac{2}{1}.$$

We express the slope as a fraction, even if it is an integer. This makes it easier to determine points on the graph. A slope of 2 means a vertical change (rise) of 2 for every horizontal change (run) of 1.

To Find the Slope of a Line

- Choose any two points (x_1, y_1) and (x_2, y_2) on the line.
- Find the difference in y-values by subtracting y_1 from y_2.
- Find the difference in x-values by subtracting x_1 from x_2.
- Write the ratio: slope $= \frac{\text{difference in } y\text{-values}}{\text{difference in } x\text{-values}}$ as $m = \frac{y_2 - y_1}{x_2 - x_1}$ or $m = \frac{\Delta y}{\Delta x}$.

> **It makes no difference which points are labeled (x_1, y_1) and (x_2, y_2); the value of m will always be the same for any pair of points on a line.**

Note the importance of the *sign* and *value* of the slope, m.

Value of m	Values of Δy and Δx	Appearance of Graph
positive	Δy and Δx have the same sign.	Line rises from left to right. /
negative	Δy and Δx have opposite signs.	Line falls from left to right. \
zero	$\Delta y = 0$	Line is horizontal. —
undefined	$\Delta x = 0$	Line is vertical. |

Reminders:

- For any given linear function, the slope provides a *constant rate of change*. Since all segments of a line have the same slope, using any two points from the line must produce the same slope.
- If a line is parallel to the y-axis, such as $x = 5$ or $x = -3$, the line is not a function and the slope of that vertical line is *undefined*, or the line is said to have *no slope*.

Having no slope is different from zero slope, just like dividing by zero is different from dividing zero by another number.

MODEL PROBLEMS

1. Draw the graph of $y = 3$ and find the slope.

SOLUTION

We have already discussed the idea that graphs of this type are parallel to the x-axis with y-intercept 3.

Draw the graph.

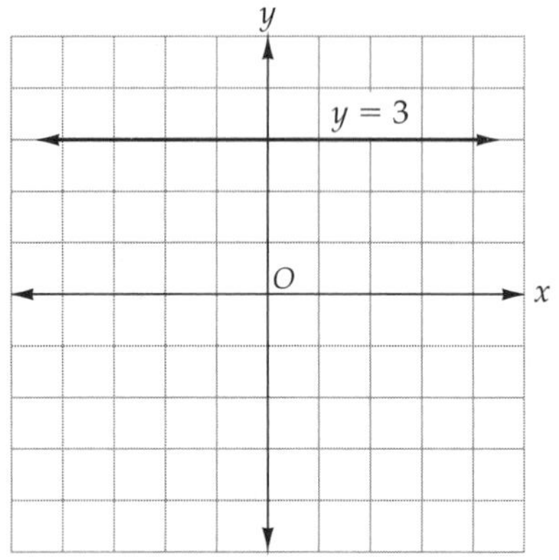

Notice that, since all y-values are the same, the change in y, or Δy, is 0.

Thus, the slope $= m = \dfrac{\Delta y}{\Delta x} = \dfrac{0}{\Delta x} = 0$.

2. Draw the graph of $x = 1$ and find the slope.

SOLUTION

We have already discussed the idea that graphs of this type are parallel to the y-axis with x-intercept 1.

Draw the graph.

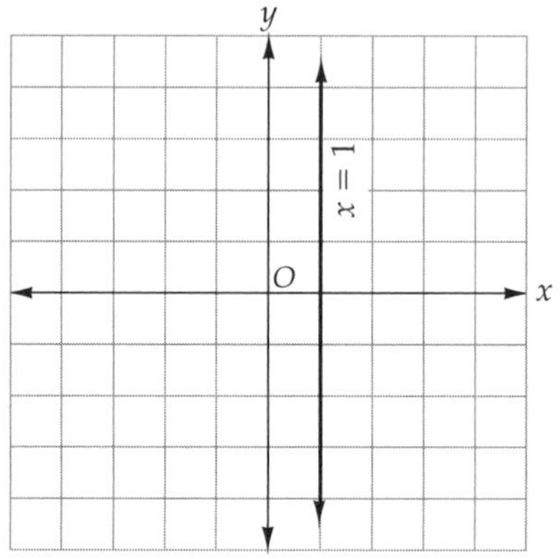

All graphs of the form $y = b$ have zero slope. The slope of all graphs of the form $x = a$ is undefined.

Notice that, since all x-values are the same, the change in x, or Δx, is 0, which means the denominator in the ratio $\dfrac{\Delta y}{\Delta x}$ is 0. Thus $\dfrac{\Delta y}{\Delta x} = \dfrac{\Delta y}{0}$. However, since division by zero is undefined, the slope is *undefined*. There is no slope.

Model Problems continue . . .

Model Problems *continued*

3. **MP 2, 4** Tommy is offered two contract jobs, but he can only accept one. Both Job A and Job B will take exactly 40 hours to complete. Job A offers a sign-on bonus of $75 and Job B does not. The tables show his pay received per hour for a given amount of time for Job A and Job B. For example, if Tommy works two hours with Job A, he will be paid $103. If he works 6 hours, he will be paid $159.

Job A

Time (in hours)	0	2	4	6
Pay (in dollars)	75	103	131	159

Job B

Time (in hours)	0	2	4	6
Pay (in dollars)	0	34	68	102

a Find the rate of change for each job. What does the rate of change mean in this situation? Check your answer by graphing.

b What does the slope represent?

c What does the y-intercept represent for each job?

d Write an equation to determine the time (in hours) when Tommy's total pay for Job A would equal the same pay he would be getting had he taken Job B. Indicate that intersection point on the graph.

e Find Tommy's total pay for the 40 hours on Job A versus Job B. Decide which job he should accept.

SOLUTION

a For Job A, the rate of change is:

$$\frac{\$103 - \$75}{2 - 0 \text{ hours}} = \frac{\$28}{2 \text{ hours}} = \$14 \text{ per hour}$$

For Job B, the rate of change is:

$$\frac{\$34 - \$0}{2 - 0 \text{ hours}} = \frac{\$34}{2 \text{ hours}} = \$17 \text{ per hour}$$

The rate of change is Tommy's hourly rate.

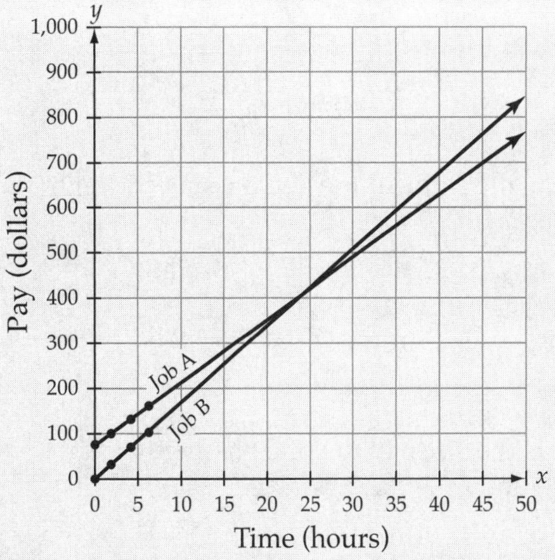

b The slope represents the rate of change, which is Tommy's hourly rate.

c For Job A, the y-intercept at (0, 75) is equal to the sign-on bonus. This means that Tommy receives $75 for showing up to the first hour of work for Job A. Job B does not have a sign-on bonus, so the y-intercept is at (0, 0).

d Write an equation to model the situation. $\$75 \text{ (bonus)} + \$14x = \$17x$

Solve for x. $\$75 = 3x$

$x = 25$ hours

Check. $75 + 14(25) = 17(25)$

$\$425 = \$425$ ✓

Model Problems continue . . .

Model Problems *continued*

e We know the rate of change remains constant on a line, so we can find how much money Tommy can make after working 40 hours at each rate.

Job A: \$75 (bonus) + 40(\$14) = 75 + 560 = \$635

Job B: 40(\$17) = \$680

Tommy should accept Job B.

PRACTICE

1. What is the slope of the line, or rate of change, represented by this table of values?

x	y
−3	1
−2	3
−1	5

A. −2
B. −0.5
C. 0.5
D. 2

2. What is the slope of the line passing through (0, 0) and (−2, −5)?

A. −2.5
B. −0.4
C. 0.4
D. 2.5

3. What is the slope of the line passing through (5, −4) and (−2, −1)?

A. −1

B. $-\frac{3}{7}$

C. $\frac{5}{3}$

D. $\frac{5}{7}$

4. Which line has a slope of 5? The line passing through

A. (0, −5) and (−5, 0)
B. (0, 10) and (2, 0)
C. (0, −10) and (2, 0)
D. (0, 5) and (5, 0)

Exercises 5–8: Find the slope of the line or rate of change represented by each table of values.

5.

x	y
0	0
1	−1
2	−2

6.

x	y
−5	1
−5	3
−5	5

7.

x	y
1	4
2	4
3	4

8.

x	y
−2	0
0	−2
2	−4

Exercises 9–18: Find the slope of the line passing through the following pairs of points. State whether the slope is positive, negative, zero, or undefined.

9. (1, 1), (6, 7)

10. (2, −5), (4, 0)

11. (4, −3), (6, −5)

12. (−3, −5), (−2, −4)

Practice Problems continue . . .

13. (4, −7), (−7, 4)

14. (−1, 2), (−3, 6)

15. (6, −2), (7, −2)

16. (0, 0), (5, 5)

17. (4, 1), (1, 4)

18. (5, 3), (7, 3)

Exercises 19–22: Graph the given point and use the given slope, *m*, to draw a line.

19. $(-2, 3); m = \frac{1}{3}$

20. $(1, 5); m = -\frac{2}{3}$

21. $(2, -4); m = \frac{2}{3}$

22. $(-4, -1); m = 3$

23. **MP 2, 4** The rates to rent a lane at the Thunder Bowling Alley are shown in the table:

a Use the information in the table to find the *rate of change* and indicate the units.

b There is a 25% discount for any time that exceeds the first 10 hours of use during the week. If George and Georgette bowl a total of 16 hours during a certain week, what was the cost? How much was the discount?

Time (in hours)	2	4	6
Cost (in dollars)	14	23	32

24. Points $A(-2, 0)$, $B(0, 3)$, and $C(4, -3)$ are the vertices of triangle *ABC*. Find the slope of each side of the triangle.

25. **MP 7** Write the equation of a line passing through the point (1, 2) but not (0, 0). Explain how you know your equation is correct.

The Slope of Parallel and Perpendicular Lines

If two lines in the coordinate plane have the *same slope* and *different* y-intercepts, or if they are vertical lines that have different x-intercepts, then the lines are parallel.

For example, the graphs of the following pairs of linear equations are *parallel.*

1. $y = 3x + 5$ and $y = 3x - 1$

The slope for both lines is 3 and the y-intercepts are 5 and -1.

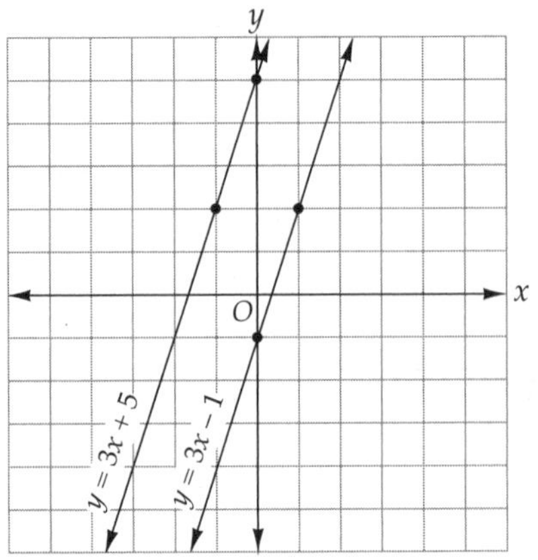

2. $y = \frac{2}{3}x - 2$ and $y = \frac{2}{3}x + 4$

The slope for both lines is $\frac{2}{3}$ and the y-intercepts are -2 and 4.

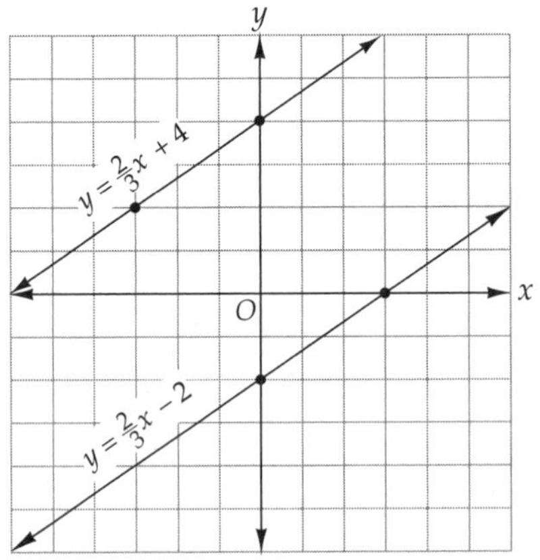

3. $y = -\frac{1}{3}x + 1$ and $y = -\frac{1}{3}x - 2$

The slope for both lines is $-\frac{1}{3}$ and the y-intercepts are 1 and -2.

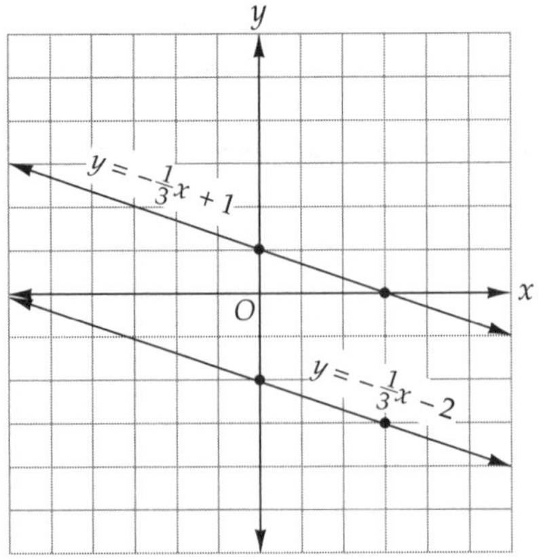

If two lines in the coordinate plane have slopes that are *negative reciprocals* of each other, then the two lines are **perpendicular**. The y-intercepts can be any real numbers. If two lines are *perpendicular*, then the product of their slopes is -1. For example, $\frac{3}{5} \bullet \left(-\frac{5}{3}\right) = -\frac{15}{15} = -1$.

> **The product will not be -1 if one of the lines has an undefined slope, as is the case with lines parallel to the y-axis.**

The graphs of the following pairs of linear equations are *perpendicular*.

1. $y = \frac{2}{3}x + 2$ and $y = -\frac{3}{2}x - 1$

The slopes are $\frac{2}{3}$ and $-\frac{3}{2}$.

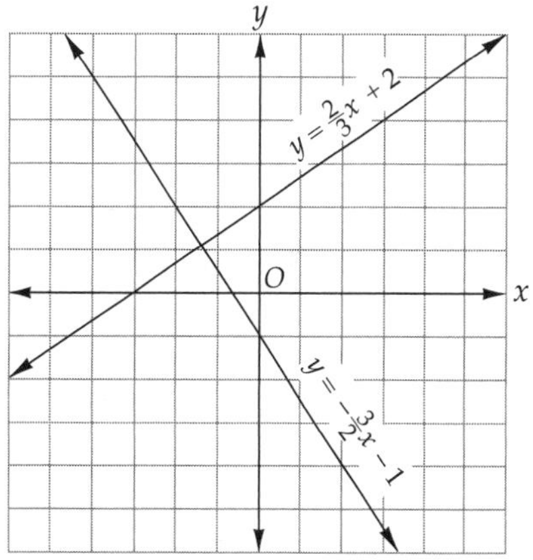

2. $y = -4x + 3$ and $y = \frac{1}{4}x + 1$

The slopes are -4 and $\frac{1}{4}$.

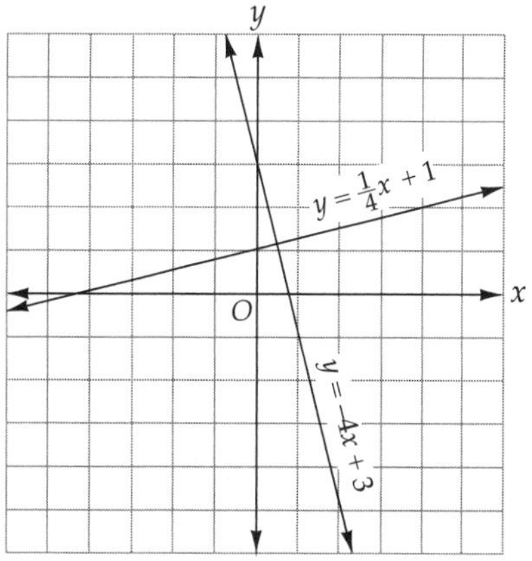

3. $y = x + 2$ and $y = -x + 2$

The slopes are 1 and -1.

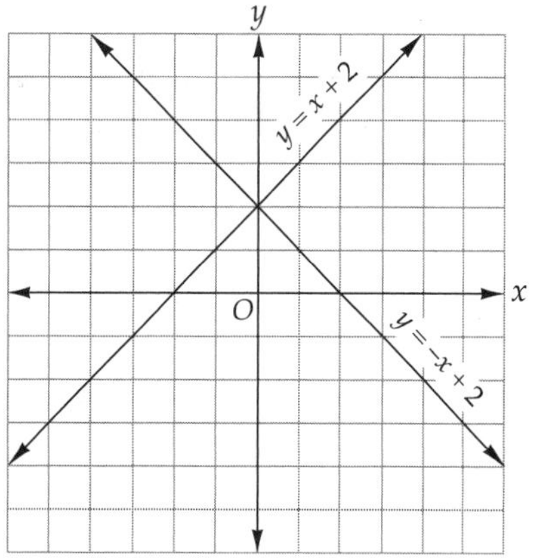

MODEL PROBLEM

Find two lines that are perpendicular to each other by comparing slopes.

A. $2x + y = 4$ B. $2x - y = -4$ C. $x + 2y = 4$

SOLUTION

Rewrite each equation in $y = mx + b$ form:

A. Given. $2x + y = 4$
Subtract $2x$. $2x - 2x + y = -2x + 4$
Simplify. $y = -2x + 4$
Slope is -2.

B. Given. $2x - y = -4$
Subtract $2x$. $2x - 2x - y = -2x - 4$
Multiply both sides by -1. $-y = -2x - 4$
Simplify. $y = 2x + 4$
Slope is 2.

C. Given. $x + 2y = 4$
Subtract x. $x - x + 2y = -x + 4$
Divide both sides by 2. $2y = -x + 4$
Solve for y. $y = -\frac{1}{2}x + 2$
Slope is $-\frac{1}{2}$.

Since 2 and $-\frac{1}{2}$ are negative reciprocals (their product is -1), $2x - y = -4$ and $x + 2y = 4$ are perpendicular.

Answer: B. $2x - y = -4$ and C. $x + 2y = 4$

PRACTICE

Exercises 1–8: State whether the given lines are parallel, perpendicular, or neither. Solve for y if necessary.

1. $y = \frac{2}{3}x - 5$
$y = -\frac{2}{3}x + 5$

2. $y = 3x - 5$
$y = 3x + 7$

3. $y = 7$
$x = 6$

4. $y = 5x$
$y = -5x$

5. $4x - 5y = 20$
$15x + 12y = 60$

6. $3y + 5 = 14$
$y = -1$

7. $y = -\frac{1}{2}x - 1$
$x + 2y = -4$

8. $x + y = 9$
$y - x = 13$

Practice Problems continue . . .

Exercises 9–15: State the slope of a line that is:

a parallel to the given line

b perpendicular to the given line

9. $y = 5x - 2$

10. $y = -2x + 7$

11. $y = -\frac{4}{3}x + 3$

12. $x - y = 6$

13. $4x + 6y = 12$

14. $x = 8$

15. $y = -3$

Exercises 16–18: In each of the following sets, select the one equation whose graph would *not be parallel* to the other two.

16. $\{y - 6x = 3, 2y = 12x, x = 6y\}$

17. $\{5x - y = 2, y - 5x = 2, 5x - y = 2\}$

18. $\{3x + y = 8, 2y = 8 - 6x, x - 3y = 8\}$

Exercises 19–21: In each of the following, select the one equation (*a*) or (*b*) that is *not perpendicular* to the first equation.

19. $y = -\frac{3}{5}x + 1$:

$\left\{(a)\ 3y = 5x + 6; (b)\ y = -\frac{5}{3}x + 1\right\}$

20. $2y - x = 0$: $\left\{(a)\ y = -2x, (b)\ y = -\frac{1}{2}x\right\}$

21. $y + 5x = 4$: $\left\{(a)\ y = -5x, (b)\ y = \frac{1}{5}x + 4\right\}$

LESSON 3.4

3.4 Graphing and Writing Linear Equations Using the Slope-Intercept and Point-Slope Forms

Certain forms of a linear equation can provide enough information to easily graph the corresponding line. Consider the table of values for each of the three given graphs and their linear equations. The slopes and y-intercepts are easily found from looking at the linear equation. There is a pattern.

1. Equation: $y = 2x - 1$

x	0	1	2
y	−1	1	3

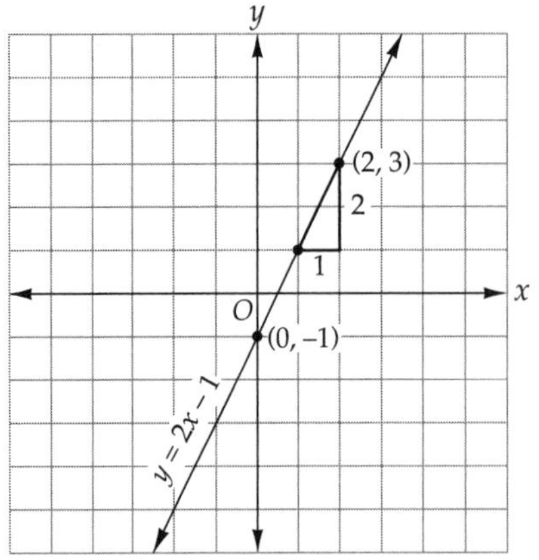

The slope is 2 or $\frac{2}{1}$ and the y-intercept is −1.

2. Equation: $y = -\frac{2}{3}x + 3$

x	−3	0	3
y	5	3	1

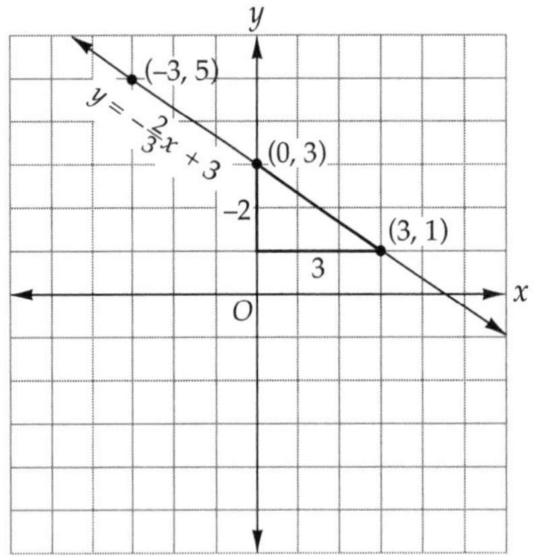

The slope is $-\frac{2}{3}$ and the y-intercept is 3.

3. Equation: $y = \frac{1}{2}x + 2$

x	−2	0	2
y	1	2	3

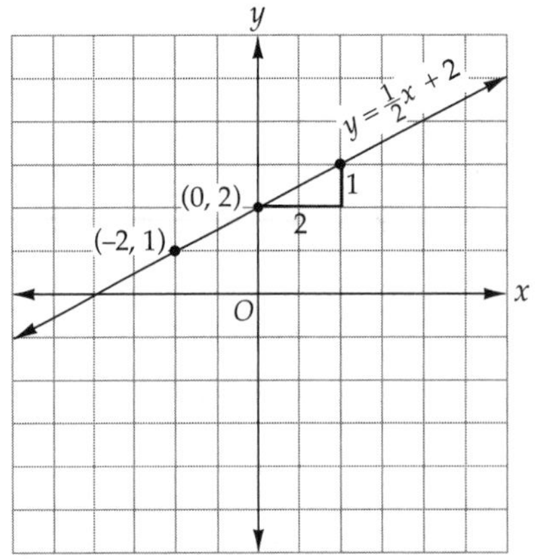

The slope is $\frac{1}{2}$ and the y-intercept is 2.

Slope-Intercept Form

In several of the examples discussed in this and previous sections, the first step in graphing the equation was to solve the equation for y. You may have noticed that in each of these examples, the value of the slope equaled the coefficient of x, and the y-intercept equaled the numeric constant. These statements are always true when y is by itself.

> If a linear equation is expressed in the form $y = mx + b$, then m represents the slope of the line and b represents the y-intercept. $y = mx + b$ is called the **slope-intercept form** of the equation.

> Direct variation is a special case of the slope-intercept form when $b = 0$.

We can identify the slope and intercept in the equation:

$$y = \frac{-2}{3}x + 4:$$

The slope is $\frac{-2}{3}$ and the y-intercept is 4.

If we are told that the slope of a line is $\frac{3}{4}$ and the y-intercept is -2,

then the equation of the line is $y = \frac{3}{4}x - 2$.

> A negative slope can be written as
>
> $-\frac{2}{3}$ or $\frac{-2}{3}$ or $\frac{2}{-3}$
>
> but not $\frac{-2}{-3}$.

The slope-intercept form is an easy form to use when a graph of the line is required. We graph $y = \frac{3}{4}x - 2$:

(1) *Remember that b is the value of y where the graph crosses the y-axis.* The y-intercept (-2), is at the point $(0, -2)$ when $y = \frac{3}{4}x - 2$.

(2) To find a second point, use the slope, $m = \frac{3}{4}$. Remember that $\frac{3}{4} = \frac{\Delta y}{\Delta x}$. This means that when y changes $+ 3$, x changes $+ 4$. So starting at the y-intercept $(0, -2)$, the next point would be $(0 + 4, -2 + 3)$ or $(4, 1)$. Plot that point.

(3) We can repeat the procedure by adding 3 to y and 4 to x. The next point would then be $(8, 4)$. Plot that point and draw a line connecting the three points.

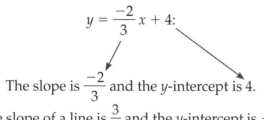

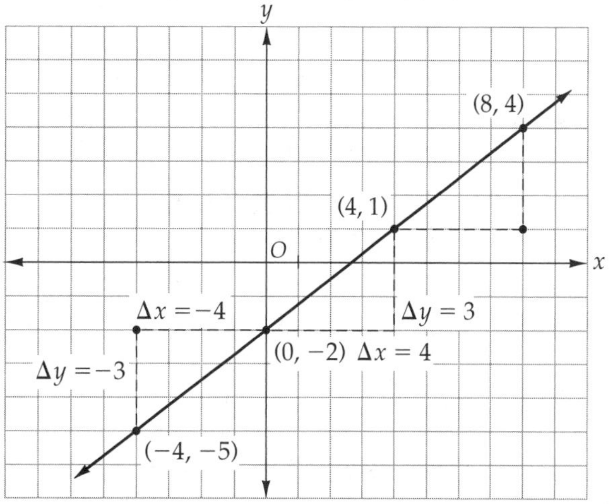

MODEL PROBLEMS

1. Find the slope and y-intercept of $4x + 3y = 3$.

SOLUTION

Solve for y.

$$4x + 3y = 3$$
$$3y = 3 - 4x$$
$$y = 1 - \frac{4}{3}x$$

Rewrite in slope-intercept form: $y = mx + b$.

$$y = -\frac{4}{3}x + 1$$

Answer: Slope $m = -\frac{4}{3}$ and y-intercept $b = 1$

2. **MP 7** Write the equation of a line in standard form $Ax + By = C$, if the slope is $-\frac{4}{5}$ and the y-intercept is 5.

SOLUTION

Begin with the slope-intercept form $y = mx + b$ and replace m with $-\frac{4}{5}$ and b with 5. Thus, $y = -\frac{4}{5}x + 5$. To change into standard form, add $\frac{4}{5}x$ to both sides.

Rewrite as $\frac{4}{5}x + y = 5$

Multiply every term by 5, so $4x + 5y = 25$

Answer: $4x + 5y = 25$

3. **MP 5** Predict what feature of the following graphs is the same and what feature is different. Use your graphing calculator to check your prediction.

$y = 3x - 1$

$y = 3x + 1$

$y = 3x + 3$

SOLUTION

The graphs have the same slope. The slope is 3. However, each has a different y-intercept. The graphs will be parallel and cross the y-axis at -1, 1, and 3, respectively.

The graphing window on the right verifies the prediction.

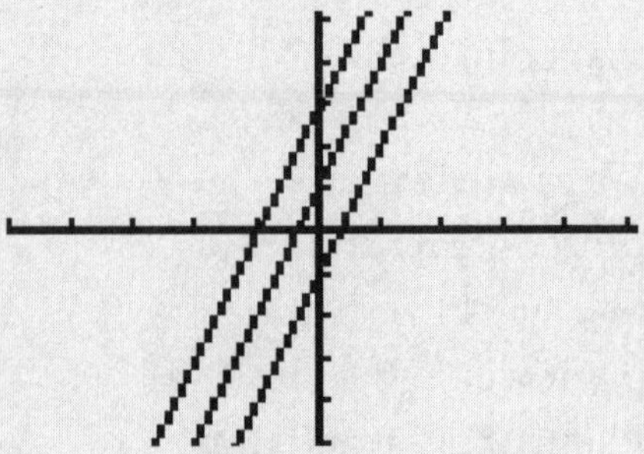

Answer: The equations are parallel lines. The y-intercepts are $(0, -1)$, $(0, 1)$, and $(0, 3)$.

Point-Slope Form

Given the slope m of line l and the coordinates (x_1, y_1) of any point on the line, it is possible to write an equation for the line. Since the slope is the same for any two points on the line, we can let (x, y) represent another point on the line and write the slope as $m = \frac{y - y_1}{x - x_1}$. By cross multiplying we get $y - y_1 = m(x - x_1)$.

If a line passes through the given point (x_1, y_1) and has slope m, the **point-slope form** of the equation of the line is $y - y_1 = m(x - x_1)$.

MODEL PROBLEMS

1. **MP 1, 2, 7** Write the equation of the line parallel to $2y = x + 3$ and passing through the point $(6, -2)$.

SOLUTION

First, solve for y. $y = \frac{1}{2}x + \frac{3}{2}$.

Since the new line is parallel, it has the *same slope*, $m = \frac{1}{2}$.

Using the point-slope method, $y - (-2) = \frac{1}{2}(x - 6)$ and $y + 2 = \frac{1}{2}x - 3$.

Thus, $y = \frac{1}{2}x - 5$.

2. **MP 1, 2, 7** Write the equation of the line perpendicular to $3y = -2x - 3$ and passing through the point $(2, -1)$.

SOLUTION

First, solve for y. $y = -\frac{2}{3}x - 1$. Since the new line is perpendicular, the slope is the *negative reciprocal* of $-\frac{2}{3}$, which is $\frac{3}{2}$. Again, using the point-slope method, $y - (-1) = \frac{3}{2}(x - 2)$ and $y + 1 = \frac{3}{2}x - 3$. Thus, $y = \frac{3}{2}x - 4$.

Model Problems continue . . .

Model Problems *continued*

3. **MP 6** Given a line with point $P(4, 6)$ and slope of $m = 3$:

a Write the correct linear equation in slope-intercept form.
b Graph the equation by creating a table of values.
c Identify the key features of the graph, such as the slope and x- and y-intercepts..

SOLUTION

a Substitute (4, 6) in the slope equation $m = \frac{y - y_1}{x - x_1}$, and substitute 3 for m. $3 = \frac{y - 6}{x - 4}$

Multiply both sides by $x - 4$. $3(x - 4) = y - 6$

Remove parentheses. $3x - 12 = y - 6$

Rewrite the equation in slope-intercept form. $3x - 6 = y$

or $y = 3x - 6$

b Any set of three points will enable us to graph the function.
Equation: $y = 3x - 6$

x	1	2	3
y	−3	0	3

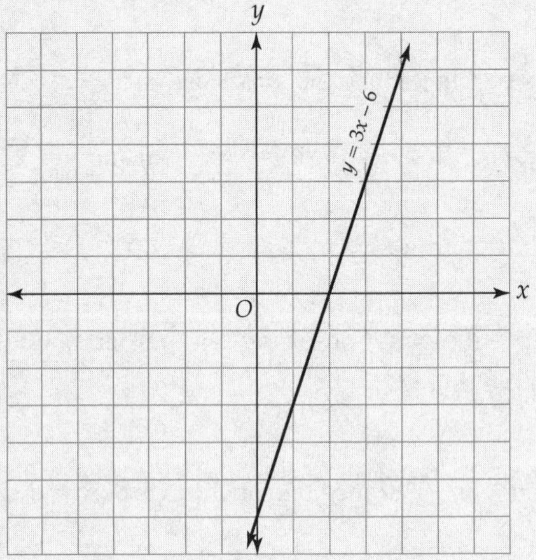

c The key features of the graph are:
x-intercept: (2, 0)
y-intercept: (0,−6)
slope (constant rate of change): 3

PRACTICE

1. Which is the graph of $x + y = 5$?

A.

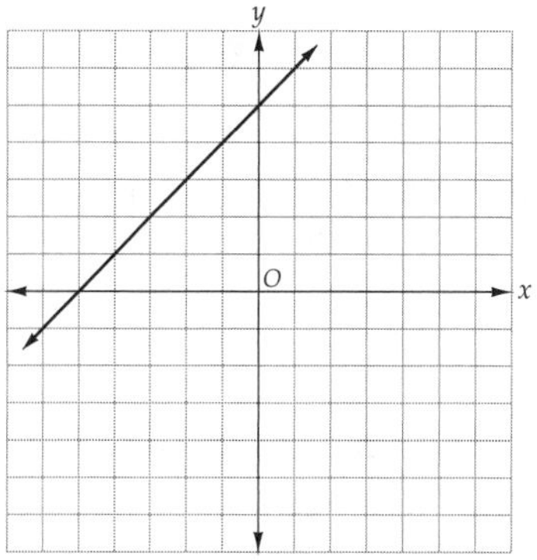

C.

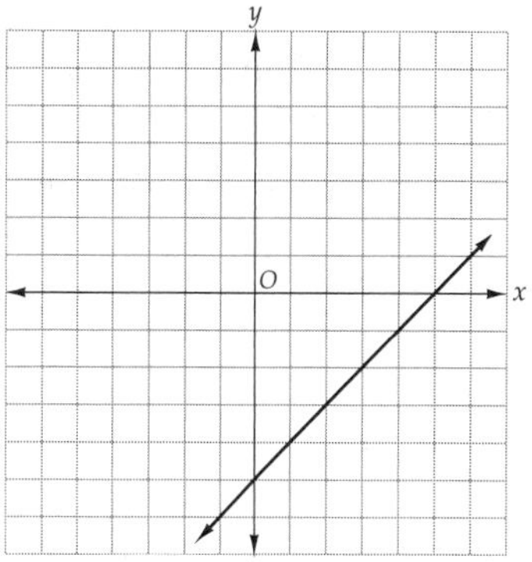

B.

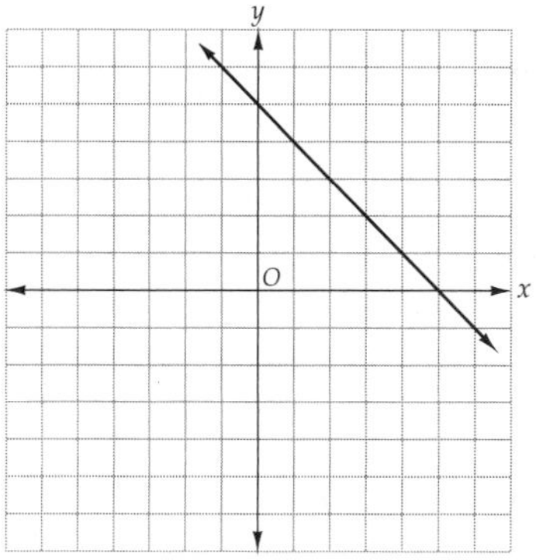

D.

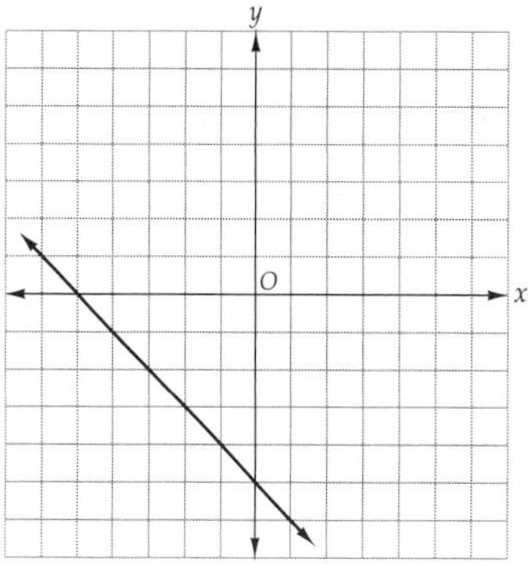

Exercises 2–5: Fill in the table.

Equation	Solve for y	Slope	y-intercept
2. $2x + 2y = 6$			
3. $3x - 3y = 12$			
4. $3x - y + 7 = 0$			
5. $3y - 7 = 0$			

Exercises 6–9: Write an equation of the line whose slope and y-intercept are given, and graph the line.

6. Slope is 4 and y-intercept is 1.

7. Slope is $-\frac{1}{2}$ and y-intercept is 0.

8. Slope is -1 and y-intercept is 1.

9. Slope is 0 and y-intercept is 6.

Exercises 10–11: Using the point-slope form, write an equation of the line with the given slope that passes through the given point. Transform the equation into the $y = mx + b$ form and graph.

10. $m = -2, (4, 2)$

11. $m = -\frac{1}{2}, (-4, -2)$

Practice Problems continue . . .

Exercises 12–13: In each of the following, write the equation of the line with the given slope and y-intercept or the given slope and given point. Then write that equation in the standard form $Ax + By = C$, where A, B, and C are integers.

12. $m = \frac{1}{2}$, $b = -4$

13. $m = -\frac{1}{4}$, $b = -2$

14. MP 2, 4 When you race a bicycle, you burn about 12 calories per minute. Draw a graph showing how many calories you burn based on how many minutes you race.

15. MP 2, 4 The formula for converting Fahrenheit to Celsius is $C = \frac{5}{9}(F - 32)$.

a Create a graph to convert from Celsius to Fahrenheit.

Use the graph to find the temperature in Fahrenheit that corresponds to:

b 0°C
c 50°C

Use the graph to find the temperature in Celsius that corresponds to:

d 81°F
e 36°F

Exercises 16–19: Given the slope and a point, write the equation of a line in $y = mx + b$ form.

16. $m = 5$, y-intercept $= (0, 3)$

17. $m = -3$, $b = 5$

18. $m = -\frac{1}{3}$, y-intercept $= (0, 0)$

19. $m = 0$, $b = 4$

Exercises 20–21: Given the slope and a point, write the equation of a line.

20. slope $= -\frac{2}{3}$; $(-9, -1)$

21. slope $= \frac{2}{5}$; $(-5, -4)$

Exercises 22–26: Write the equation for each line.

22. a line parallel to the y-axis and passing through the point (3, 5)

23. a line parallel to the x-axis and passing through the point (3, 5)

24. a line parallel to $3y - 4x = 6$ with $b = -3$

25. a line perpendicular to the line $y = -2x + 5$ and containing the point (3, 1)

26. a line perpendicular to the line $y = \frac{3}{2}x - 2$ and containing the point $(1, -4)$

Exercises 27–28: For each equation,

a Use the given coordinates (x, y) to find the value of k.
b Substitute the value for k and find the y-intercept of the equation.

27. $y = 2x + k$ and $(x, y) = (-2, 1)$

28. $5x = 3y - k$ and $(x, y) = (4, 2)$

29. If $a \neq 0$, and the slope of the line passing through $(-a, a)$ and $(3a, b)$ is 1, which of the following is an expression for b in terms of a?

A. $-3a$ C. $3a$
B. $5a$ D. $-5a$

MP 7 Exercises 30–31: If the graphs of each pair of given equations are the same, find the value of a and the value of k.

30. $3x + 2y = 18$ and $ax + ky = 6$

31. $ax - 6y = 9$ and $4x + ky = 12$

32. MP 2 If the slope of a given line is represented by the expression, $\frac{a}{b}$, write equations for lines that have y-intercepts of c and are:

a Parallel to the given line.

b Perpendicular to the given line.

Finding the Slope-Intercept Form Given Two Points

To Find the Slope-Intercept Form of a Line Given Two Points

Method 1

- Use the two points to find slope m of the line.
- Use slope m and either one of the given points to substitute for x and y in the slope-intercept formula: $y = mx + b$.
- Solve for b, the y-intercept.
- Substitute the values for m and b in $y = mx + b$.

Method 2

- Use the two points to find slope m of the line.
- Then use slope m and either one of the given points to substitute in the point-slope formula: $y - y_1 = m(x - x_1)$
- Simplify and change into $y = mx + b$ form.

MODEL PROBLEMS

1. MP 1 Find the equation of the line that joins the points (1, 3) and (2, 5).

SOLUTION

METHOD 1 (Slope-Intercept)

Substitute and find slope m:

$$m = \frac{y_2 - y_1}{x_2 - x_1} = \frac{5 - 3}{2 - 1} = \frac{2}{1} \text{ or } 2$$

Now substitute 2 for slope m, and point (1, 3) for (x, y) in the slope-intercept formula $y = mx + b$.

Solve for b:

$3 = 2(1) + b$, and $b = 1$

Once again, substitute 2 for m, and 1 for b in $y = mx + b$:

The equation of the line is $y = 2x + 1$.

Check. Check by substituting the coordinates of the other point (2, 5) for (x, y) in the equation of the line.

$5 = (2)(2) + 1$

$5 = 5$ ✓

METHOD 2 (Point-Slope)

Substitute and find the slope m:

$$m = \frac{y_2 - y_1}{x_2 - x_1} = \frac{5 - 3}{2 - 1} = \frac{2}{1} \text{ or } 2$$

Now substitute 2 for slope m and point (1, 3) for (x_1, y_1) in the point-slope formula:

$$y - y_1 = m(x - x_1)$$
$$y - 3 = 2(x - 1)$$

If we had chosen the point (2, 5), then

$$y - y_1 = m(x - x_1)$$
$$y - 5 = 2(x - 2)$$

In fact, these are dependent lines; that is, they have the same graph. If we convert each equation to slope-intercept form, the result is the same equation.

$y - 3 = 2(x - 1)$	$y - 5 = 2(x - 2)$
$y - 3 = 2x - 2$	$y - 5 = 2x - 4$
$y = 2x + 1$	$y = 2x + 1$

Model Problems continue . . .

2. Find the equation of the line if the y-intercept is (0, 6) and the line passes through the point (2, −4).

SOLUTION

METHOD 1

Use (0, 6) and (2, −4) and find the slope $m = \frac{6 - (-4)}{0 - 2} = \frac{10}{-2} = -5$.

Now substitute in 6 for b and −5 for m so that $y = -5x + 6$.

METHOD 2

Use $y = mx + b$ and substitute 6 for b and (2, −4) for (x, y) and solve for m.

$-4 = m(2) + 6, -10 = 2m, m = -5$

Now use $y = mx + b$ again and substitute in 6 for b and −5 for m: $y = -5x + 6$.

3. Write the equation of the line where the x-intercept is (2, 0) and the y-intercept is (0, −4).

SOLUTION

Since the intercepts are (2, 0) and (0, −4), the slope is $\frac{-y}{x} = \frac{-(-4)}{2} = 2$.

Now substitute in −4 for b and 2 for the slope m. The equation is $y = 2x - 4$.

4. Write an equation of a line whose x-intercept is $\left(\frac{5}{2}, 0\right)$ and y-intercept is (0, −5).

SOLUTION

Since the x-intercept is $\frac{5}{2}$ and the y-intercept is −5, the slope $\frac{-y}{x} = \frac{-(-5)}{\frac{5}{2}} = 5 \times \frac{2}{5} = 2$.

Now substitute in −5 for b and 2 for the slope m. The equation is $y = 2x - 5$.

5. **MP 3** Why does it make sense to substitute 0 for y if we want to find the x-intercept? Why does it make sense to substitute 0 for x if we want to find the y-intercept?

Answer: Where the line crosses the x-axis, the y-value is 0, and where the line crosses the y-axis, the x-value is 0.

Model Problems continue . . .

6. **MP 2, 3, 4** Abdullah takes a taxi to visit his grandparents and his cousins. The rate is the same for both trips. There is a flat fee for bringing the cab to a residence and then a charge per mile. The x-coordinate is the independent variable (distance in miles). The y-coordinate is the dependent variable (cost of the ride).

Trip to grandparents: (3, 15)
Trip to cousins: (4, 19)

a In what quadrant(s) is this graph meaningful?
b Plot the coordinate pairs and sketch a graph. Record the y-intercept and the slope. What does the y-intercept represent? What does the slope represent?
c Use an algebraic method for finding the equation of a line given two points. Does your equation for the line match? How do you know?

SOLUTION

a This graph is meaningful only in quadrant 1. The distance and the cost are always non-negative.

b

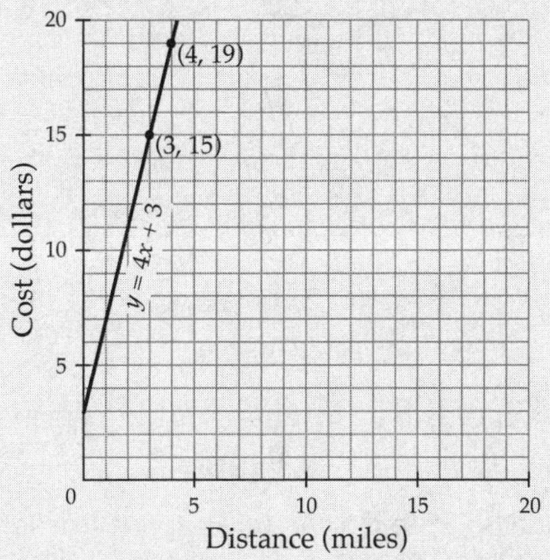

The y-intercept is (0, 3). There is a flat fee of \$3.00 to use the taxi service.

The slope is $\frac{19-15}{4-3} = \frac{4}{1} = 4$. This is the constant rate of change for the graph. The charge is \$4.00 per mile. The equation of the sketched graph appears to be $y = 4x + 3$.

c Algebraic solution:

Slope: $m = \frac{y_2 - y_1}{x_2 - x_1} = \frac{19-15}{4-3} = \frac{4}{1} = 4$

Choose either point. The calculation below uses (3, 15).

$$\begin{aligned} y &= mx + b \\ 15 &= 4(3) + b \\ 15 &= 12 + b \\ -12 &= -12 \\ \hline 3 &= b \end{aligned}$$

The calculation verifies that the equation of the line representing taxi fare is $y = 4x + 3$ because the slope and y-intercept of this equation match the slope and y-intercept of the graph.

PRACTICE

1. Which equation passes through $(3, -5)$ and $(-1, 3)$?

A. $y + 5 = x - 3$
B. $y = 2x + 1$
C. $y - 3 = -2(x + 1)$
D. $y = x + 2$

Exercises 2–6: Write the linear equation determined by the following pairs of points. Put your answer in $y = mx + b$ form and then $Ax + By = C$ form, where A, B, and C are integers.

2. $(1, 3)$ and $(-2, -6)$

3. $(3, 5)$ and $(4, 7)$

4. $(-2, 3)$ and $(1, 5)$

5. $(2, 3)$ and $(2, 5)$

6. $(-1, -2)$ and $(2, 2)$

7. If the vertices of triangle ABC are located at $(2, -2)$, $(6, 4)$, and $(-4, 2)$, what are the slopes of the three lines that determine the triangle?

Exercises 8–11: Write the linear equation determined by the following information.

8. y-intercept $(0, 3)$ and point $(1, 2)$

9. y-intercept $(0, -2)$ and point $(2, 5)$

10. $b = 5$ and point $(3, -2)$

11. $b = -4$ and point $(3, 1)$

Exercises 12–17: Find the x- and y-intercepts of the following equations.

12. $x + 2y = 2$

13. $2x - 5y = 20$

14. $y = \frac{3}{5}x + 5$

15. $y = 10$

16. $y = -\frac{2}{3}x + 3$

17. $3x + y - 3 = 0$

Exercises 18–20: Given the x- and y-intercepts, write the linear equation.

18. $(2, 0)$ and $(0, -6)$

19. $(4, 0)$ and $(0, 1)$

20. $(-5, 0)$ and $(0, -3)$

MP 1, 4, 5, 7 The graph below shows Michelle driving to work.

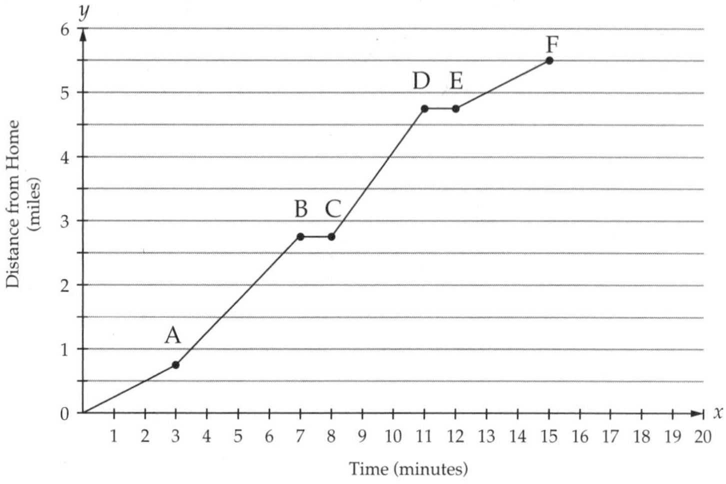

21. Which of the following could describe what happened between B and C?

A. Michelle drove away from home.
B. Michelle drove toward her home.
C. Michelle increased her speed.
D. Michelle stopped at a stoplight.

22. Which of the following describes what happened at A?

A. Michelle reduced her speed.
B. Michelle drove toward her home.
C. Michelle increased her speed.
D. Michelle stopped at a stoplight.

3.5 Functions

A function pairs each element of the **domain** with one and only one element of the **range**. In other words, no two ordered pairs have the same x-value.

Relations That Are Functions

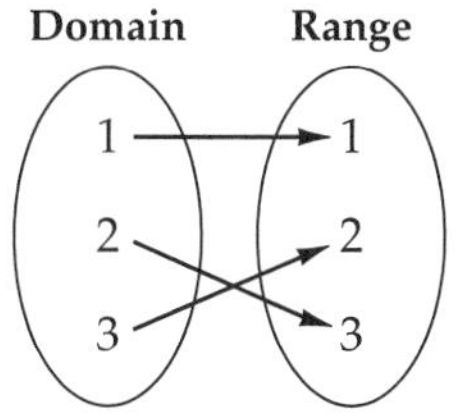

Domain x	Range y
1	4
2	7
3	10

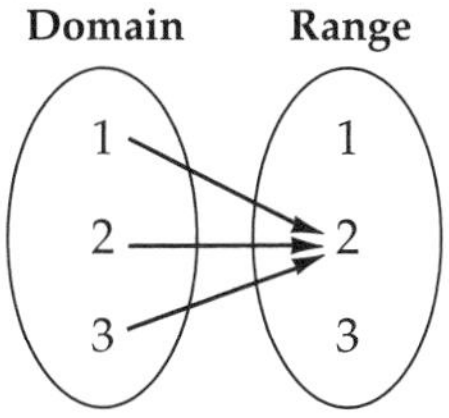

Relations That Are Not Functions

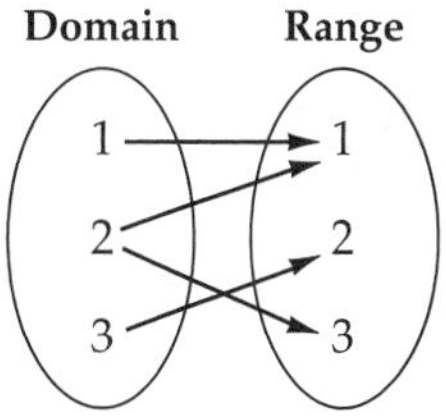

Domain x	Range y
1	4
1	7
2	10

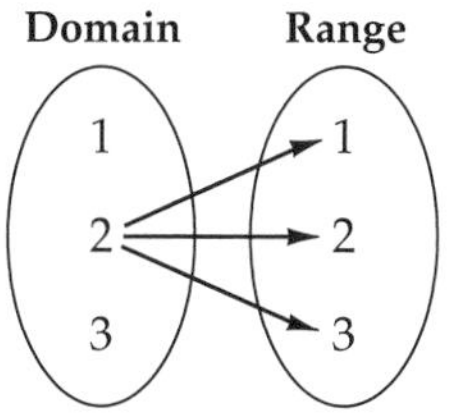

Graphing Functions

- With a function, the y is replaced by $f(x)$, so in $y = 2x + 1$ we can write $f(x) = 2x + 1$. Any letter may be used in function notation, so $g(x)$, $h(t)$, $F(m)$, etc., may each represent a function.
- We can call the value of x the input to the function, and the value of $f(x)$ is the output.
- Substituting values for x has the same result, whether one writes $f(x) = 2x + 1$ or $y = 2x + 1$. If $x = 4$, $y = f(4) = 2(4) + 1 = 9$.
- The graph is the set of all points $(x, f(x))$. When this is graphed, $f(x)$ is the vertical axis, instead of y.

If you are able to draw a vertical line through any part of the graph and have the vertical line cross the graph more than once, the graph is not a function.

input	output
x	$f(x)$
−2	−3
−1	−1
0	1
1	3
2	5

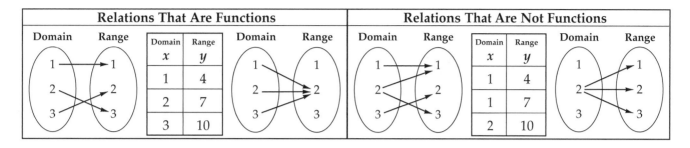

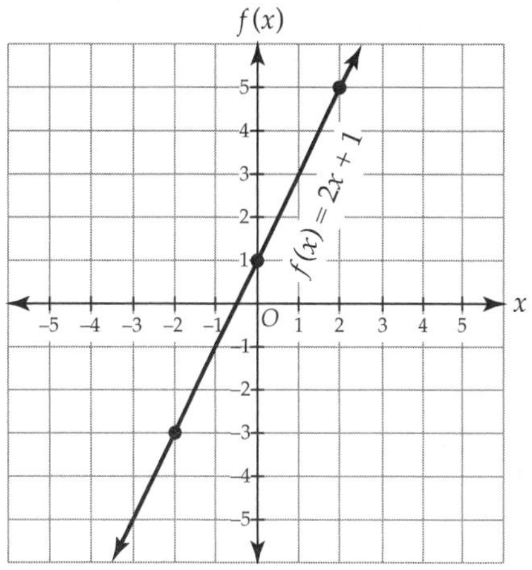

For any function $y = f(x)$, when x, the input, takes on all the values in the domain, the set of all the values of $f(x)$ is called the *range of the function*. In other words, the range of a function is the set of outputs (i.e., the values of the dependent variable, $f(x)$).

input = independent
output = dependent

Domain Restrictions

- Domains are important and are often discussed with functions. For the function $f(x) = 2x + 1$, there are no restrictions because the domain could be any real number.

- If the function describes a real-world formula, then the "real world" may create domain restrictions. For instance, if x represents time during a process that begins at time $x = 0$, then x cannot be negative.

- Domain restrictions can also come from the expression. For instance, the domain of the function $f(x) = \dfrac{1}{x - 3}$ has a restriction. The value of x cannot be 3, since 3 would make the denominator equal zero, and dividing by zero is undefined. The domain is all real numbers, except for 3.

- Desired values of the range may determine the domain. For the function $f(x) = -2x$, if the range is all the positive numbers, then the domain is all negative numbers, since any negative number multiplied by a negative number is positive.

MODEL PROBLEMS

1. **MP 1, 2** If $x \geq 0$ is the domain for the function $f(x) = -\dfrac{1}{2}x + 5$, what is the range?

SOLUTION

Substituting some friendly integers such as {0, 2, 4, 8} we find a range of {5, 4, 3, 1}. As x gets larger, $f(x)$ appears to get smaller. It is often helpful to evaluate input values that are among the smallest values in the domain and among the largest values in the domain. Zero is the smallest number in the domain, $f(0) = 5$ and $f(10{,}000) = -4995$. The range is $y \leq 5$ or $f(x) \leq 5$.

2. **MP 1, 2, 7** Consider the following four functions. Identify the domain and range for each and determine if the domain is restricted by the expression:

a $f(x) = 2x + 3$
b $f(x) = x^2 - 1$
c $f(x) = (x - 1)^2 + 2$
d $f(x) = \sqrt{x + 3}$

SOLUTION

a $f(x) = 2x + 3$
There are no restrictions.
Domain: all real numbers
Range: all real numbers

b $f(x) = x^2 - 1$
Domain: all real numbers
$x^2 \geq 0$, therefore $x^2 - 1 \geq -1$, so Range: $f(x) \geq -1$.

> Any real number squared will be positive or zero. It cannot be negative.

c $f(x) = (x - 1)^2 + 2$
Domain: all real numbers
Once again, we can say $(x - 1)^2$ will be a positive number or zero.
Thus, $f(1) = (1 - 1) + 2 = 0 + 2 = 2$. Hence, Range: $f(x) \geq 2$.

d $f(x) = \sqrt{x + 3}$
Domain: the square root is only defined for non-negative numbers and zero.
$x + 3 \geq 0$; $x \geq -3$, so Range: The principal root is always positive. $f(x) \geq 0$.

Model Problems continue . . .

Model Problems *continued*

3. **a** Graph the function $f(x) = 3x - 5$ with the restricted domain $1 < x < 3$.

b Identify the range.

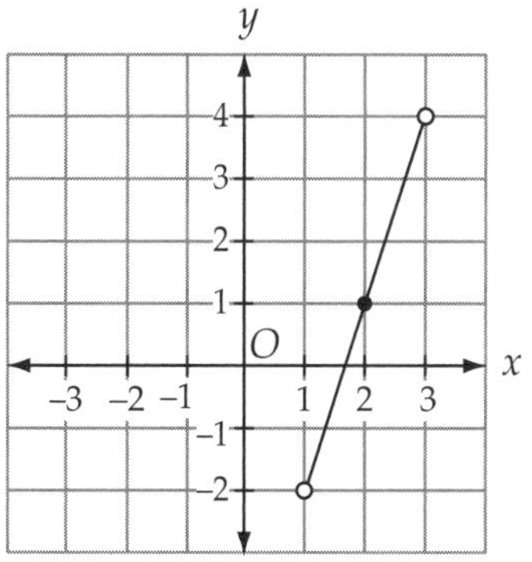

SOLUTION

a Determine some coordinate pairs that fit the function, such as $(1, -2)$, $(2, 1)$, and $(3, 4)$, plot those points, and draw the line segment. Note the open circles at $(1, -2)$ and $(3, 4)$.

b Range: $-2 < y < 4$

PRACTICE

1. If we say that the cost, c, of mailing a first-class letter depends on the weight, w, of the letter, identify the dependent and independent variables.

2. MP 2 If theater tickets cost \$80 each and you plan on buying as many as 6 tickets,

a Write a function for the cost, C, as a function of the number of tickets, t, that you might buy.

b Identify the independent and dependent variables.

c Identify the domain and range and the set of ordered pairs.

3. If $f(x) = 4x + 3$ and $f(x) = 10$, what is the value of x?

4. If $f(x) = 2x + 5$, then what is the value of $f(-9) - f(0)$?

Exercises 5–8: Use the given information to write a function in the form $f(x) = mx + b$.

5. $f(-1) = 3$ and $f(2) = 9$

6. $m = -2$ and $f(-2) = 8$

7. $f(0) = -5$ and $m = 2$

8. $f(0.5) = 6.5$ and $f(-1.5) = 10.5$

9. Each of the following functions has a given domain. Identify the range of the function.

a $y = x - 2$ with D: $\{1, 2, 3, 4\}$

b $f(x) = 2x$ with D: $\{1, 3, 5, 7\}$

c $y = x + 3$ with D: $\{2, 4, 6, 8\}$

d $y = 2x - 3$ with D: $\{-3, -2, -1, 0, 1\}$

e $f(x) = \frac{1}{3}x + 2$ with D: $\{-6, -3, 0, 3, 6\}$

10. For each of the following use the given domain to find the range.

a $y = -2x + 3$ D: $x \leq 0$

b $y = x^2 - 1$ D: $x \geq 1$

c $f(x) = -3x + 1$ D: $x \leq 0$

d $f(x) = 2x - 3$ D: $x \geq 0$

11. MP 7 For each function use the given domain to find the range.

a $y = \frac{1}{2}x - 5$, domain $-8 \leq x < 10$

b $g(x) = 3 - \frac{x}{2} - 2$, domain $-2 < x \leq 6$

Practice Problems continue . . .

Exercises 12–14: Write the equation for each graph. State the domain and range if it is the graph of a function.

12.

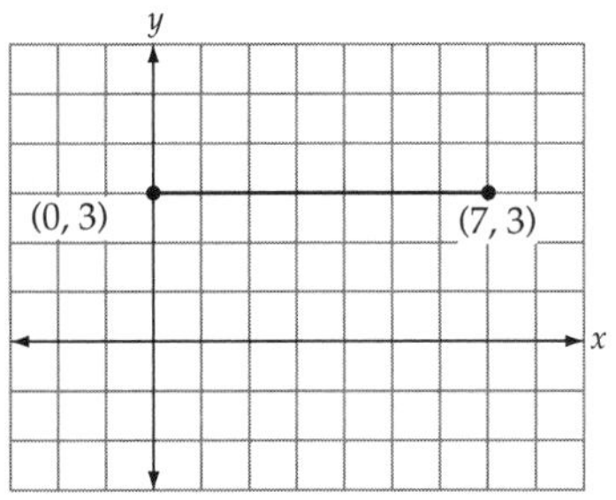

13.

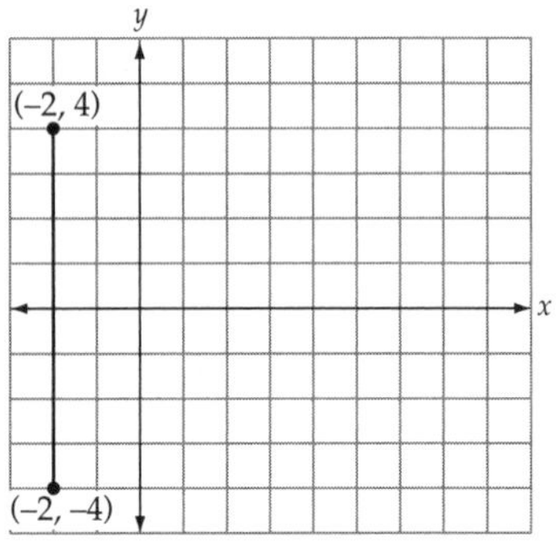

14.

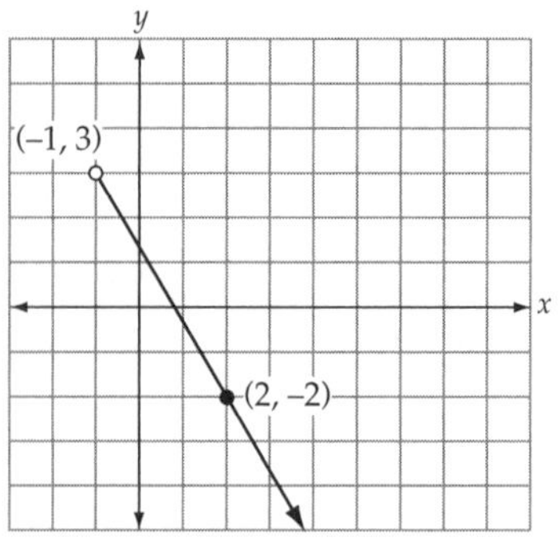

LESSON 3.6

3.6 The Algebra of Functions

We defined functions with real-number domains and ranges and graphed them on a rectangular coordinate system. Just as it is possible to perform operations on real numbers, it is also possible to perform the four basic operations $(+, -, \times, \div)$ on functions.

If the domains and ranges of functions f and g are the set or a subset of the real numbers, then

- The *sum* of f and g, written as $f + g$, is defined by $(f + g)(x) = f(x) + g(x)$
- The *difference* of f and g, written as $f - g$, is defined by $(f - g)(x) = f(x) - g(x)$
- The *product* of f and g, written as $f \times g$, is defined by $f \times g(x) = f(x) \times g(x)$
- The *quotient* of f and g, written as f/g, is defined by $f/g(x) = \dfrac{f(x)}{g(x)}$, where $g(x) \neq 0$

Performing an operation on two functions *f*(*x*) and *g*(*x*) produces a new function *h*(*x*).

MODEL PROBLEMS

1. If $f(x) = 3x^2 + 1$ and $g(x) = 5x - 2$, find the sum $f + g$ and difference $f - g$ of the functions.

SOLUTION

$h(x) =$ the sum $f(x) + g(x) = 3x^2 + 1 + 5x - 2$
$= 3x^2 + 5x - 1$
$h(x) = 3x^2 + 5x - 1$

$h(x) =$ the difference $f(x) - g(x)$
$= 3x^2 + 1 - (5x - 2) = 3x^2 + 1 - 5x + 2$
$= 3x^2 - 5x + 3$
$h(x) = 3x^2 - 5x + 3$

2. If $f(x) = 4x + 1$ and $g(x) = 3x$, find the product $f(x) \cdot g(x)$ and quotient $\frac{f(x)}{g(x)}$ and state any restrictions.

SOLUTION

$h(x) =$ the product $f(x) \times g(x) = (4x + 1)3x$
$= 12x^2 + 3x$

$h(x) = 12x^2 + 3x$

$h(x) =$ the quotient $\frac{f(x)}{g(x)} = \frac{4x + 1}{3x}$ and since the denominator $3x \neq 0$, $x \neq 0$.

$h(x) = \frac{4x + 1}{3x}$

PRACTICE

1. If $f(x) = 2x$ and $g(x) = 3x - 1$ for each of the following, find the function $h(x)$ and state any restrictions.

a $f + g$

b $f - g$

c $f \bullet g$

d $\frac{f}{g}$

2. If $f(x) = 3x - 2$ and $g(x) = x$ for each of the following, find the function $h(x)$.

a $f + g$

b $f - g$

c $f \bullet g$

d $\frac{f}{g}$

3. If $f(x) = 10$ and $g(x) = \frac{1}{5}x - 2$, find $h(x) = f(x) \bullet g(x)$.

4. MP 2 If $f(x) = 4x - 1$ and $g(x) = -3x + 2$,

a Find $h(x) = f(x) + g(x)$.

b Find $h(x) = f(x) - j(x)$.

c Complete the table and draw a conclusion regarding $h(x)$.

x	$f(x) + g(x)$	$h(x) =$
-2		
-1		
0	$-1 + 2 = 1$	$0 + 1 = 1$
1	$3 + -1 = 2$	$1 + 1 = 2$
2		

5. MP 2, 4 In the first year of after-school golf instruction, 8 girls and 11 boys enrolled. Each year thereafter, 3 more girls and 5 more boys enrolled. If t is the time (in years) since the first year of instruction,

a Write a rule for each of the following functions:
$G(t)$, the number of girls enrolled as a function of time t
$B(t)$, the number of boys enrolled as a function of time t
$T(t)$, the total enrollment as a function of time t

b After 6 years what was $G(t)$, $B(t)$, and $T(t)$?

3.7 Inverse Functions

A function f has an inverse if it passes the *horizontal line test*. In other words, if we have graphed a function and every horizontal line intersects the graph of that function in at most one point, then an inverse of the function exists. That inverse is denoted by the symbol f^{-1}, and the given function f is said to be a *one-to-one function*.

We show the graphs of two functions, $y = 2^x$ and $y = x^2$. Only the exponential function $y = 2^x$ is one-to-one and has an inverse function. The quadratic function $y = x^2$ is not one-to-one since it fails the horizontal line test.

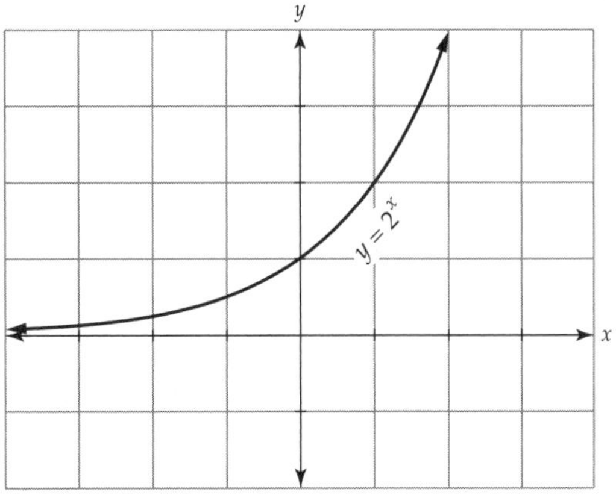

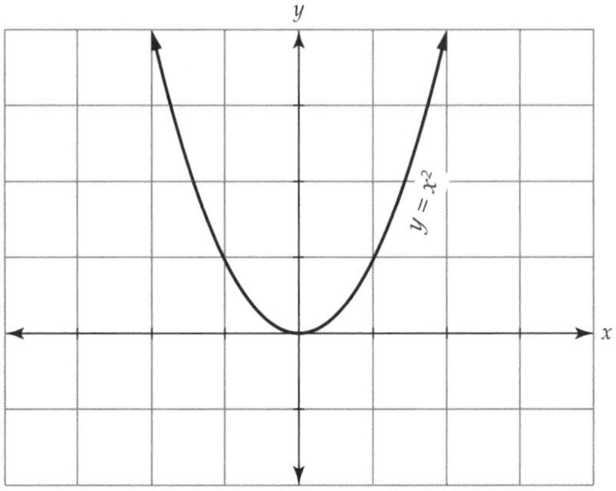

If the point (a, b) is on the graph of f, and f is a 1 – 1 function, then (b, a) is a point on the graph of f^{-1}, the inverse. In other words, the inverse function maps the outputs of the original inputs back to the original inputs.

> The identity function, $y = x$, is its own inverse.

The domain of the function, f, equals the range of its inverse f^{-1}. The range of the function, f, is the domain of its inverse, f^{-1}. We show the function $f(x) = 2x - 1$ and its inverse $f^{-1}(x) = \dfrac{x+1}{2}$.

x	$f(x)$
−1	−3
0	−1
1	1
2	3
3	5

x	$f^{-1}(x)$
−3	−1
−1	0
1	1
3	2
5	3

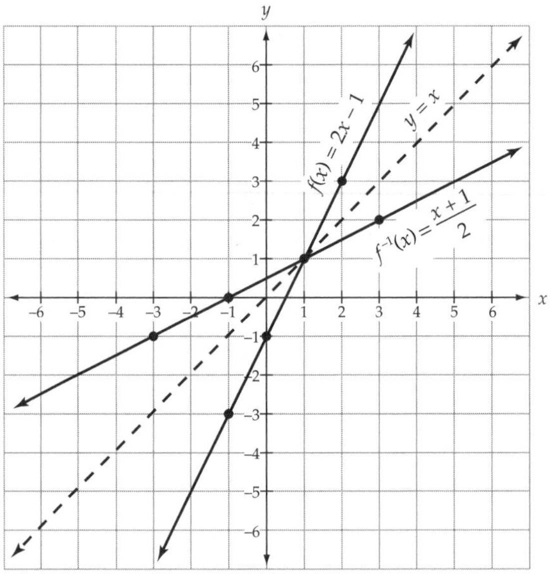

The graphs of f and f^{-1} are reflections of each other across the line, $y = x$. We could also say that the graphs of f and f^{-1} are always symmetric with respect to the line $y = x$.

To find the inverse of a one-to-one function algebraically, we first replace $f(x)$ with y, then interchange x and y, solve for y, and, lastly, replace y with $f^{-1}(x)$.

MODEL PROBLEMS

1. Write the inverse of the function $\{(3, -8), (4, 1), (0, -5), (-2, 6)\}$.

SOLUTION

Interchange the x-coordinate and y-coordinate of each pair in the given function to find the inverse.

Answer: $\{(-8, 3), (1, 4), (-5, 0), (6, -2)\}$

2. What is the inverse of the function $f(x) = \dfrac{3x - 2}{5}$?

SOLUTION

Replace $f(x)$ with y in the given equation. $\quad y = \dfrac{3x - 2}{5}$

Interchange the x and y in the given equation. $\quad x = \dfrac{3y - 2}{5}$

Solve for y. $\quad 5x = 3y - 2$

$$5x + 2 = 3y$$

$$y = \frac{5x + 2}{3} \text{ or } f^{-1}(x) = \frac{5x}{3} + \frac{2}{3}$$

3. **MP 2, 7** Find the inverse of $f(x) = \dfrac{x + 6}{3}$. Graph the function and its inverse.

SOLUTION

Replace $f(x)$ with y. $\quad y = \dfrac{x + 6}{3}$

Switch x and y. $\quad x = \dfrac{y + 6}{3}$

Solve for y. $\quad 3x = y + 6$

$$y = 3x - 6 \text{ or } f^{-1}(x) = 3x - 6.$$

We can now graph the two functions along with the identity function $y = x$ as a broken line along the diagonal. Notice that $f(x)$ contains the points $(-6, 0)$, $(-3, 1)$, $(0, 2)$, and $(3, 3)$, and by reflecting $f(x)$ across the line $y = x$, we can graph the inverse function that contains the points $(0, -6)$, $(1, -3)$, $(2, 0)$, and $(3, 3)$.

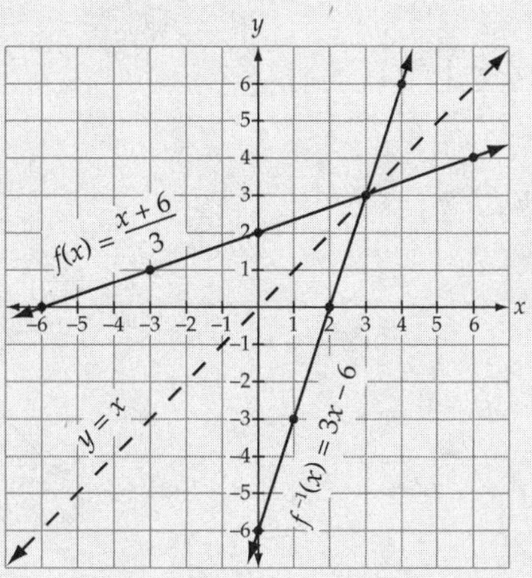

PRACTICE

1. If $f(x) = 6x - 2$, then the inverse function is

A. $f^{-1}(x) = \frac{x+2}{6}$

B. $f^{-1}(x) = \frac{x}{6} + 2$

C. $f^{-1}(x) = \frac{x+1}{3}$

D. $f^{-1}(x) = \frac{x}{3} + 1$

2. What is the inverse of the function $x + 2y + 3 = 0$?

A. $y = -\frac{1}{2}x - \frac{3}{2}$

B. $y = -2x - 3$

C. $y = -2x - \frac{3}{2}$

D. $y = 2x + 3$

3. What is the inverse of $f(x) = -\frac{3}{2}x$?

A. $f^{-1}(x) = \frac{3}{2}x$

B. $f^{-1}(x) = \frac{2}{3}x$

C. $f^{-1}(x) = \frac{2}{3}x - 1$

D. $f^{-1}(x) = -\frac{2}{3}x$

4. **MP 1, 2** Which is the equation of the line formed when the function $f(x) = 3x + 1$ is reflected in the line $y = x$?

A. $y = 3x - 1$

B. $y = \frac{x}{3} - 1$

C. $y = \frac{x-1}{3}$

D. $x = y$

5. Which function is one-to-one?

A.

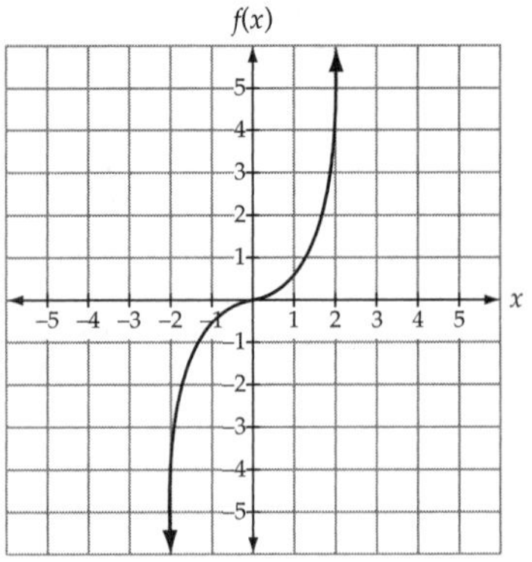

B.

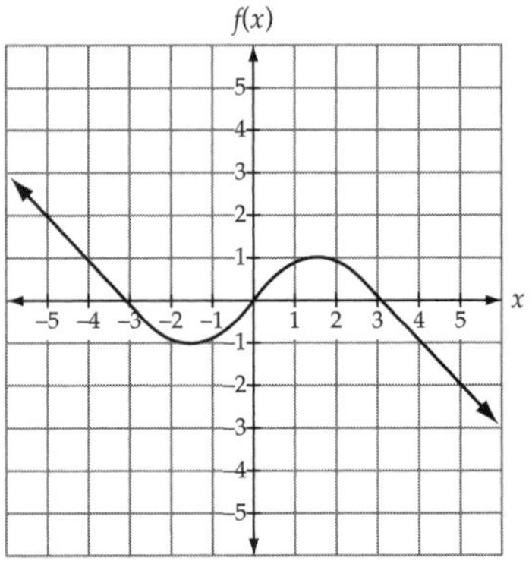

C.

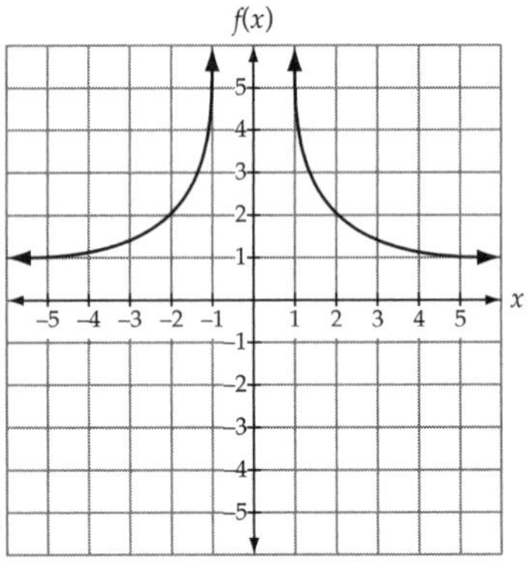

D.

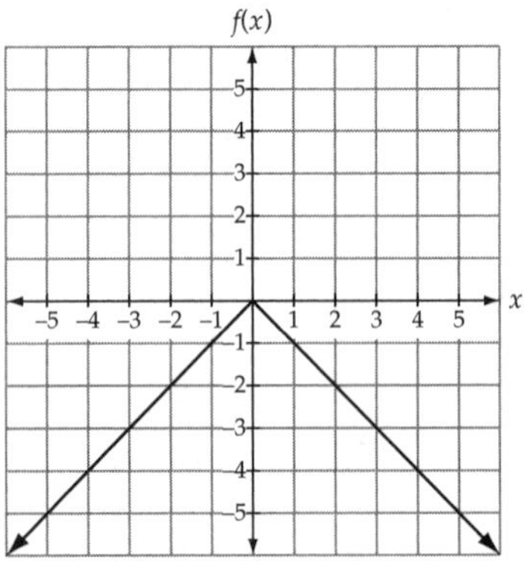

Practice Problems continue . . .

6. Which relation is a 1–1 function?

A. $\{(a, b), (a, c), (a, d)\}$

B. $\{(a, b), (a, c), (b, d)\}$

C. $\{(a, c), (b, c), (a, b)\}$

D. $\{(a, b), (b, c,) (c, d)\}$

7. Find the inverse of each of the following.

a $\{(-1, 2), (0, 5), (3, -2), (5, 6)\}$

b $\{(1, 2), (2, 3), (3, 4), (4, 5)\}$

c $\{(1, a), (2, c), (3, d), (4, g)\}$

d $\{(1, k), (2, k+1), (3, k+2)\}$

8. If $g = \{(3, -2), (4, -2), (5, -1)\}$,

a Write the relation formed by interchanging the x-coordinate and y-coordinate of g.

b Is this new relation a function? If not, explain why.

9. Write in the form $y = mx + b$ the equation of the inverse for each of the given functions:

a $y = 6x$

b $y = 2x - 12$

c $y = -\frac{1}{3}x + 3$

d $y = 2x + 6$

e $2x + 3y = 6$

10. a If $f(x) = 3x - 7$, evaluate $f^{-1}(-1)$.

b If $g(x) = \frac{2}{3}x + 4$, evaluate $g(-3)$, and evaluate $g^{-1}(2)$.

c What conclusion can be drawn from the answers to **a** and **b**?

11. MP 3

a Graph $f(x) = 2x - 1$.

b Find and graph on the same coordinate system the inverse function, f^{-1}.

c Graph $y = x$ and find the common intersection of the three linear equations.

d Set $f(x) = f^{-1}(x)$ and solve algebraically for the values of x and y.

e What conclusion can be drawn from the answers to **c** and **d**?

12. MP 3 Explain why a function needs to be one-to-one in order to have an inverse.

LESSON 3.8

3.8 Modeling with Linear Functions

Graphs are used to represent relationships between two variables. They help us understand relationships and generalize beyond the data supplied. In functions, a value of y or $f(x)$ is assigned to each value of x. The primary relationship in a function is that the y-value depends on the x-value. For this reason, the x-axis is called the **independent axis** and the y-axis is called the **dependent axis**. The relationship can also be seen in terms of *slope*, as the rate of change between the *dependent* y-axis and the *independent* x-axis: $\frac{\text{dependent } \Delta y}{\text{independent } \Delta x}$.

Drawing the Graph of a Situation. In dealing with real situations, it becomes necessary to think of the x-axis as some independent variable, such as time, and to think of the y-axis as a dependent variable, such as height or distance. Whenever it is clear that one variable depends on the other, the **dependent variable** should be the y and the **independent variable** should be the x. If a graph is comparing air pressure at different altitudes, then the pressure (y) depends on the altitude (x). But if a graph is charting a mountain climber's progress, then the altitude (y) depends on the time spent climbing (x).

It is important to label each axis of a graph you create.

MODEL PROBLEM

MP 2, 8 Deluxe Limousine Service charges \$2 for the initial pickup of a passenger and then \$1 per mile. Make a graph of this situation.

SOLUTION

Note that the fee for the ride *depends* on the number of miles traveled. Therefore, the fee will be represented by the variable y and distance will be represented by the variable x. The change per mile is the fraction that represents the change in price per change in miles traveled, or $\frac{\Delta y}{\Delta x}$, the slope, which equals $\frac{\$1}{1 \text{ mile}}$ or 1. The equation will then be $y = \$2 + \$1x$.

We can make a table of miles and fees for Deluxe Limousine Service. The label for the x-axis is *miles traveled*, and the label for the y-axis is *limo fee in dollars*.

Miles Traveled x	Limo Fee in Dollars y
0	2
1	3
2	4

The graph starts where the number of miles traveled is 0. The fee at zero miles is \$2. Thus, the point (0, 2) is on the graph. A 1-mile trip costs \$3 and a 2-mile trip costs \$4. When we plot these points, we see a linear pattern. We can extend the graph in the first quadrant, and we can read the fees for longer trips. Note that the graph is only in the first quadrant because we are limited by the situation. The limo cannot travel negative miles nor owe money to the passenger.

Answer:

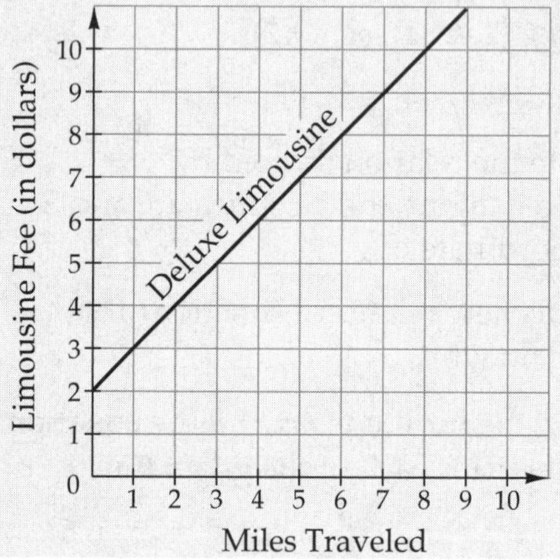

Reading the Graph of a Situation When considering the graph of a situation, remember:

- Questions that involve rates (time per room painted, daily charge) or speeds (miles per hour, births per year) will usually require information about the slope.
- Questions that involve starting times, opening deposits, beginning locations, or similar initial conditions are usually asking questions about the y-intercept.

MODEL PROBLEM

MP 2, 4 This graph represents the billing structure for Friendly Taxi. What is the initial pickup fee and charge per mile for this service?

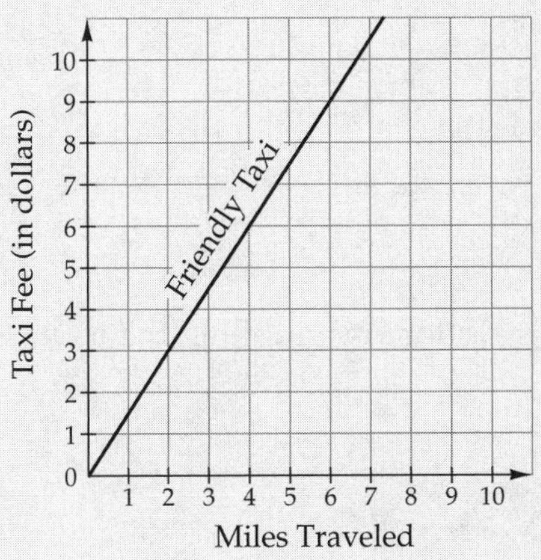

SOLUTION

The initial pickup fee is the charge before any driving is done, in other words, when x is 0. The point on the graph with an x-value of zero is the origin, (0, 0). Therefore, the pickup fee is $0.

The charge per mile is the change in price per change in miles, or $\frac{\Delta y}{\Delta x}$, the slope. Two points on the line are (0, 0) and (2, 3), so $\frac{\Delta y}{\Delta x} = \frac{3-0}{2-0} = \frac{3 \text{ dollars}}{2 \text{ miles}} = 1.5$ dollars per mile.

Answer: There is no pickup fee, and the charge per mile is $1.50.

Situations Involving Graphs of Systems When two equations are graphed on the same coordinate plane, many types of questions involve comparing the graphs.

- Questions that ask "When is situation A better/lower than situation B?" want you to find an inequality involving x that describes what part of the graph satisfies the situation. For example, the answer might be "When the time is longer than 5 days."
- Questions that ask "When are the values the same?" want you to find the coordinates of the point of intersection.
- Questions that ask about differences at specific values of x require you to subtract the y-value of one line from the other.

MODEL PROBLEM

MP 2, 4 Deluxe Limousine Service charges $2 for the initial pickup of a passenger and then $1 per mile. By comparison, Friendly Taxi does not have an initial pickup fee but charges $1.50 per mile. Graph the fee schedule for Deluxe Limousine on the same coordinate plane as the graph for Friendly Taxi. Then answer the following questions:

a For what length trips is it cheaper to use Friendly Taxi?

b At what mileage is the cost the same for both services? What is the cost?

c What is the difference in cost at the 6-mile mark?

SOLUTION

The graphs of the costs of each service were discussed earlier in this section. By graphing them on the same coordinate plane, you can answer the three questions.

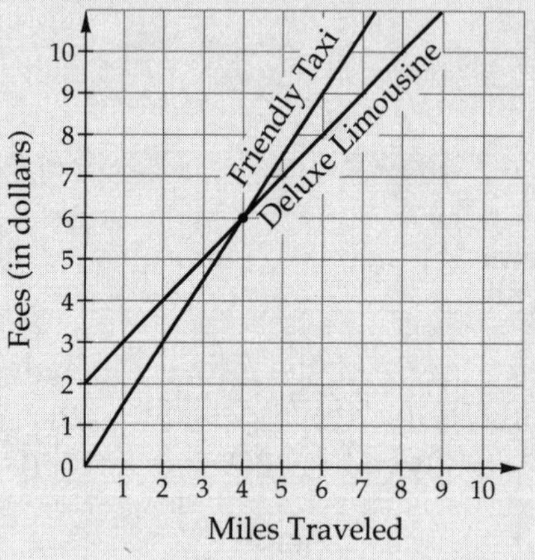

Answer:

a The graph for Friendly Taxi is below the graph for Deluxe Limousine up to the 4-mile mark. So for trips under 4 miles long, it is cheaper to use Friendly Taxi.

b The lines intersect at (4, 6). So at 4 miles, the cost for both services is $6.

c At 6 miles, the graph shows the cost for Deluxe Limousine is $8 and the cost for Friendly Taxi is $9. The difference is $9 − $8 = $1.

PRACTICE

1. The graph represents the number of books read by Claire and Terry over a 4-week period. Who reads faster, and by how much?

A. Claire reads 8 more books per week than Terry.
B. Claire reads 2 more books per week than Terry.
C. Claire reads 1 more book per week than Terry.
D. Claire reads twice as many books per week as Terry.

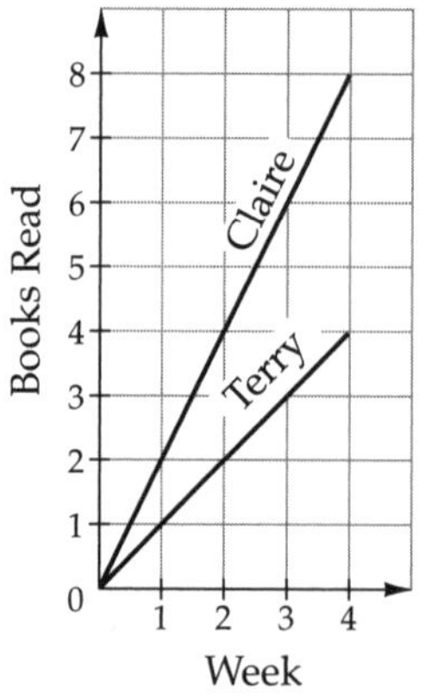

Practice Problems continue . . .

2. **MP 4, 8** Alyssa bicycled for 2 hours at 4 miles per hour. She stopped for one hour to visit a friend. She bicycled for another hour at 5 miles per hour. Which graph best represents Alyssa's trip if the horizontal axis is time and the vertical axis is distance?

A. 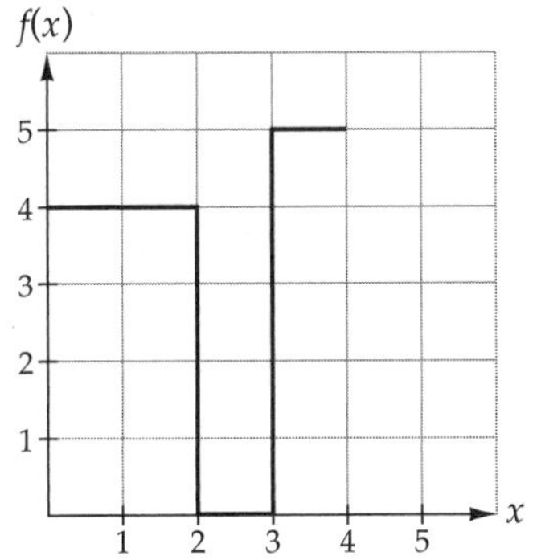

B. 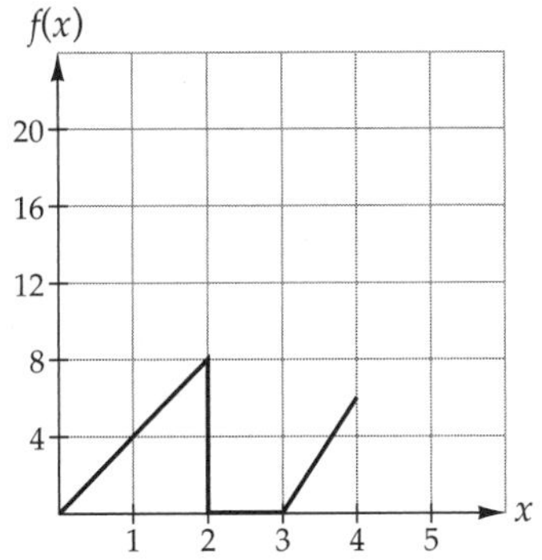

C. 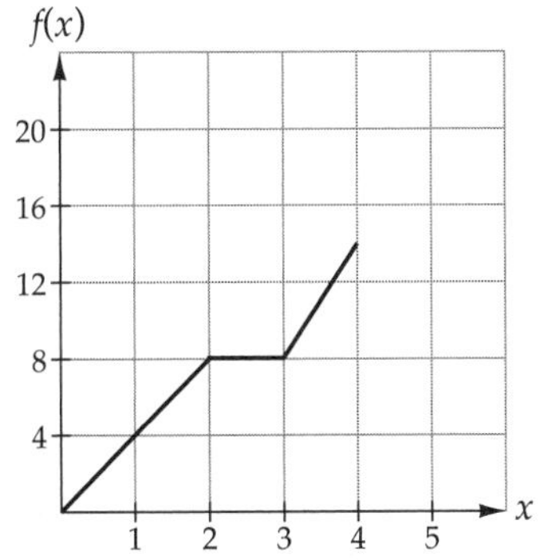

D. 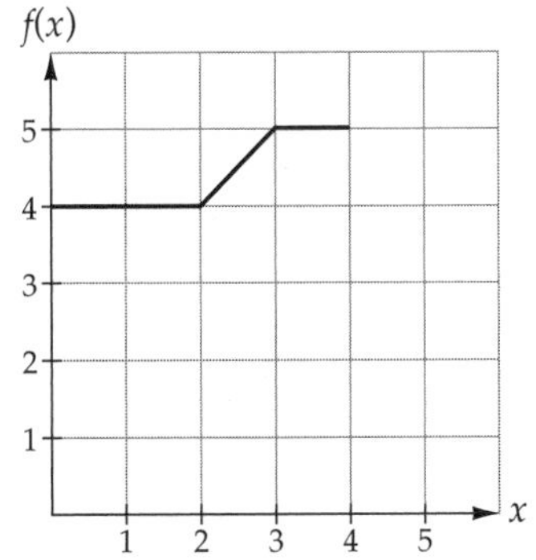

3. Both Janine and Fran used exercise equipment at their gym. Fran walked on a treadmill and Janine rode a stationary bicycle. Their times and calories burned are shown in the graph below. In calories burned per hour, how much faster was Janine than Fran?

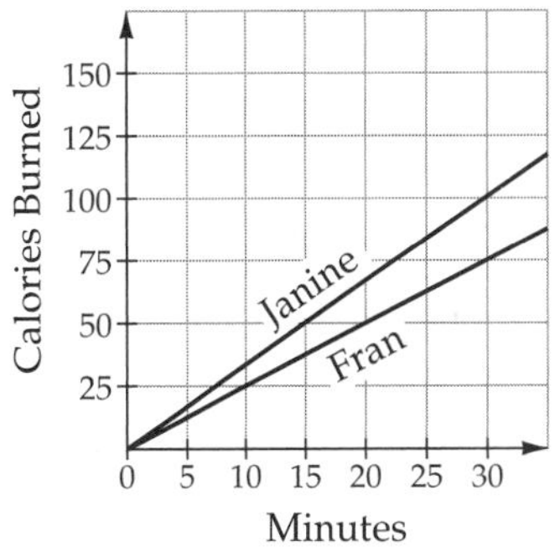

4. The figure below shows the cost of membership for two recreational clubs. For each club, the cost includes an initial fee to join the club plus a monthly charge.

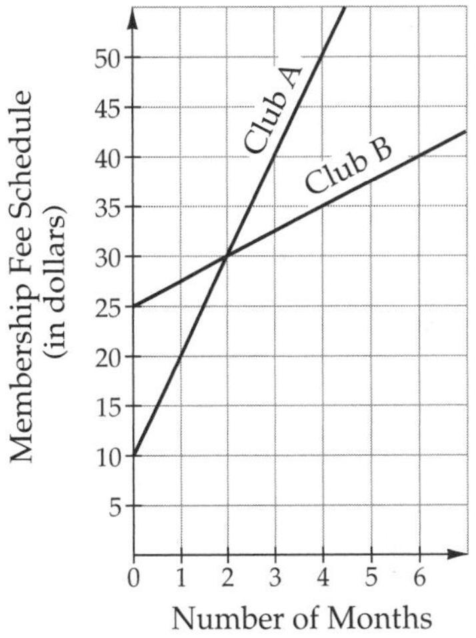

a What is the initial fee for Club A? for Club B?

b For which month will the total expenses be the same for both clubs? What is that total cost?

c What is the monthly charge for Club A? for Club B?

Practice Problems continue . . .

5. MP 2, 4 Two different health clubs have the following rates. Sammy's Spa charges a flat fee of \$350 a year for the use of the club, machines, the pool, and the classes. Shape Up! charges \$150 a year for the use of the club, machines, and pool, plus \$20 per exercise class.

- **a** Write an equation to represent each health club's yearly fees.
- **b** Graph each equation with appropriate labels for the axes.
- **c** Under what circumstances is it more economical to join Shape Up?

6. The graph below shows the relationship between the depreciated value (v) of a car (in thousands of dollars) and the passage of time (t).

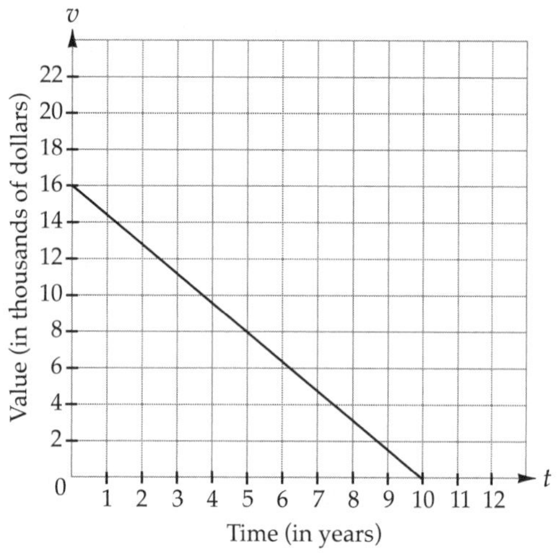

- **a** Write a linear equation to represent the depreciated value of the car.
- **b** Use that equation to find the value of the car after 4.5 years.

7. The graph below shows the relationship between the cost, C, (in thousands of dollars) of manufacturing DVD players and the number of DVD players produced, N.

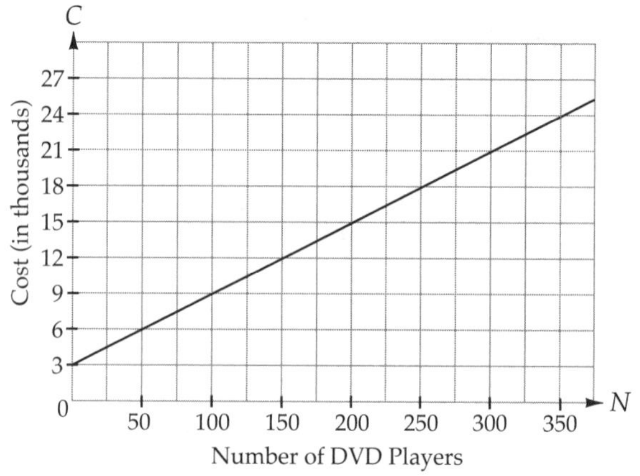

- **a** Write a linear equation to represent the cost of manufacturing the DVD players.
- **b** Use that equation to find the cost of manufacturing 300 DVD players.

8. MP 2, 4 George goes walking at noon at a rate of 3 miles an hour. At 2 P.M., Pete follows George on a bicycle at the rate of 5 miles an hour. The graph below shows both the time (in hours) and distance (in miles) of both George and Pete.

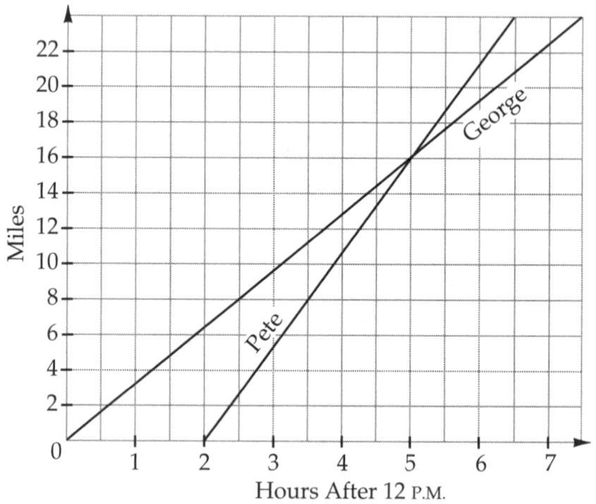

- **a** Write a linear equation to represent the distance traveled in terms of rate and time for each person.
- **b** After how many hours does Pete finally catch up to George?
- **c** After how many *more* hours will George be 8 miles behind Pete?

Practice Problems continue . . .

9. MP 2, 4, 6 To repair a hybrid car, a service station charges \$50 an hour for labor plus the cost of parts. If the parts come from the original dealership they cost \$250, but if they come from the station's in-house storage they cost just \$150. The two functions below give the total cost $C(t)$ for a repair using either source for parts and where t is the time spent on the job.

Dealership: $C(t) = \$50t + \$250$;
Storage: $C(t) = \$50t + \$150$

a Explain the functions in words.

b Graph both equations on the same xy-coordinate system using the x-axis for time and the y-axis for cost. Describe the graphs.

c What is the difference in cost between the two if the repair takes 2 hours, 3 hours, or 5 hours?

d What conclusion can you draw from those differences? Explain.

10. MP 2, 4 Consider the table below, which records steady rainfall over a period of four hours.

Length of Storm (in hours), *x*	1	2	3	4
Amount of Rainfall (in inches), *y*	0.4	0.8	1.2	1.6

Although the time is given in whole numbers, we can talk about the amount of rain after any period of time during the storm. The graph should be a line segment (a continuous function).

a Write the equation that represents the rainfall as a function of time.

b What is the rate of change?

c Graph the function.

d In any given two and one-half hours, how much rain fell? Explain where you see this on the graph.

e Show a different place on the graph that also shows this information.

11. MP 1, 2, 4 Get Fit Now, Witness Fitness, and Beech Tree Gym all have a constant monthly rate after the inital fee.

a Compare Get Fit Now, Witness Fitness, and Beech Tree Gym to determine which fitness center has the lowest monthly rate. The cost of Beech Tree Gym is represented by the equation $C = 22.5M + 30$, where C is the total cost and M is the number of months. The costs for Get Fit Now and Witness Fitness are displayed below.

b Which fitness center would cost the least for 6 months of use?

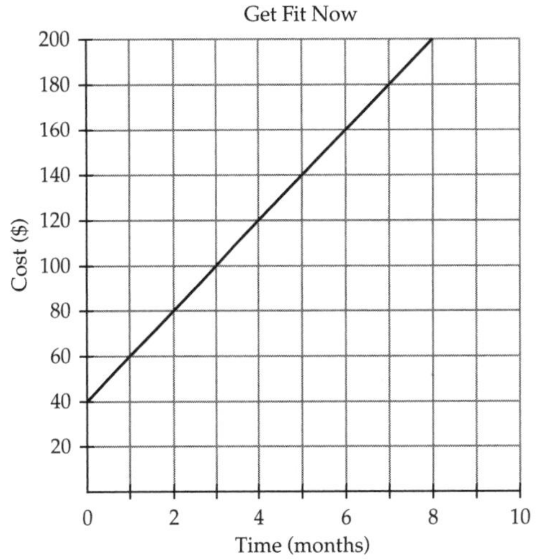

Witness Fitness	
Time (months)	**Cost (\$)**
3	86
5	130
8	196
9	218

CHAPTER 3 REVIEW

1. Which graph does *not* represent a function?

A.

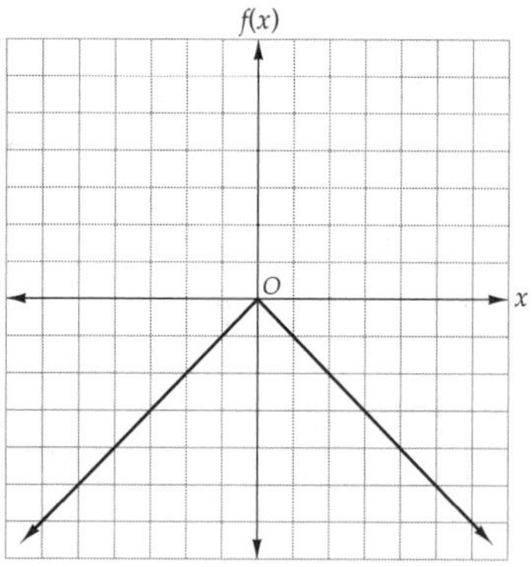

B.

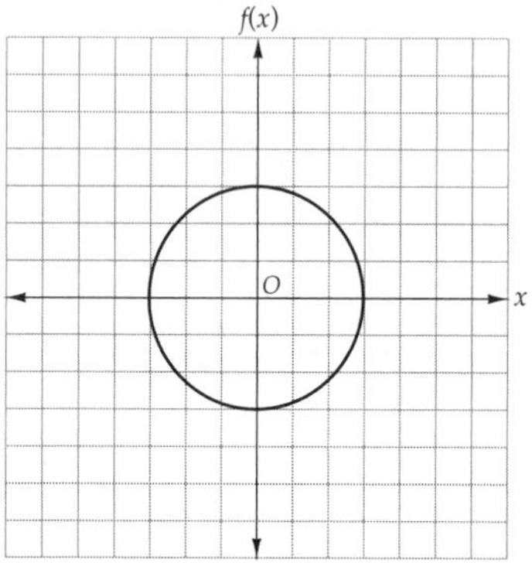

C.

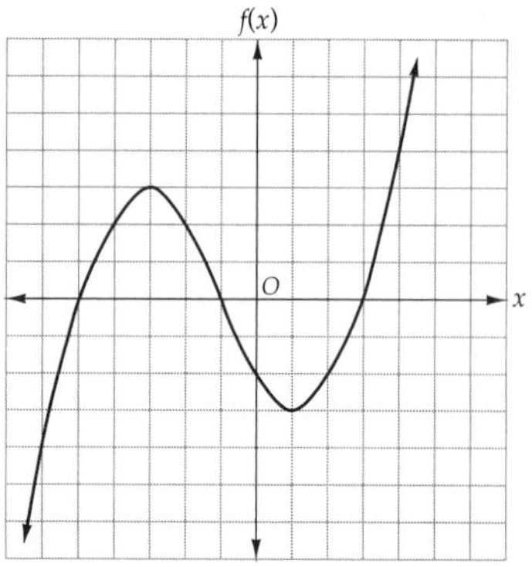

D.

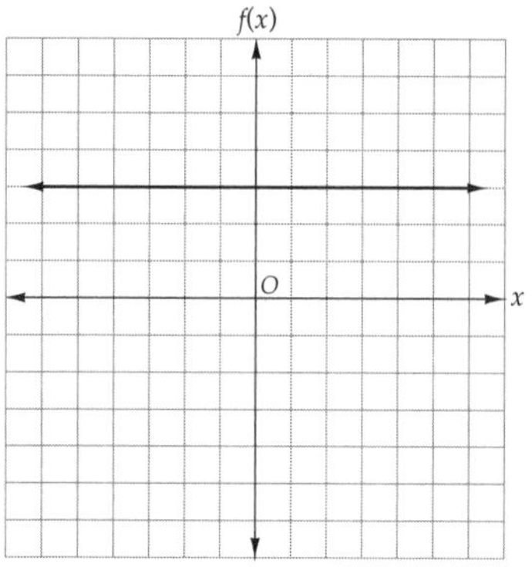

2. What is the slope of the line in the graph? Both axes have the same units.

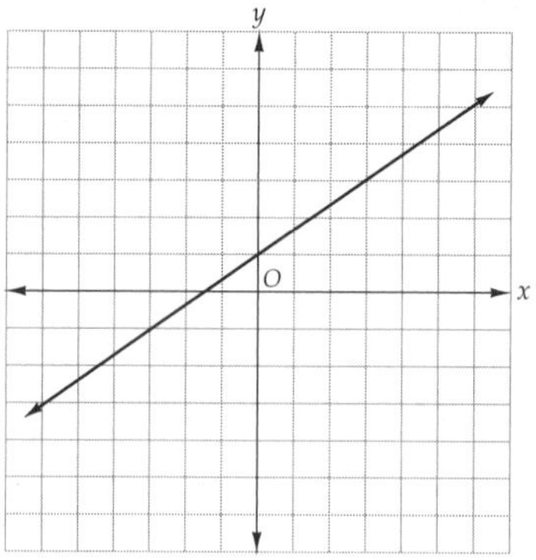

A. $\frac{3}{2}$

B. 1

C. $\frac{2}{3}$

D. $-\frac{2}{3}$

3. If the point $A(x, -y)$ is in quadrant IV, then which of the following is correct?

A. $x > 0, y > 0$

B. $x > 0, y < 0$

C. $x < 0, y > 0$

D. $x < 0, y < 0$

4. If x varies directly as y and $x = 2.4$ when $y = 6$, which is a possible ordered pair for (x, y)?

A. (24, 6)

B. (0.4, 1)

C. (0.4, 2.5)

D. (1, 2.4)

5. What is the value of c so that the line $y = 5x + c$ will pass through the point (3, 7)?

Chapter Review continues . . .

6. Categorize the slope of the seven line segments (a–g) in the figure as positive, negative, zero, or undefined.

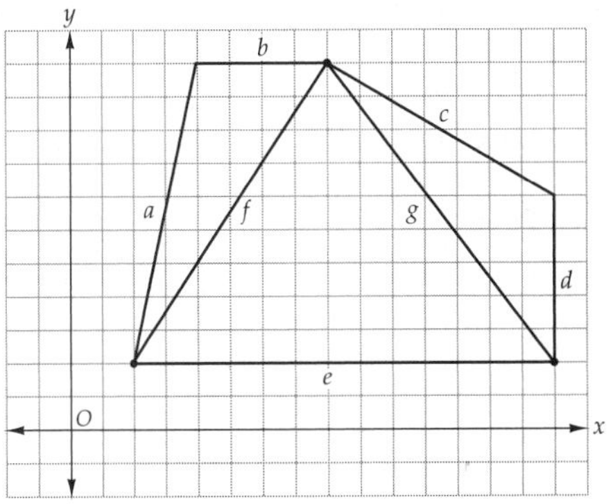

7. What is the slope of the line representing the equation $x + 3y + 6 = 0$?

Exercises 8–9: Create a table of at least three value pairs for each equation. Graph the line using those ordered pairs. State the x- and y-intercepts.

8. $5y = 9x$

9. $12 - 4y = 2x$

10. State the intersection point of each given pair of lines.

a the x-axis and the y-axis

b $x = -1, y = -4$

11. What is the slope of the line $y = 8$?

12. MP 3 If two points on line h are $(-2, 3)$ and $(4, -1)$ and two points on line k are $(1, 1)$ and $(3, 4)$, is it true that lines h and k are perpendicular? Support your conclusion.

13. MP 3, 4 A taxi ride costs \$2.50 for the first quarter of a mile and \$0.75 for each subsequent quarter of a mile.

a A ride that costs \$10.50 is how many miles longer than a ride that costs \$7.75? Explain your procedure.

b If n represents the number of quarter miles traveled and $C(n)$ represents the total cost of the trip, which function would best describe $C(n)$?

A. $C(n) = 2.50n$

B. $C(n) = 2.50 + 0.75n$

C. $C(n) = 2.50 + 0.75(n - 1)$

D. $C(n) = 2.50n + 0.75n$

14. Given the relation $\{(-1, 4), (-2, 5), (-3, 5), (-4, 4)\}$, determine:

a The domain and range.

b If the relation is a one-to-one function.

15. MP 2, 4 The depth of water in a tub varies directly as the length of time the taps are on. If the taps are left on for six minutes, the depth of the water is 24 cm.

a Write an equation that expresses the functional relationship between depth (d) and time (t).

b Graph the equation.

c Find the depth of the water if the taps are left on for 8 minutes.

d Find the length of time the taps were left on if the depth of water is 44 cm.

Chapter Review continues . . .

16. If line k is represented by the linear equation $y = 2x - 1$ and line r is represented by the linear equation $y = -\frac{2}{5}x + 2$,

a Identify the slope of line k and of line r.

b What are the x-intercept and y-intercept of line k and of line r?

c Write a linear equation *parallel* to line k and another equation *parallel* to line r.

d Write a linear equation *perpendicular* to line k and another equation *perpendicular* to line r.

e If point $(10, y)$ lies on line k and point $(x, -3)$ lies on line r, what is the missing y-coordinate for line k and the missing x-coordinate for line r?

17. Write the point-slope form of a line where m is the slope and the point is (x_1, y_1).

18. Graph the linear function f defined by $y = f(x) = 3x - 1$ by using the slope and y-intercept.

19. **MP 7**

a Describe the graph of a constant function.

b Give two different examples.

c Explain why a constant function is different from a function with a constant rate of change.

20. Use the x- and y-intercepts to graph the line $3x - 2y = 6$.

Exercises 21–23: Identify the slope and y-intercept.

21. $y = \frac{3}{5}x - 7$

22. $y + x - 8 = 0$

23. $x = -4$

Exercises 24–27: Use the given conditions to write a function in the form $f(x) = mx + b$.

24. $m = \frac{2}{3}$, and $f(0) = -2$

25. slope $= -\frac{1}{3}$, and $f(9) = 2$

26. $f(3) = -2$, and $f(1) = 6$

27. Perpendicular to $3x + y - 1 = 0$ and passing through $(3, -1)$

28. Write an equation of the line passing through the point $(2, -3)$ and

a parallel to the x-axis

b parallel to the y-axis

29. Which function describes the line l in the given diagram?

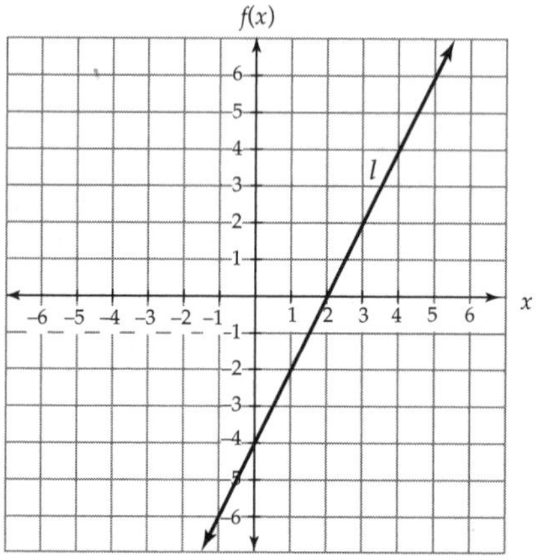

A. $f(x) = 2x + 2$

B. $f(x) = 2x - 4$

C. $f(x) = -2x - 4$

D. $f(x) = -2x + 2$

Exercises 30–31: Select the equation whose graph would *not* be parallel to the other two.

30. $2x - y = 9; 2y - x = 7; 2x - y = 2$

31. $x + 3y = 7; 3x + y = 7; y = 7 - 3x$

32. Write an equation of the line passing through the points $(2, -3)$ and $(3, -1)$ in

a point-slope form

b slope-intercept form

c general linear form $Ax + By = C$

33. The x- and y-intercepts of a line are $(-5, 0)$ and $(0, -2)$. Write a linear equation for the line in the form $y = mx + b$.

34. Find the x- and y-intercepts of the equation $5x - y - 5 = 0$.

Chapter Review continues . . .

35. If $f(x) = -3x$ and $g(x) = 4x - 7$, find $h(x) = f(x) + g(x)$.

36. If $f(x) = 5x - 3$ and $g(x) = -x + 2$, find $h(x) = f(x) - g(x)$.

37. If $f(x) = -3$ and $g(x) = 6x - 5$, find $h(x) = f(x) \times g(x)$.

38. If $f(x) = \frac{4}{3}$, $g(x) = 11x - 6$, and $h(x) = x$, find $m(x) = f(x)[g(x) + h(x)]$.

39. y varies directly with x. Write the equation and find the indicated values.

a If $y = 6$ when $x = 48$, what is the value of y when $x = 20$?

b If $y = 5$ when $x = -10$, find the value of y when $x = 50$.

c If $y = -10$ when $x = -4$, what is the value of x when $y = -12$?

40. If y varies directly with x, and $x = 24$ when $y = 4$, write a direct variation equation that relates x and y.

41. As a weekend security guard, Steve works only whole-hour shifts and works no more than 12 hours. He gets paid $21 an hour. His pay P is a function of the number of hours n that he works. What is the range of this function?

A. $0 \leq n \leq 12$

B. $0 \leq P \leq 252$

C. {0, 1, 2, 3, 4, 5, 6, 7, 8, 9, 10, 11, 12}

D. {0, 21, 42, 63, 84, 105, 126, 147, 168, 189, 210, 231, 252}

42. **a** Graph $f(x) = \frac{x - 1}{2}$.

b On the same coordinate system, graph the inverse function, $f^{-1}(x)$.

c Graph $y = x$ and find the common intersection of the three linear equations.

d Set $f(x) = f^{-1}(x)$ and solve algebraically for the values of x and $f(x)$.

43. The function P for the perimeter of an equilateral triangle varies directly as the length of a side s. If the sides have only integer lengths of {1, 2, 3, 4, 5},

a Write a linear function expressing this relationship.

b State the ordered pairs.

c In an xy-coordinate system, draw the graph of the linear function.

d Is this function continuous or discrete?

44. Determine if $f^{-1}(x) = \sqrt{x}$ is the inverse of $f(x) = x^2$. Justify your response.

45. **MP 2** The use of g gallons of water in taking a shower is directly proportional to the number of minutes m of showering. If the average time per shower is 12.5 minutes and 68.2 gallons of water is used, how many gallons of water would be saved if a shower took only 9.4 minutes?

46. **MP 4, 7** The supply of Crazy Coffee Beans can be described with the equation $S = 4(P - 2.5) + 10$, where S represents the amount of the supply in tons and P represents the price in dollars per pound. The supply of Jolt Coffee Beans can be described with the equation $S = 6(P - 4) + k$, where k is an unknown value. The supply of Jolt Coffee Beans equals 6 tons when the price is $4 per pound.

a Find the value of k and write an equation for the supply of Jolt Coffee Beans.

b Graph both equations. Place P on the horizontal axis and S on the vertical axis.

c Use the graph to answer the question: If the price of coffee is $8, will there be a greater supply of Crazy Coffee Beans or Jolt Coffee Beans?

Chapter Review continues . . .

47. MP 2, 4 You are traveling in Mexico and need to exchange some U.S. dollars for Mexican pesos. To do this, you go to a bank and give them dollars. In exchange, they give you Mexican pesos. How many pesos they give you is a function of three things:

(1) How many dollars you give the bank.

(2) The exchange rate. For example, the rate might be that a dollar is worth 9.8 pesos. (This is not the exchange rate shown in the graph.)

(3) The bank also charges you a fixed fee for any exchange they do. For instance, they might charge you 35 pesos anytime you exchange money.

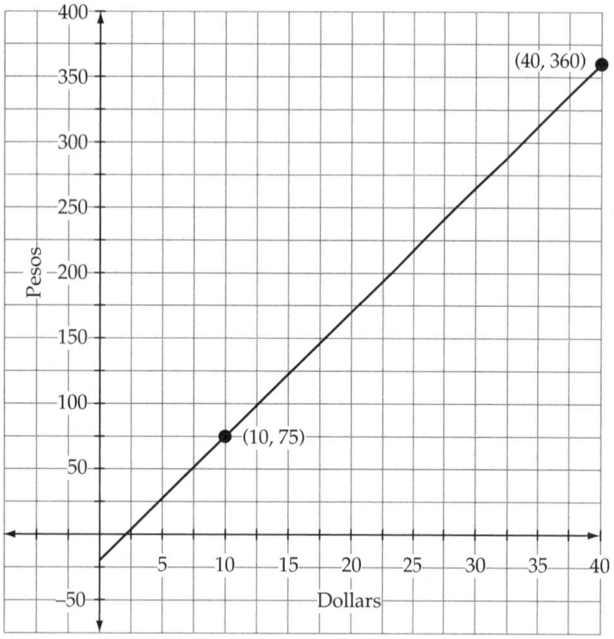

Above, you see a graph that reflects the exchange of dollars to pesos at El Mathematico bank. Use the graph to answer these questions:

a What is the exchange rate between dollars and pesos?

b What fixed fee in pesos does the bank charge for an exchange of dollars into pesos?

c Write an equation for the exchange in $y = mx + b$ form, with y being pesos and x being dollars.

Cumulative Review for Chapters 1–3

1. If $-1 < a < 0$, which of the four expressions would have the largest value?

A. a C. a^3

B. a^2 D. a^4

2. In the given figure, if PR is $4x + 5$, RS is $2x + 3$, and Q is the midpoint of $\overline{PS}$, then QR is

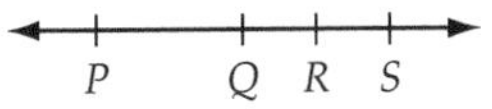

A. $6x + 8$

B. $3x + 4$

C. $2x + 2$

D. $x + 1$

3. If $\frac{a}{b} = 1$ and $a + b = 10$, then ab equals

A. 1

B. 5

C. 10

D. 25

4. If the points (2, 3) and (5, y) lie on a line whose slope is $-\frac{7}{6}$, what does y equal?

A. -6.5 C. 0.5

B. -0.5 D. 6.5

5. Which of the following is *not* a function?

A. $\{(-2, 0), (2, 2), (2, -2), (7, 3)\}$

B. $\{(-1, -2), (0, -3), (1, -2), (2, 1)\}$

C. $\{(-2, 2), (-1, 1), (0, 0), (1, 1)\}$

D. $\{(-1, -2), (0, -3), (1, -2), (2, 1)\}$

6. Which of the following inequality transformations is *not* correct?

A. $2x + 1 < 8 \rightarrow 2x < 7$

B. $4(x + 1) < -5 \rightarrow 4x < -9$

C. $3x - 4 > 0 \rightarrow 3x > 4$

D. $5x - 7 < 0 \rightarrow 5x > 7$

7. Find the equation of a line containing the point (3, 3), and parallel to the line passing through the points (−2, 0) and (0, 8).

A. $y = 4x$

B. $y = 4x - 9$

C. $y = -4x - 15$

D. $y = 4x + 9$

8. Which of the following is correct?

A. $\sqrt{5} + \sqrt{20} = 5$

B. $\sqrt{24} + \sqrt{48} = 5\sqrt{6}$

C. $\sqrt{18} - 2\sqrt{2} = \sqrt{2}$

D. $\sqrt{27} - \sqrt{18} = 3$

9. If the function h is defined by $h(x) = x^2 - x$, which of the following has a negative value?

A. $h(-1)$

B. $h\left(-\frac{1}{2}\right)$

C. $h\left(\frac{1}{2}\right)$

D. $h(1)$

10. If (4, 5) is a point on the graph of $y_1 = f(x)$, find a point on the graph of $y_2 = -f(x) - 2$.

11. If x is $\frac{1}{3}$ of y and y is $\frac{3}{5}$ of z and $5x + 3 = 4$, what is the value of $z + 5$?

12. Lines g and y are perpendicular. Line g passes through the points (0, 0) and (3, –1). Line y passes through the points (3, –1) and (0, k). What is the value of k?

13. In the figure shown, the area of $\triangle CAB$ is equal to the area of $\triangle OAC$.

What is the value of $\frac{n}{a}$?

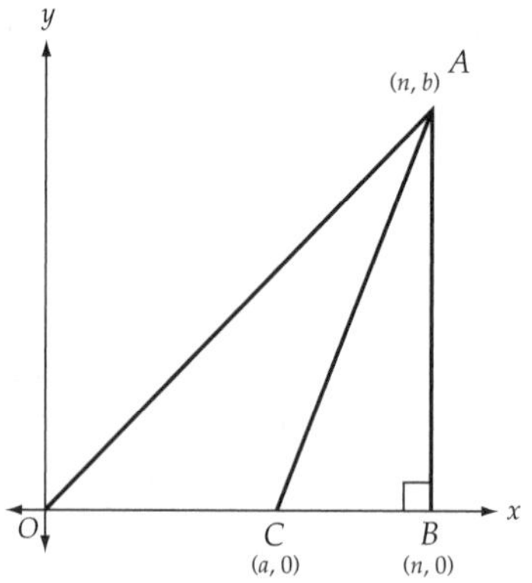

14. The length of a rectangle is 5 inches less than 4 times the width. If the perimeter is 85 inches, what is the area of the rectangle?

15. In the xy-plane, the two points $A(-3, 4)$ and $B(5, 2)$ on line k are each reflected across the line $y = x$ to points A' and B'. What is the slope, the y-intercept, and the equation of the inverse function containing the points A' and B'?

16. **MP 3, 7** Simplify each of the following. Show your work.

a $x^5 + x^5$

b $(-3x^4)^3$

c $-ab^2(-4a^2b)^2$

d $\dfrac{36x^4y^2}{-9xy^2}$

17. **MP 2** Write the equation or inequality, and then solve for x.

a Eight less than one-third of x is equal to eight more than 3 times x.

b Five times x decreased by 18 is greater than or equal to 3 times x.

18. **MP 2** George travels 126 miles at 60 mph. If he traveled the same amount of time at 50 mph, how far would he have traveled?

19. **MP 2** The annual simple interest on a savings account of \$5400 is \$180. At the same rate, what is the amount of interest on \$8700?

20. **MP 3, 7** Solve for x in each of the following and show your work.

a $\frac{3}{5}(x - 10) = 6(x + 3) + 3$

b $\frac{2}{3}x + 1 + \frac{5}{3}x = \frac{13}{3}x - 1$

c $2(x + 4) - 3 = \frac{1}{2}(10 + 4x)$

21. **MP 2** One side of a triangle is 5 inches greater than twice a second side, and the third side is 5 inches less than twice the second side. All the sides of the triangle are integers.

a If the perimeter must be at least 50 inches, what is the *smallest possible value* of each side?

b What is the smallest possible perimeter?

22. **MP 2** The weight of a uniform steel cylinder is directly proportional to its length. If a length of 3 feet weighs 3.5 pounds, what is the weight (to the nearest tenth) of a length of steel 8.7 feet?

23. **MP 2** The weight of 24 grams stretches a hanging spring 3 cm. If the distance (d) that spring is stretched is directly proportional to the weight (w), what is the weight needed to stretch the spring 8 cm?

24. **MP 2** The distance from a lightning bolt is directly proportional to the time elapsed from the instant the bolt is seen to the instant the sound of thunder is heard. If you hear the thunder 3 seconds after you see the bolt, then the bolt is approximately 0.6 miles away. If you hear the thunder 11 seconds after you see the bolt, approximately how far away is the lightning bolt?

25. **MP 7** Write the equation of the inverse function f^{-1} solved for y, if $f(x) = \frac{1}{2}x + 1$.

26. **MP 3** Dave has decided that if c and d are positive numbers and $\frac{c}{d} > cd$, then each of these statements **must** be true:

(1) $c > 1$

(2) $d < 1$

(3) $d < c$

For each incorrect conjecture, give a counterexample. For each correct conjecture, justify why it is correct.

27. **MP 2, 4** A homeowner plans on making a profit P of one-eighth of what his house originally cost C. Hence, his selling price SP is placed at $630,000.

a Write a set of equations to represent the profit P, based on the cost, profit, and selling price.

b What was his original cost?

c What was his profit?

28. **MP 2, 3, 4** The weekly demand D for a certain electronic toy is related to the price x in dollars by the function $D = 1000 - 8x$. The weekly supply S is given by the function $S = 2x + 100$.

a Graph the functions and determine the price at which the supply will equal demand.

b How many of these items will be sold at that price?

c If the price is set at $125 for each toy, what is the demand? What does this mean?

29. **MP 7** In each literal equation, solve for the indicated variable.

a Solve for m in the slope-intercept form of a linear equation.

b Solve for c in $m = \frac{a}{2}(b + c)$.

c Solve for p in the following: $A = p + prt$.

30. **MP 3** Eric and Wendy disagreed about the number line representation for $2(x + 4) < 10$.

Eric said the representation is:

Wendy said the representation is:

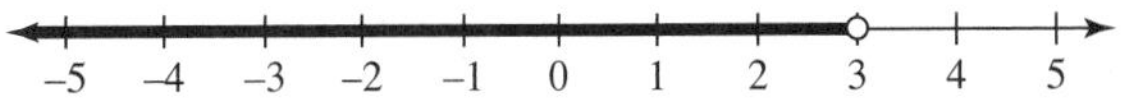

Who is correct? Explain your reasoning.

Chapter 4 Inequalities, Absolute Value, Piecewise and Step Functions

Chapter Focus

In this chapter we will write, graph, and apply functions that have different equations for different portions of the domain. We will graph inequalities and special functions in the xy-coordinate plane as well as absolute value inequalities on the number line. Our study of special functions will include piecewise functions, absolute value functions, step functions, and greatest integer functions.

Chapter Content

Chapter Vocabulary

absolute value	**greatest integer function**	**step function**
axis of symmetry	**half plane**	**transformation**
boundary line	**horizontal translation**	**vertex**
conjunction	**parent function**	**vertical shrinking**
disjunction	**piecewise function**	**vertical stretching**
end behavior	**reflection**	**vertical translation**

LESSON 4.1

4.1 Graphing Linear Inequalities

A line graphed in the coordinate plane divides the plane into two regions, called **half planes**. When the equation of the line is written in slope-intercept form, or $y = mx + b$ form, the half plane *above* the line is the graph of $y > mx + b$, and the half plane *below* the line is the graph of $y < mx + b$. If a half plane is to be included in a solution set, we show this by shading its entire region. The line itself, considered a **boundary line** (or plane divider), is drawn as a solid line when it is part of the solution set, and as a dashed line if it is not.

To Graph a Linear Inequality

- Graph the boundary line for the inequality by expressing the inequality as an equation in slope-intercept form or by creating a table of values.

  If the sign is $>$ or $<$, the boundary line will be broken or dashed, which means points on the line are not a solution. - - - - - -

  If the sign is $\geq$ or $\leq$, the boundary line will be solid, which means points on the line are solutions to the inequality. ———

- Shade the half plane of the inequality.

  Method 1: Select two points, one on each side of the boundary line, and substitute them into the inequality. Shade the half plane with the point that makes the inequality true.

  Method 2: Solve the inequality for y so that you can graph the line in the form of $y = mx + b$.

  In general, if the inequality begins with $y >$ or $y \geq$, shade the half plane *above* the boundary line.

  If the inequality begins with $y <$ or $y \leq$, shade the half plane *below* the boundary line.

> The origin (0, 0) is a point that is especially easy to use when determining which side of the boundary line the graph is located.

MODEL PROBLEMS

1. Graph the inequality $x - 3y > 6$.

SOLUTION

Step 1. Rewrite the inequality in $y = mx + b$ form:

$x - 3y > 6$

$x - 6 > 3y$ or $3y < x - 6$

$y < \frac{x}{3} - 2$

Step 2. Create a table of values for $y = \frac{x}{3} - 2$.

x	−3	0	3
y	−3	−2	−1

Step 3. Graph the inequality.

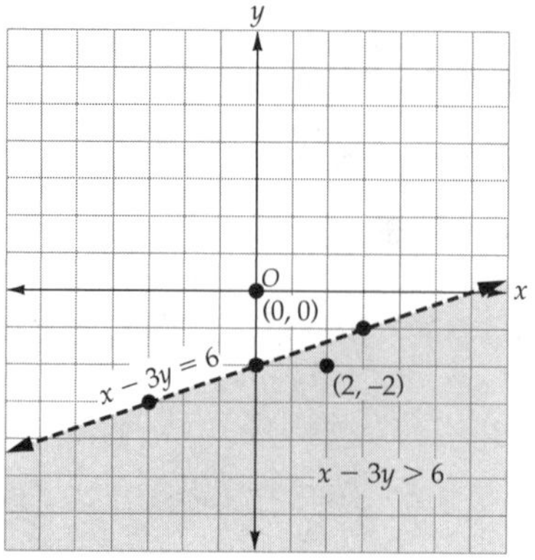

Step 4.

Check (2, −2) by substituting.

$x - 3y > 6$

$(2) - 3(-2) > 6$

$2 + 6 > 6$

$8 > 6$ ✓

Check (0, 0) from outside the solution set.

$x - 3y > 6$

$(0) - 3(0) > 6$

$0 \not> 6$ (not in solution set) ✓

2. Graph the following inequalities:

a $y > 2x + 1$

b $y \leq 2x + 1$

SOLUTION

a

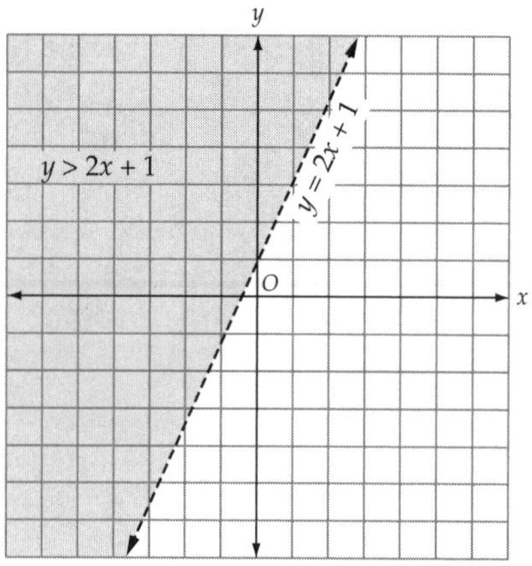

b

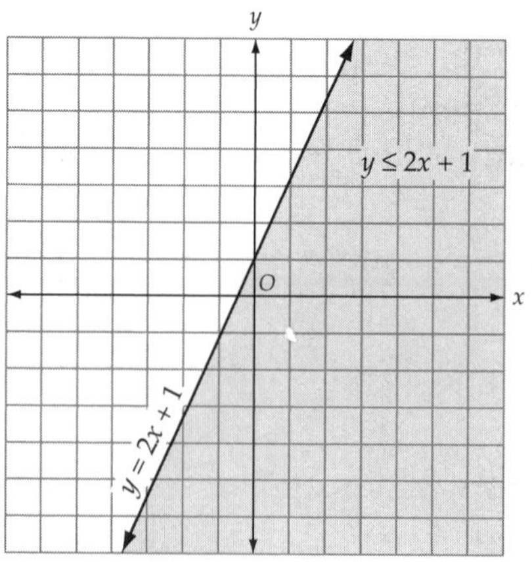

Model Problems continue . . .

3. **MP 2, 4, 6** At Barney's Garage, it takes an average of 1 hour for a tune-up and oil change and an average of 6 hours to replace a transmission. If Emilie, the chief auto mechanic, puts in no more than 42 hours a week,

a Write an inequality that describes the possible number of tune-up and oil changes (x) and transmission replacements (y) that she can do.

b Graph your answer to part **a** on the xy-coordinate system.

c What is the maximum number of each job she can do?

d What is the meaning of the ordered pair (12, 4)? How many hours does she have left to attend to other mechanical tasks?

SOLUTION

a In words, we can say that 1 hour times each tune-up (x) plus 6 hours times each transmission job (y) is less than or equal to 42 hours. We write this as the inequality $x + 6y \le 42$. Converting the inequality into slope-intercept form gives us $y \le -\frac{1}{6}x + 7$.

b

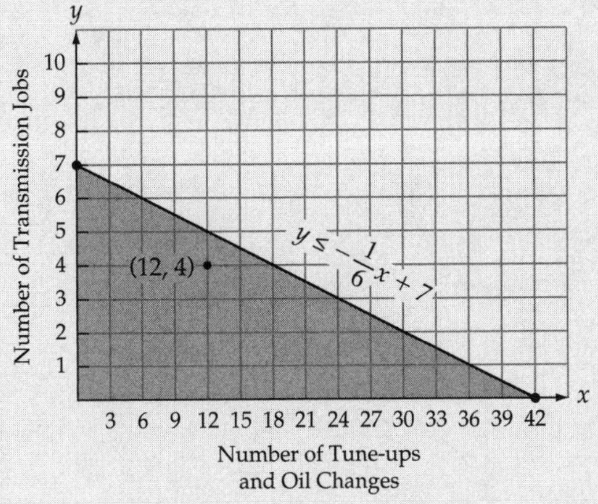

The graph is a model of this situation. Models do not always strictly represent the situation. This graph looks continuous and shows fractional jobs, but only integers make sense in this context.

Since we know the slope-intercept form of the inequality, we know that the inequality crosses the y-axis at 7 and the slope is $-\frac{1}{6}$. The solutions only occur in the 1st quadrant, because negative numbers do not make sense.

c To find the maximum possible number of tune-up and oil changes (x), we set $y = 0$. If $y = 0$, then $x + 6(0) \le 42$ and $x = 42$ tune-up and oil changes. To find the maximum possible number of transmission replacements (y), we set $x = 0$. If $x = 0$, then $0 + 6y \le 42$ and $y = 7$ transmission jobs.

d The ordered pair $(x, y) = (12, 4)$ means 12 tune-up and oil changes and 4 transmission jobs; that means Emilie has worked for 12 hours + 24 hours = 36 hours. She has 6 hours of work left.

PRACTICE

1. Which graph shows $y < 3x$?

A.

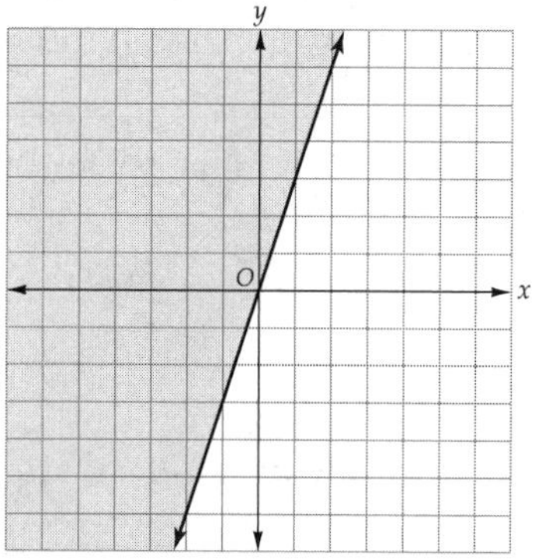

B.

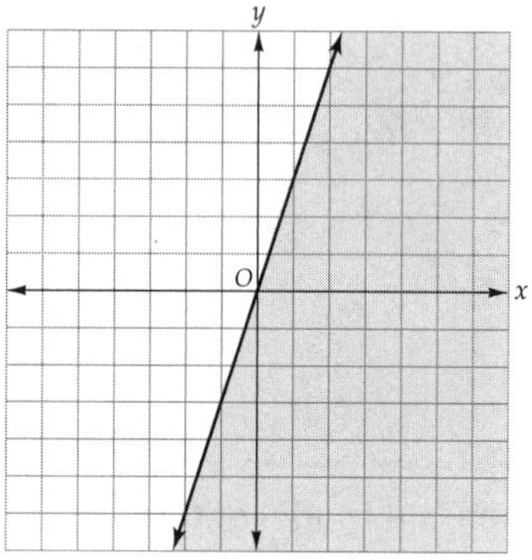

C.

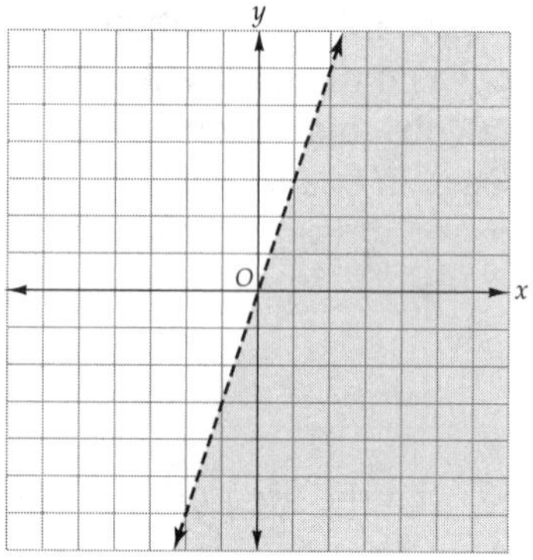

D.

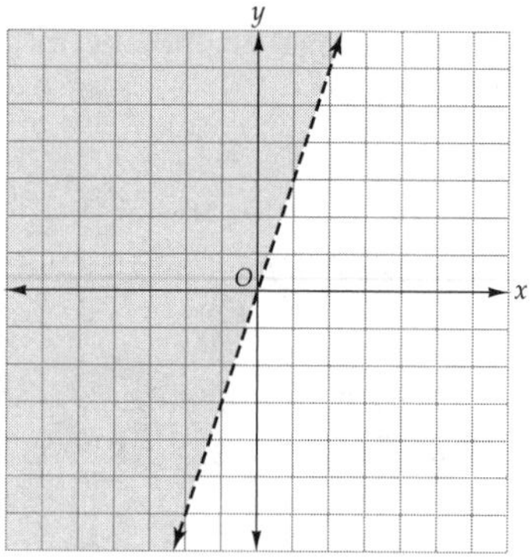

2. Which graph shows $y > -x - 1$?

A.

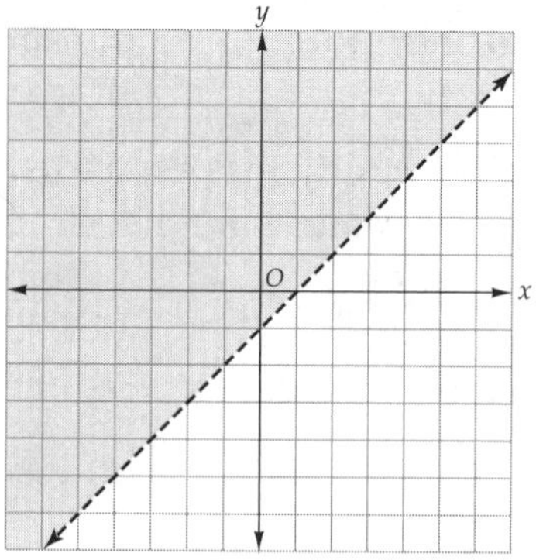

B.

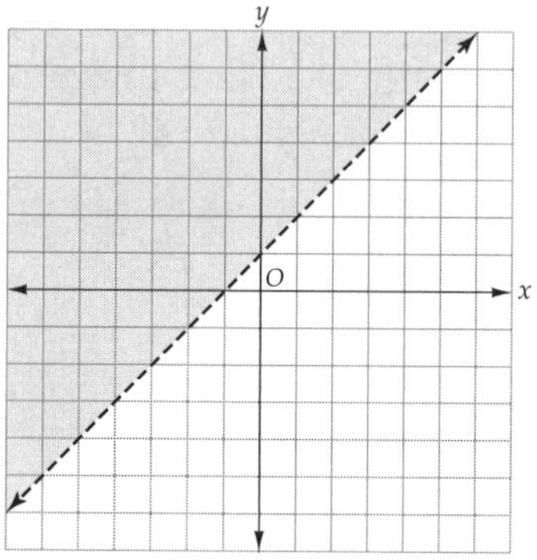

C.

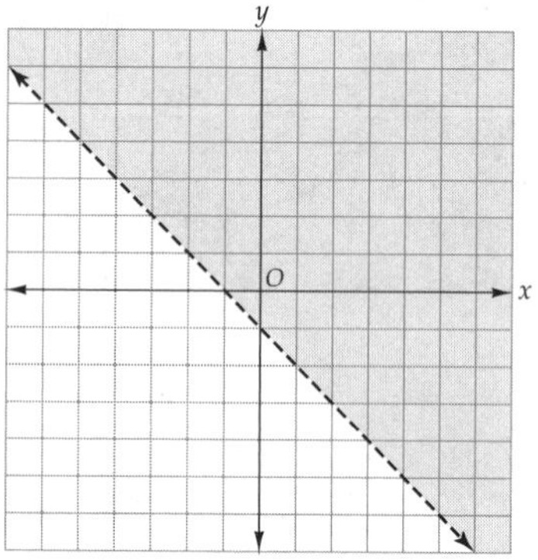

D.

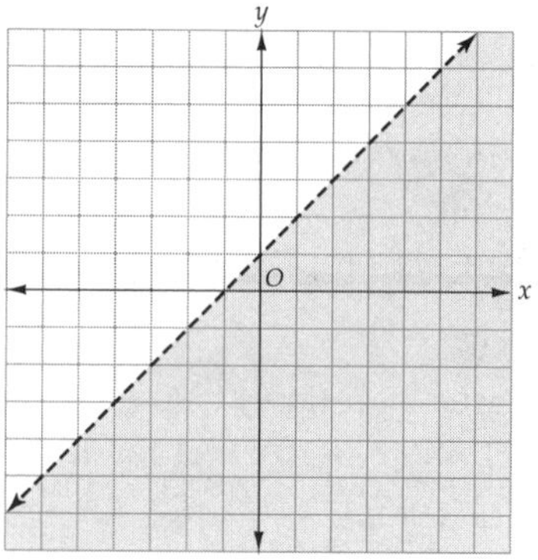

Practice Problems continue . . .

3. Which equation describes the shaded area of the graph?

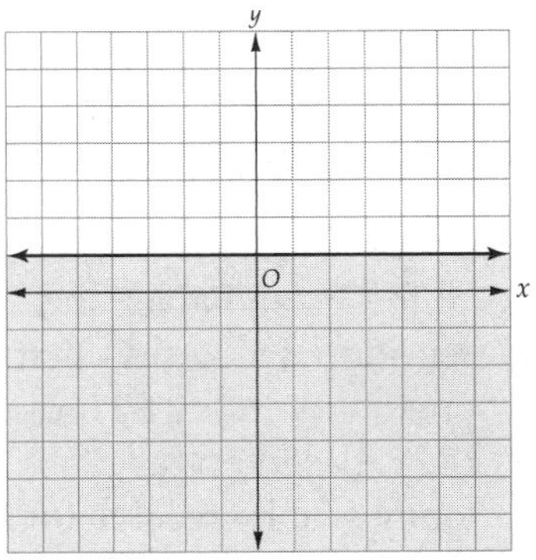

A. $y > 1$ C. $y \leq 1$
B. $y < 1$ D. $y \geq 1$

4. Which equation describes the shaded area of the graph?

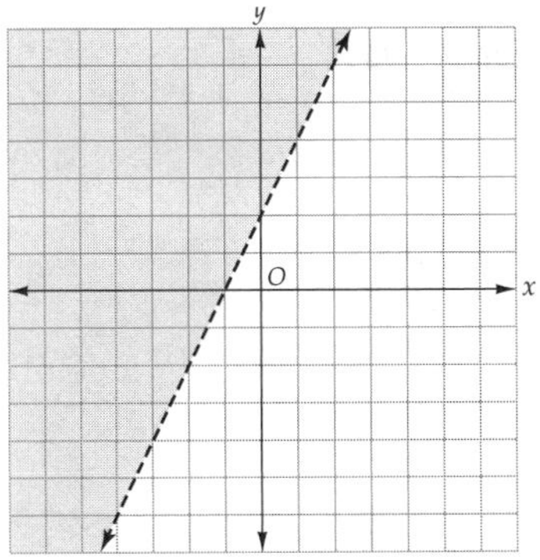

A. $y \leq \frac{1}{2}x + 2$

B. $y \geq -\frac{1}{2}x + 2$

C. $y < -2x + 2$

D. $y > 2x + 2$

Exercises 5–10: Solve for y. Graph each inequality in the coordinate plane.

5. $y \leq -2x$

6. $x + y \geq 1$

7. $2x + y > -4$

8. $2x - y < 3$

9. $x \leq 0$

10. $x < 1 + y + x$

Exercises 11–15: Write each verbal sentence as an inequality. Solve and graph the inequality.

11. The y-coordinate of a point is greater than 2 less than the x-coordinate.

12. The sum of the x-coordinate and the y-coordinate of a point is greater than or equal to 4.

13. Twice the y-coordinate of a point decreased by the x-coordinate is less than or equal to -1.

14. The y-coordinate of a point decreased by half the x-coordinate is greater than 0.

15. The x-coordinate of a point decreased by the y-coordinate is less than or equal to 3.

16. Which ordered pair is in the solution set of $2x - y < 6$?

A. (3, 0) C. (6, −6)
B. (−3, 0) D. (0, −6)

17. Which ordered pair is *not* in the solution set of $x - y > -1$?

A. (−1, 0) C. (0, −1)
B. (0, 0) D. (1, 0)

18. Which ordered pair is *not* in the solution set of $3x + 2y \geq 6$?

A. (0, 6) C. (0, −6)
B. (2, 0) D. (6, 6)

19. **MP 2, 4, 6** On the first day of spring, Garden World sold more than \$5000 worth of ornamental trees. Six-foot red maples cost \$200 each and 5-ft white birch cost \$250 each.

a Write an inequality that shows the possible number of maple trees (x) and birch trees (y) that were sold.

b Graph your answer.

c If no birch trees were sold, what is the least amount of red maples that could have been sold?

d If the sales results are represented by an ordered pair, what would (21, 13) mean?

e By how much is the value of (21, 13) greater than \$5000?

Practice Problems continue . . .

20. MP 2, 4 Retirees ages 62 to 65 can earn as much as \$15,120 and still receive their full Social Security benefits. If their annual earnings exceed \$15,120, then their benefits are reduced. Charlie, who is 64 and retired, works two part-time jobs: one in the evening answering phones for the local Pizza Palace and a morning job as a barista at a nearby coffee shop. The Pizza Palace pays \$360 for a 5-day week; the coffee shop pays \$540 for a 7-day week.

a Write an inequality representing the number of weeks he can work at each job during the year without losing any of his Social Security benefits: use (x) for the weeks at the Pizza Palace and (y) for the weeks as a barista.

b Graph the inequality on the xy-plane.

c What is the maximum number of weeks he can work at the Pizza Palace? at the coffee shop?

d What is the relationship of the inequality and the point (30, 20)?

e Charlie says he plans on working 30 weeks at the Pizza Palace and 20 weeks at the coffee shop. He knows that he will lose \$1 in benefits for every \$2 he earns over the \$15,120. Based on his plan, how much total money will he receive for the year?

LESSON 4.2

4.2 Absolute Value Inequalities and Graphing on the Number Line

The **absolute value** of a number, $|n|$, is the distance from n to the origin. Since $+7$ and -7 are each a distance of 7 units from zero on the number line, the absolute value $|+7|$ and $|-7|$ each have a value of 7. In other words, $|+7| = |-7| = 7$.

> If $n \geq 0$, $|n| = n$, and if $n < 0$, $|n| = -n$.
> If n is positive, the absolute value of n is n.
> If n is negative, the absolute value of n is the opposite of n.

Compare the examples of absolute value inequalities to $|x| = 4$. Remember that if $|x| = 4$, then the values for x are 4 or -4.

(1) $|x| < 4$

- The statement $|x| < 4$ means that the distance between x and 0 is *less* than 4, so that we have the **conjunction** $x < 4$ *and* $x > -4$. We write this as a compound inequality, $-4 < x < 4$, which means the number is larger than -4, but smaller than 4.
- We graph the conjunction below. The inequality is true for any number less than 4 and greater than -4, such as 2 or -3.1.

(2) $|x| > 4$

- The statement $|x| > 4$ means that the distance between x and 0 is *greater* than 4, so that we have the **disjunction** $x < -4$ *or* $x > 4$.
- We graph the disjunction below. A number cannot be both less than -4 and greater than 4. For instance, the inequality is true for 7.2, where $x > 4$, but not where $x < 4$. The number 7.2 is not less than -4, so it fulfills only one of the inequalities.

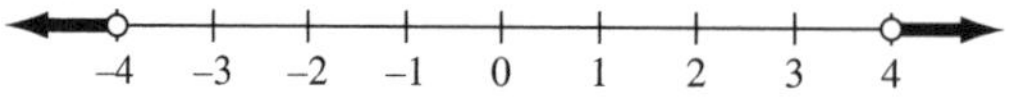

MODEL PROBLEMS

Model Problems 1–4: Solve the inequality, state the solution as a compound inequality, and graph the solution set.

1. $|x + 2| \geq 3$

SOLUTION

Rewrite as a compound inequality and solve each.

$x + 2 \geq 3$ *or* $x + 2 \leq -3$

Answer: $x \geq 1$ or $x \leq -5$

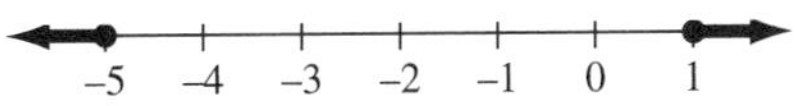

2. Solve the compound inequality using two methods: $|2x - 3| < 7$

SOLUTION

Rewrite as a compound inequality and solve each.

METHOD 1

$2x - 3 < 7$ and $2x - 3 > -7$

$2x < 10$ and $2x > -4$

$x < 5$ and $x > -2$

Answer: $-2 < x < 5$

METHOD 2

$-7 < 2x - 3 < 7$

$-7 + 3 < 2x - 3 + 3 < 7 + 3$

$-4 < 2x < 10$

Answer: $-2 < x < 5$

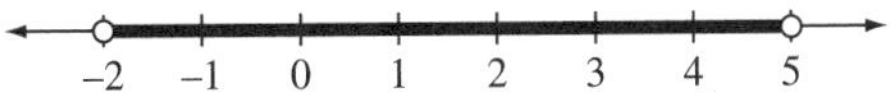

3. Solve the compound inequality: $2|6 - x| < 4$

> Remember, when dividing by a negative number, the inequality will reverse.

SOLUTION

Given. $2|6 - x| < 4$

First divide by 2. $|6 - x| < 2$

Now rewrite as a compound inequality. $-2 < 6 - x < 2$

Subtract 6 from each expression. $-8 < -x < -4$

To solve for x, divide each expression by -1, so $8 > x > 4$, which can be rewritten as $4 < x < 8$.

Answer: $4 < x < 8$

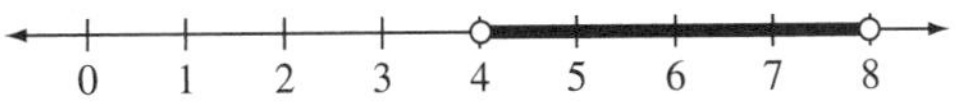

4. $5 + 3|2x - 1| \leq 17$

SOLUTION

In this more complex problem, we must isolate the absolute value expression first.

Given. $5 + 3|2x - 1| \leq 17$

Subtract 5 from both sides. $3|2x - 1| \leq 12$

Divide by 3. $|2x - 1| \leq 4$

Now rewrite as a compound inequality. $2x - 1 \leq 4$ and $2x - 1 \geq -4$

Rewrite. $x \leq 2.5$ and $x \geq -1.5$

Answer: $-1.5 \leq x \leq 2.5$

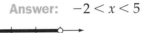

Model Problems continue . . .

Model Problems *continued*

5. At a spring-water bottling plant, machine X fills the plastic bottle and machine Z caps the bottle if the number of fluid ounces, n, is between $9\frac{7}{8}$ and $10\frac{1}{8}$ ounces. Which of the following relations best describes the possible values of acceptable fluid ounces?

A. $|n - 10| = \frac{1}{8}$ B. $|n - 10| < \frac{1}{8}$ C. $|n + 10| = \frac{1}{8}$ D. $|n - 10| > \frac{1}{8}$

SOLUTION

We will use the method called *average and difference.* First find the average of the two extremes: the average of $9\frac{7}{8}$ and $10\frac{1}{8}$ ounces is 10 ounces. Now find the positive difference between that average 10 and either extreme (9.875 or 10.125). The difference is 0.125 or $\frac{1}{8}$. Thus, to determine if any given ounces, n, is allowable, the difference between n and 10 must be less than $\frac{1}{8}$. Since that difference could be positive or negative, we take the absolute value of that difference. Hence, we write $|n - 10| < \frac{1}{8}$ which is choice B. However, we should observe that $|10 - n| < \frac{1}{8}$ is also correct, since absolute value takes the positive difference.

Answer: B.

PRACTICE

Exercises 1–10: Solve each inequality, and graph the solution set.

1. $|x| > 3$

2. $|x - 3| \leq 5$

3. $|x + 4| > 1$

4. $|5 - x| < 8$

5. $|6x + 1| \geq 2$

6. $|3m - 6| \geq 9$

7. $3|3x + 5| \leq 12$

8. $|3 - 2x| \leq 1$

9. $|4 - 4x| < 5$

10. $|5x - 20| > 10$

11. The graph represents which inequality?

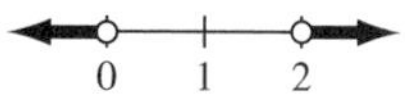

A. $|x + 1| > 1$ C. $|x - 1| > 1$

B. $|x - 1| < 1$ D. $|x + 1| < 1$

12. If $2|x| + 1 > 7$, which of the following could be true?

A. $x = -3.5$ C. $x = -2$

B. $-3 < x < 0$ D. $x = -1$

13. If $|n| > -1$, which statement represents all possible values of n?

A. $n > -1$ C. $-3 < n < 3$

B. $n > 3$ or $n < -3$ D. all real numbers

14. Which of the following is the graph of the solution set for $|4 - 2x| < 12$?

A.

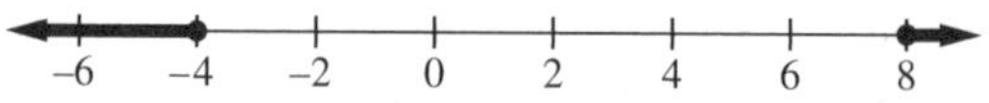

B.

C.

D.

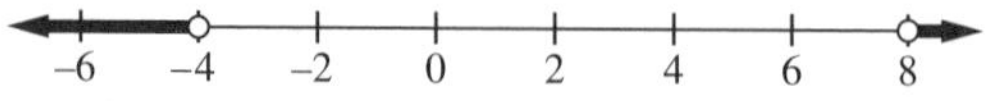

Practice Problems continue . . .

15. Which graph represents the solution set for $\left|\frac{4x-5}{3}\right| > 1$?

A. 

B. 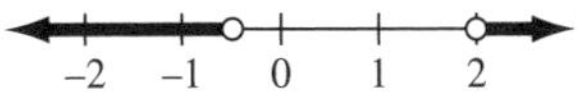

C. 

D. 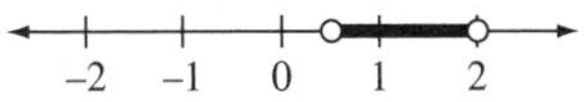

Exercises 16–19: Solve each inequality, and graph the solution set.

16. $|x - 1| - 3 \le 4$

17. $5|x + 8| - 6 > 14$

18. $7 + 3|2x - 4| > 13$

19. $4|2x + 11| + 2 \le 18$

Exercises 20–23: Show two methods to solve the inequalities.

20. $-6 \le 2x - 7 \le -3$

21. $9n - 1 < 17$ or $3n + 1 \ge 16$

22. $-5 < -5x + 8 < 12$

23. $-4y + 10 \ge 8$ or $5y - 13 > -3$

24. MP 1, 7 Write an absolute value inequality with the given solution.

a $2 \le x \le 8$

b $-1 < x < 9$

c $-2 \le x \le 8$

d $x > 3$ or $x < -7$

25. Which inequality expresses the fact that the daily December temperature, T, stayed within 5 degrees of the mean winter temperature of 12 degrees?

A. $|T - 5| < 12$

B. $|T - 12| < 5$

C. $|T + 5| < 12$

D. $|T - 12| > 5$

26. The amount of medicine a doctor prescribes for a certain patient must be no less than 2.95 ounces and no more than 3.05 ounces. If a variable fluid dispenser provides x fluid ounces of this medicine, which of the following statements could be used to describe all possible acceptable values for x?

A. $|x - 3| = .05$ C. $|x - 3| \le .05$

B. $|3 - x| < .05$ D. $|x - 3| \ge .05$

27. The required diameter of a solid copper pipe is 3.25 cm, and the diameter tolerance, or error allowance, is 0.004 cm. If d represents the actual diameter of each pipe produced, which of the following describes all the possible acceptable values for d?

A. $|d - 3.25| \le .004$ C. $|3.25 - d| = .004$

B. $|d + 3.25| \le 3.254$ D. $|d - .004| = 3.25$

28. MP 1 If $f(x) = |3x - 15|$, for what interval is it true that $f(x) < x$?

a State the answer as a compound inequality.

b List the set of integer values for which $f(x) < x$.

29. MP 2, 3, 5 Graph $|x| \le 5$ and $x \le |-5|$. Compare and contrast the graphs.

30. MP 2, 6 When Jamal played basketball this season, the points (p) that he scored in each of his team's basketball games stayed within 10 points of his season average of 28.

a Write an absolute value inequality that represents that fact.

b Explain the meaning of each term and symbol in the context of the problem.

31. MP 3, 6 In the following problems, show your proof with algebraic steps and make a clear argument for your answer.

a If $a > 0$, $m = p$, and k is a constant, how many solutions are there to this absolute value equation: $a|x + k| + m = p$?

b If $a < 0$, $m > p$, and k is a constant, how many solutions are there to this absolute value equation: $a|x + k| + m = p$?

LESSON 4.3

4.3 Graphing Piecewise and Step Functions

Piecewise Functions

A **piecewise function** is defined by more than one condition for distinct intervals in its domain. Here are three examples of piecewise functions and their corresponding graphs.

(1) $h(x) = \begin{cases} 3 & \text{if } x < 0 \\ -3 & \text{if } x \geq 0 \end{cases}$

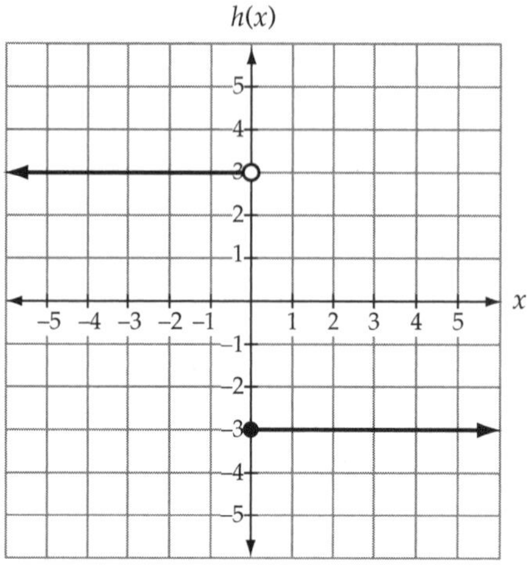

One can think of piecewise functions as disjunctions. In example 1, $h(x)$ is 3 if $x < 0$ or $h(x)$ is -3 if $x \geq 0$.

From the graph and the defining function $h(x)$, we can see that there is a constant for each condition.

- For the first condition, we graph $h(x) = 3$. The first condition tells us that for all negative x, where $x < 0$, we graph the constant $y = 3$. This expression is not defined for 0, so the empty circle means at $x = 0$, $h(x)$ does not equal 3.
- For the second condition, we graph $h(x) = -3$ for $x \geq 0$. Since $h(0) = -3$, there is a closed circle at the point $(0, -3)$.

(2) $f(x) = \begin{cases} 1 & \text{if } x < 1 \\ x - 1 & \text{if } x \geq 1 \end{cases}$

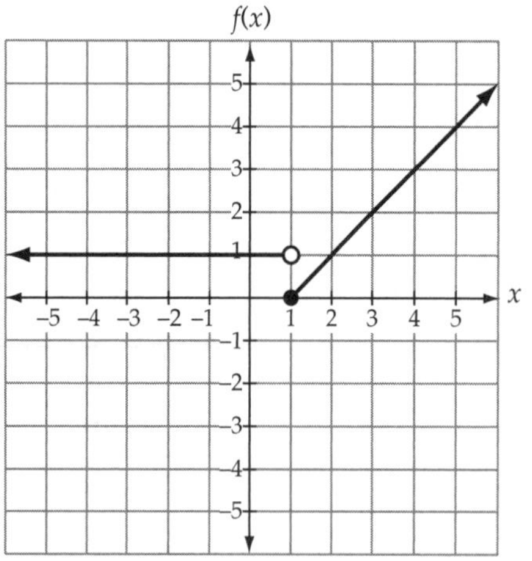

- For the first condition, $f(x) = 1$, for all x less than 1. Since $x \neq 1$, there is an open circle at 1.
- For the second condition, $f(x) = x - 1$, for all x greater than or equal to 1. Start at the closed circle $(1, 0)$ and graph the linear function $f(x) = x - 1$ for values of x greater than one.

(3) $g(x) = \begin{cases} 0 & \text{if } x \leq 0 \\ x & \text{if } x > 0 \end{cases}$

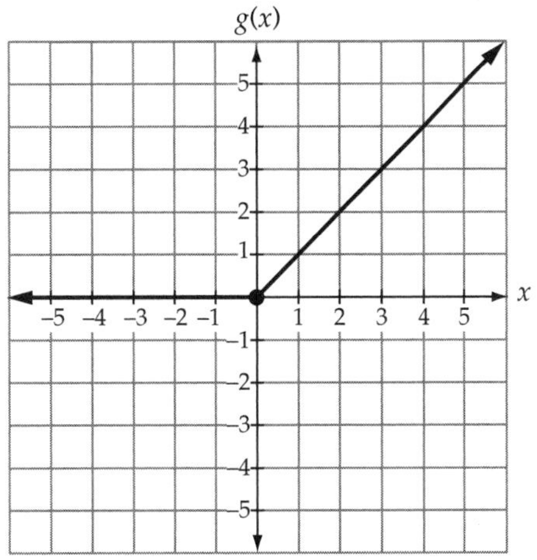

Although the graph is continuous, it is piecewise because it has more than one condition.

- For the first condition, for all non-positive x, $g(x) = 0$ with a closed circle at 0.
- For the second condition, for all positive numbers, we graph the ray $g(x) = x$. The endpoint is already filled in by the first rule.

MODEL PROBLEMS

1. Use the graph below to:

   a Determine the x-values where the rules change.
   b Write the piecewise function that describes the given graph.
   c Within the piecewise function, what types of functions are there?

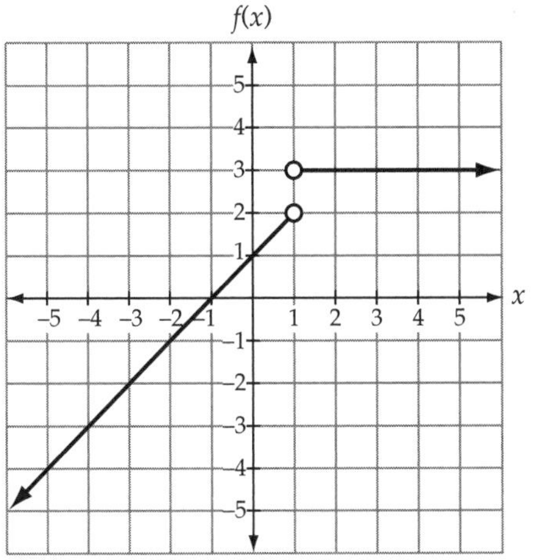

SOLUTION

a The rules change for the piecewise function at $x = 1$.

b $f(x) = \begin{cases} 3 & \text{if } x > 1 \\ x + 1 & \text{if } x < 1 \end{cases}$

c Both piecewise functions are linear functions.

Model Problems continue . . .

2. For the following piecewise function: $f(x) = \begin{cases} -2 & \text{if } x < -2 \\ -x+1 & \text{if } -2 \le x \le 0 \\ x+1 & \text{if } 0 \le x \le 3 \\ 1 & \text{if } 3 < x \end{cases}$

a Graph the piecewise function.

b Determine the x-values where the rules change.

SOLUTION

a

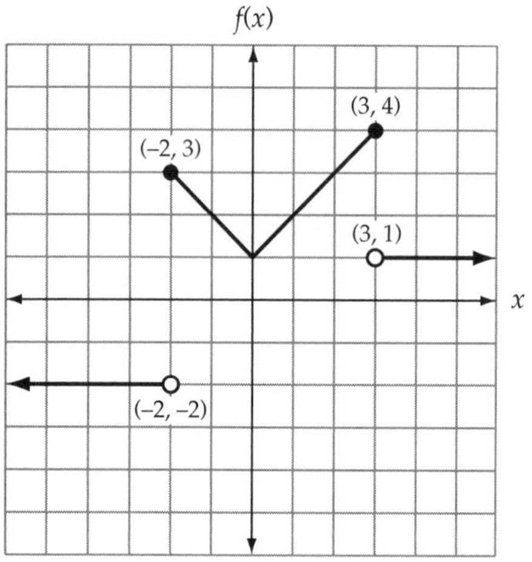

The absolute value function we will study later can also be defined algebraically as a piecewise function:

$$f(x) = |x| = \begin{cases} x & \text{if } x \ge 0 \\ -x & \text{if } x < 0 \end{cases}$$

b The rules change when $x = -2$, $x = 0$, and $x = 3$.

3. If $f(x) = \begin{cases} -x, & \text{if } x < 0 \\ x+1 & \text{if } x \ge 0 \end{cases}$, find

a $f(-4)$ **c** $f(1.4)$

b $f(-0.5)$ **d** $f(3)$

SOLUTION

a Since $-4 < 0$, then $-x = -(-4) = 4$

b Since $-0.5 < 0$, then $-x = -(-0.5) = 0.5$

c Since $1.4 > 0$, then $x + 1 = 1.4 + 1 = 2.4$

d Since $3 > 0$, then $x + 1 = 3 + 1 = 4$

Model Problems continue . . .

Model Problems *continued*

4. MP 2 At Eagle Nest Golf Club, golf clubs are rented by the day, and you pay for the whole day even if you return your clubs early. The first day is $20, and then $20 more for a second day. For every day after the second day, the rental is only $10. Construct a graph that shows the cost of renting golf clubs for different periods of time.

a What should we label the x- and y-axes?

b How will the ordered pairs appear, and what will they mean?

c What are the independent and dependent variables?

d What is the cost of renting clubs for 2 days? for 3.5 days? How long can you rent the clubs if you have only $75?

e Define the rental as a piecewise function.

SOLUTION

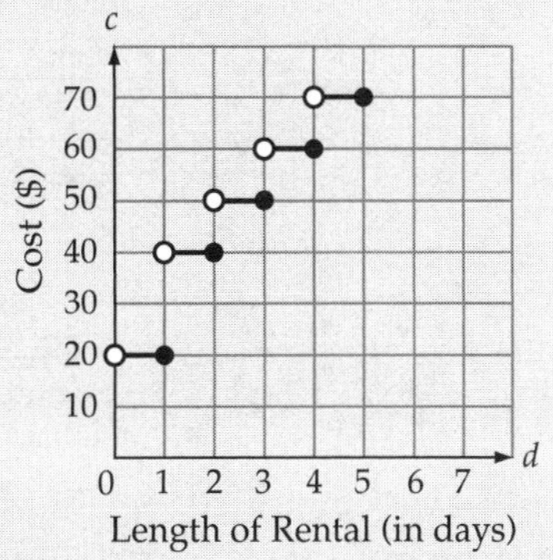

a The horizontal axis is labeled with the variable d. This reinforces the fact that it is associated with the number of days the clubs will be rented. The vertical axis is labeled with the letter c (for cost).

b In this case, the ordered pairs on the graph will be of the form (d, c). For example, the point (3, 50) would tell us that for 3 days the rental cost is $50.

c Since the days are unknown, the d variable is independent. The cost, c, is dependent on the number of days rented.

d 2-day rental is $40; 3.5 days is $60; for $75 you can only rent for 5 days.

e $$c(d) = \begin{cases} 20 & \text{if } 0 < d \leq 1 \\ 40 & \text{if } 1 < d \leq 2 \\ 50 & \text{if } 2 < d \leq 3 \\ 60 & \text{if } 3 < d \leq 4 \\ 70 & \text{if } 4 < d \leq 5 \end{cases}$$

PRACTICE

1. Consider the function defined:

$$g(x) = \begin{cases} x - 2 & \text{if } -4 \leq x \leq 1 \\ -x + 1 & \text{if } x > 1 \end{cases}$$

What is the value of $g(-4) + g(1)$?

A. -7 C. -5

B. -6 D. 5

Practice Problems continue . . .

2. **MP 3** Which of the following is the piecewise graph of the given function? Explain your reasoning. $f(x) = \begin{cases} 2 & \text{if } x < 0 \\ 1 & \text{if } x = 0 \\ 0 & \text{if } x > 0 \end{cases}$

A.

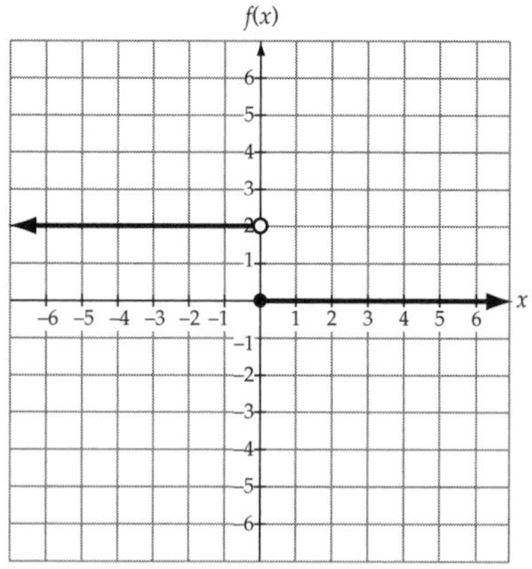

B.

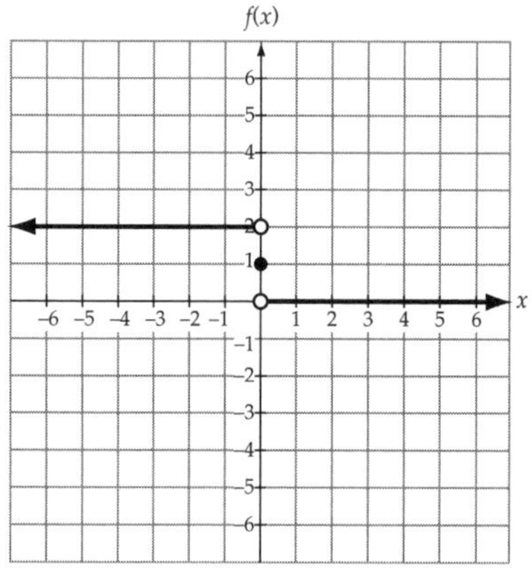

C.

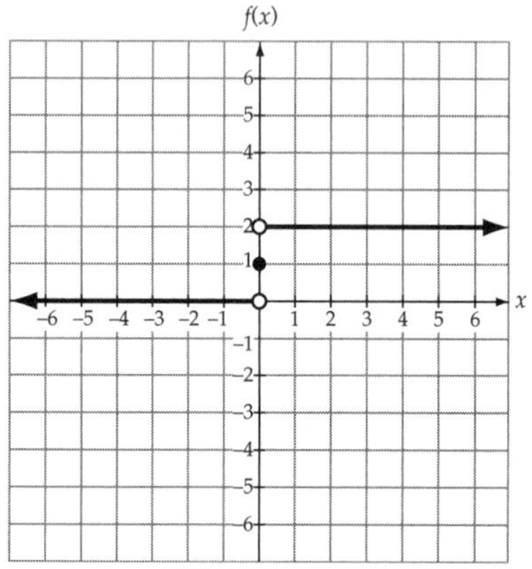

D.

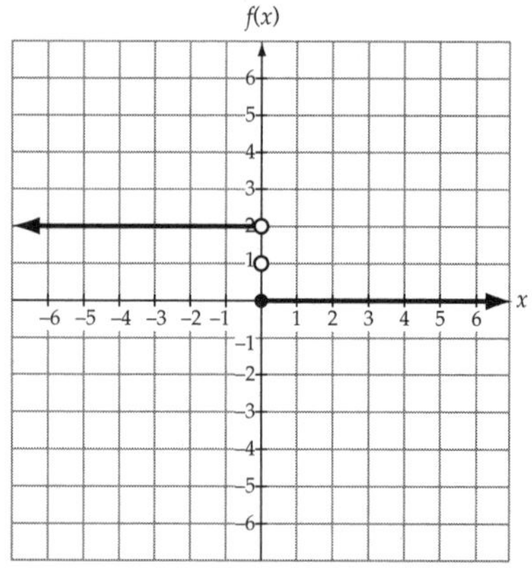

3. Write the piecewise function that describes the given graphs.

a

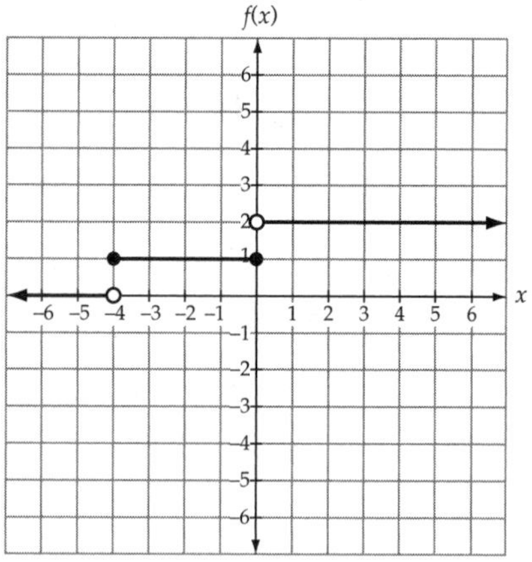

b

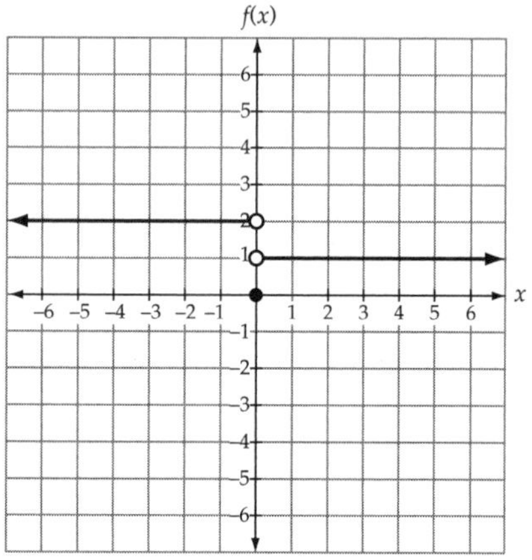

c

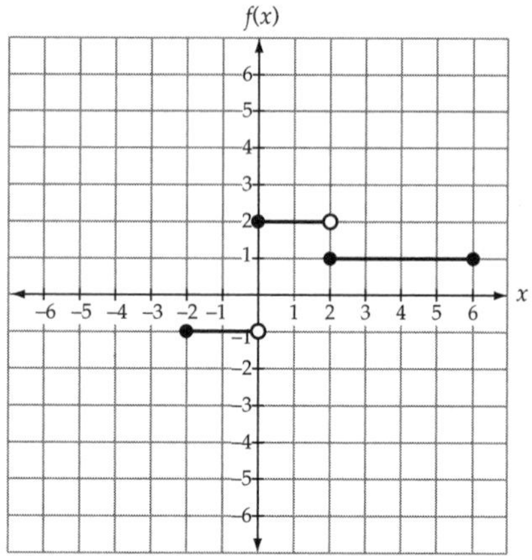

d

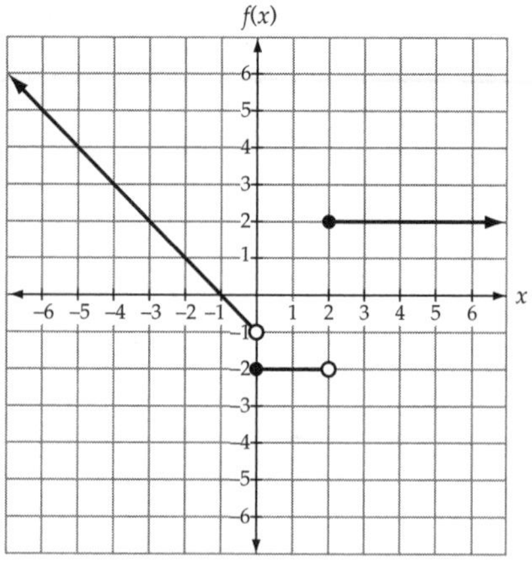

Step Functions

Another type of piecewise function is called a **step function**. The graphs of these functions appear to "step" from one change to another, usually horizontally because they appear to be a constant function at each interval. The following problem and graph show a typical example of a step function:

Example of a Real-World Step Function	Graph of a Step Function
The Star Packaging Co. charges \$11 for shipping and handling any package weighing one pound or less. Each additional pound or fraction of a pound will cost \$3 more, as indicated by the graph.	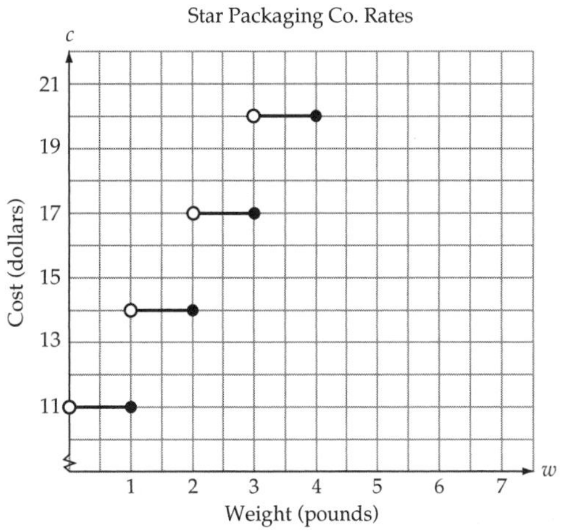

Among step functions, one of the most important is the **greatest integer function**.

The greatest integer function is a step function f such that $f(x) = [x]$, where $[x]$ means the greatest integer not greater than x (or the greatest integer less than or equal to x).

$f(x) = [x]$	
x	$f(x)$
−2.5	−3
−1.1	−2
−0.8	−1
3	3
3.7	3
4.8	4
5.9	5

If x is a positive number in a greatest integer function, such as $x = 3.7$ and $f(x) = [x]$, then $f(3.7) = [3.7] = 3$, because 3 is the greatest integer not bigger than 3.7. The coordinates $(x, f(x))$ would be $(x, [x])$ or, in this case, $(3.7, 3)$.

However, in the case of negative numbers, the numbers for $[x]$ are to the left. For example, if $x = -1.1$, then $f(-1.1) = [x]$ would mean $(-1.1, -2)$, since the greatest integer not greater than -1.1 would have to be -2.

We show a graph of the greatest integer function $f(x) = [x]$, where the domain is the real numbers and the range is integers only. Note the locations of the closed and open dots. They show that $f(3) = 3$, for instance, and that $f(3.999) = 3$, but $f(4) = 4$.

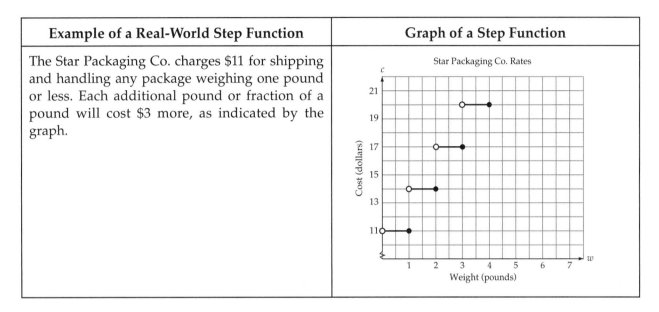

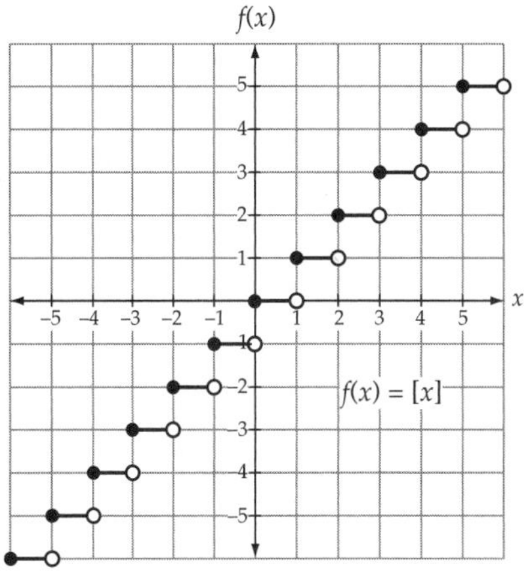

MODEL PROBLEMS

1. The following graph of $f(x)$ is a typical illustration of a step function. Describe the set of rules for this graph.

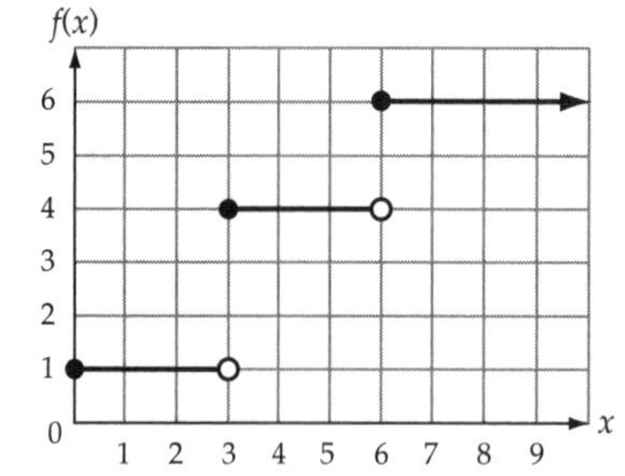

SOLUTION

$$f(x) = \begin{cases} 1 & \text{if } 0 \leq x < 3 \\ 4 & \text{if } 3 \leq x < 6 \\ 6 & \text{if } x \geq 6 \end{cases}$$

2. **MP 2, 4** A long-distance phone call to a city in Eastern Europe initially costs $4.50 up to the first minute. For one full minute up to two minutes, the cost increases by $0.50; it increases by another $0.50 for two full minutes up to three minutes, and so on. The greatest integer step function graphed below illustrates this pricing.

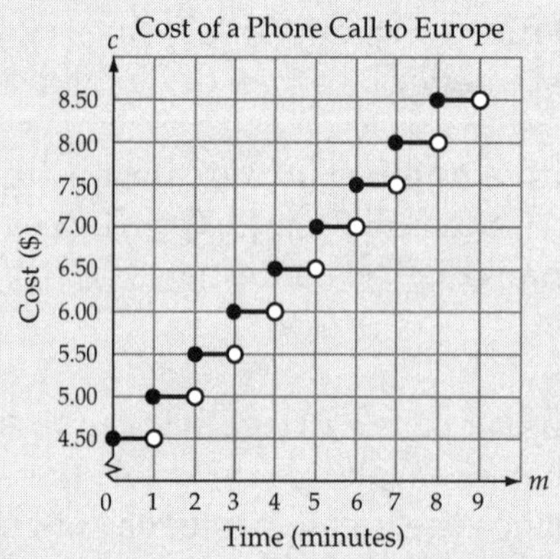

a What is the cost of a 5-minute-and-40-second call?

b What is the difference between the cost of the call in part **a** and the cost of an 8-minute call?

c About how many minutes could you talk for on a phone call that cost $7.50? Give two possible answers.

d Write the function $c(m)$ to represent the cost for any given time.

SOLUTION

a $7.00

b 8-minute call = $8.50. The difference is $1.50.

c time, m, spent talking: 6 min $\leq m <$ 7 min

d $c(m) = \$4.50 + 0.50\,[m]$

PRACTICE

1. MP 3, 4 Which of the following applications could *not* be represented by the graph of a typical step function? Explain your reasoning.

a Postage rates per ounce

b Charges at a parking lot per hour

c Taxicab fares determined by the distance traveled

d Temperatures over the course of an afternoon

2. For the greatest integer function $f(x) = [x]$, complete the following table of values.

x	$[x]$	$f(x)$
−3.1	[−3.1]	
−3	[−3]	
−2.8	[−2.8]	
−2.3	[−2.3]	
−1.8	[−1.8]	
−1	[−1]	
−0.8	[−0.8]	
0	[0]	
0.7	[0.7]	
0.9	[0.9]	
1	[1]	
1.1	[1.1]	
1.9	[1.9]	
2	[2]	
2.4	[2.4]	
3.7	[3.7]	
4	[4]	
4.5	[4.5]	

3. The Star Packaging Co. charges \$11 for shipping and handling any package weighing one pound or less. Each additional pound or fraction of a pound will cost \$3 more, as indicated by the graph.

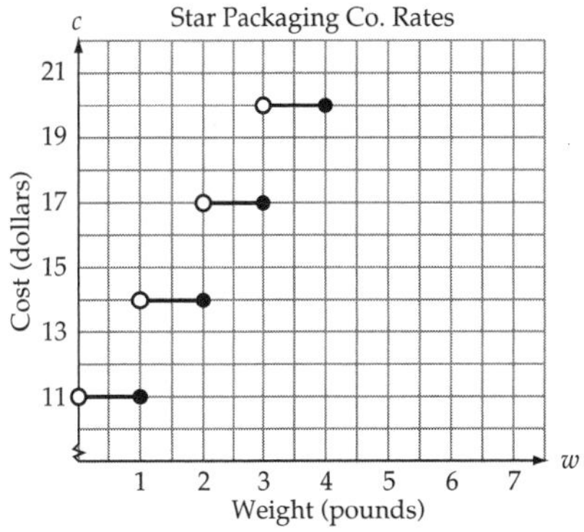

a What is the total cost of sending three separate packages weighing 1.8 pounds, 3.7 pounds, and 4 pounds?

b If it costs \$17 to send a particular package, what could have been the weight of that package?

c Mary reasons that since an additional pound costs \$3, an additional half-pound will cost \$1.50. Is this true? Justify your response.

4. On a city taxi meter, the cost begins at \$2.50 per person for the first mile plus \$1.25 for every additional mile or fraction of a mile thereafter. The following step function graph illustrates this distance/cost relationship. Using the graph, answer the following:

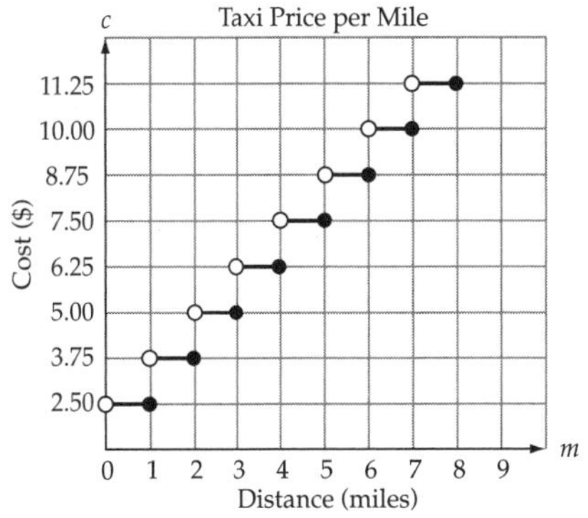

a If Mark takes the city taxi and travels a distance of 3.7 miles, what is his cost for the taxi ride?

b If the cost to travel from the airport to his office is \$8.75, how many miles did he travel? If he also gave a 15% tip to the driver, what did it cost him (rounded to the nearest dollar)? *Practice Problems continue . . .*

5. MP 2, 3, 4 The following step function graph represents a section of the income tax table of Center City for those earning \$50,000 to \$51,000.

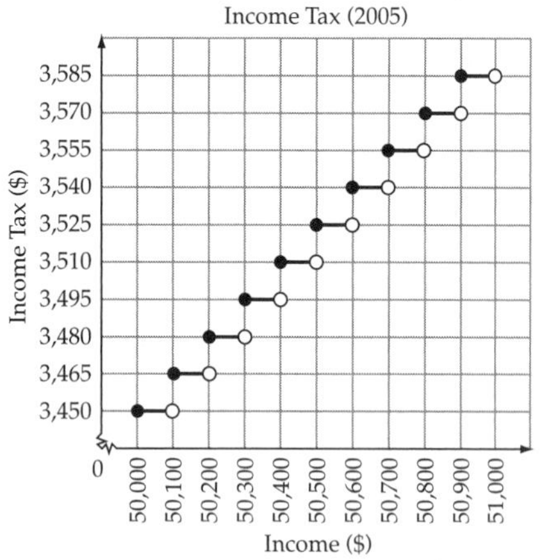

Using the graph above, answer the following questions.

a If Stacy Johnson earned \$50,825 in 2005, how much was her income tax?

b What was the approximate tax rate she paid (taxes paid/income earned)?

c Her brother, Thomas, paid \$3,510 in taxes. Express his income as an inequality.

d If Stacy's dad's taxes came to \$3,540, which of the following could *not* represent his earnings: \$50,610, \$50,675, \$50,701, or \$50,695? Explain your reasoning.

6. MP 1 Construct the graph that illustrates this step function.

a $f(x) = \begin{cases} -2 & \text{if } -5 < x \leq -1 \\ 1 & \text{if } -1 < x < 2 \\ 5 & \text{if } x \geq 2 \end{cases}$

b What is the value of $f(-4.1) + f(-1.1) + f(0) + f(1.1) + f(2)$?

MP 7, 8 Exercises 7–15: Sketch the graph of each of the following step functions.

7. $y = [x + 1]$

8. $y = [x + 2]$

9. $y = [x + 3]$

10. $f(x) = 2[x]$

11. $f(x) = 3[x]$

12. $f(x) = 4[x]$

13. $f(x) = [x] + 1$

14. $f(x) = [x] + 2$

15. $f(x) = [x] + 3$

16. MP 2, 3, 4 Prompt Service Co. has delivery charges for the shipping and handling of packages at the following rates.

Weight (w)	0.5 lb or less	Greater than 0.5, less than or equal to 1 lb	Greater than 1 lb, less than or equal to 2 lb	Over 2 lb
Cost $C(w)$	\$15	\$20	\$25	\$40

a Construct the graph of a step function based on the given data.

b If the weights (w) of three separate packages are 0.25 lb, 1 lb, and 2.1 lb, what was the total cost for delivery?

c If shipping and handling charges for two packages were \$45, which of the following could *not* be the total weight of the packages? Defend your choice.
1.6 lb, 2.1 lb, 2.5 lb, or 3.1 lb

4.4 Graphing Absolute Value Functions

Key Features of the Graph

We will look at the *key features* of graphs of absolute value functions of the form $f(x) = |x|$.

x	$f(x)$
−6	6
−4	4
−2	2
0	0
2	2
4	4
6	6

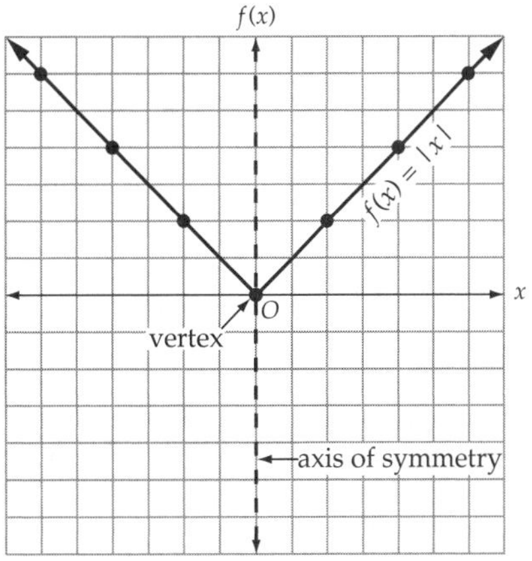

When graphing on an xy-coordinate system, the *domain* is the x-axis and the *range* is the y-axis. And the graph of the function y = f(x) is the set of all points (x, f(x)).

The axis of symmetry is an equation of a line, not just a number.

1. **axis of symmetry:** The graph of $f(x) = |x|$ is symmetric with respect to the y-axis, also called the **axis of symmetry**.
2. **vertex,** or **turning point:** The graph of $f(x) = |x|$ is a V-shaped union of two rays with a common endpoint called the **vertex**. The vertex is the *lowest point* (minimum) if the graph opens upward, and it is the *highest point* (maximum) if the graph opens downward.
3. **end behavior of the graph:** Absolute value functions open up or down. The graph of $f(x) = |x|$ opens up.
4. ***y*-intercept:** The y-intercept is where $x = 0$. The y-intercept in $f(x) = |x|$ is the origin.
5. ***x*-intercept** or ***x*-intercepts:** The x-coordinates are the x-values when $y = 0$. The x-intercept in $f(x) = |x|$ is the origin.
6. **average rate of change:** To find the average rate of change, we calculate the slope of a line between those points.
   - When $x < 0$ in the absolute value function $f(x) = |x|$, we see that function has a negative slope. We confirm this by calculating the average rate of change over an interval using $\frac{y_2 - y_1}{x_2 - x_1}$ or $\frac{f(x_2) - f(x_1)}{x_2 - x_1}$. The average rate of change from the point (−6, 6) to the point (−4, 4) is $\frac{y_2 - y_1}{x_2 - x_1} = \frac{6 - 4}{-6 - (-4)} = \frac{2}{-2} = -1$.
   - When $x > 0$ in the absolute value function $f(x) = |x|$, we see that function has a positive slope. The average rate of change from the point (4, 4) to the point (6, 6) is $\frac{y_2 - y_1}{x_2 - x_1} = \frac{6 - 4}{6 - 4} = \frac{2}{2} = 1$.

Transformations of Absolute Value Functions

As we continue to observe patterns in functions, we will examine **transformations** of the most basic absolute value parent function, $f(x) = |x|$, compared to the general form $f(x) = a|x - h| + k$.

> A **parent function** is the simplest form of a function. In this case, $a = 1$, $h = 0$, and $k = 0$ in the parent function.

1. **Reflection about the *x*-axis:** If $a < 0$, the coefficient is negative, and the graph opens downward, as in the graph of $g(x) = -|x|$. The vertex remains the same but is now the maximum.

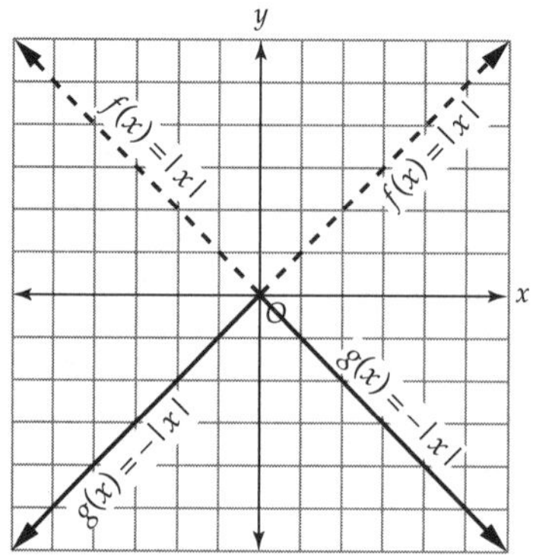

2. **Vertical stretching:** If $a > 1$, the coefficient is greater than 1, the graph is steeper (or narrower) than the parent function, as is the case in $g(x) = 2|x|$, and the slopes of the two rays are -2 and 2.

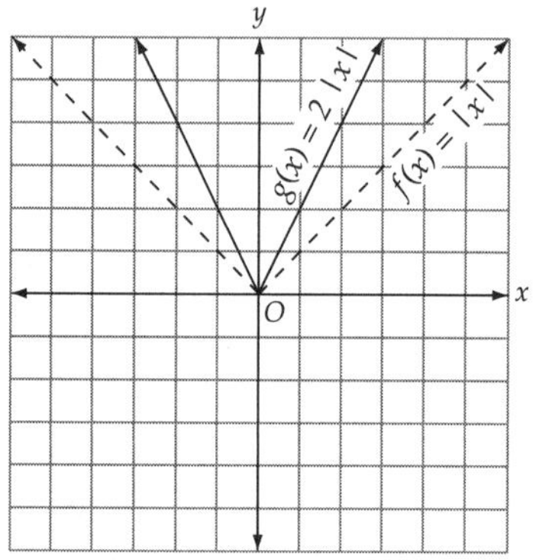

3. **Vertical shrinking:** If $0 < a < 1$, the coefficient is between 0 and 1, and the graph is wider (less steep) than the parent function, as is the case in $g(x) = \frac{1}{2}|x|$. The slopes of the rays are $-\frac{1}{2}$ and $\frac{1}{2}$.

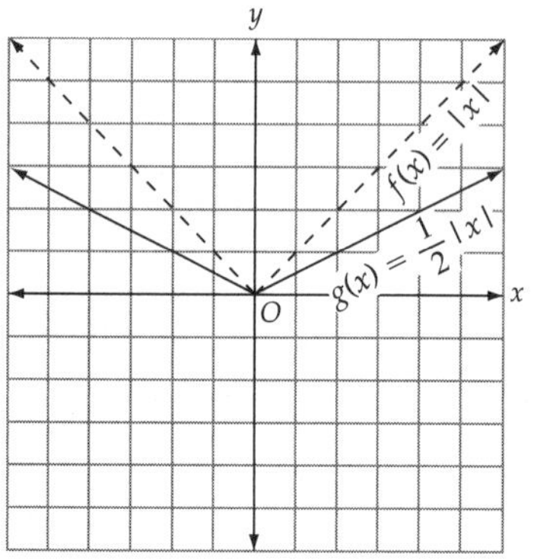

4. **Vertical translation:** If $f(x) = |x| + k$, as in the graph of $g(x) = |x| + 4$, then the parent function shifts up k units. If $f(x) = |x| - k$, as in the graph of $h(x) = |x| - 2$, then the parent function shifts down k units. This is true for all functions, including quadratic functions and exponential functions. The vertex of $g(x) = |x| + 4$ is the y-intercept (0, 4), and the vertex of $h(x) = |x| - 2$ is (0, –2).

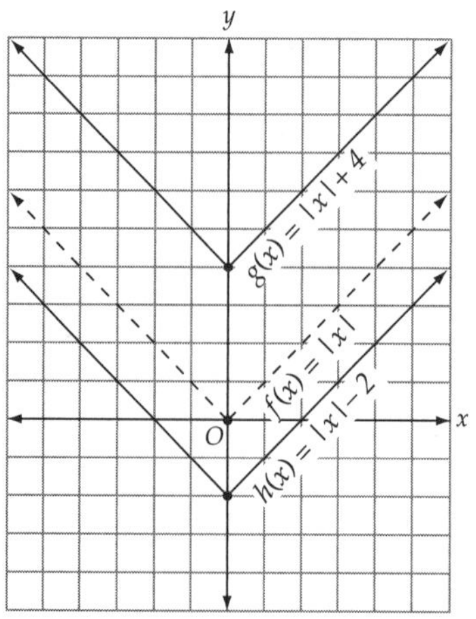

> Similar to the b in the linear function $f(x) = mx + b$, if we add or subtract constants as in $f(x) = |x| + k$, the graph moves vertically.

5. **Horizontal translation:** If $f(x) = |x + h|$, as in the graph of $g(x) = |x + 2|$, then the parent function shifts the graph to the left h units. If $f(x) = |x - h|$, as in the graph of $h(x) = |x - 4|$, then the parent function shifts the graph to the right h units. This is true for all functions. The vertex of $g(x) = |x + 2|$ is the x-intercept $(-2, 0)$, and the vertex of $h(x) = |x - 4|$ is $(4, 0)$.

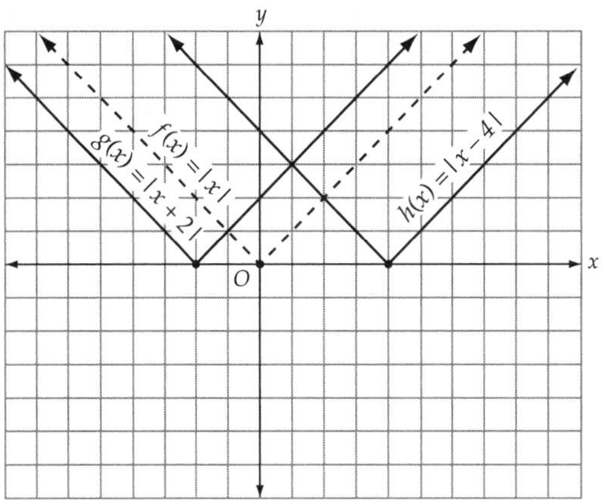

Changing the values of a, h, and k in a function has the effect of translating the graph *left* or *right* (that's the h value), *up* or *down* (that's the k value), as well as changing whether the graph *vertically stretches* or *vertically shrinks* (that's the a value). Lastly, the *sign* of the coefficient of a determines whether the function opens up or down.

MODEL PROBLEMS

1. Write the corresponding absolute value functions that describe each of the three graphs below.

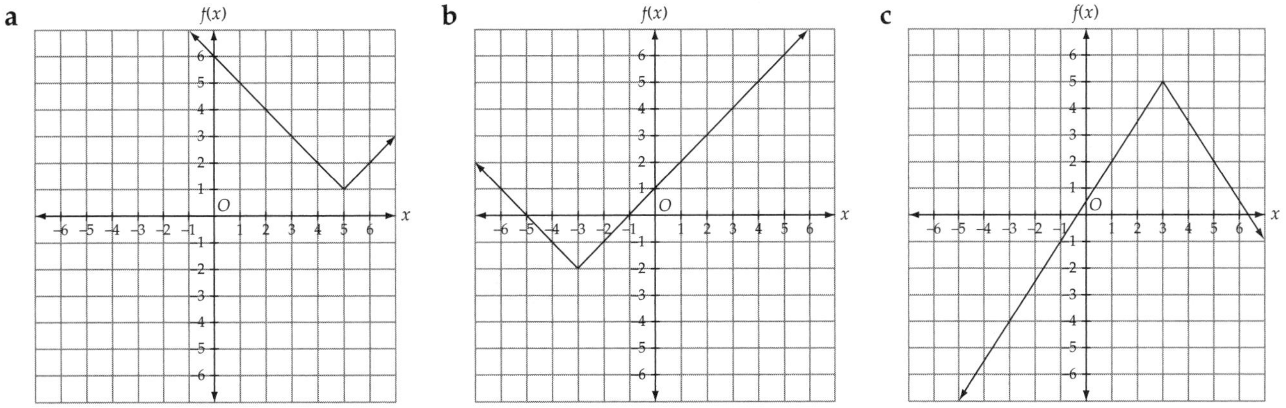

SOLUTION

a $f(x) = |x - 5| + 1$

b $f(x) = |x + 3| - 2$

c $f(x) = -\dfrac{3}{2}|x - 3| + 5$

2. **MP 7** If $f(x) = |x|$, what graphic transformation has been applied to create each of the functions $g(x)$?

a $g(x) = |x - 2|$

b $h(x) = |x - 2| - 1$

c $z(x) = |x + 4| + 3$

SOLUTION

a Move the vertex $(0, 0)$ for $f(x) = |x|$ 2 units to the right to the new vertex $(2, 0)$.

b Move the vertex $(0, 0)$ for $f(x) = |x|$ 2 units to the right and 1 unit down to the new vertex $(2, -1)$.

c Move the vertex $(0, 0)$ for $f(x) = |x|$ 4 units left and 3 units up to the new vertex $(-4, 3)$.

Model Problems continue . . .

Model Problems *continued*

3. **MP 3, 7** If Marta says that the transformation of the graph of $g(x) = -|x|$ is a reflection of the function $f(x) = |x|$ across the y-axis and that the graph opens upward and has a vertex at $(-1, 1)$, is she correct? If she is not, correctly describe the graphic transformation of the function.

SOLUTION

No, Marta is not correct. The graph of $g(x) = -|x|$ is a reflection of the function $f(x) = |x|$ across the x-axis so that the graph opens downward and has the vertex (0, 0).

4. **MP 1** The absolute value functions $f(x) = |x - 3| - 1$ and $g(x) = 2$ are graphed below.

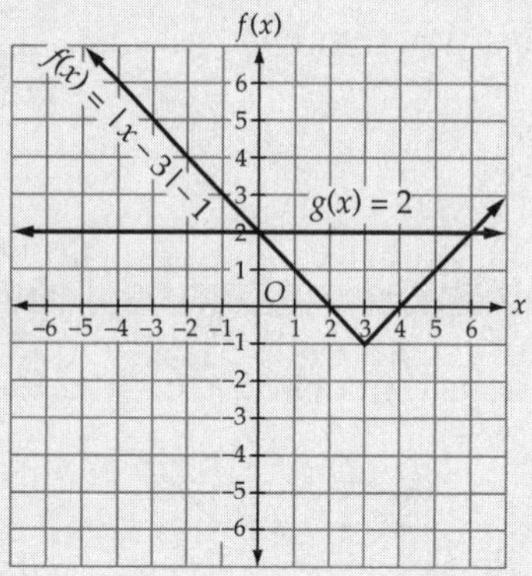

a What are the intersection points of the functions?

b Solve $|x - 3| - 1 = 2$ algebraically. What ordered pairs make both $f(x)$ and $g(x)$ true? That is, when does $f(x) = g(x)$?

c Identify the coordinates of the vertex (or turning point) for the graph. Identify (h, k) in the function $f(x) = |x - 3| - 1$. Is it the same as the vertex?

d What is the axis of symmetry?

SOLUTION

a The intersection points of the two functions are (6, 2) and (0, 2).

> The intersection points of the two functions are the solutions to the set of functions.

b $|x - 3| - 1 = 2$

$|x - 3| = 3$

$x - 3 = 3$ or $x - 3 = -3$

$x = 6$ or $x = 0$

The x-values are the x-coordinates of the intersection points in the graphs of the two functions, $g(x) = 2$ and $f(x) = |x - 3| - 1$.

c Vertex $(3, -1)$; $(h, k) = (3, -1)$; they are the same.

d The axis of symmetry is $x = 3$.

Model Problems continue . . .

Model Problems *continued*

5. **MP 1, 4, 5, 6** Let us consider the real-time event of a rolling ball striking a wall and returning. An absolute value function can be used to model the rolling ball and the distance from the wall over time. We must keep in mind that the distance from the wall decreases as the ball approaches the wall and then increases as the ball bounces back. Now, for the sake of the math (and not the physics) let us assume that the speed is a constant, so that the ball does not lose energy and slow down as it returns.

Angela is putting a ball toward a given hole in miniature golf. There is a bumper wall directly behind the hole, and Angela is standing 24 feet from the bumper wall. If the ball she putts is moving at 8 ft/sec, misses the hole, hits the bumper wall, and rolls directly back to her,

a Make a table of values and graph the function of the situation.

b Write an equation that represents the golf ball's distance d (in feet) from the wall at any given time t (in seconds). Explain the meaning of each number, term, and symbol in your equation.

c How long does it take the ball to reach the wall?

d When is the ball 4 feet from the wall? 10 feet from the wall?

e Explain one limitation of this model.

SOLUTION

a Table of values, using $t = \{0, 1, 2, 3, 4, 5, 6\}$

t (in seconds)	0	1	2	3	4	5	6
$d(t)$ (in feet)	24	16	8	0	8	16	24

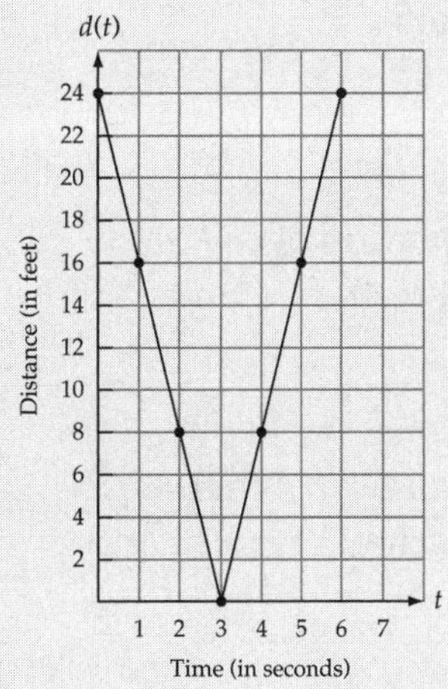

In graphing this absolute value function, we see that 24 or (0, 24) is the y-intercept, and the slope is -8 when $0 \leq t \leq 3$ and 8 when $3 \leq t \leq 6$.

b If we were merely interested in how long it would take for the rolling ball to cover 24 feet, we would use the formula $d = rt$, distance = rate × time, or in this case $24 = 8(t)$, and the answer for t would be 3 seconds.

However, we are interested in the changing distance as the ball rolls to the wall 24 feet away. So the equation becomes $d(t) = 24 - 8t$. But the distance would be negative once we go beyond 3 seconds. However, if we use absolute value notation, and now write $d(t) = |24 - 8t|$, then the equation makes sense for the real-time event and allows for the fact that the ball travels 24 feet and then back again.

Answer: $d(t) = |24 - 8t|$

c We could set $|24 - 8t| = 0$, which means the ball is zero distance from the wall. In solving, we write $24 - 8t = 0$ and $t = 3$ seconds.

Answer: 3 seconds

d Solve $|24 - 8t| = 4$; $t = 2.5$ seconds or 3.5 seconds

Solve $|24 - 8t| = 10$; $t = 1.75$ seconds or 4.25 seconds

e The ball loses energy when it hits the wall and would return at a slower speed.

PRACTICE

1. **MP 5, 7** Graph the following functions. How are these functions the same? How are they different?

   $f(x) = x + 3$ and $g(x) = |x| + 3$

2. **MP 7, 8** In each comparison, explain clearly what changes occur.

   a Compare $f(x) = |x|$ with the following three functions: $g(x) = |x| + 1$, $h(x) = |x| + 3$, and $k(x) = |x| - 2$

   b Compare $f(x) = |x|$ with the following three functions: $p(x) = |x + 1|$, $q(x) = |x + 3|$, and $s(x) = |x - 2|$

3. **MP 7** Determine the equation from the description.

   a Given the graph of $f(x) = |x - 2| + 3$, what would be the equation of this same graph if it was shifted left one unit and down two units?

   b Given the graph of $f(x) = |x + 3| + 1$, what would be the equation of this same graph if it was shifted right five units and down two units?

   c Given the graph of $f(x) = |x + 1| + 3$, what would be the equation of this same graph if it was shifted right one unit and down three units?

   d Given the graph of $f(x) = |x - 5| - 1$, what would be the equation of this same graph if it was shifted left six units and up three units?

4. **MP 8** What graphic transformation has been applied to $f(x) = |x|$ to create each of the four functions $g(x)$ given below?

   a $g(x) = |x + 2| + 3$

   b $g(x) = |x - 4| - 5$

   c $g(x) = 2|x - 1| - 4$

   d $g(x) = -3|x + 2| + 6$

5. Graph each of the following functions.

   a $f(x) = |x + 3| + 2$

   b $f(x) = |x - 2| - 3$

   c $f(x) = |x - 3| + 2$

   d $f(x) = |x + 1| + 1$

   e $f(x) = -2|x| + 1$

   f $f(x) = |x + 1| - 2$

   g $f(x) = |x - 2| + 3$

   h $f(x) = |x - 1| + 1$

6. Graph each piecewise function for the given domain.

   a $f(x) = \dfrac{x}{|x|}$ for all $x \neq 0$

   b $h(x) = \begin{cases} -1 & \text{if } x < -1 \\ |x| & \text{if } -1 \leq x \leq 2 \\ -1 & \text{if } x > 2 \end{cases}$

   c $g(x) = \begin{cases} x^2 & \text{if } -2 \leq x < 2 \\ x & \text{if } 2 \leq x \leq 5 \end{cases}$

Practice Problems continue . . .

7. Write the corresponding absolute value function that describes each of the following four graphs.

a

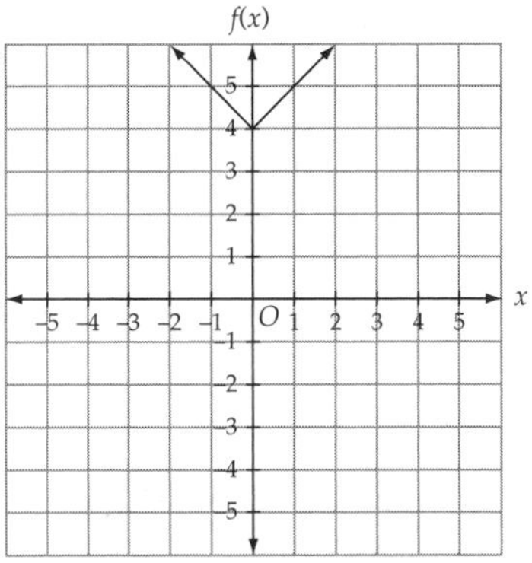

b

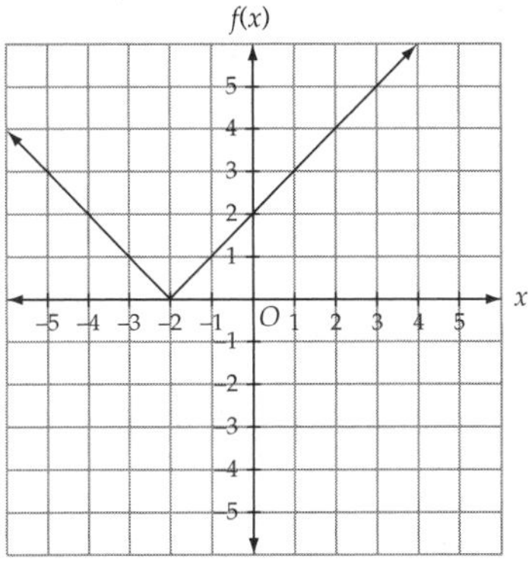

c

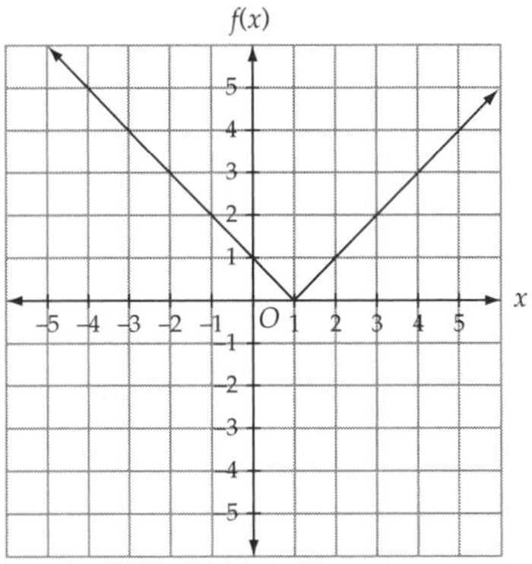

8. Write the corresponding absolute value function that describes each of the four graphs shown below.

a

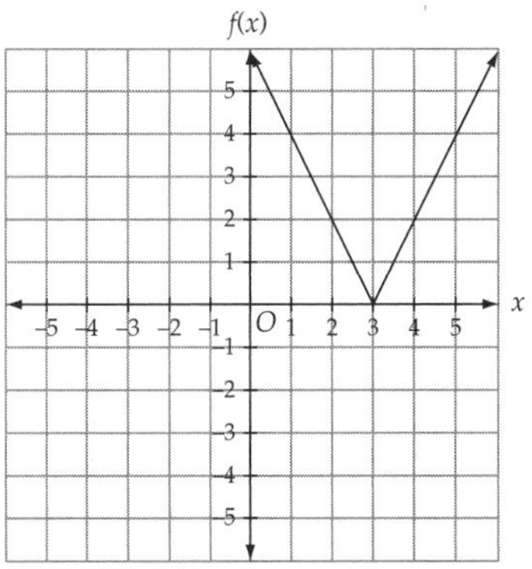

b

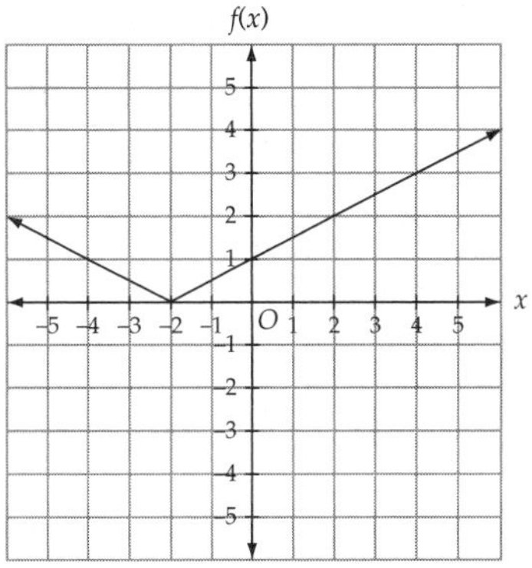

c

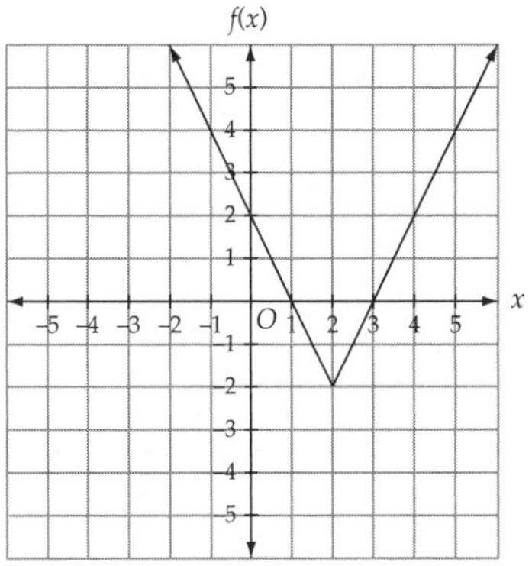

d

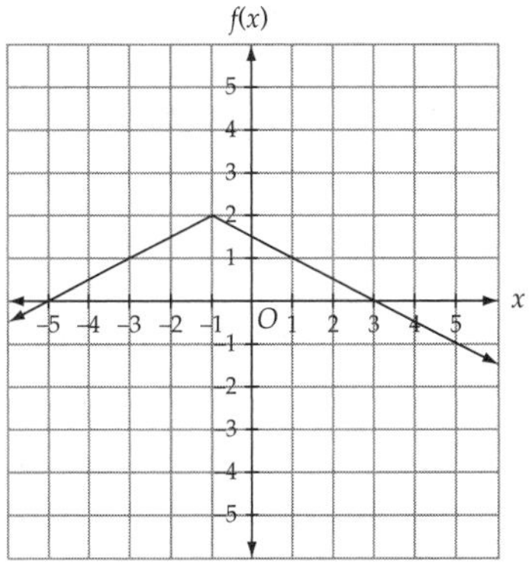

Practice Problems continue . . .

9. Identify the vertex of the function, and the axis of symmetry.

a $3|x+4|-7=y$

b $-|x+1|-5=y$

c $2|x-5|+1=y$

10. MP 1, 5 Given $f(x)=|x-4|$ and $f(x)=2.5$,

a Draw the graphs of the functions on one coordinate plane and describe the methods used to create the graphs.

b How many x-intercepts occur?

c What are the coordinates of any intersections?

d State the coordinates of the vertex and the axis of symmetry of $f(x)=|x-4|$.

11. Given $|x-3|+2=8$,

a Solve algebraically for the values of x.

b Graph the functions $f(x)=|x-3|+2$ and $f(x)=8$ in the same coordinate plane.

c Find the $(x, f(x))$ intersection points.

d Find the coordinates of the vertex and the axis of symmetry of $f(x)=|x-3|+2$.

12. Given $2|x-3|+1=5$,

a Solve algebraically for the values of x.

b Graph the functions $f(x)=2|x-3|+1$ and $f(x)=5$ in the same plane.

c Find the intersection points of the two functions.

d Find the coordinates of the vertex of $f(x)=2|x-3|+1$.

13. If $-2|x+1|+6=-6$,

a What are the (x, y) coordinates of the intersections of $y=-6$ and $y=-2|x+1|+6$?

b Identify the turning point, or vertex, of $y=-2|x+1|+6$.

c What is the axis of symmetry?

14. If $0.5|x-2|+3=5$,

a Solve for x.

b Identify the (x, y) coordinates of the intersections of $y=0.5|x-2|+3$ and $y=5$.

c Find the coordinates of the vertex of $y=0.5|x-2|+3$.

15. If $|x+3|-3=-3$,

a Solve for x.

b Find the coordinates of the vertex and the axis of symmetry of $y=|x+3|-3$.

c Identify the (x, y) coordinates of the intersections of $y=|x+3|-3$ and $y=-3$.

d If there is only one intersection point, describe what the graphs of these two functions look like.

16. MP 1, 3 Given the equations, predict the differences in the graphs. Confirm your predictions by graphing the set of functions on the same xy-plane.

(1) $y=2|x|$

(2) $y=|x|+2$

(3) $y=-|x|-2$

17. MP 1, 3 Graph the equations on the same xy-plane. Compare and contrast the transformations of the graphs.

(1) $y=|x|-3$

(2) $y=|x+3|$

(3) $y=|x-3|$

18. MP 1, 3 Graph the equations on the same xy-plane. Compare and contrast the transformations of the graphs. What is the area of the enclosed figure formed by these two graphs?

(1) $y=\frac{1}{3}|x-1|-1$

(2) $y=-2|x-1|+6$

Practice Problems continue . . .

19. MP 1, 5, 6 At MiniGolfWorld, Kyle putts a golf ball toward a par 2 hole with a wall behind it. The ball misses the hole, hits the wall, and rolls 18 feet directly back to him.

If the golf ball rolls at a constant rate of 4 ft/sec,

- **a** Write an absolute value equation that represents the golf ball's distance d from the wall at any given time t (in seconds).
- **b** Graph the absolute value function that represents this event. Describe the method used to complete the graph.
- **c** Write an equation to find the time it takes for the golf ball to reach the wall.
- **d** When does the ball return to Kyle? Write an equation that models the situation. Solve it. Describe the meaning of the solutions.
- **e** When is the golf ball 6 feet from the wall? 10 feet from the wall? Write and solve the suitable equations.
- **f** If you graph the function you found in part **a** and the function $f(x) = 6$ or $f(x) = 10$ on the same xy-plane, what do the intersections represent?

LESSON 4.5

4.5 Solving Absolute Value Equations Algebraically

We apply the concepts learned in graphing absolute value inequalities on the number line, graphing absolute value functions, and piecewise functions to solving absolute value equations algebraically.

To Solve Absolute Value Equations Algebraically

	$\|x + 1\| = 6$	
• Choose a method.	**Method 1 Number Line.** The number $(x + 1)$ has a distance of 6 from zero. This means $(x + 1)$ could be at 6 or -6. $x + 1 = 6$ or $x + 1 = -6$	**Method 2 Piecewise.** $f(x) = \|x + 1\|$ and $g(x) = 6$. $f(x)$ is a piecewise function: $f(x) = \begin{cases} x + 1 & \text{if } x \geq -1 \\ -(x + 1) & \text{if } x \leq -1 \end{cases}$ Check for intersections: $x + 1 = 6$ or $-(x + 1) = 6$
• Solve for x.	$x = 5$ or $x = -7$	
• Check answers using the original equation.	Substituting 5 for x, we get $\|5 + 1\| = 6$. Substituting -7 for x, we get $\|-7 + 1\| = 6$.	

The domains are found by setting each piece to ≥ 0 and solving for x.

MODEL PROBLEMS

1. Solve for x: $|2x - 5| = 3$

SOLUTION

$2x - 5 = 3$ or $2x - 5 = -3$

$x = 4$ or $x = 1$

Check.

$$|2x - 5| = 3 \qquad |2x - 5| = 3$$
$$|2(4) - 5| = 3 \qquad |2(1) - 5| = 3$$
$$|8 - 5| = 3 \qquad |2 - 5| = 3$$
$$|3| = 3 \qquad |-3| = 3$$
$$3 = 3 \checkmark \qquad 3 = 3 \checkmark$$

Answer: $x = 4$ or $x = 1$

2. Solve for n: $|4n - 5| = -2$

SOLUTION

The solution is the empty set, or $\varnothing$, since the absolute value cannot yield a negative solution. Graphically, $f(n) = |4n - 5|$ will open up and stay above the x-axis. Thus, it will not cross $g(n) = -2$.

3. Solve for m: $|3 - 4m| = 15$

SOLUTION

$3 - 4m = 15$ or $3 - 4m = -15$

$-4m = 12$ or $-4m = -18$

$m = -3$ or $m = 4.5$

Check. $|3 - 4m| = 15$

$$|3 - 4(-3)| = 15 \quad \text{or} \quad |3 - 4(4.5)| = 15$$
$$|3 + 12| = 15 \quad \text{or} \quad |3 - 18| = 15$$
$$|15| = 15 \checkmark \quad \text{or} \quad |-15| = 15 \checkmark$$

Answer: $m = -3$ or $m = 4.5$

4. Solve for x. Show your work. $|x + 5| - 16 = 2x$

SOLUTION

First, we isolate the absolute value expression on one side of the equation. Write the two cases and solve for each case given $|x + 5| = 2x + 16$.

$$x + 5 = 2x + 16 \quad \text{or} \quad x + 5 = -(2x + 16) = -2x - 16$$
$$5 = x + 16 \quad \text{or} \quad 5 = -3x - 16$$
$$-11 = x \qquad 21 = -3x$$
$$-7 = x$$

> **It is important to check the answers in the original equation. An answer may not actually be a solution.**

Check.

$$|-11 + 5| - 16 = 2(-11) \qquad |-7 + 5| - 16 = 2(-7)$$
$$|-6| - 16 = -22 \qquad |-2| - 16 = -14$$
$$6 - 16 = -22 \qquad 2 - 16 = -14$$
$$-10 = -22 \times \qquad -14 = -14 \checkmark$$

Answer: $x = -7$; only one solution works because the line and absolute value graph only intersect once.

PRACTICE

1. Solve: $|x| = 5$

A. 5 C. $\{5, -5\}$

B. -5 D. $\{0, 5\}$

2. Solve: $|-x| = 6$

A. $\{\ \}$ C. -6

B. 6 D. $\{6, -6\}$

3. Solve: $|x| = -3$

A. $\{\ \}$ C. 3

B. -3 D. $\{3, -3\}$

4. Solve: $|n + 3| = 1$

A. 4 C. $\{-2, -4\}$

B. -2 D. $\{2, 4\}$

5. Solve: $|m - 5| = 8$

A. $\{13, -13\}$ C. $\{3, -13\}$

B. 3 D. $\{13, -3\}$

6. Solve: $|2x - 8| = 6$

A. $\{7, 1\}$ C. $\{-7, 1\}$

B. $\{7, -1\}$ D. $\{-7, -1\}$

7. Solve: $|2 - 3x| = 3$

A. $\left\{-\frac{1}{3}, -\frac{5}{3}\right\}$ C. $\left\{\frac{5}{3}, -\frac{5}{3}\right\}$

B. $\left\{-\frac{1}{3}, \frac{5}{3}\right\}$ D. $-\frac{1}{3}$

8. Solve: $|6 - 4x| = 6$

A. 0 C. $\{3, -3\}$

B. $\{0, 3\}$ D. $\{0, -3\}$

9. Solve: $|5 - y| + 2 = 6$

A. $\{1, 9\}$ C. $\{1, -1\}$

B. $\{-1, -9\}$ D. $\{9, -9\}$

10. Solve: $|2x - 3| + 2 = 5$

A. $\{-3, 0\}$ C. $\{-2, 4\}$

B. $\{3, -3\}$ D. $\{3, 0\}$

Exercises 11–25: In each of the following, $f(x) = g(x)$. Graph both functions and then determine any common solutions.

11. $|x - 3| = 5$

12. $|2x + 4| = 10$

13. $|3x - 3| = 15$

14. $\left|\frac{1}{2}n - 5\right| = 2$

15. $|3 - 2x| = 15$

16. $|7 - 3x| = 8$

17. $|2x - 2| + 8 = 15$

18. $|3m - 7| + 3 = 8$

19. $3|4 - x| + 7 = 28$

20. $5|2x - 3| - 8 = 22$

21. $|5x - 4| = 3x$

22. $|4x + 1| = 5x$

23. $|2x + 4| = x$

24. $|4x - 2| = 3x+2$

25. $|3x - 5| = 4x-2$

26. If the domain for x is $\{-2, -1.7, 0, 1.8, 3.1\}$, find the range for $f(x)$ when $f(x) = |x| + x - [x]$.

CHAPTER 4 REVIEW

1. What is the range of the function $g(x) = x^2 + 1$ when the domain is $\{0, 2, 4\}$?

A. $\{1, 3, 5\}$ C. $\{1, 9, 25\}$

B. $\{1, 5, 9\}$ D. $\{1, 5, 17\}$

2. The graph of $y = f(x)$ is shown below. If $f(-2) = k$, what could be the value of $f(k)$?

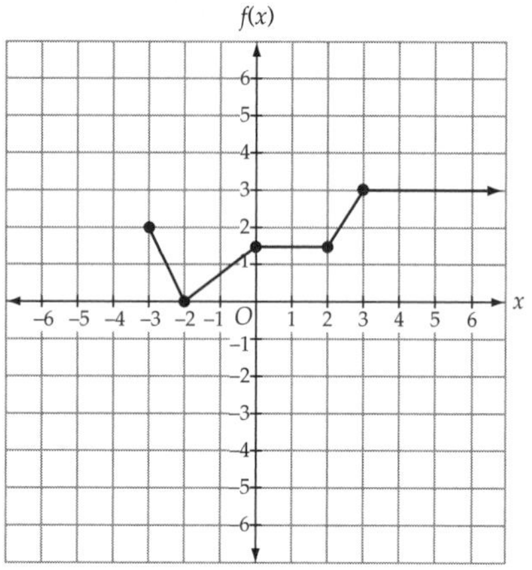

A. -2 C. 1.5

B. 0 D. 2

3. If $|a| = |b|$ and $a \neq b$, which of the following must be true?

I. $a^2 = b^2$ II. $a + b = 0$ III. $ab < 0$

A. III only

B. I only

C. II and III only

D. I, II, III

4. For which of the following functions is $g(-2) > g(2)$?

A. $g(x) = 6x^2$ C. $g(x) = \dfrac{6}{x}$

B. $g(x) = 6$ D. $g(x) = 6 - x^3$

5. The given graph is the graph of which of the following inequalities?

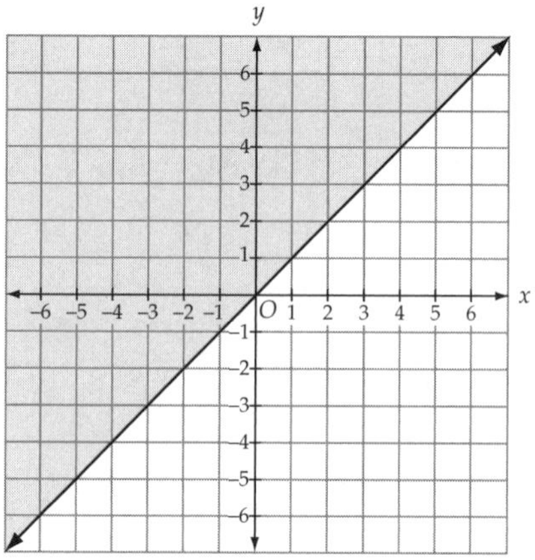

A. $y > x$ C. $y \geq x$

B. $y < x$ D. $y \leq x$

6. How many quadrants have solution points for $x + y < 4$?

A. 1 B. 2 C. 3 D. 4

7. How many quadrants have solution points for $x + y > 4$?

A. 1 B. 2 C. 3 D. 4

8. Using the given diagram, which of the lettered points has coordinates (x, y) such that $|x| - |y| = -3$?

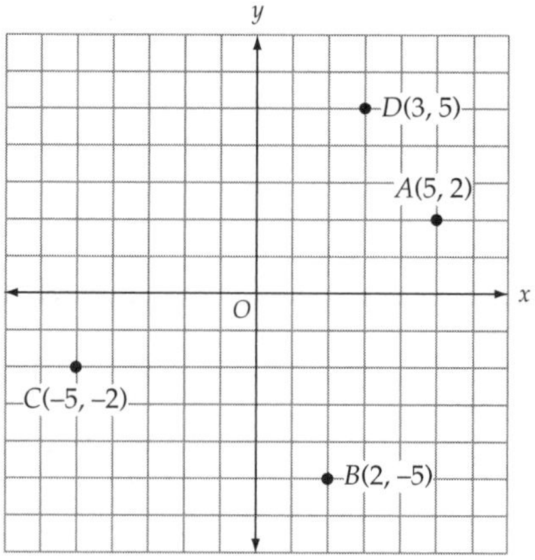

A. A B. B C. C D. D

Chapter Review continues . . .

9. What is the least value of x that satisfies $|x - 2| = \frac{1}{4}$?

A. 2.75 B. 2.25 C. 1.75 D. 1.25

10. What is the greatest value of x that is a solution to $|x - 4| + 8 = 16$?

A. −4 B. 4 C. 8 D. 12

11. If $f(x) = |x - 4|$, what is the value of $f(8) - f(-8)$?

A. −8 B. −4 C. 0 D. 4

12. Which of the following is the solution set for $|x - 1| < 6$?

A. $\{x|\ -7 < x < 5\}$

B. $\{x|\ -5 < x < 7\}$

C. $\{x|\ x < -5 \text{ or } x > 7\}$

D. $\{x|\ x < -7 \text{ or } x > 5\}$

13. Which function would produce the given graph?

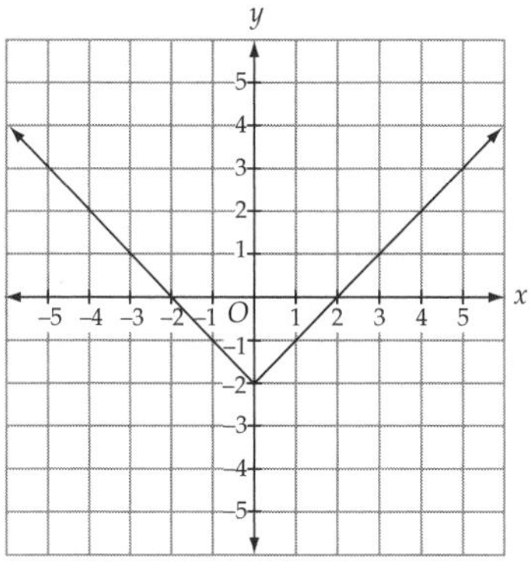

A. $f(x) = |x - 2|$ C. $f(x) = |x + 2|$

B. $f(x) = |x| - 2$ D. $f(x) = |x| + 2$

14. Which of the following is the solution to the statement $|x - 3| < 2$?

A. $x < 5$

B. $x < -1$

C. $1 < x < 5$

D. $-1 < x < 5$

15. Which of the following is the solution of $|2x - 3| \geq 4$?

A. $x \geq 3.5$

B. $x \leq 3.5$ or $x \geq 0.5$

C. $-0.5 \leq x \leq 3.5$

D. $x \leq -0.5$ or $x \geq 3.5$

16. Which of the following is the graph of the solution set for $|1 - 2x| > 7$?

A. 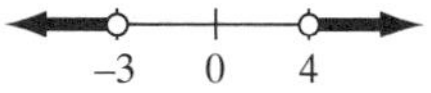

B. 

C. 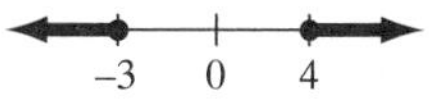

D. 

17. A regulation for getting on a child's ride in Fun Park requires that a child's height, h, must be between 36 and 54 inches. Which of the following inequalities can be used to determine whether or not a child's height, h, satisfies the regulation for this ride?

A. $|h - 9| < 54$

B. $|h - 18| < 45$

C. $|h - 36| < 18$

D. $|h - 45| < 9$

18. At the ABC Bottling Company, the number of fluid ounces, w, of spring water allowed to fill a bottle is between 10.75 and 11.25 ounces. If the capping machine will only accept a bottle containing water that falls within that range, which of the following describes all possible acceptable values of w?

A. $|w - 11| < 0.25$

B. $|w - 11| = 0.25$

C. $|w - 0.25| = 11$

D. $|w - 11| > 0.25$

Chapter Review continues . . .

19. Which of the following is the graph of $g(x) = |x - 3| + 2$?

A.

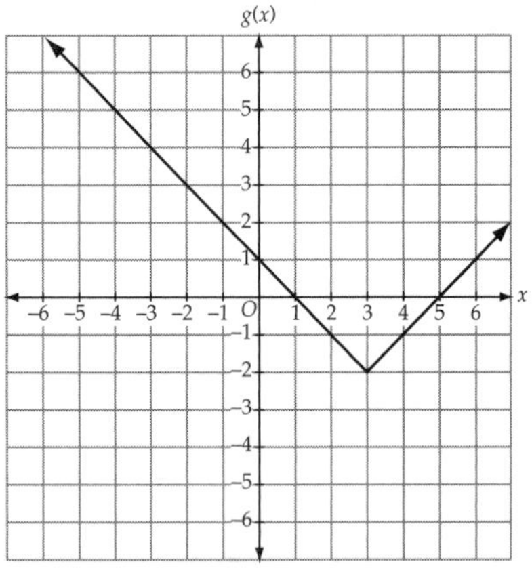

B.

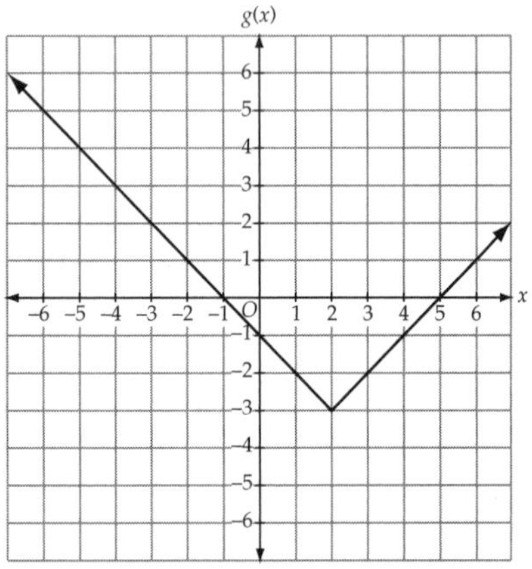

C.

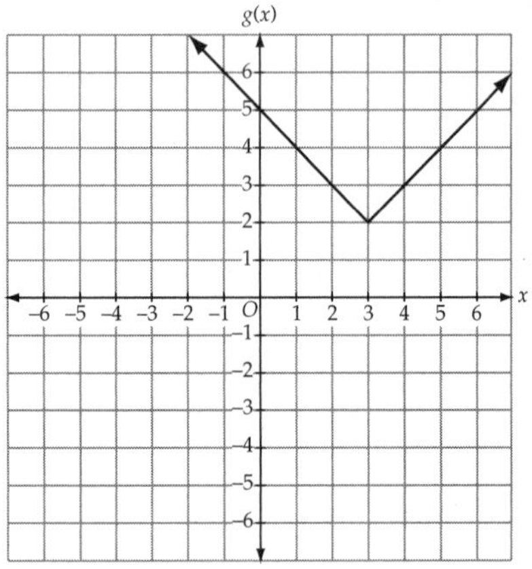

D.

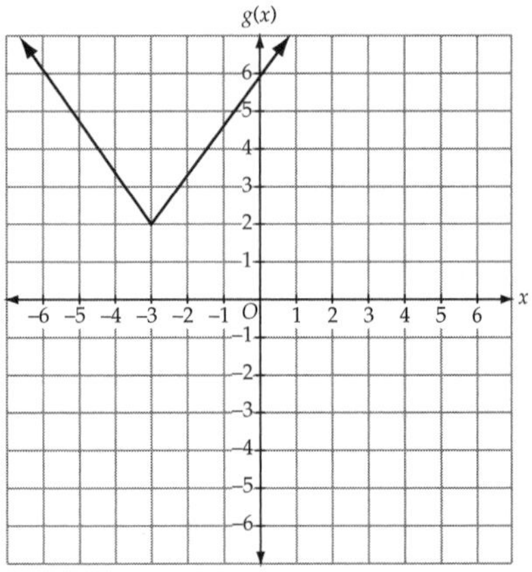

20. The given figure is the graph of which of the following absolute value inequalities?

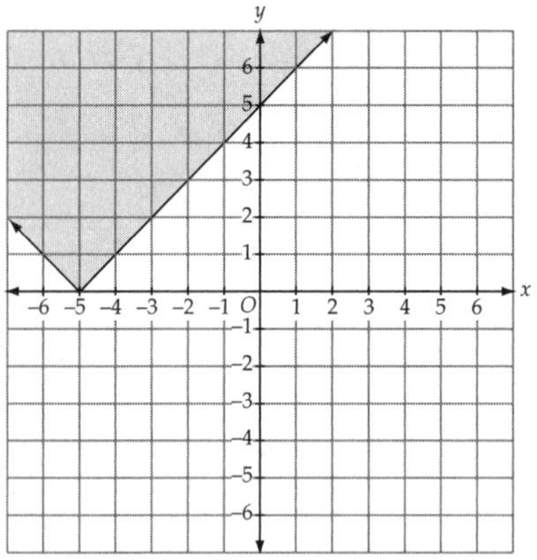

A. $y \geq |x + 5|$ C. $y \geq |x - 5|$

B. $y \leq |x + 5|$ D. $y \leq |x - 5|$

21. If $x = -1.7$, find the value of $f(x) = |x| - x^2 - [x]$.

22. If $x = -0.5$, find the value of $f(x) = |x| - x^2 - [x]$.

23. Given this piecewise function

$$f(x) = \begin{cases} 5x - 1 & \text{if } x \geq 4 \\ 1 - 5x & \text{if } x < 4 \end{cases}$$

what is the value of $f(5) + f(-5)$?

Chapter Review continues . . .

24. Match the following five equations with the given graphs.

(1) $y = |x| - 2$

(2) $y = \left|\frac{1}{2}x\right|$

(3) $y = 2|x|$

(4) $y = |x - 2|$

(5) $y = 3|x| - 3$

A.

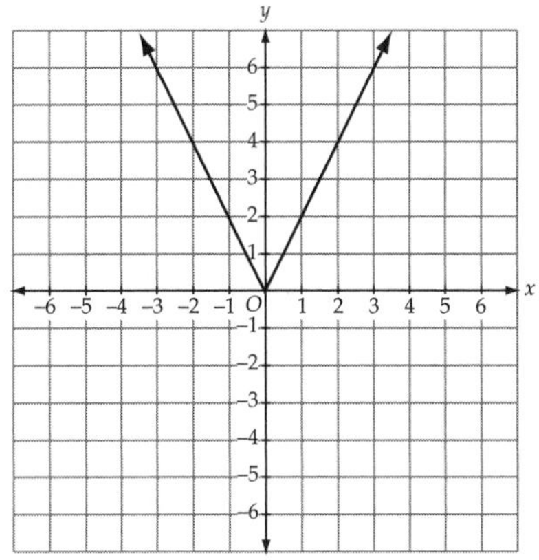

B.

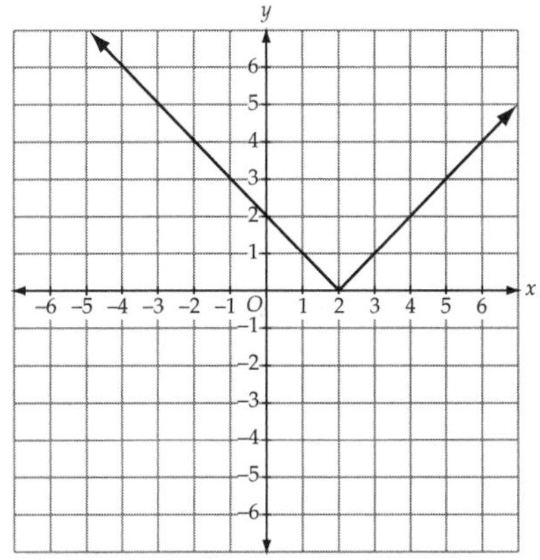

C.

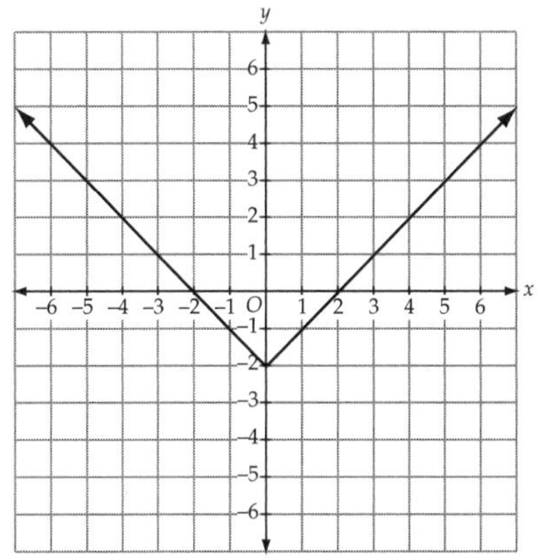

D.

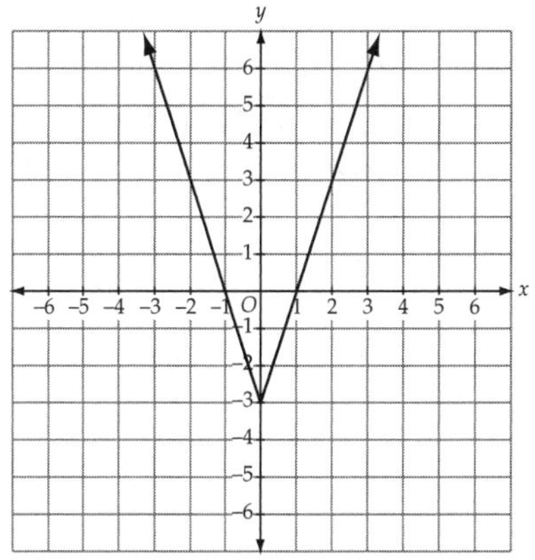

E.

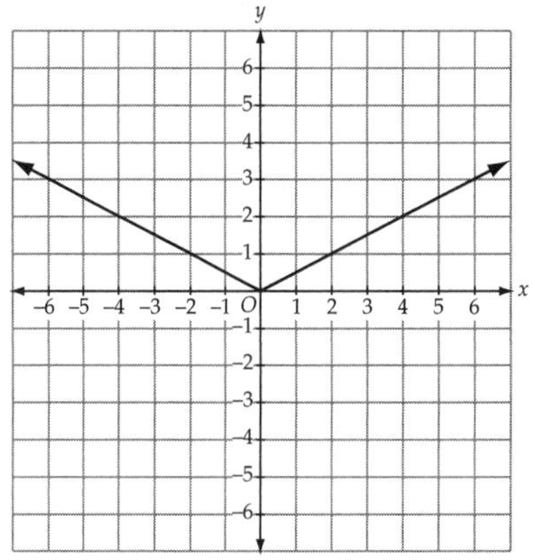

25. For each inequality, solve, express the solution as an equivalent compound inequality, and graph the solution set on a number line.

a $|x + 3| < 3$

b $|x + 1| \geq 4$

c $|x - 9| \leq 5$

d $|2x - 9| - 1 > 11$

e $|3 - x| + 6 > 7$

26. Graph the following function for the given domain: $f(x) = \begin{cases} -2 & \text{if } x < 0 \\ 0 & \text{if } x = 0 \\ 2 & \text{if } x > 0 \end{cases}$

27. Graph the piecewise function for the given domain: $f(x) = \begin{cases} x + 1 & \text{if } x \leq 0 \\ x - 2 & \text{if } x > 0 \end{cases}$

28. Graph the function $f(x) = [x] + |x|$ over the given domain: $-3 \leq x \leq 3$. Include a table of values. Hint: Use integers and half-integers.

Chapter Review continues . . .

29. MP 3 Kate purchases a refrigerator on an installment plan. She pays $60 a month until the appliance is paid off. Which of the following graphs could describe the relationship between months and the unpaid balance? Explain your reasoning.

A.
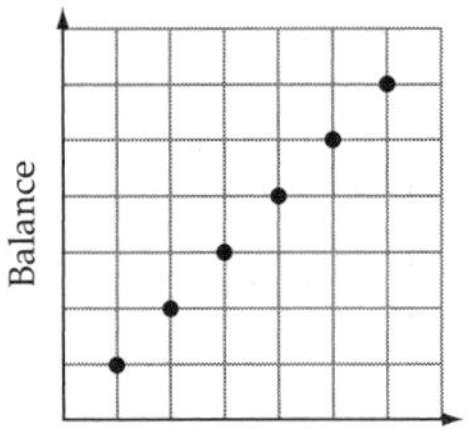

B.
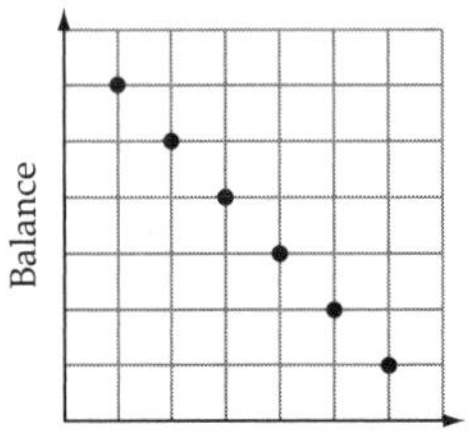

C.
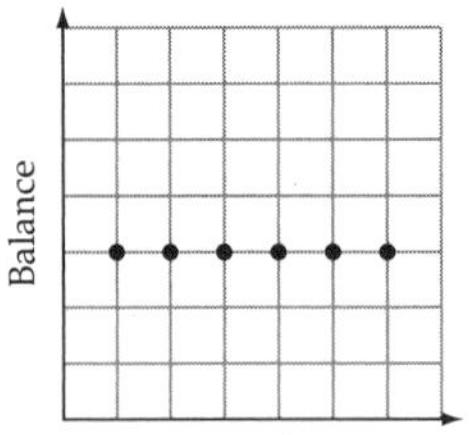

D.
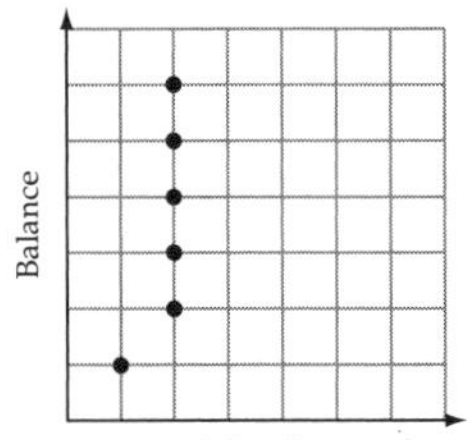

30. MP 3 Let g be a function such that $g(x) = |x| - a$, where a is a constant. If $g(-5) = 7$, what is the value of $g(7)$? Explain your reasoning.

31. MP 2, 6 If $f(x) = |2x - 9|$, then all of the possible values for which $f(x) \leq x$ can be found in what interval? Explain your reasoning.

32. MP 2 Define the basic absolute value function $f(x) = |x|$ as a continuous piecewise function. State the domain and range of that function.

33. Graph the following inequalities in the xy-coordinate system, label clearly, and shade appropriately each inequality.

a $y \leq -3x + 1$

b $y > \frac{1}{2}x - 3$

c $y \leq 4$

34. MP 2, 4, 5 At Acadia Bike Rental in Maine, the bikes rent for $7.50 a day (or any fraction of a day).

a Identify the domain and range.

b Construct a *step function* to illustrate the rental of a bike for 5 days.

c What would be the cost of renting a bike for two and a half days?

d If a vacation renter was charged $30.00, for how many days did he rent the bike?

Chapter Review continues . . .

35. **MP 1, 2, 4, 6** A washer for an outdoor hose is manufactured with the inner and outer rims having a radius of 3 cm and 6 cm, respectively. If the acceptable tolerance is $\pm 3\%$ of the required dimensions,

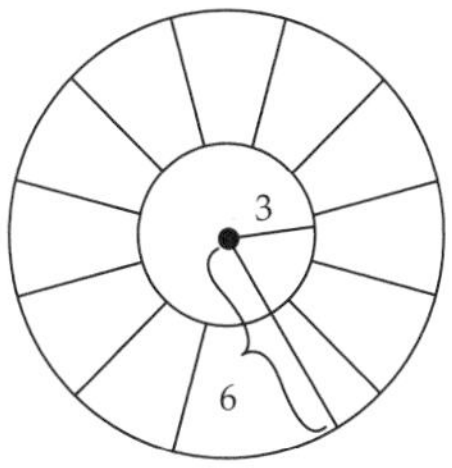

- **a** Write an absolute value inequality to represent the possible acceptable dimensions of the inner radius r and the outer radius R.
- **b** Solve and state the results as compound inequalities.
- **c** Write an equation to represent the surface area, or face, of this washer.
- **d** To the nearest tenth, write a compound inequality to represent the range of possible surface areas A (from the smallest to the largest).

36. **MP 2, 5** The rates charged by a hardware company for the rental of floor-sanding equipment for a maximum of 5 days is as follows.

Rental Time (*d*)	Rental Fee (C)
One day or a portion thereof	\$15
More than 1 day but no more than 3 days	\$25
More than 3 days	\$50

- **a** Construct a graph to represent time (d) and cost C.
- **b** Define the piecewise function $C(d)$.

37. **MP 1, 2, 5, 6** The Sometime Taxi Co. charges \$4 for the first mile, and a lower constant rate of \$2.50 for each subsequent mile or part of a mile after that.

- **a** Construct a graph that illustrates this distance/cost relationship for a trip of 4.5 miles.
- **b** What is the total cost for Ana if she and three other friends share the cost of a 4.5-mile ride and give the driver a generous 20% tip?

38. **MP 2, 3, 4**

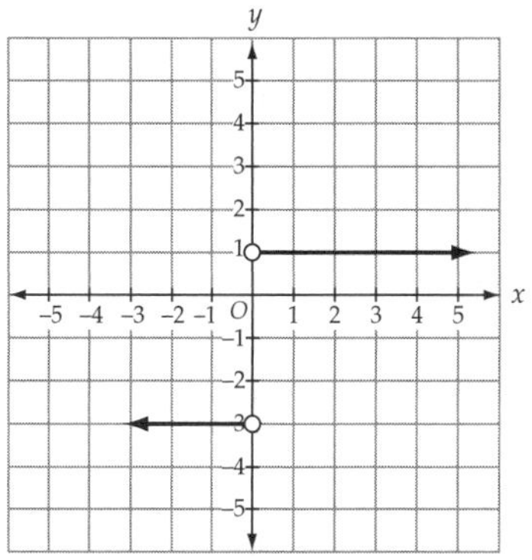

- **a** Write the piecewise function.
- **b** Describe a scenario that fits the graph.

Cumulative Review for Chapters 1–4

1. If x is an integer, which of the following is the solution set of $-1 \le x < 2$?

A. $\{-1, 0, 1, 2\}$ C. $\{0, 1, 2\}$

B. $\{-1, 0, 1\}$ D. $\{0, 1\}$

2. For which of the following compound inequalities is the solution set the empty set?

A. $\{x|\, x > 3\} \vee \{x|\, x < -2\}$

B. $\{x|\, x < 3\} \wedge \{x|\, x < -2\}$

C. $\{x|\, x > 3\} \wedge \{x|\, x < -2\}$

D. $\{x|\, x < 3\} \vee \{x|\, x < -2\}$

3. Which graph represents the solution to the inequality $-3x + 1 \le 13$?

A. 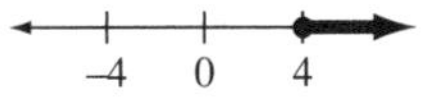

B. 

C. 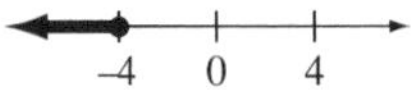

D. 

4. During a holiday sale, one pumpkin costs n dollars. Each additional pumpkin purchased at the same time costs d dollars less than the first one. Which of the following represents the cost, in dollars, of x pumpkins bought during this sale, if x is an integer greater than 1?

A. $n + (x - 1)(n - d)$

B. $nx - x(n - d)$

C. $n + x\,(n - d)$

D. $n(x + dx)$

5. What is the solution set of the inequality $|3 - 2x| \ge 4$?

A. $\left\{x \middle| \frac{7}{2} \le x \le -\frac{1}{2}\right\}$

B. $\left\{x \middle| -\frac{1}{2} \le x \le \frac{7}{2}\right\}$

C. $\left\{x \middle| x \le -\frac{1}{2} \text{ or } x \ge \frac{7}{2}\right\}$

D. $\left\{x \middle| \le \frac{7}{2} \text{ or } x \ge -\frac{1}{2}\right\}$

6. Which table is an example of y varying directly with x?

A.

x	y
3	5
4	6
5	7

B.

x	y
3	5
4	4
5	3

C.

x	y
3	9
4	16
5	25

D.

x	y
3	6
4	8
5	10

7. Which function best represents this graph?

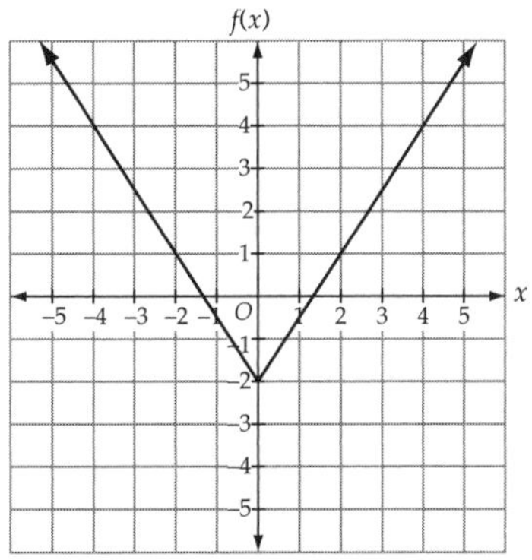

A. $f(x) = \left|\frac{3}{2}x\right| - 2$

B. $f(x) = \left|\frac{3}{2}\right|x - 2$

C. $f(x) = \frac{3}{2}\,|x - 2|$

D. $f(x) = \left|\frac{3}{2}x - 2\right|$

8. If $y = \left[\,|x|\,\right]$ for the domain $-2 < x < -1$, then $y =$

A. 2 C. -1

B. 1 D. -2

9. If $3\,|x + 5| = 15$ and $5\,|3 - y| = 20$, then $x + y$ could equal each of the following except

A. -11 C. 3

B. -1 D. 7

10. The graph below is represented by which of the following functions?

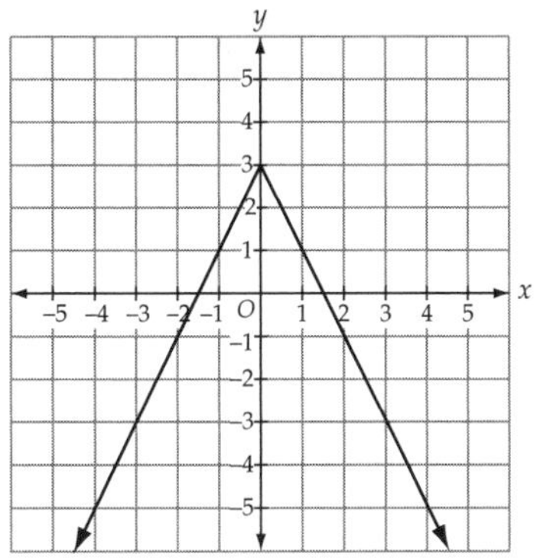

A. $y + 3 = -2|x|$ C. $y = 2|x| - 3$

B. $y = |-2x| + 3$ D. $y = -2|x| + 3$

11. MP 3 Write the missing reasons in the proof. All variables represent numbers. Prove: If $a + c = b + c$, then $a = b$.

Statement	Reasons
1. $a + c = b + c$	1. Given
2. $(a + c) + (-c) = (b + c) + (-c)$	2.
3. $a + [c + (-c)] = b + [c + (-c)]$	3.
4. $a + 0 = b + 0$	4.
5. $a = b$	5.

12. MP 7

a Given the function $f(x) = |x - 1| - 2$, what would be the new equation if the graph was shifted right two units and up 3 units?

b If $f(x) = |x + 4| + 4$ is shifted left 3 units and down 3 units, what is the new function?

13. MP 2, 7

a What is the slope of a line perpendicular to the line containing the points $(-6, -1)$ and $(3, 7)$?

b If the line $y = ax + 7$ is parallel to the line $5x + 8y = 10$, what is the value of a?

c Find the value of k so that the line joining $(-2, k)$ and $(3, 7)$ is horizontal.

d Find the x- and y-intercepts of the linear equation $2x - 7y - 14 = 0$.

14. If $[x]$ denotes the greatest integer function, what is the value of each of the following?

a $[-3.2] + [2.7]$

b $[-2.3] + [1.6]$

c $[-1.7] + [3.4]$

d $[-4.5] - [2.3]$

15. Using the given information, write an equation for each function in the form $f(x) = mx + b$.

a $f(2) = 22$ and $f(-4) = 1$

b $f(-3) = 2$ and $f(1) = -6$

16. The ratio of students to teachers at a high school musical event is 15 to 1. If there are 18 teachers present, what is the total number of people at the event?

17. **MP 2, 4** A train leaves the town of Legend and will eventually pass the town of Epic 420 miles away. The train travels at the speed of 55 mph.

- **a** If $d(t)$ represents distance, and t represents the number of hours since the train left Legend, write an expression to represent how far the train must still travel to reach Epic.
- **b** If the train has been traveling for more than 5 hours, how far is the train from Epic?
- **c** For what range of time is the train at least 66 miles but no more than 99 miles from Epic? Express your answer as a compound inequality.

18. Graph the following function, $g(x) = [x] - 2$, over the domain: $-2 \leq x \leq 5$.

19. Based on the given table,

x	y
–1	–4
1	2
3	8
4	11

- **a** Express the relationship between x and y as an equation.
- **b** Provide three additional pairs of values, including x-value 0.

20. The charge for a telephone call from Chicago to Cairo is \$0.52 for the first minute or less and \$0.35 for each additional minute or portion thereof.

- **a** Graph this step function for charges on calls lasting 6 minutes or less. Let x represent the time and $f(x)$ the charge.
- **b** For the domain $0 < x \leq 6$, what is the range?
- **c** What is the charge for a 1-hour phone call from Chicago to Cairo?
- **d** If the charge for a Chicago-Cairo call is \$6.12, what was the maximum time in minutes for this call?
- **e** Is the relation formed by interchanging x and $f(x)$ from part **a** also a function? If not, explain why.

21. **MP 2, 3, 4, 6** For each of the following, identify the variable and write an algebraic equation or system of equations or inequalities that could be used to answer the question. Solve the equation or inequality and justify your reasoning.

- **a** Terri rented a car for \$84 a week plus \$0.16 for each mile the car is driven. What is the greatest number of miles Terri can drive the car if she wishes to spend at most \$140?
- **b** In $\triangle ABC$, the measures of angles A and B are in the ratio of $1:3$, and the measure of angle C is twice the measure of angle B. What is the measure of each angle?
- **c** The perimeter of a rectangular garden is 66 feet. If w represents the width and the length is 3 feet more than 4 times the width, what equation can be used to find the dimensions of the garden?

22. a On the same set of axes, graph the following system of equations:

$y = x + 4$

$x + y = 6$

$y = 2$

b Find the area of the triangle whose vertices are the points of intersection of the lines graphed in part **a**.

23. MP 2, 4 Before the start of a football game, the football must be inflated to an air pressure P of 12.1 pounds per square inch (psi) within an absolute error span of no more than 0.5 psi.

a What are the maximum and minimum acceptable air-pressure values?

b Which of the following is an equation by which the pressure P of the football can be judged acceptable?

A. $|P - 12.1| > 0.5$

B. $|P - 12.1| \leq 0.5$

C. $|P - 0.5| \leq 12.1$

D. $|P + 0.5| \leq 12.1$

24. Graph the solution set for the inequality $x^2 > x^3$.

25. Graph this piecewise function.

$$f(x) = \begin{cases} -1 & \text{if } x < 0 \\ x + 2 & \text{if } x \geq 0 \end{cases}$$

26.

x	−1	0	1	2
$f(x)$	$\frac{1}{36}$	$\frac{1}{3}$	4	

The table above describes the following function: $f(x) = km^x$ for some constants k and m.

a What are the values for k and m?

b What is the value of $f(2)$?

27. a If $a = b$ and $y = x - 5$ and x is 6 less than b, then y is how much less than a?

b If $a + b = 30$, $\frac{b}{c} = 3$, $\frac{1}{3}b = -7$, and $c \neq 0$, what is the value of $a + c$?

28. Karl's Car Rental charges a car rental fee of \$45 plus \$6 per hour or fraction of an hour. Ramona's Real Wheelz charges a car rental fee of \$30 + \$8.50 per hour or fraction of an hour. Under what conditions does it cost *less* to rent from Karl's Car Rental?

29. In each of the following, solve for x.

a $22 = 1 - \frac{7x}{2}$

b $2x + 5 - x = 7 + x - 2$

c $m = a(x + b)$

d $12 + 3(2x - 1) = 2(3x + 1)$

e $\frac{x}{3} - \frac{x}{6} = 4 + \frac{x}{2}$

30. Given the equations $f(x) = |x - 2| - 1$ and $f(x) = 2$,

a Graph the two equations and find the common solutions.

b If $f(x) = 2$ is replaced with $f(x) = -1$, how many common solutions are there? Name any common solutions.

31. Graph this piecewise function.

$$f(x) = \begin{cases} 1 & \text{if } x \text{ is an integer} \\ 0 & \text{if } x \text{ is not an integer} \end{cases}$$

Chapter 5 Systems of Linear Equations and Inequalities

Chapter Focus

Often, mathematics problems will include information relating two quantities without providing a value for either one. To find the solution, we need sets of information in the form of equations or inequalities. A system of equations or inequalities is a set of two or more equations or inequalities containing two or more variables. The solution is true for all equations or inequalities in the system. A system can have any number of equations or inequalities and any number of variables. In order to solve the system, there must be as many equations or inequalities as there are variables. For instance, if there are three unknowns, or variables, we must have three distinct equations or inequalities to find the solution. We will work on systems containing two linear equations or inequalities that have two variables. We will solve the systems using three different methods: graphing, substitution, and elimination. For all procedures, we will apply the mathematics to real-world problems.

Chapter Content

Chapter Vocabulary

consistent systems

dependent systems

elimination method

inconsistent systems

intersection

solution of the system

substitution method

LESSON 5.1

5.1 Solving Systems of Linear Equations by Graphing

When graphing simultaneous equations in the same coordinate plane, we must remember that

- Each straight-line graph is the solution for one equation.
- Every point on each graph represents the (x, y) values that satisfy the given equation.

To Solve Systems of Linear Equations Graphically

- Write both equations in slope-intercept form.
- Draw the graph of each equation on the same coordinate plane. Make sure the scale, or units, are the same for each line graphed.
- Be careful about a *restricted domain*. Do not extend the graph to domain values that cannot occur. For instance, if both the variables must represent positive numbers, make sure to limit your graph to the first quadrant.
- The coordinates of the point of **intersection**, or points of intersection, of the lines define the **solution of the system**.
- Check the solution in both equations.

Two lines do not always intersect at a point. What does that mean for the number of solutions?

(1) **Consistent systems.** If two distinct lines intersect, one point (x, y) of intersection makes both equations true.

- Lines have different slopes.
- Lines intersect in exactly one point.

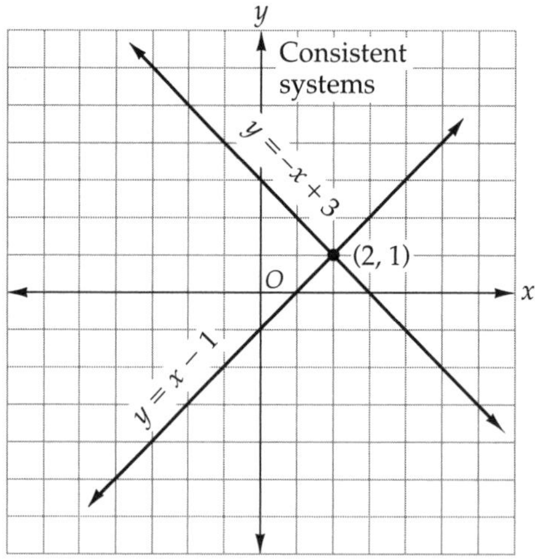

Check to make sure the point is a solution to both equations.
Substitute the coordinates (2, 1) in each equation.

$y = -x + 3$	$y = x - 1$
$1 = -2 + 3$	$1 = 2 - 1$
$1 = 1$ ✓	$1 = 1$ ✓

(2) **Inconsistent systems.** If two lines have the same slope, but different y-intercepts, they are parallel and will not intersect. There is no solution to these systems.

- Lines have the same slope but different y-intercepts.
- Lines are parallel and do not intersect.

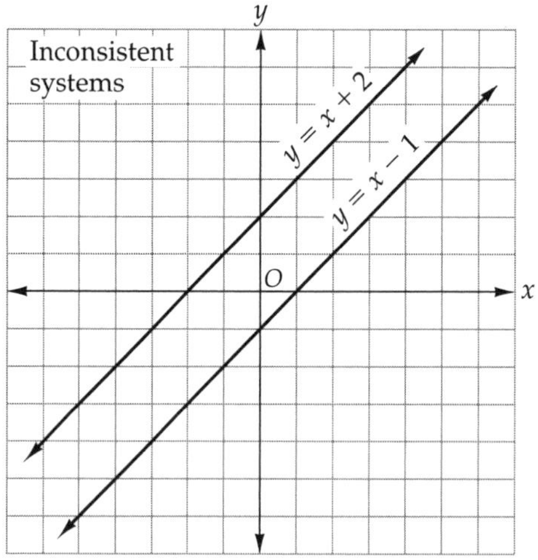

(3) **Dependent systems.** If the two lines coincide (different representations of the same line), there are infinitely many solutions. Every point on the line is a solution.

- Lines have the same slope and the same y-intercept.
- Lines are identical and share all points in common.

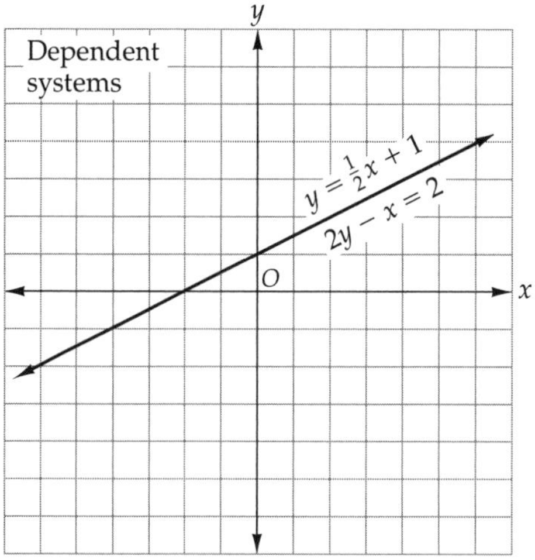

MODEL PROBLEM

MP 1, 2, 4, 5 The Senior Citizen Sunshine Club is planning a fund-raiser to help a day care center. They have to decide whether to make embroidered napkin sets or placemat sets. Most supplies are donated. The initial cost of extra supplies for the napkin sets is $500. The initial cost of extra supplies for the placemats is $1,500. The napkin sets will sell for $8.00 each and the placemat sets will sell for $14.00 each. The time and staff for producing each product is the same.

a Write equations for the profit P for each product based upon the number N of items sold.

b The start-up cost for the placemat sets is much higher than for the napkin sets. Use a graphing calculator to determine the number of placemat sets that must be sold to make it more profitable to make placemats than napkins.

SOLUTION

a The profit equation for the napkins is $P = -500 + 8N$.

The profit equation for the placemats is $P = -1500 + 14N$.

b Rewrite the equations in terms of x and y.

$y = -500 + 8x$

$y = -1500 + 14x$

Use a graphing calculator to find the value of x (number of items) where the linear functions intersect. Experiment with windows, assuming that the intersection will be in the first quadrant. The window shown is an example of a useful setting.

```
Plot1  Plot2  Plot3          WINDOW
\Y1■ -500+8X                   Xmin=0
\Y2■ -1500+14X                 Xmax=200
\Y3=                           Xscl=1
\Y4=                           Ymin=0
\Y5=                           Ymax=1500
\Y6=                           Yscl=1
\Y7=                          ↓Xres=1
```

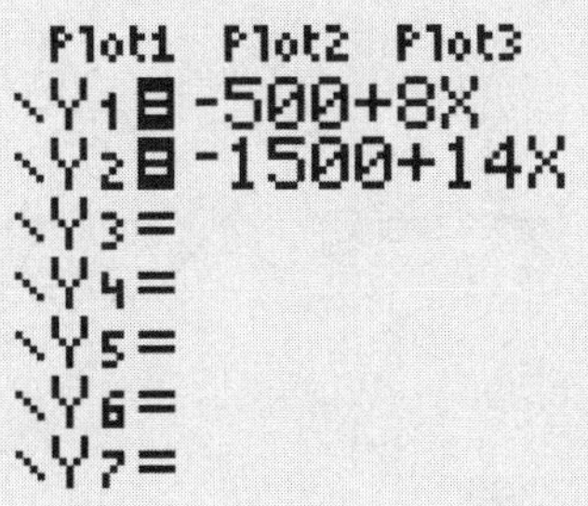

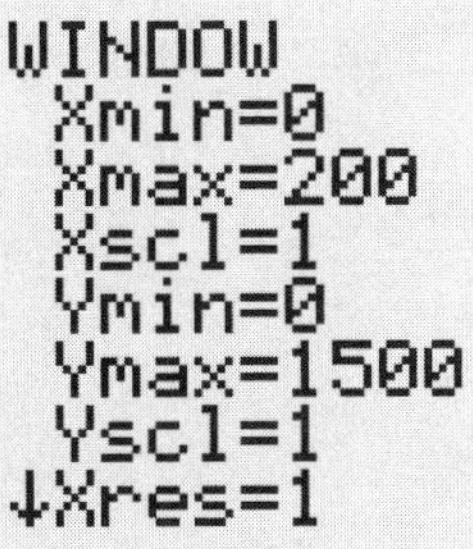

Press GRAPH.

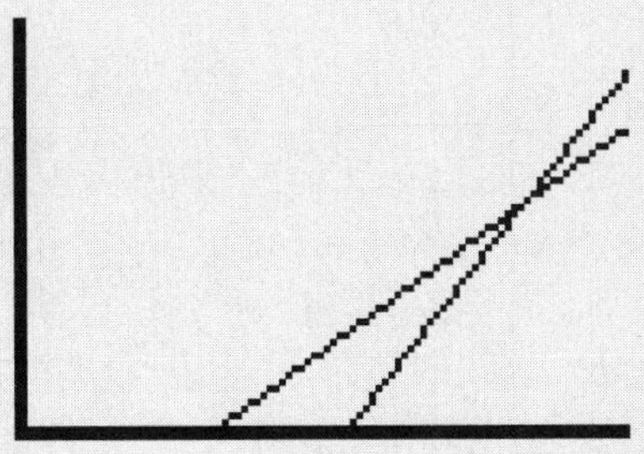

From 2nd [CALC], choose 5: Intersect and press ENTER. Continue to press ENTER until the intersection is shown in the lower border of the window.

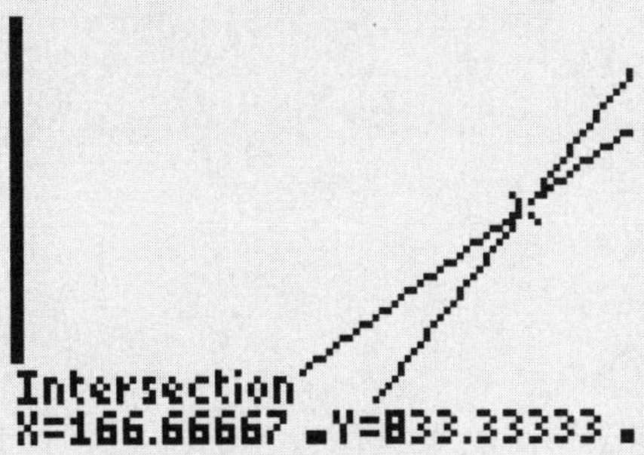

Answer: The group would have to sell at least 167 placemat sets for the profit for placemat sets to exceed the profit for napkin sets.

PRACTICE

1. 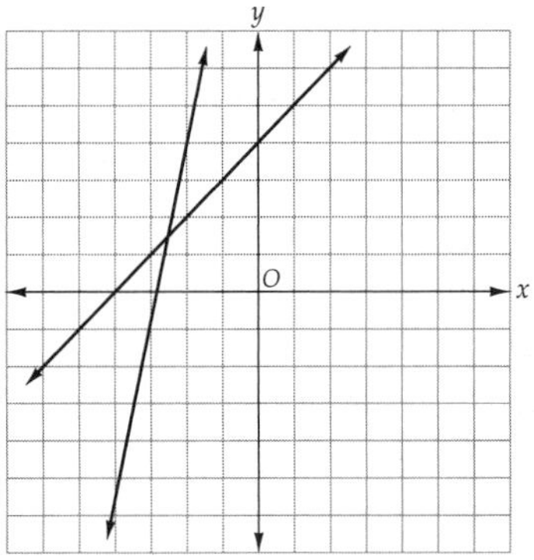

The system of equations represented by this graph is

A. consistent

B. inconsistent

C. dependent

D. codependent

2. 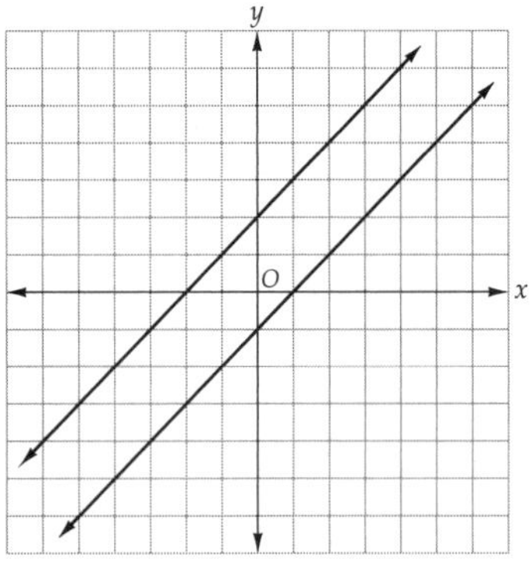

The system of equations represented by this graph is

A. consistent

B. inconsistent

C. dependent

D. codependent

3. The simultaneous solution to $y = 5$ and $y = 4x - 3$ is

A. (5, 17)

B. (2, 5)

C. (0, 5)

D. $\varnothing$, since the lines have different y-intercepts

4. The lines $y = 2x + 2$ and $y = 3x - 1$ intersect at point

A. $(-3, -8)$ C. $(1, 4)$

B. $(-1, -4)$ D. $(3, 8)$

Exercises 5–7: Identify each system of linear equations as *consistent* or *inconsistent*. Explain your reasoning.

5. 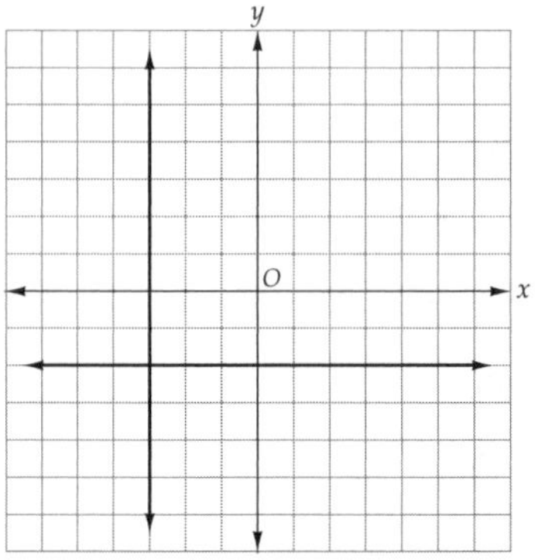

6. 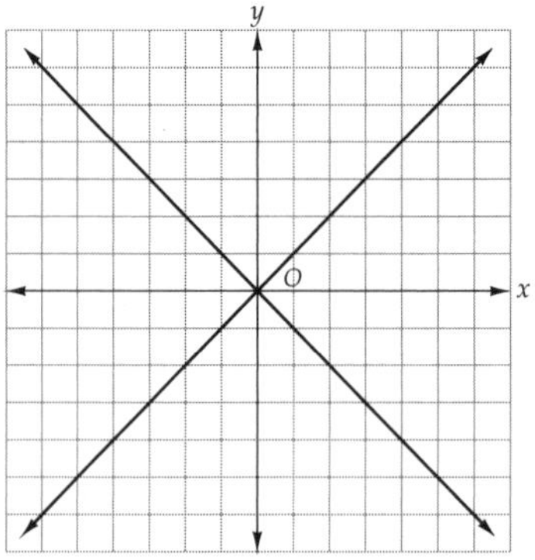

7. 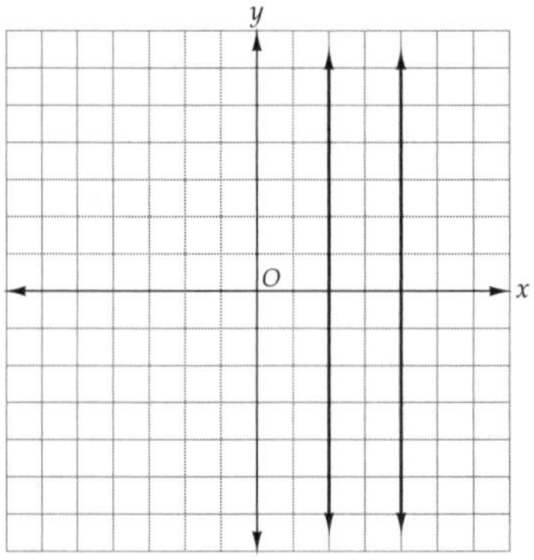

Practice Problems continue . . .

Exercises 8–21: Solve each system graphically. Check and state whether each system is *consistent*, *inconsistent*, or *dependent*.

8. $x + y = 4$
$y = 3x$

9. $y = -x + 7$
$y = 2x + 1$

10. $x - y = 4$
$y = \frac{1}{2}x$

11. $-2x + y = 1$
$-2x + y = 2$

12. $-2x + y = 1$
$2y = 4x + 2$

13. $2x + y = 2$
$y - x = 5$

14. $y - x = 2$
$y - 2x - 2 = 0$

15. $x = 0$
$y = -3$

16. $y = 3x - 3$
$y - 3x - 1 = 0$

17. $x + y = 1$
$-x + y = 1$

18. $y = \frac{1}{2}x + 4$
$2y = x - 6$

19. $2y = 4x - 6$
$4y + 12 = 8x$

20. $y = -3x$
$2x + y + 2 = 0$

21. $y = -2x - 1$
$x + y + 4 = 0$

Exercises 22–30: In the following problems:

a Write a system of two first-degree equations involving the variables x and y that represent the conditions stated.

b Solve the system graphically.

22. If the sum of two numbers is 13 and their difference is 7, what are the numbers?

23. The sum of two numbers is 8. If three times the first number is equal to the second number, find the numbers.

24. If five pencils and three erasers cost 65 cents, and three pencils and two erasers cost 40 cents, what is the cost of one pencil and one eraser?

25. If Robert has ten coins, all nickels and dimes, worth 70 cents, how many of each kind of coin does he have?

26. The difference between two numbers is 24, and the sum of those numbers is 48. What are the numbers?

27. The difference between two numbers is 4. If twice the larger number is equal to two more than three times the smaller number, what are the numbers?

28. The perimeter of a rectangle is 18. If the length is twice the width, what are the dimensions of the rectangle?

29. **MP 1, 2, 4** Rita joined the Venus gym with no initiation fee and a monthly charge of \$75. Robert joined the Mars gym with an initiation fee of \$60 and a monthly fee of \$50. After how many monthly payments will Rita have the less expensive total cost?

30. **MP 1, 2, 4** Carol and Harry rode go-carts around a National Park Service path. Carol rode at 12 miles per hour. Harry left 15 minutes later and rode at 16 miles per hour. After how many miles did Harry catch up to Carol?

LESSON 5.2

5.2 Solving Systems of Linear Equations by Substitution

Graphing systems may make for approximate solutions if the lines do not intersect at integer values. In this case, your answer will be an approximation. The **substitution method** or **elimination method** will give a precise solution.

To Solve Systems of Equations with the Substitution Method

- Solve one of the equations for one of the variables.
- Substitute the expression found in place of this variable in the second equation. You now have the second equation in one variable.
- Solve the second equation by isolating that one variable.
- Substitute the resulting value for that variable in either original equation.
- Solve for the other variable.
- Check by substituting both variable values in both equations.
- Your answer is typically an ordered pair if the system is consistent. However, the question may ask for something different. Always double-check to be certain of what was asked.

MODEL PROBLEMS

1. Solve this system of equations: $3x - 4y = 2$ and $x = 14 - 2y$

SOLUTION

Since the solutions are the same for each equation, $x = 14 - 2y$ is true in both equations.

Write the first equation.	$3x - 4y = 2$
Substitute $14 - 2y$ for x.	$3(14 - 2y) - 4y = 2$
Distribute the 3.	$42 - 6y - 4y = 2$
Combine like terms.	$42 - 10y = 2$
Add $10y$ to both sides.	$42 = 10y + 2$
Subtract 2 from both sides.	$40 = 10y$
Solve.	$4 = y$

Substitute 4 for y in either equation.

$x = 14 - 2y$

$x = 14 - 2(4)$

$x = 14 - 8 = 6$

Check by substituting 6 for x and 4 for y in both original equations.

$3x - 4y = 2$	$x = 14 - 2y$
$3(6) - 4(4) = 2$	$6 = 14 - 2(4)$
$18 - 16 = 2$ ✓	$6 = 14 - 8$ ✓

Answer: $(x, y) = (6, 4)$

Model Problems continue . . .

2. Henrietta has seven bills, all tens and twenties, that total \$100 in value. How many of each bill does she have?

SOLUTION

Let x represent the number of tens and y represent the number of twenties.

Henrietta's number of bills can be shown by $x + y = 7$.

The cash value of the bills can be shown by $10x + 20y = 100$.

Now we have the system $x + y = 7$ and $10x + 20y = 100$.

Write the first equation. $x + y = 7$

Solve for x.

$$\begin{aligned} x + y &= 7 \\ -y &= -y \\ \hline x &= 7 - y \end{aligned}$$

Write the second equation. $10x + 20y = 100$

Substitute $(7 - y)$ for x. $10(7 - y) + 20y = 100$

Solve.

$$\begin{aligned} 70 - 10y + 20y &= 100 \\ 70 + 10y &= 100 \\ -70 &= -70 \\ \hline 10y &= 30 \\ y &= 3 \end{aligned}$$

Substitute 3 for y in one of the original equations and solve for x.

$$\begin{aligned} x + y &= 7 \\ x + (3) &= 7 \\ -3 &= -3 \\ \hline x &= 4 \end{aligned}$$

To check, substitute 3 for y and 4 for x in each equation.

$$\begin{aligned} 10x + 20y &= 100 \\ 10(4) + 20(3) &= 100 \\ 40 + 60 &= 100 \checkmark \end{aligned} \qquad \begin{aligned} x + y &= 7 \\ 4 + 3 &= 7 \checkmark \end{aligned}$$

Check the original problem.

4 bills + 3 bills = 7 bills

$(4 \times 10) + (3 \times 20) = 40 + 60 = 100$

Answer: Henrietta has 4 ten-dollar bills and 3 twenty-dollar bills.

Model Problems continue . . .

Model Problems *continued*

3. **MP 3, 4** Larry is driving through a red light traveling at 40 miles per hour. Officer Ollie, traveling in the same direction, is 0.25 miles behind Larry and chasing him at 50 miles per hour. Larry will be out of Ollie's jurisdiction in two miles. Will Ollie catch Larry in time?

SOLUTION

We first have to find how far the men will travel when their distance, d, from Larry's current spot is the same. In order for Ollie to catch Larry, the distance Larry travels must be less than or equal to two miles.

For Larry: $d = 40t$ (distance in miles, time in hours)

For Ollie: $d = -0.25 + 50t$ (Ollie starts out 0.25 miles behind)

We want to find the distance, d. We set the two expressions equal to each other and solve for time, t.

$$-0.25 + 50t = 40t$$
$$\underline{+0.25 \quad = \quad +0.25}$$
$$50t = 40t + 0.25$$
$$\underline{-40t = -40t}$$
$$10t = 0.25$$
$$t = 0.025 \text{ hours}$$

Use the first equation to solve for d, using $t = 0.025$ hours: $d = 40t$

$$d = 40(0.025)$$
$$d = 1 \text{ mile}$$

Check in both equations:

$d = 40t$	$d = -0.25 + 50t$
$1 = 40(0.025)$	$1 = -0.25 + 50(0.025)$
$1 = 1$ ✓	$1 = 1$ ✓

Ollie catches Larry in one mile, and the jurisdiction line is two miles away.

Answer: Yes.

When you are solving word problems, be sure that your answer fits the problem, not just your equations.

PRACTICE

Exercises 1–16: Solve each system of equations by substitution, and check.

1. $y = 2x$
$x + y = 9$

2. $y = -3x$
$5x - y = 8$

3. $y = 2x$
$3x + 2y = 28$

4. $y = x - 3$
$2x + 3y = 16$

5. $x = y - 4$
$4y - 3x = 14$

6. $x + 2y = 10$
$2x - y = 5$

7. $x - 5y = 4$
$2x + 14 = y$

8. $x + y = 6$
$3x - 4y = 4$

9. $8x = 2y$
$2x + 3y = 42$

10. $y = -4x$
$x - 2y = 27$

11. $x = 2y + 14$
$y - 4x = 0$

Practice Problems continue . . .

12. $x = 2y - 13$
$3x + y = 3$

13. $x = 2 - 2y$
$2x - 3y = 25$

14. $x + 3y = 0$
$2x + 5y = 3$

15. $x + 3y = 9$
$4x + 5y = 22$

16. $4y - 3 = x$
$4x + 1 = 6y$

Exercises 17–28: Use x and y to identify clearly the unknowns in each problem. Set up a system of linear equations and solve each system algebraically. Check your answers.

17. The sum of two numbers is 78. Their difference is 18. Find the numbers.

18. The sum of two numbers is 24. If 4 less than 6 times the smaller number equals 5 more than 3 times the larger number, what are the numbers?

19. The sum of John and Harry's ages is 19 years. If the difference of their ages is 5 years, what are their ages?

20. The Chrysler Building is 491 feet taller than the Washington Monument. If the height of the Chrysler Building is 64 feet less than twice the height of the Washington Monument, how tall is each structure?

21. At an amusement park, the cost of 3 adult tickets and 4 children's tickets is $126.50. Another customer paid $120.50 for 2 adult tickets and 5 children's tickets. What is the price of each kind of ticket?

22. In the vote for school president, 476 seniors voted for one or the other of the two candidates. The candidate who won had a majority of 94. How many seniors voted for the winner?

23. The factory foreman makes $9 more per hour than Janet, the most senior worker. If one dollar is subtracted from the foreman's rate of pay, the resulting amount is $\frac{3}{2}$ of what Janet makes. Find the rate of pay for Janet and for the foreman.

24. Thomas has a collection of 25 coins; some are dimes and some are quarters. If the total value of all the coins is $5.05, how many of each kind of coin are there?

25. Carlos and Sam together unpacked cartons for 3 hours at a rate of 8 cartons per hour. During that time, Carlos unpacked twice as many cartons as Sam. How many cartons did each of them unpack?

26. In a vegetable store, a customer paid $8.80 for 3 pounds of tomatoes and 5 pounds of potatoes. A second customer paid $15.15 for 7 pounds of tomatoes and 6 pounds of potatoes. What is the *positive difference* in the price per pound of tomatoes and potatoes?

27. A motorist paid $26.50 for 10 gallons of gas and 2 quarts of oil. Another customer paid $23.58 for 8 gallons of gas and 3 quarts of oil. Find the cost of 1 gallon of gas and of 1 quart of oil.

28. Marie went out with $10.75 to cover the exact cost of a certain number of 25-cent stamps and 10-cent stamps. However, by mistake, she interchanged the number of 25-cent stamps and the 10-cent stamps and came back home with $3.30 in change. How many stamps of each kind was she supposed to buy?

29. **MP 3** A student was given the following two equations and asked to determine if they were equivalent: $n + \frac{m}{9} = \frac{1}{4}$ and $9n + m - \frac{1}{4} = 2$. Show how they are or are not equivalent. Explain your answer clearly.

Practice Problems continue . . .

30. Temperatures measured in degrees Celsius and degrees Fahrenheit are related by the formula $F = 1.8C + 32$, where F represents degrees Fahrenheit and C represents degrees Celsius. Jacques has a quick approximation: "Double the Celsius temperature and add 30 degrees." For what Celsius and Fahrenheit temperatures is his method exact?

31. MP 1, 2, 4 Riverview is 240 miles north of Lakeside. Seaford is 20 miles north of Lakeside. A red car left Riverview, traveling south toward Lakeside at 1.2 miles per minute. A white car left Seaford, traveling north at 1 mile per minute.

a Using d_r to represent the distance the red car is from Lakeside and d_w to represent the distance the white car is from Lakeside and t to represent time in minutes, write equations showing d_r and d_w in terms of t.

b After how many minutes will the two cars be the same distance from Lakeside?

32. MP 1, 2, 4 A chemist has a solution that is 40% acid and another solution that is 90% acid. He wants to make 100 milliliters (mL) of a 70% acid solution. How many mL of each solution should he use?

33. MP 1, 2, 4 A craft store sells solid beads at \$10 per pound and marble beads at \$15 per pound. The store wants to mix 200 pounds of beads and sell the mixture for \$12 per pound. How many pounds of each bead variety should they use?

LESSON 5.3

5.3 Solving Systems of Linear Equations by Elimination

Elimination is another way to solve a system of equations. It is particularly efficient when the coefficients of one variable are the same in both equations, or one is an integer multiple of the other.

To Solve Systems of Equations with the Elimination Method

- Rewrite the equations in the standard form of a linear equation, $Ax + By = C$.
- Line up the equations one under the other, so like terms lie in the same columns. You may need to rewrite one or more equations to get like terms in the same column.
- If like terms have opposite coefficients, such as $2x$ and $-2x$, you can simply add the equations to eliminate a variable.

- If no like terms match the description above, multiply one or both equations by constants, so the coefficients of the variable you want to eliminate are additive opposites. Add the columns. This will result in a single equation in one variable.
- Solve the resulting equation by isolating the variable.
- Substitute the resulting value into either *original* equation.
- Solve the resulting equation for the second variable.
- Check by substitution in *both original equations*.

If both variables cancel out when the columns are added, the system of equations is either inconsistent (parallel lines) or dependent (lines that coincide), so that a single solution is not possible.

MODEL PROBLEMS

1. Solve the system of equations $x + y = 8$ and $x - y = 2$.

SOLUTION

The equations are already in standard form, and the y terms are already opposites.

Set up the equations in columns.

$$\begin{array}{r} x + y = 8 \\ \underline{x - y = 2} \end{array}$$

Add the columns.

$$2x = 10$$

Solve for x.

$$\frac{2x}{2} = \frac{10}{2}$$

$$x = 5$$

Substitute 5 for x in the first equation.

$$(5) + y = 8$$

Solve for y.

$$\begin{array}{r} \underline{-5 \qquad = -5} \\ y = 3 \end{array}$$

Check. Substitute 5 for x and 3 for y in the original equations.

$$\begin{array}{rr} x + y = 8 & \qquad x - y = 2 \\ (5) + (3) = 8 & \qquad (5) - (3) = 2 \\ 8 = 8\checkmark & \qquad 2 = 2\checkmark \end{array}$$

Answer: (5, 3)

Model Problems continue . . .

2. Find the solution of the system $x - 2y = 1$ and $x + y = 10$.

SOLUTION

The coefficients of x are the same.

Write the first equation. $x - 2y = 1$

Multiply each term by -1. $(-1)x + (-1)(-2y) = (-1)1$

Simplify. $-x + 2y = -1$

Set up the equations in columns and add.

$$\begin{aligned} -x + 2y &= -1 \\ x + y &= 10 \\ \hline 3y &= 9 \end{aligned}$$

Solve. $y = 3$

Replace y in either equation.

$$\begin{aligned} x + y &= 10 \\ x + 3 &= 10 \\ x &= 7 \end{aligned}$$

Check by substituting 3 for y and 7 for x in both original equations.

$$\begin{aligned} x - 2y &= 1 \\ 7 - 2(3) &= 1 \\ 7 - 6 &= 1 \checkmark \end{aligned} \qquad \begin{aligned} x + y &= 10 \\ 7 + 3 &= 10 \checkmark \end{aligned}$$

Answer: $(x, y) = (7, 3)$

3. Solve the system $5x - 2y = 10$ and $2x + y = 31$.

SOLUTION

More work is involved to make the y coefficients cancel.

Write the second equation. $2x + y = 31$

Multiply each term by 2. $(2)2x + (2)y = (2)31$

Simplify. $4x + 2y = 62$

Set up the equations in columns and add.

$$\begin{aligned} 5x - 2y &= 10 \\ 4x + 2y &= 62 \\ \hline 9x &= 72 \end{aligned}$$

Solve. $x = 8$

Replace x in either equation.

$$\begin{aligned} 2x + y &= 31 \\ 2(8) + y &= 31 \\ 16 + y &= 31 \\ y &= 15 \end{aligned}$$

Check by substituting 15 for y and 8 for x in both original equations.

$$\begin{aligned} 5x - 2y &= 10 \\ 5(8) - 2(15) &= 10 \\ 40 - 30 &= 10 \checkmark \end{aligned} \qquad \begin{aligned} 2x + y &= 31 \\ 2(8) + (15) &= 31 \\ 16 + 15 &= 31 \checkmark \end{aligned}$$

Answer: $(x, y) = (8, 15)$

Model Problems continue . . .

Model Problems *continued*

4. **MP 2, 3, 4** Karlene invests \$3,900 at two different rates: 4% and 6%. If she receives a total of \$210 in annual interest from her two investments, how much does she invest at each rate? Reason about the number and nature of the solutions to the system. Determine the best method to solve the system. Check your answers.

SOLUTION

Step 1. We start by writing equations for the situation.
Let x = amount invested at 4%. $0.04x$ = annual income from 4% investment.
Let y = amount invested at 6%. $0.06y$ = annual income from 6% investment.
Then, $x + y = 3{,}900$ and $0.04x + 0.06y = 210$.

Step 2. Let's think about the number of solutions and the nature of the solutions. Looking at the coefficients of the variables in each equation, it is clear that the lines will be distinct. If we write the equation in slope-intercept form, we can see that the slope of the first equation is -1, since $y = -x + 3{,}900$, and the slope of the second equation is a different value. Therefore, we have a pair of consistent equations. We will find one solution.

Step 3. We can assume the values for x and y will be quite large. Graphing by hand would be difficult due to scaling considerations. The elimination technique is also difficult due to the mix of coefficients, some integer and some decimal. Clearly, the addition-subtraction method is the best choice.

Step 4. Solve the system of equations. More work is involved to make the x coefficients cancel.

Write the second equation.	$0.04x + 0.06y = 210$
Multiply each term by 100 to get rid of the decimals.	$(100)0.04x + (100)0.06y = (100)210$
Simplify.	$4x + 6y = 21{,}000$
Write the first equation.	$x + y = 3{,}900$
Multiply each term by 4.	$(4)x + (4)y = (4)3{,}900$
Simplify.	$4x + 4y = 15{,}600$
Set up the equations in columns and subtract equation #2 from #1.	$4x + 6y = 21{,}000$ $-(4x + 4y = 15{,}600)$ $2y = 5{,}400$
Solve.	$y = 2{,}700$
Replace y in either equation.	$x + y = 3{,}900$ $x + 2{,}700 = 3{,}900$ $x = 1{,}200$

Step 5. Check by substituting 2,700 for y and 1,200 for x in both original equations.

$x + y = 3{,}900$	$0.04x + 0.06y = 210$
$1{,}200 + 2{,}700 = 3{,}900$	$0.04(1{,}200) + 0.06(2{,}700) = 210$
$3{,}900 = 3{,}900$ ✓	$48 + 162 = 210$
	$210 = 210$ ✓

PRACTICE

Exercises 1–20: Find the ordered pair (x, y) that satisfies each system, and check.

1. $x + y = 5$
$2x - y = 7$

2. $2x + 3y = 2$
$4x + 3y = 3$

3. $x - 3y = 1$
$2x + 3y = 20$

4. $4x - y = 8$
$4x - 3y = 8$

5. $5x + y = 15$
$3x + y = 11$

6. $2x - 5y = 7$
$4x - 5y = 19$

7. $2x - 3y = -4$
$2x + 5y = 12$

8. $-5x - 4y = 23$
$2x - 4y = 2$

9. $6x + 2y = 18$
$3x - 2y = 6$

10. $2x + y = 6$
$5x + 3y = 17$

11. $2x + 3y = 5$
$5x - 4y = 2$

12. $x + 7y = 15$
$2x + 9y = 20$

13. $3x + 5y = 7$
$7x - y = 29$

14. $x + y = 4$
$2x + 3y = 7$

15. $7x - 2y = 39$
$5x = 21 - 2y$

16. $6(x + y) = 12$
$x = 6y - 6$

17. $7x - 2y = 2$
$3x + 4y = 30$

18. $3x - 2y = -5$
$5x + 2y = -19$

19. $4x + y = 12$
$2x - \frac{1}{2}y = 2$

20. $x + y = 1{,}500$
$0.04x + 0.06y = 74$

MP 1, 2, 4 Exercises 21–30:

a Write a system of two first-degree equations involving the variables x and y that represent the conditions stated.

b Solve the system algebraically, and check.

21. George invested \$2,000 at two different rates, 5% and 6%. If his total interest income was \$106, how much did he invest at each rate?

22. Pauline invested \$10,000 at two different rates, 4% and 6%. If her total interest income was \$470, how much did she invest at each rate?

23. Amanda made two different investments that totaled \$6,000. The rate for one investment was 4.5%, while the other was 7.5%. If the total return on these investments came to \$366, how much was invested at each rate?

24. If two angles are complementary and the measure of one is 36° more than the measure of the other, what is the measure of each angle?

25. Two angles are supplementary. If the measure of the first angle is twice the measure of the second, what is the measure of each angle?

26. The perimeter of a rectangular garden is 320 yards. If the length is 8 yards less than 3 times the width, what are the dimensions of the garden?

27. To raise money, a high school musical sold adult and student tickets. The cost of an adult ticket was \$6.20 and the cost of a student ticket was \$3.00. The number of student tickets sold was 50 more than twice the number of adult tickets sold. If the total income was \$4,237, how many of each type of ticket were sold?

Practice Problems continue . . .

28. Two angles are supplementary. If the degree measure of the larger angle is 60 less than twice the measure of the smaller angle, what is the degree measure of each angle?

29. Derek invested some money at 5% interest and another amount at 8.25% interest. The amount invested at 5% was $1,000 more than the amount invested at 8.25%. If the total interest income at the end of one year from these two investments was $315, how much was invested at each rate?

30. Kate deposited x dollars in a bank paying 8.5% interest and y dollars at a second bank paying 10.75% interest. If the x amount was $4,000 less than twice the y amount, and the total interest income for one year was $1,880, how much money did she invest at each rate?

LESSON 5.4

5.4 Solving Systems of Linear Inequalities by Graphing

The graph of the solution of a system of linear inequalities is the shaded region of the plane containing all points that are common solutions of all the inequalities in the system.

To Find the Solution Set of a System of Two Linear Inequalities

- Solve each inequality for y.
- Identify slope and y-intercept and graph the boundary lines for each inequality.
- The boundary line is solid if the inequality symbol is $\leq$ or $\geq$ and is broken or dashed if the inequality symbol is $<$ or $>$.
- Shade the correct *half plane* for each inequality.
- Shade the common region shaded by both half planes and label with a capital letter, such as S, for *solution*.
- If the two regions do not overlap, indicate that there is no solution.
- Make sure the shaded common region conforms to the constraints of the problem.

MODEL PROBLEMS

1. Graph the following system of inequalities and label the solution set S:

$y > x + 4; x + y \leq 0$

SOLUTION

The graph of $y > x + 4$ is a dashed line, with y-intercept or $b = 4$ and a slope of $m = 1$. The shading is above the line.

The second inequality $x + y \leq 0$, must be rewritten as $y \leq -x$. The graph is a solid line, with y-intercept at the origin or $b = 0$ and a slope of $m = -1$. The shading is below the line.

The solution to the system is the common region, marked S.

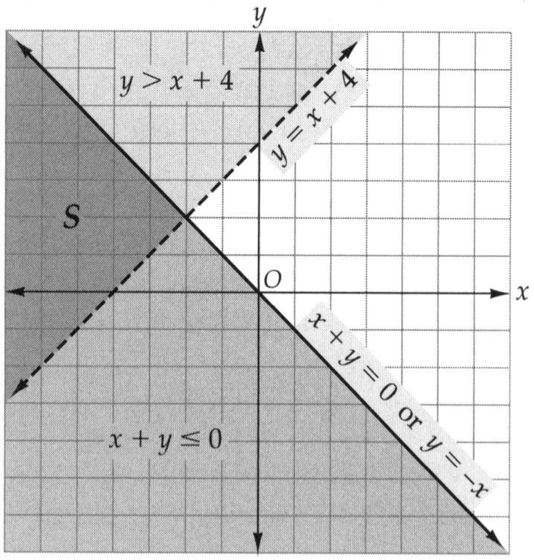

2. **MP 1, 2, 4, 5** On Fridays, every child admitted to the game room at Billy's Beach Shack must bring at least one adult. Fire codes restrict the number of people in the game room to 80.

- **a** Show all allowable combinations of adults and children on a graph.
- **b** Show on the graph and name a combination that is allowable according to the chaperone rule but not the fire code.
- **c** Show on the graph and name a combination that is not allowable according to the chaperone rule but okay under the fire code.
- **d** Show on the graph and name a combination that is allowable according to both the chaperone rule and fire code.

SOLUTION

a Let A = number of adults. Let C = number of children.
Since every child must be accompanied by an adult, $A \geq C$.
The fire code tells us that $A + C \leq 80$ or $A \leq -C + 80$.

We will use the calculator for this graph. Substitute y for A and x for C. We know the maximum number of people is 80, so the window is set for all first quadrant, extending slightly beyond 80.

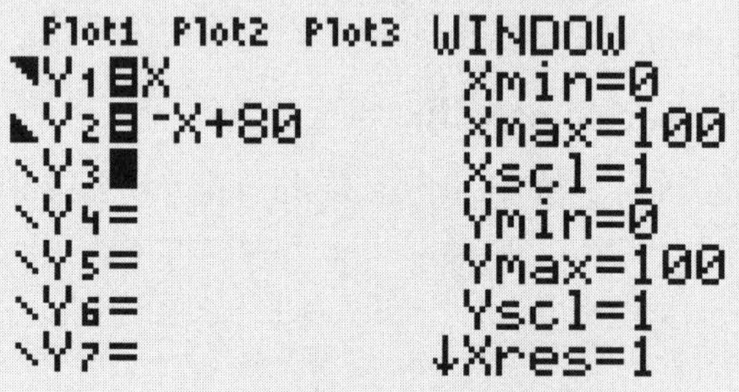

Using the trace key and the intersect function in y, we get the anticipated results. There can be no more than 40 children, in which case each adult is accompanied by exactly one child.

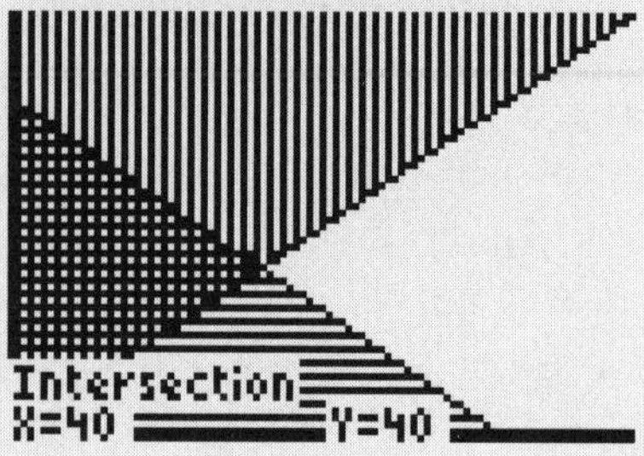

b All combinations that are solutions to the chaperone rule, but not solutions to the fire code, are correct answers. One example is (40, 45).

c All combinations that are solutions to the fire code, but not the chaperone rule, are correct answers. One example is (35, 20).

d All combinations that are solutions to both the fire code and chaperone rule are solutions. One example is (26, 40).

PRACTICE

1. Which graph shows the solution to the system $y \geq -3x + 2$ and $x < 0$?

A.

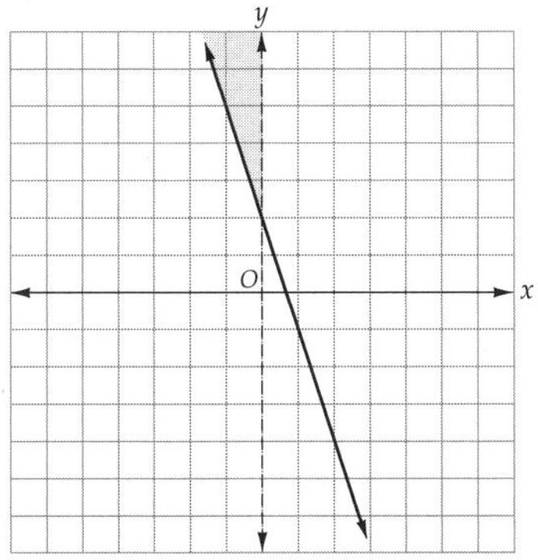

B.

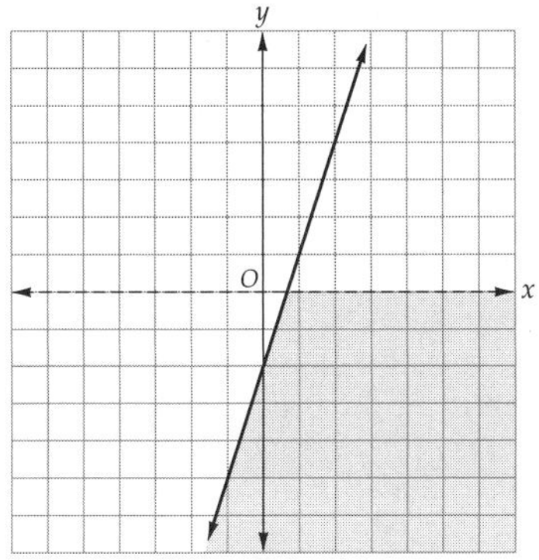

C.

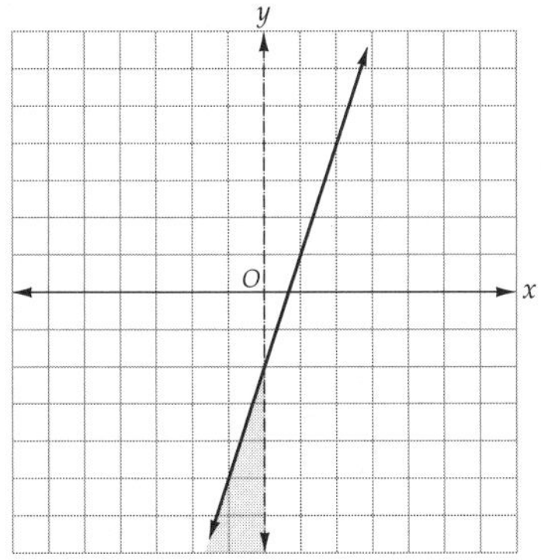

D.

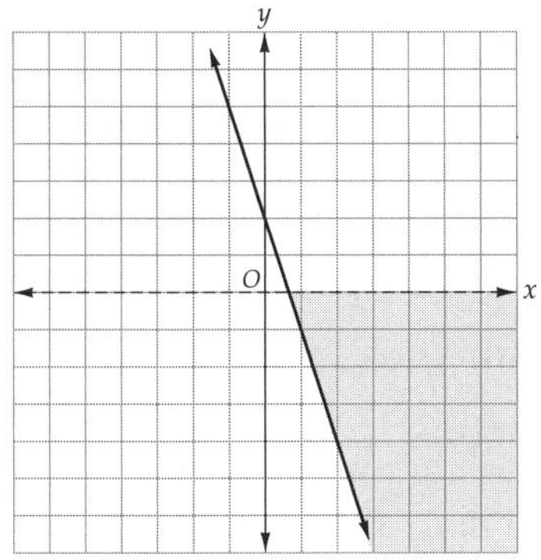

2. Which graph shows the solution set of $y \leq 1$ and $x + y \geq 2$?

A.

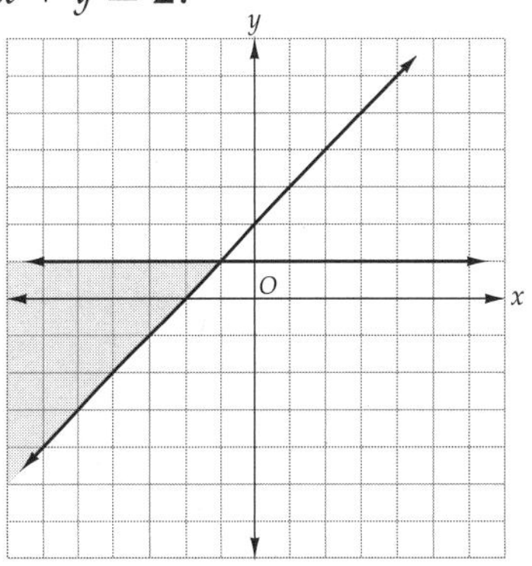

B.

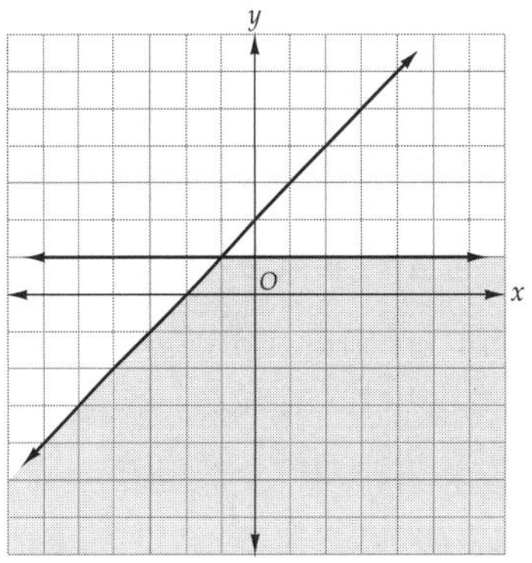

C.

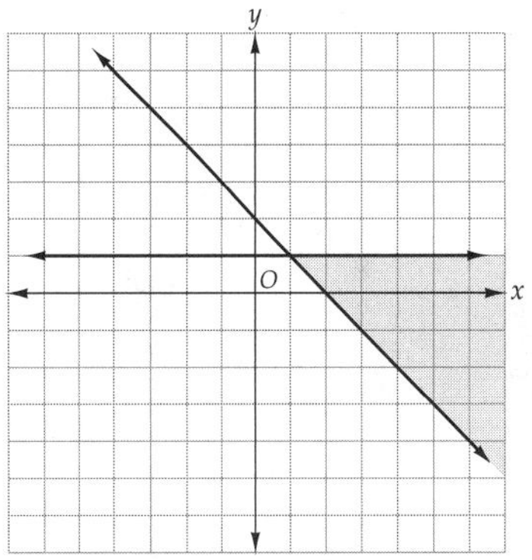

D.

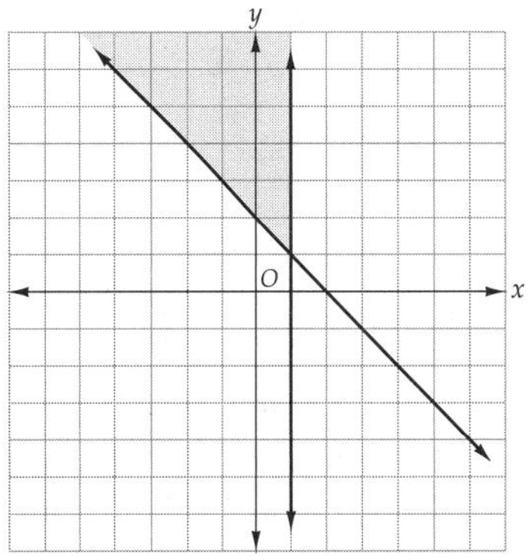

Practice Problems continue . . .

3. Which set of inequalities describes the shaded area of the graph?

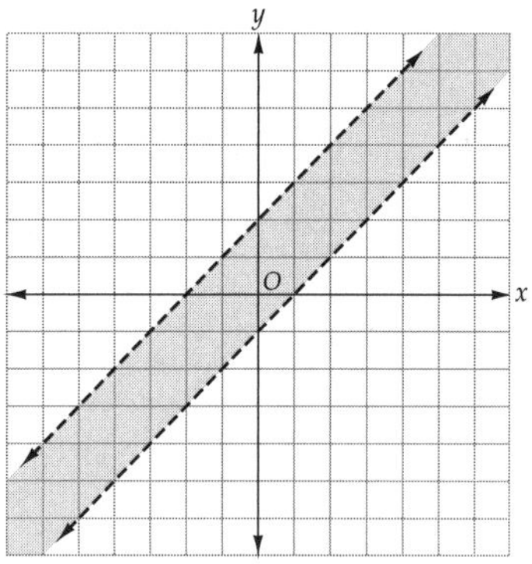

A. $y > x - 1$ and $y < x + 2$

B. $y < x - 1$ and $y > x + 2$

C. $y < x - 1$ or $y > x + 2$

D. $y > -1$ and $y < 2$

4. Which set of inequalities describes the shaded area of the graph?

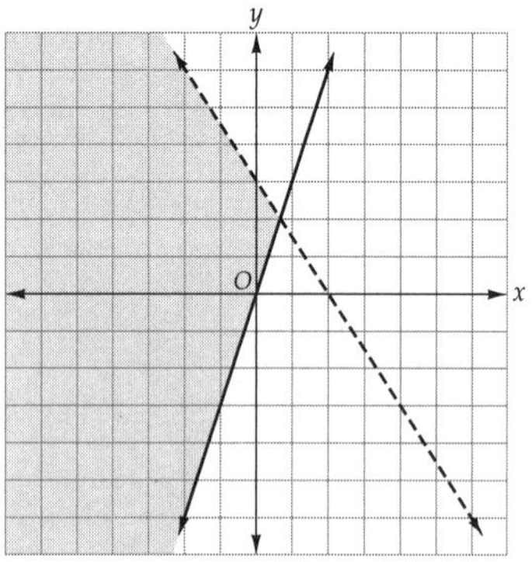

A. $y < 3x$ and $y \geq -\frac{3}{2}x + 3$

B. $y > \frac{1}{3}x$ and $y \geq -\frac{3}{2}x - 3$

C. $y \leq 3x$ and $y < -\frac{3}{2}x + 3$

D. $y \geq 3x$ and $y < -\frac{3}{2}x + 3$

Exercises 5–20: Graph each system of inequalities and label the solution set *S*. Pick a point in the solution set, if any, and verify that it satisfies both inequalities.

5. $y > x - 3$
$y < x + 5$

6. $y > -2x - 8$
$x - y > 1$

7. $y < x$
$y > 0$

8. $y \geq x + 5$
$x > -5$

9. $x + y < 7$
$x - y > 3$

10. $y > -x$
$x + 2y < 4$

11. $x + y \geq -2$
$3x + 2y > 1$

12. $y > 2x + 1$
$y < x - 2$

13. $2x + 3y > 6$
$x - y < 2$

14. $x \geq 2$
$y \leq x$

15. $2y - 4x > -6$
$3y - x \leq -9$

16. $x \geq 4$
$y \geq 4$

17. $-2x - y \leq 1$
$y \leq -3$

18. $y < \frac{3}{2}x - 2$
$y < -x + 3$

19. $3x - 3 \leq y \leq \frac{1}{2}x - 3$

20. $y \geq -2x + 5$
$x \leq 5$
$y \leq 4$

21. On Friday, every adult admitted to the Play as You Eat Restaurant must be accompanied by *at least* one child. The restaurant has a safety seating capacity of 100 diners.

a What are the variables?

b What are the constraints?

c Write the inequalities for the constraints.

d Graph the inequalities and shade the solution set showing all possible combinations of adults and children.

Practice Problems continue . . .

22. At a Math Day for small children, every child must be with an adult and every adult must bring at least 1 child but no more than 3. Fire laws limit the number of people to 180. Graph all possible combinations of adults and children.

a What are the variables?

b What are the constraints?

c Write the inequalities for the constraints.

d Graph the inequalities and shade the solution set showing all possible combinations of adults and children.

23. MP 7

a Write a system that represents the graph shown below.

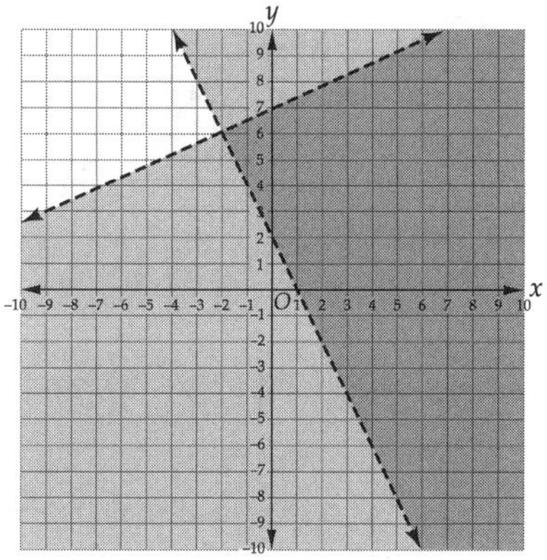

b Rewrite your system so that the solution now lies in the unshaded region.

c Write a system for which $(-2, 6)$ is the only solution.

24. MP 1, 2, 4, 5, 6 Write a system of inequalities to create a shaded triangular solution with vertices at $(1, 1)$, $(5, 9)$, and $(3, -3)$. Draw the graph.

25. MP 1, 2, 4, 5, 6 The Care Club has 25 cups of flour to make cookies and tarts. They can get as much as they need of other ingredients. A tray of cookies requires 2 cups of flour; a tray of tarts requires 1 cup of flour. It takes one-half hour to make a tray of cookies and 1 hour to make a tray of tarts. The club can allocate 10 hours to the project.

a What are the variables?

b What are the constraints?

c Write the inequalities for the constraints.

d Graph the inequalities and shade the solution set showing all possible combinations of trays of cookies and trays of tarts.

e Suppose the Care Club can sell a tray of cookies for \$2.00 and a tray of tarts for \$5.00. How would the club decide how many trays of each dessert to make?

26. Graph $x - 2y > 0$, $x + y \geq 4$, and $x \leq 3$. Is the point $(3, 1)$ in the solution set?

CHAPTER 5 REVIEW

1. You want to solve the system below by eliminating y. You multiply the first equation by 7. By what number should you multiply the second equation?

$2x - 5y = 1$

$-3x + 7y = -3$

A. -7

B. -5

C. 5

D. 7

2. What is the solution to this system of equations?

$2x + y = 7$

$3x - y = 3$

A. $(4, 1)$

B. $(2, -1)$

C. $(2, 3)$

D. $(3, 2)$

Chapter Review continues . . .

3. Prestige Parking charges $5 for the first hour or any part of that hour and $3 for each additional hour or part of an hour. Paradise Parking charges $8 for the first hour or any part of that hour and $1.50 for each additional hour or part of an hour. For how many hours of parking will the charge be the same in both garages?

A. From 1 hour and 1 minute to 2 hours

B. From 2 hours and 1 minute to 3 hours

C. From 3 hours and 1 minute to 4 hours

D. From 4 hours and 1 minute to 5 hours

4. MP 1, 4 A circus act has 3 times as many elephants as acrobats. Jorge noticed that all together, there were 56 legs in the circus ring. How many elephants were in the show?

5. Write the point-slope form of a line where m is the slope and the point is (x_1, y_1).

6. Graph the linear function f defined by $y = f(x) = 3x - 1$ by using the slope and y-intercept.

7. Describe the graph of a constant function. Give two different examples.

8. Use the x- and y-intercepts to graph the line $3x - 2y = 6$.

Exercises 9–11: Identify the slope and y-intercept.

9. $y = \frac{3}{5}x - 7$

10. $y + x - 8 = 0$

11. $x = -4$

Exercises 12–15: Write an equation of the line that satisfies the given conditions.

12. $m = \frac{2}{3}$, and y-intercept $(0, -2)$

13. slope $= -\frac{1}{3}$, and passing through $(9, 2)$

14. Passing through the points $(3, -2)$ and $(1, 6)$

15. Perpendicular to $3x + y - 1 = 0$ and passing through $(3, -1)$

16. Write an equation of the line passing through the point $(2, -3)$ and

a parallel to the x-axis

b parallel to the y-axis

17. Write an equation in point-slope form of a line with $m = 5$ and that passes through the point $(-1, 1)$. Verify that $(-2, -4)$ is on that line.

Exercises 18–19: Select the equation whose graph would *not* be parallel to the other two.

18. $2x - y = 9; 2y - x = 7; 2x - y = 2$

19. $x + 3y = 7; 3x + y = 7; y = 7 - 3x$

20. Write an equation of the line passing through the points $(2, -3)$ and $(3, -1)$ in

a point-slope form

b slope-intercept form

c general linear form $Ax + By = C$

21. The x- and y-intercepts of a line are $(-5, 0)$ and $(0, -2)$. Write a linear equation for the line in the form $y = mx + b$.

22. Find the x- and y-intercepts of the equation $5x - y - 5 = 0$.

Exercises 23–25: Solve the systems of equations graphically, and check.

23. $y = -2x$
$3x - y = 5$

24. $x - y = 5$
$y = -2x + 4$

25. $3x + 2y = -5$
$2x + 4y = 2$

26. MP 3 Explain how to identify if a system is *consistent*, *inconsistent*, or *dependent* without solving.

Chapter Review continues . . .

Exercises 27–30: Find the ordered pair (x, y) that satisfies each system (if possible) and check. Identify the system of linear equations as *consistent*, *inconsistent*, or *dependent*.

27. $5x + 3y = 12$
$x + 2y = 8$

28. $2y = 2x + 2$
$-x + y = 1$

29. $x + 2y = 0$
$3x - 2y = 16$

30. $3x + 12 = y$
$8x - 2y = 40$

31. On the same coordinate axes, graph the system of inequalities. Pick a point in the solution set, if any, and verify that it satisfies both inequalities.

$x - y > 3$
$x - y < -2$

32. Graph the following inequalities on the same coordinate plane.

$x - y \leq 2; 2x + 3y \geq 9$

Find the following points:

a a point *not* in either solution set

b a point that lies in only $x - y \leq 2$

c a point that lies in only $2x + 3y \geq 9$

d a point in the solution set that satisfies both inequalities

33. If Josh has 8 quarters and dimes with a combined value of \$1.25, how many quarters and dimes does he have?

34. Three times Simon's age is 58 more than Max's age. One-third the sum of their ages is 10 less than Simon's age. What are their ages?

35. The difference between two numbers is 2. When the sum of the smaller number plus 3 is multiplied by 3, the result is equal to two times the sum of the larger number and 2. Find the numbers.

36. Graph the following set of inequalities and record one point in the solution set.

$x \geq 0; y < 3; 2x + y > 5$

37. **MP 1, 2, 4** Valerie stayed at a working farm for 30 days. She received \$25 for each day she worked, but she had to pay \$3 for each day she did not work. At the end of her stay, she was \$498 richer than when she started. For how many days did she work?

38. **MP 1, 2, 4, 5, 6** There is a simple formula you can use to discover your maximum pulse rate when you work out. Just take 220 and subtract your age. If you are 14 years old, then your maximum pulse rate would be 206, but it is dangerous to maintain that heart rate. A safe range is between 50% and 80% of your maximum.

a Write an equation relating age and maximum pulse rate during exercise.

b Write an inequality for the recommended high pulse rate during exercise.

c Write an inequality for the recommended low pulse rate during exercise.

d Graph the safe workout pulse range for people of any age.

e Select and justify an appropriate domain for this problem.

39. At the town Fourth of July fireworks show, every child must be with an adult, and every adult may bring at most two children. The show arena can safely seat 240 people. Graph all combinations of parents and children the event can accommodate.

Chapter Review continues . . .

40. MP 1 Consider two linear equations.

The graph of $f(x)$ is shown below.

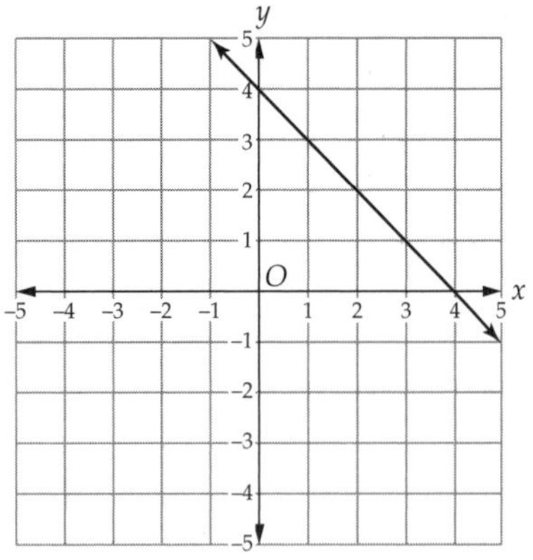

Some values of $g(x)$ are shown in the table.

x	−3	0	3	6	9
$g(x)$	−5	−4	−3	−2	−1

a Find the common solution for the two linear equations.

b Name one point that is a solution to $f(x)$ and not $g(x)$.

41. Ninth- and tenth-graders went to a school assembly. All together, there were 880 students. There were 30 more ninth-graders than tenth-graders. Using elimination, find the number of ninth-graders and tenth-graders, and then solve again using substitution.

42. MP 1, 2, 4 Sam had 4 times as many model cars as his friend Peter. After Sam gave away half his cars and Peter bought 10 more cars, they each had an equal number of cars. Write a system to describe the situation, and solve the system. Solve the problem another way by drawing a diagram.

Cumulative Review for Chapters 1–5

1. MP 6 Two racing karts practiced for a competition. Kart A traveled at 40 miles per hour. Kart B traveled at 60 feet per second. Which statement is true?

   A. Kart A traveled $\frac{2}{3}$ the speed of Kart B.

   B. Kart B traveled $\frac{2}{3}$ the speed of Kart A.

   C. Kart A traveled slightly faster than Kart B.

   D. Kart B traveled slightly faster than Kart A.

2. MP 1, 2, 4 Household cleaners are often mixed with water. Information about four products is listed below. The concentration indicates the percent of active cleaning ingredient in the product. Rank the cost per fluid ounce of active cleaning ingredient from least to greatest.

	Concentration	Fluid Ounces in the Container	Price of the Container
Miss Magic	6%	128	$11.99
Shiny Sheen	22%	64	$15.99
Tough Thomas	35%	32	$12.99

   A. Shiny Sheen < Tough Thomas < Miss Magic

   B. Tough Thomas < Shiny Sheen < Miss Magic

   C. Miss Magic < Tough Thomas < Shiny Sheen

   D. Miss Magic < Shiny Sheen < Tough Thomas

3. The height, S, of a ball thrown straight up in the air is given by the product of -16 and the time in seconds squared, plus the product of the initial velocity in feet per second and time in seconds, plus the initial height in feet. Let t = time, v = initial velocity, and h = initial height. Then S =

   A. $16t^2 + vt + h$

   B. $-16t^2 + vt + h$

   C. $-16t + t(v + h)$

   D. $-16t + vt^2 + h$

4. The price of a pet sitter is $40 plus $8 per half hour. If Diana uses the pet sitter for h hours, which of the following algebraic expressions represents the cost?

   A. $40 + \frac{8h}{2}$

   B. $40 + 16h$

   C. $48h$

   D. $56h$

5. The solution set for $-3(x - 7) - 2x < -9$ is

   A. $x > -\frac{12}{5}$

   B. $x < 10$

   C. $x < 6$

   D. $x > 6$

6. Cristina bought a bag of coffee for $8.47. The weight of the bag was $\frac{7}{8}$ of a pound. What was the price, per pound, of the coffee?

   A. $9.68

   B. $15.13

   C. $7.41

   D. $9.35

7. Which pair of lines are *not* perpendicular?

A. $y = 3x + 2$ and $y = -3x + 2$

B. $y = 2x + 7$ and $y = -0.5x + 1$

C. $2y = 3x - 6$ and $3y + 2x = 0$

D. $y = 8$ and $x = 8$

8. Write an equation of the line containing the points $(1, -7)$ and $(-2, 5)$.

A. $y = -4x - 11$

B. $y = -4x - 3$

C. $y = 4x - 11$

D. $y = 4x + 13$

9. What are the x- and y-intercepts of $y = \frac{2}{3}x + 2$?

A. $(0, -3)$ and $(2, 0)$

B. $(0, 3)$ and $(0, -2)$

C. $(3, 0)$ and $(0, -2)$

D. $(-3, 0)$ and $(0, 2)$

10. Which is a ratio comparing 6 hours to 2 days?

A. 6 to 2

B. 6 to 48

C. 24 to 2

D. 12 to 1

11. The price of a dozen plants is $30. At that rate, how many plants can you buy for $12.50?

A. 4

B. 5

C. 6

D. 8

12. Find the solution to the equations
$12x - 4y = 24$
$6x + 2y = -2$

A. $x = \frac{5}{6}, y = -3\frac{1}{2}$

B. $x = 0.4, y = -3.6$

C. $x = \frac{10}{7}, y = 5$

D. $x = 1.1, y = 2$

13. A newspaper delivery service uses a car and a van to deliver newspapers. The car can hold *a* newspapers and the van can hold *b* newspapers. Last month, the car was used *c* days and the van was used *v* days. Which expression represents how many newspapers were delivered last month?

A. $c + v$

B. $a + b$

C. $ac + bv$

D. $\frac{ac + bv}{a + c}$

14. Solve: $2|x - 5| + 2 = 6$

15. Solve: $6 - 3x > 12 - x$

16. Solve: $|x + 3| - 2 > 5$

17. If the domain is $\{-1.5, -0.7, 0, 1.8, 2\}$, find the range for $f(x)$ when $f(x) = [2x] - |x|$.

18. The table below shows values for the linear function $g(x)$. Write the equation for the function.

x	-4	-2	2	4
$g(x)$	9	5	-3	-7

19. Write an equation for a line parallel to the line $y = 3x - 4$ and passing through the point $(-2, 0)$.

20. MP 2, 4, 5 Marc rode his bicycle on the bike path through a state park. He traveled at 15 miles per hour for 1 hour, rested for 1 hour, and then continued riding at ten miles per hour for another 2 hours. Sketch a position-time graph showing Marc's trip.

21. MP 3, 7 The area of a rectangular garden is 60 ft^2. The length is an irrational number. Explain why or why not the width must be a fraction, whole number, irrational number, or non-real number.

22. MP 2, 3, 4 The number of members at the beach club is represented by $f(t) = 0.25|t - 60| + 20$ where t is the number of minutes since the facility opened at 11:00 A.M.

a What is the minimum number of members at the club? Explain.

b At what time do you expect to find the fewest number of members present? Explain.

c At what times would you expect 25 members to be present? Explain.

d How many members would you expect when the club opens each day? Explain.

23. MP 1, 2, 4 Jose decided to join a gym. The Training Station charges $48 to join and $59 each month. Giant Gym has no joining fee, but charges $65 each month.

a Which gym should Jose join?

b If Jose made his decision on January 1 and has a poor record of keeping New Year's resolutions, does that change your answer to part **a**?

c How many months does Jose need to keep his resolution for Giant Gym to be more expensive?

24. A function is defined as follows:

$$f(x) = \begin{cases} \frac{x}{2} \text{ if } x < 0 \\ 2x \text{ if } x > 0 \end{cases}$$

a Graph the function.

b Find the value of $f(-4) + f(0.5)$.

25. MP 4, 5, 6 A saw is used to make a notch in a 20-centimeter-tall piece of wood. It cuts down a centimeter for every centimeter it moves to the right until it has moved down 16 centimeters, the desired location of a notch. It then moves up a centimeter for every centimeter it moves to the right.

a Graph the saw position function first in order to recognize it. The input of the function, x, is the distance that the saw has moved to the right, and the output of the function, $f(x)$, is the height of the cut from the bottom of the piece of wood.

b Describe its path with a function.

Chapter 6 Operations with Polynomials

Chapter Focus

In this chapter we will learn to perform operations [+, −, ×, ÷] with polynomials. In the process, we will apply the rules of exponents for positive and negative integers in order to rewrite and simplify algebraic expressions. We will also use our skills with polynomial operations in working with word problems.

Chapter Content

Chapter Vocabulary

binomial	**monomial**	**square of a binomial**
box method	**perfect square trinomial**	**standard form of a polynomial**
difference of two squares	**polynomial**	**trinomial**
FOIL method		

LESSON 6.1

6.1 Adding and Subtracting Polynomials

A *term* is an algebraic expression written as the product or quotient of numbers, variables, or both. A term that has no variables is often called a *constant*.

- 5, x, cd, $6mx$, $\frac{4x^2y}{-3m^3}$ are all terms. Of these, 5 is a constant.

An algebraic expression of exactly one term is called a **monomial**.

- Examples of monomials include 7, a, and $2x^2$.

Like terms contain the *same variables* with corresponding variables having the *same exponents*. Terms are separated by plus (+) and minus (−) signs.

- $7x^3y^4$ and x^3y^4 are like terms; 5 and 100 are like terms. y and x are not like terms; n and n^3 are not like terms.

Since algebraic expressions themselves represent numbers, they can be added, subtracted, multiplied, and divided. When algebraic expressions are added or subtracted, they can be combined only if they have like terms.

Adding or Subtracting Monomials with Like Terms

A monomial is an expression of the form ax^n, where a represents a real number and n represents a positive integer. The real number a is the *coefficient*, and the number n is called the *degree of the monomial*.

For example:

- $7x^2$ has a coefficient of 7 and degree of 2.
- $-9m$ has a coefficient of −9 and degree of 1.
- k has a coefficient of 1 and degree of 1.
- 24 has a degree of 0, since $24 = 24x^0$.

A monomial with a degree of 0 is a constant.

If more than one variable appears in a term, such as $6x^2y^3$, the degree of the monomial is the number of variable factors. The monomial $6x^2y^3$ can be written as $6 \bullet x \bullet x \bullet y \bullet y \bullet y$, so it has five variable factors and its degree is 5.

For example:

- $8x^4y^3$ is a monomial that has a coefficient of 8 and degree of $4 + 3$ or 7.
- $5xm^3$ is a monomial that has a coefficient of 5 and degree of $1 + 3$ or 4.

To find the degree of a multivariable term, sum the exponents of the variables.

To Add or Subtract Monomials with Like Terms

- Use the distributive property and the rules of signed numbers to add or subtract the coefficients of each term.
- Write this sum with the variable part from the terms.

MODEL PROBLEMS

1. MP 7 Show how to add $-2x^3$ and $5x^3$ using the distributive property.

SOLUTION

$-2x^3 + 5x^3 = (-2 + 5)x^3 = 3x^3$

2. MP 7 Show how to subtract $7mn^2$ from $4mn^2$ using the distributive property.

SOLUTION

$4mn^2 - 7mn^2 = (4 - 7)mn^2 = -3mn^2$

Standard Form of Polynomials

An algebraic expression of one or more unlike terms is a **polynomial**. **Binomials** are polynomials with *two* unlike terms. $7v + 9$ and $3x^2 - 8y$ are both binomials. **Trinomials** are polynomials with *three* unlike terms. $x^2 - 3x - 5$ and $3a^2bx - 5ax - 2ab$ are both trinomials.

A polynomial with one variable is said to be in **standard form** when it has no like terms and is written in order of descending exponents. For example, $4x + 9 - 5x^2 + 3x^3$ in standard form is $3x^3 - 5x^2 + 4x + 9$.

To Write a Polynomial in Standard Form

- Combine like terms.
- Arrange the terms in order of descending exponents. The "+" and "−" signs belong to the coefficient to the right of the sign. When you are arranging the terms, treat the terms as positive or negative based on the sign in front of the term.

When you are asked to *simplify* a polynomial, you should always write it in standard form.

The *degree of a polynomial* is the degree of the term with the greatest degree.

For example:

- $-2x^5 + 3x^3 + 6x^2 + 8$ is a polynomial of degree 5, taken from x^5.
- $a^4 + a^3b^4 + ab^5$ is a polynomial with two variables, a and b. The degree of the first term is 4, the second term is $3 + 4$ or 7, and the third term is $1 + 5$ or 6. The degree of the polynomial is 7.

MODEL PROBLEMS

1. MP 7 Given the polynomial $6x + 2x^2 - (11 + 3x^2)$

a Write the polynomial in standard form.

b Identify the degree of each term.

c Identify the degree of the polynomial.

SOLUTION

a $-x^2 + 6x - 11$

b The degree of $-x^2$ is 2, $6x$ is 1, and -11 is 0.

c 2

2. MP 7 Given the polynomial $(9 - 2a^2b^2) + (4a^3b + 3ab^3)$

a Write the polynomial in standard form.

b Identify the degree of each term.

c Identify the degree of the polynomial.

SOLUTION

a $4a^3b - 2a^2b^2 + 3ab^3 + 9$

b The degree of $4a^3b$ is 4, $-2a^2b^2$ is 4, $3ab^3$ is 4, and 9 is 0.

c 4

If there is more than one variable in the polynomial, arrange the terms in descending order of one of the variables.

PRACTICE

MP 7 Exercises 1–10: In each of the following,

a Write the polynomial in standard form.
b Name the coefficient of each term.
c State the degree of each term.
d State the degree of the polynomial.

1. $x^3 + 3x + 3x^2 + 1$

2. $2a^3 - 3 - 6a^2 + 5a$

3. $5x - 4x^3 + 15x^2 + 10$

4. $6y + 4y^3 + 11 - 2y^2$

5. $7 - 2x - 8x^3 + 10x^2 - 15x^4$

6. $a^3 - ab^3 + 3a^4b^2 - 3a^2b$

7. $3xy + y^4 - x^2y^2 + x^3y^3$

8. $5x^3y^2 + 8xy - 6 + 4x^2y$

9. $2x^4y - x^3y^2 + x^2y^3 - xy^4 + 1$

10. $-abc + 7 + 5a^5b^4c^3 - 2a^3b^2c$

Adding and Subtracting Polynomials

To Add Polynomials

- Use the commutative property to rearrange the terms so like terms are beside each other.
- Combine like terms.

To Subtract Polynomials

- Change the sign of every term in the subtracted polynomial and remove parentheses.
- Combine like terms.

> Remember, $a - b$ is the same as $a + (-b)$.

MODEL PROBLEMS

1. Add $-3x^2 + 4y$ and $5x^3 - 6x^2 - 3y$.

SOLUTION

$$(-3x^2 + 4y) + (5x^3 - 6x^2 - 3y)$$
$$= -3x^2 + 4y + 5x^3 - 6x^2 - 3y$$
$$= 5x^3 - 3x^2 - 6x^2 + 4y - 3y$$
$$= 5x^3 + (-3 - 6)x^2 + (4 - 3)y$$
$$= 5x^3 - 9x^2 + 1y$$
$$= 5x^3 - 9x^2 + y$$

2. Subtract $9x^2 - 5x$ from $-4x^2 - 8x$.

SOLUTION

First, rewrite the problem to show the subtraction as $(-4x^2 - 8x) - (9x^2 - 5x)$. Change the signs in the subtracted polynomial and remove the parentheses.

$$(-4x^2 - 8x) - (9x^2 - 5x)$$
$$= -4x^2 - 8x - 9x^2 + 5x$$
$$= (-4 - 9)x^2 + (-8 + 5)x$$
$$= -13x^2 - 3x$$

Check. $(-13x^2 - 3x) + (9x^2 - 5x)$

$$= -13x^2 - 3x + 9x^2 - 5x$$
$$= (-13x^2 + 9x^2) + (-3x - 5x)$$
$$= -4x^2 - 8x \checkmark$$

3. **MP 2, 7** Write the missing length as an expression and show your work.

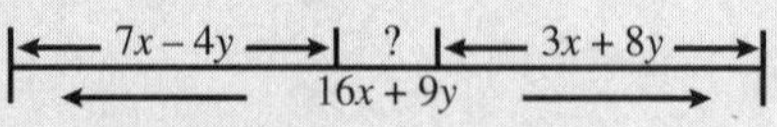

SOLUTION

Subtract the sum of the two shorter lengths from the entire length. $16x + 9y - [(7x - 4y) + (3x + 8y)]$

Use the distributive property and simplify. $16x + 9y - 7x + 4y - 3x - 8y$

$= 6x + 5y$

Answer: $6x + 5y$

PRACTICE

1. Simplify $(7x + 6x) - 12x$.

A. x
B. $2x$
C. x^2
D. 1

2. Simplify $m - [2 - (2 - m)]$.

A. -4
B. 0
C. $2m - 2$
D. $2m$

3. Find the sum of $-3x^2 - 4xy + 2y^2$ and $-x^2 + 5xy - 8y^2$.

A. $-2x^2 + xy - 6y^2$
B. $-4x^2 + xy - 6y^2$
C. $-4x^2 - 9xy - 6y^2$
D. $-2x^2 - 9xy + 10y^2$

4. What is the result when $-4x + 6$ is subtracted from $8x + 6$?

A. $12x + 12$
B. $12x$
C. $4x + 6$
D. $4x$

5. Simplify $5x - 3y - 7x + y$.

6. What is the result when $10x - 7$ is subtracted from $9x - 15$?

7. What is the result when $3 - 2x$ is subtracted from the sum of $x + 3$ and $5 - x$?

8. Add $2x - 3x^2 - 7$, $3 - 5x - 5x^2$, and $2x^2 + 12 + x - x^2$.

9. Find the sum of $4x^2 - 6x - 3$ and $3x^2 - 5x + 7$.

10. From $16x^2 + 25y + 12z$ subtract $16x^2 - 5y + 8z$.

Exercises 11–17: Remove parentheses and find each sum or difference.

11. $(x^2 + 3x + 1) + (2x^2 - x - 2)$

12. $(-3x^2 + 4x - 8) + (4x^2 + 5x - 11)$

13. $(4x^2 - 4) + (x^2 - x + 4)$

14. $(-3x^2 + 6x + 1) - (4x^2 + 7x - 3)$

15. $(x^2 - x - 9) - (-2x^2 + x + 4)$

16. $(x^2 + 2x - 3) - (x^2 - 4)$

17. $(x^3 - 3x^2 + 2x + 5) - (-5x^3 + x^2 + 3x - 2)$

18. What polynomial will produce the sum $6x^2 - x + 2$ when added to $4x^2 - 6x + 3$?

MP 7, 8 Exercises 19–26: Use the distributive property, remove the parentheses, and solve each of the following equations.

19. $13x - (x + 21) = 39$

20. $3a - (5 - 2a) = 35$

21. $7x - (x^2 - x - 9) = 17 - x^2$

22. $19m - (1 - 2m - m^2) = 20 + m^2$

23. $10 - (x + 6) - 2 = -5x + 9 - (-5x + 3)$

24. $0.5a + (a - 1) - (0.2a + 10) = 0.2a - (0.2a - 28)$

25. $2x - [5x - (6x + 2)] = 14 - x$

26. $7x - [x - (2x + 8)] = 3x - 7$

27. What polynomial must be added to $a^2 - 3a + 8$ to obtain the sum $3a^2 + 5a - 9$?

28. **MP 2, 7** The perimeter of the given isosceles trapezoid, $ABCD$, is $20x^2 + 18$. Base $AD = 8x^2 + 1$ and base $BC = 4x^2 + 3$.

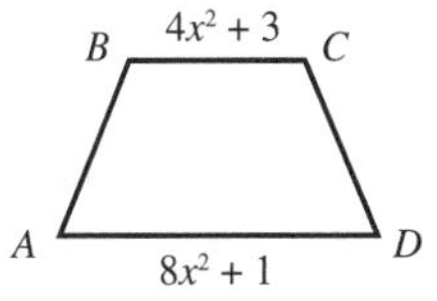

a What is the length of one of the legs, either AB or DC?

b Let $x = 2$. Substitute and check if your answer is plausible.

29. **MP 2, 7** The measures of two sides of a triangle are $8x + 8$ and $2x^2 + 7$.

a If the perimeter, P, measures $10x^2 - 3x + 12$, what is the measure of the third side?

b Let $x = 3$ and show that your answer makes sense.

6.2 Multiplying a Monomial by a Monomial

Multiplying Powers with Like Bases

When multiplying powers with like bases, count the number of times that the base is used as a factor or simply add the exponents.

The following is a list of guidelines for working with exponents.

Rules for Operations on Terms with Exponents

Operation	Rule	Examples
Addition and subtraction $x^n + x^m = x^n + x^m$ $x^n - x^m = x^n - x^m$	Like bases with unlike exponents *cannot* be added or subtracted unless they can be evaluated first.	$2^2 + 2^3 = 4 + 8 = 12$ $3^3 - 3^2 = 27 - 9 = 18$ $a^2 + a^3 = a^2 + a^3$ $a^3 - a^2 = a^3 - a^2$
Multiplication $x^n \bullet x^m = x^{n+m}$	To multiply powers of like bases, add the exponents.	$3^4 \times 3^5 = 3^9$ $a^2 \bullet a^3 = a^{2+3} = a^5$ $a^{-4} \bullet a^5 = a^{-4+5} = a^1 = a$
Division $\frac{x^n}{x^m} = x^{n-m}, x \neq 0$	To divide powers of like bases, subtract the exponent of the divisor from the exponent of the dividend.	$\frac{4^7}{4^5} = 4^{7-5} = 4^2$ $\frac{a^5}{a^2} = a^{5-2} = a^3$ $\frac{a^3}{a^8} = a^{3-8} = a^{-5} = \frac{1}{a^5}$
Raising a power to a power $(x^m)^n = x^{mn}$	To raise a term with an exponent to some power, multiply the exponents.	$(5^2)^3 = 5^{2 \times 3} = 5^6$ $(a^4)^3 = a^{4 \bullet 3} = a^{12}$
Raising a fraction to a power $\left(\frac{x}{y}\right)^n = \frac{x^n}{y^n}$	To raise a fraction to a power, raise the numerator and the denominator to that power.	$\left(\frac{3}{5}\right)^2 = \frac{3^2}{5^2} = \frac{9}{25}$ $\left(\frac{a}{b}\right)^7 = \frac{a^7}{b^7}$
Raising a product to a power $(xy)^n = x^n y^n$	To raise a product to a power, raise each factor to that power.	$(5 \bullet 2)^3 = 5^3 \bullet 2^3 = 1{,}000$ $(4a)^2 = 4^2 \bullet a^2 = 16a^2$ $(ab)^5 = a^5 b^5$

MODEL PROBLEMS

	SOLUTION
1. $(10^5)(10^6)$	$10^{5+6} = 10^{11}$
2. $y^{106} \bullet y^{14}$	$y^{106+14} = y^{120}$
3. $b \bullet b^4 \bullet b^{10}$	$b^{1+4+10} = b^{15}$

To Find Powers of a Power

- Raise the numerical coefficient to the indicated power.
- Follow the rule for signs in multiplication.
- Multiply the exponents of the given literal factors by the power.
- If any given term is a fraction, raise both the numerator and the denominator to the indicated power.

MODEL PROBLEMS

MP 7, 8 Model Problems 1–9: Simplify and show your work.

SOLUTION

1. $(3a^2xy^3)^2$ — $(3a^2xy^3)(3a^2xy^3) = (3)(3)(a^2)(a^2)(x)(x)(y^3)(y^3) = 9a^4x^2y^6$

2. $(-3xy^4)^2$ — $(-3xy^4)(-3xy^4) = (-3)(-3)(x)(x)(y^4)(y^4) = 9x^2y^8$

3. $(4bx^2)^3$ — $(4bx^2)(4bx^2)(4bx^2) = (4)(4)(4)(b)(b)(b)(x^2)(x^2)(x^2) = 4^3b^3x^6 = 64b^3x^6$

4. $(-3m^4)^3$ — $(-3)^3m^{12} = -27m^{12}$

5. $(-2c^3x)^4$ — $(-2)^4[(c^3)x]^4 = (-2)^4(c^3)^4(x^4) = (-2)^4c^{12}x^4 = 16c^{12}x^4$

6. $(-2x^2a)^5$ — $(-2)^5x^{10}a^5 = -32x^{10}a^5$

7. $\left(\frac{2}{3}a^2b^3\right)^2$ — $\left(\frac{2^2}{3^2}\right)a^4b^6 = \frac{4}{9}a^4b^6$

8. $(0.3a^3x^5)^2$ — $0.3^2a^6x^{10} = 0.09a^6x^{10}$

9. $\left(\frac{x^2m}{5a^2b^5}\right)^2$ — $\frac{x^4m^2}{25a^4b^{10}}$

PRACTICE

Exercises 1–20: Simplify.

1. $(3ab^3)^2$
2. $(-3x^2y^3)^2$
3. $(am^4x)^3$
4. $(-x^3)^3$
5. $(-2m^3x)^4$
6. $(5a^3b^{10})^2$
7. $(-5x^4)^2$
8. $(-3a^2x^5)^3$
9. $(4a^5x^4)^3$
10. $(2x^4y^6)^5$
11. $(-0.5ab^4)^2$
12. $(-3x^2y^4)^5$
13. $\left(\frac{1}{3}a^4b^5\right)^5$
14. $(-0.3x^2)^3$
15. $\left(\frac{3}{5}ab^3x^2\right)^2$
16. $\left(\frac{4ab^2}{-5c^3}\right)^2$
17. $\left(\frac{-3x^2y^4}{2a^2}\right)^2$
18. $(abc)^x$
19. $(a^xb^x)^m$
20. $(6x^2y^b)^a$

Multiplying a Monomial by a Monomial

To Find the Product of Monomials

- Multiply the numerical coefficients using the rule of signs for multiplication.
- Multiply variables of the same base by adding the exponents.
- Multiply these two products together.

MODEL PROBLEMS

MP 7 Model Problems 1–2: Simplify and show your work.

1. Multiply $-4a^2b^3$ and $3a^3b$.

SOLUTION

$(-4a^2b^3)(3a^3b)$

$= (-4 \bullet 3)(a^2 \bullet a^3 \bullet b^3 \bullet b^1)$

$= -12a^5b^4$

2. Simplify $(3x^a)^2(4x^b)$.

SOLUTION

$(3x^a)^2(4x^b) = 3^2x^{2a} \bullet 4x^b = (9 \bullet 4)(x^{2a} \bullet x^b) = 36x^{2a+b}$

PRACTICE

Exercises 1–25: Simplify.

1. $5x^2 \bullet 2x^4$

2. $(-3a^3)(-4x^2)$

3. $(5a^3)(-4a^7)$

4. $(-8r^4)(2r^3)$

5. $(-3ab^2c^2)(2a^2bc^3)$

6. $(-4x^5y)(x^7y)$

7. $(-x^2)(-1)$

8. $(2xb^2)(5b^4)$

9. $-a^b(a^{3b})(a^n)(a^{4n})$

10. $-5x^{10}(20x^{20})$

11. $-6a^3b^2(8a^2b^5)$

12. $\left(\frac{1}{4}x^4y^2\right)(2x^3y^5)$

13. $(-x)^3(-2x)^5$

14. $(8a)(-2a^x)$

15. $(2y^a)(-7y^{3a})$

16. $(5a^3)(2a^2)^3$

17. $(-x^2)(3xy^2)$

18. $(5a^n)^2(3xy^2)$

19. $(-4m^{t+2})(5m^{2t})^2$

20. $(-xyz)^2(-4x^4)^2$

21. $(3xy)^3(-2x^2)^3(-x^2y)^3$

22. $(7x^2y^3z^4)^2(-2x^4y^3z^2)^3$

23. $\left(\frac{1}{2}a^2b^3\right)^3\left(-\frac{2}{3}a^4b^5\right)^2$

24. $(5x^2y^3z)(2xy^2z^4)(-xyz)$

25. $2am(-mr^2)^3(-3a^2r^2)$

Practice Problems continue . . .

Exercises 26–30: Rewrite the expressions as a monomial. Show your work.

26. $(-2x^2y)^3 + (3x^3)(5xy)^3$

27. $(-2a)(-3ab)^3 + (3a)^2(ab)^2(-6b)$

28. $(2x)^2(-25x^4) + (-4x^4)(-x)^2 + (-10x^3)^2$

29. $x^a(x^b)(x^c) + 3x^ax^bx^c - 2x^ax^bx^c$

30. $(-3ax^2)(3ax^3)(ax)^2 + (-2ax)^2(ax^4)(4ax)$

31. MP 2 Represent the distance an airplane flies in 8 hours at the rate of $75x$ miles an hour.

32. MP 2 If the length of a rectangle is $5a^2$ and the width is $7ab^2$, what is the area of the rectangle?

33. MP 2 Find the area of a square if a side is $12k$.

34. MP 2 What is the volume of a rectangular solid with a length of $10n$, a width of $3n$, and a height of $\frac{1}{6}n$?

35. MP 2 What is the cost of $5m$ dozen golf balls at $3m^2$ dollars per dozen?

LESSON 6.3

6.3 Multiplying a Polynomial by a Monomial

To Find the Product of a Polynomial and a Monomial

- First use the distributive property, where $a(b + c) = ab + ac$, to remove parentheses.
- After multiplying each term of the polynomial by the monomial, simplify the product sums, if possible.

MODEL PROBLEMS

MP 7 Model Problems 1–4: Simplify and explain your reasoning.

1. Simplify $-7x(x^2 - 2) - 9x$.

SOLUTION

Write the expression.	$-7x(x^2 - 2) - 9x$
Use the distributive property.	$-7x(x^2) - 7x(-2) - 9x$
Multiply.	$-7x^3 + 14x - 9x$
Add like terms.	$-7x^3 + 5x$

2. Simplify: $\frac{1}{4}r^2x(8r^2 + 12rx - 4x^2)$

SOLUTION

Use the distributive property.	$\frac{1}{4}r^2x(8r^2) + \frac{1}{4}r^2x(12rx) + \frac{1}{4}r^2x(-4x^2)$
Multiply.	$2r^4x + 3r^3x^2 - r^2x^3$

Model Problems continue . . .

Model Problems *continued*

The quantity $(5x + x + 4)$ is immediately preceded by the coefficient $-3x$ and not by the term $5x^2$.

3. Simplify $5x^2 - 3x(5x + x + 4) + (2x)^2$.

SOLUTION

Simplify in the parentheses first.	$5x^2 - 3x(6x + 4) + (2x)^2$
Apply the exponent in the last term.	$5x^2 - 3x(6x + 4) + 4x^2$
Remove parentheses using distributive property.	$5x^2 - 18x^2 - 12x + 4x^2$
Combine like terms.	$-9x^2 - 12x$

4. Simplify $b^2 - 4[2b - 3(b - 5)]$.

SOLUTION

Simplify in the inner parentheses first.	$b^2 - 4[2b - 3b + 15]$
Simplify within the brackets.	$b^2 - 4[-b + 15]$
Remove brackets using distributive property.	$b^2 + 4b - 60$

PRACTICE

Exercises 1–24: Simplify.

1. $5(3b + 1)$

2. $8(3x - 4)$

3. $-3(5w + 6)$

4. $-4(-5x - 1)$

5. $7(-2x^2 - 4x)$

6. $x^2(3x^3 - 5)$

7. $5x(3x^2 + 2)$

8. $a(a^2 - 2ab + b^2)$

9. $-x^2(5x^2 - x + 3)$

10. $-3a^2(a^2 - 6a + 9)$

11. $-3x^4(-4x^2 - 3x + 2)$

12. $ax(6x - a)$

13. $4xy(5x^2 - 7y^2)$

14. $-x(-x^2 - x)$

15. $-a^2n(-a^2n - 5)$

16. $2y^a(3y^b - y^3)$

17. $\frac{1}{2}b(4b^2 - 8b + 16)$

18. $a(a^x - 3)$

19. $x^a(5x^{3a} - x)$

20. $-n^x(2n^x - 3n^4)$

21. $xy(3x^2 + 6xy - 4y^2)$

22. $-5a^3(2a^2 - 3a - 1)$

23. $2x^2y(x^2 - 3xy - 2y^2)$

24. $5x^{4a}(3x^{2a} + x^a + x)$

MP 7 Exercises 25–29: Rewrite the following products as equivalent polynomials.

25. $a^2b(a^3b - 4a^2b^2 - 5ab^3)$

26. $-4a^2x(5a^2 - ax - 5x^2)$

Practice Problems continue . . .

27. $-\frac{1}{3}ab(9a^2 - 6ab - 18b^2)$

28. $\frac{2}{5}m^3(10m^3 - 5m^2 - 20m + 5)$

29. $0.4a(0.5a^2 - 0.3a - 0.1a^3)$

30. Multiply
$x^5 + 2x^4 - 3x^3 + x^2 - x + 1$ by $3x^2$.

Exercises 31–50: Simplify.

31. $-5(4x - 3) + 6x - 4$

32. $4 + 7(m - 3) + 3m$

33. $9 - 4(3c + 10) - 10$

34. $8b - b(2b - 1)$

35. $4x - 3x(5x - 6) + 8x^2$

36. $9x + 4 - (2x - 6)$

37. $4x^2 - 3x - (4x - 9x^2) + (3x)^2$

38. $-a - 4[2a - (3x - 5)]$

39. $x + 3(x - 2) - (x - 1) - 1$

40. $x - (x^2 - x - 6) - (x^2 - 6x + 5)$

41. $2x - [3x + 8 + 2(3 - 5x)]$

42. $3x + [2x - 3(5 - 4x)]$

43. $2 + 3[5x - 3(4y + x)]$

44. $-7x[5(2x - y) - (3x + 2y)]$

45. $-2[5 + 2(2x - 1)]$

46. $2x - [-3x - (3x + 4) + 5]$

47. $5[3a - 4(a - 2)]$

48. $\frac{x}{2}[2a - (x - 1)a]$

49. $2a - [-2(x - 1(a - 1) - 1)]$

50. $5 - x[x - x[(x - 1) - x] - x]$

LESSON 6.4

6.4 Multiplying a Polynomial by a Polynomial

When multiplying polynomials, each term of one polynomial must multiply each term of the other polynomial. The following are three common methods for multiplying polynomials:

1. **Distributive property** (horizontal method)
2. **FOIL method** (used only to multiply two binomials)
3. **Box method** (rectangular area)

All the methods use the distributive property. After using any one of these methods, combine like terms.

Using the Distributive Property for Multiplying Polynomials

- Distribute the first polynomial over the terms of the second.
- Solve as before.

MODEL PROBLEMS

1. $(x + 2)(x + 3)$

SOLUTION

Given.	$(x + 2)(x + 3)$
Distribute $(x + 2)$ over x and 3.	$= (x + 2)x + (x + 2)3$
Distribute x over the first $(x + 2)$ and 3 over the second.	$= x^2 + 2x + 3x + 6$
Combine like terms.	$= x^2 + 5x + 6$

2. MP 7 $(2x - 3)(3x^2 - 5x + 4)$

SOLUTION

$(2x - 3)(3x^2 - 5x + 4)$
$= (2x - 3)3x^2 + (2x - 3)(-5x) + (2x - 3)4$
$= 6x^3 - 9x^2 - 10x^2 + 15x + 8x - 12$
$= 6x^3 - 19x^2 + 23x - 12$

The distributive property can also be used this way: Distribute the first term to each term in the second parentheses and then the second term to each term in the second parentheses.

3. $(x + 4)(2x - 3)$

SOLUTION

$(x + 4)(2x - 3)$
$= x(2x) + x(-3) + 4(2x) + 4(-3)$
$= 2x^2 - 3x + 8x - 12$
$= 2x^2 + 5x - 12$

Using the FOIL Method for Multiplying Polynomials

Use the FOIL method to multiply $(2x + 1)(3x - 1)$.

F Multiply the first terms. $(2x \bullet 3x) = 6x^2$

O Multiply the outer terms. $(2x) \bullet (-1) = -2x$

I Multiply the inner terms. $(1 \bullet 3x) = 3x$

L Multiply the last terms. $1 \bullet (-1) = -1$

> **FOIL stands for First, Outer, Inner, Last.**

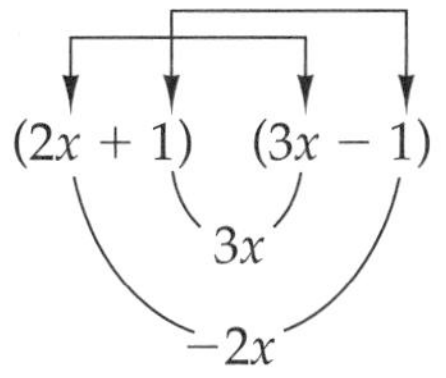

Next, combine like terms, so $6x^2 + (-2x) + 3x + (-1) = 6x^2 + x - 1$.

MODEL PROBLEMS

1. $(x + 3)(x + 4)$

SOLUTION

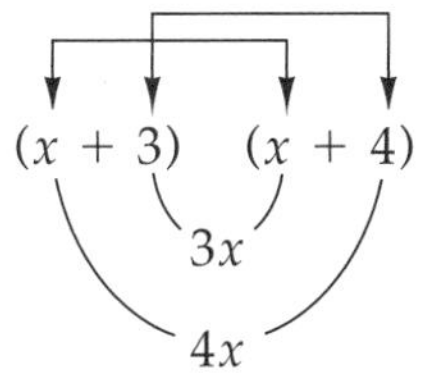

$x^2 \quad + \quad 7x \quad + \quad 12$

product of first terms $x \bullet x$	sum of inner and outer $3x + 4x$	product of last terms $3 \bullet 4$

2. $(2a - 3)(5a + 2)$

SOLUTION

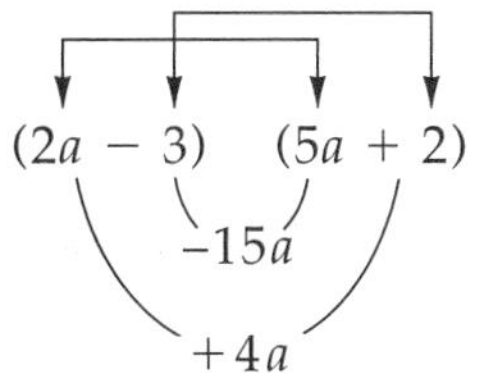

$10a^2 \quad - \quad 11a \quad - \quad 6$

Using the Box Method for Multiplying Polynomials

To Use the Box Method

- Make a table of products.
- List the areas of the four inside rectangles, and then combine to find the total area of the whole rectangle.

MODEL PROBLEMS

1. Multiply $(x + 1)$ by $(3x + 2)$.

SOLUTION

	$3x$	$+\ 2$
x	$3x^2$	$2x$
$+\ 1$	$3x$	2

Combine the items in the boxes: $3x^2 + 2x + 3x + 2 = 3x^2 + 5x + 2$

Answer: $3x^2 + 5x + 2$

2. Multiply $(x + 2)(2x^2 + x - 3)$.

SOLUTION

	$2x^2$	$+\ x$	-3
x	$2x^3$	x^2	$-3x$
$+\ 2$	$4x^2$	$2x$	-6

Combine the items in the boxes: $2x^3 + x^2 - 3x + 4x^2 + 2x - 6 = 2x^3 + 5x^2 - x - 6$

Answer: $2x^3 + 5x^2 - x - 6$

PRACTICE

MP 8 Exercises 1–25: Find the product.

1. $(x + 4)(x - 3)$
2. $(a + 5)(a + 6)$
3. $(b - 7)(b - 4)$
4. $(x + 3)(x + 3)$
5. $(x + 8)^2$
6. $(c - 2)^2$
7. $(x + y)(x + y)$
8. $(a - b)(a - b)$
9. $(2x - 6)(4x + 3)$
10. $(3x + 5)(x - 1)$
11. $(2x + 3)(5x + 5)$
12. $(3ax - 2)(ax - 5)$
13. $(2x + 3d)(4x + d)$
14. $(x^2 + x)(x + 1)$
15. $(3x^2 + 2)(x + 5)$
16. $(a + b)(a + x)$
17. $(2x^2 + 5)(x - 1)$
18. $(x - 1)(x^2 - 2x + 1)$
19. $(8ab + x)(3ab + x)$
20. $(2x^2 - 3x)(x - 1)$
21. $(x + 1)(x^2 + 2x + 1)$
22. $(x + 3)^3$
23. $(a - b)(a^2 + 2ab + b^2)$
24. $(x + 3)(5x^2 + 3x - 2)$
25. $(2x - 5)(x^3 - 2x^2 - x + 3)$

Practice Problems continue . . .

MP 7 Exercises 26–30: Simplify. Identify the method you used to simplify the expression. Show your work.

26. $x(x - 2) + (x + 2)^2$

27. $7a^3 + a(a - 3)^2$

28. $10x^2 - (3x + 1)(3x - 1)$

29. $5m^2 - 2(m + 1)(m + 1) + 4$

30. $(x + 1)^2 - (x - 1)^2$

MP 2 Exercises 31–35: Write an algebraic expression that represents the answer. Express the answer as a polynomial in simplest form.

31. a If the length of a square measures $3x - 2$, express the *area* of the square as a polynomial.

b Let $x = 2$. Show that the expressions for length and area are consistent.

32. a If the sides of a rectangle are $4x + 9$ and $x - 8$, express the *area* of the rectangle as a polynomial.

b Let $x = 10$. Show that the expressions for length and area are consistent.

33. a If the edge of a cube is $x - 1$, express the *volume* of the cube as a polynomial.

b Let $x = 3$. Show that the expressions for length and volume are consistent.

34. a If three consecutive integers are represented as x, $x + 1$, and $x + 2$, write the product of those three integers as a polynomial in simplest form.

b If $x = 2$, determine the three consecutive integers.

35. A truck travels at the average rate of $10x + 25$ miles per hour.

a Represent the distance traveled in $x + 5$ hours.

b If $x = 4$, how fast does the truck travel?

c If $x = 4$, how far does the truck travel in $x + 5$ hours?

LESSON 6.5

6.5 Special Products of Binomials

Certain binomial products appear so often that you should know them on sight. You should be able to recognize the structure of the binomial and easily simplify it.

MODEL PROBLEMS

MP 7, 8 Model Problems 1–5: Use the structure of the binomial product to simplify. Show your work.

1. $(m - 4)(m + 4)$

SOLUTION

$(m)^2 - (4)^2 = m^2 - 16$

2. $\left(\frac{1}{2}x + 3\right)\left(\frac{1}{2}x - 3\right)$

SOLUTION

$\left(\frac{1}{2}x\right)^2 - 3^2 = \frac{1}{4}x^2 - 9$

3. $(3y + 4)^2$

SOLUTION

$(3y + 4)(3y + 4) = (3y)^2 + 2(3y)(4) + 4^2$
$= 9y^2 + 24y + 16$

4. $(5x - 3)^2$

SOLUTION

$(5x - 3)(5x - 3) = (5x)^2 + 2(5x)(-3) + (-3)^2$
$= 25x^2 - 30x + 9$

5. $(a - b)(a + b)(a^2 - b^2)$

SOLUTION

$(a^2 - b^2)(a^2 - b^2) = (a^2)^2 + 2(a^2)(-b^2) + (b^2)^2$
$= a^4 - 2a^2b^2 + b^4$

Product of a Sum and a Difference: $(x + y)(x - y) = x^2 - y^2$

<table>
<tr><th>Distributive Method</th><th>FOIL Method</th><th>Box Method</th></tr>
<tr>
<td>Distribute the first term, x, to each term in the second parentheses. Then distribute the second term, y, to each term in the second parentheses.
$(x + y)(x - y)$
$= x(x - y) + y(x - y)$
$= x^2 - xy + yx - y^2$
$= x^2 - y^2$</td>
<td><u>F</u> Multiply the first terms:
$(x)(x) = x^2$
<u>O</u> Multiply the outer terms:
$(x)(-y) = -xy$
<u>I</u> Multiply the inner terms:
$(y)(x) = yx$
<u>L</u> Multiply the last terms:
$(y)(-y) = -y^2$
Product:
$x^2 - xy + yx - y^2 = x^2 - y^2$</td>
<td>Find the product: $(x + y)(x - y)$
<table><tr><td></td><td>x</td><td>$+ y$</td></tr><tr><td>x</td><td>x^2</td><td>xy</td></tr><tr><td>$- y$</td><td>$-xy$</td><td>$-y^2$</td></tr></table>Add up the boxes:
$x^2 + xy - xy - y^2 = x^2 - y^2$
Answer: $x^2 - y^2$</td>
</tr>
</table>

The product of the sum and difference of the same terms always results in the **difference of two squares**. The middle term is always <u>zero</u>.

Square of a Binomial: $(x + y)^2 = x^2 + 2xy + y^2$ and $(x - y)^2 = x^2 - 2xy + y^2$

<table>
<tr><th>Distributive Method</th><th>FOIL Method</th><th>Box Method</th></tr>
<tr>
<td>To find the first term, square the first term of the binomial:
x^2
To find the middle term, double the product of the two terms of the binomial:
$2xy$ or $-2xy$
To find the third term, square the second term of the binomial:
$(y)(y) = y^2$ or $(-y)(-y) = y^2$
Products:
$(x + y)^2 = (x + y)(x + y)$
$= x^2 + 2xy + y^2$
$(x - y)^2 = (x - y)(x - y)$
$= x^2 - 2xy + y^2$</td>
<td>$(x + y)^2$ or $(x - y)^2$
<u>F</u> Multiply the first terms:
$(x)(x) = x^2$
<u>O</u> Multiply the outer terms:
$(x)(y) = xy$ or $(x)(-y) = -xy$
<u>I</u> Multiply the inner terms:
$(y)(x) = yx$ or $(-y)(x) = -yx$
<u>L</u> Multiply the last terms:
$(y)(y) = y^2$ or $(-y)(-y) = y^2$
Products:
$(x + y)^2 = x^2 + xy + yx + y^2$
$= x^2 + 2xy + y^2$
$(x - y)^2 = x^2 - xy - yx + y^2$
$= x^2 - 2xy + y^2$</td>
<td>Find the product: $(x + y)(x + y)$
<table><tr><td></td><td>x</td><td>$+ y$</td></tr><tr><td>x</td><td>x^2</td><td>xy</td></tr><tr><td>$+ y$</td><td>xy</td><td>y^2</td></tr></table>Add up the boxes:
$x^2 + xy + xy + y^2 = x^2 + 2xy + y^2$
Answer:
$x^2 + 2xy + y^2$</td>
</tr>
</table>

1. When you take the **square of a binomial**, the trinomial product is known as a **perfect square trinomial.**
2. When squaring a binomial, the first and third terms are always positive, and the middle term is twice the product of the two terms involved.

PRACTICE

1. Which is the simplified form of $(x + 10)(x - 10)$?

A. $x^2 + 20x + 100$
B. $x^2 + 10x + 100$
C. $x^2 - 100$
D. $x^2 - 10x + 100$

2. Simplify $(2m + 3)^2$.

A. $2m^2 + 6m + 9$
B. $2m^2 + 12m + 9$
C. $4m^2 + 9$
D. $4m^2 + 12m + 9$

3. Simplify $\left(\frac{2}{3}v - 2\right)\left(\frac{2}{3}v - 2\right)$.

A. $\frac{2}{3}v^2 - 4v + 4$
B. $\frac{4}{9}v^2 - \frac{8}{3}v + 4$
C. $\frac{4}{9}v^2 - \frac{4}{3}v + 4$
D. $\frac{4}{9}v^2 + \frac{4}{3}v - 4$

4. Find the product of $(1.2a + 0.3b)$ and $(1.2a - 0.3b)$.

A. $0.0144a^2 - 7.2ab + 0.09b^2$
B. $1.2a^2 + 0.3b^2$
C. $1.44a^2 - 0.09b^2$
D. $1.44a^2 + 7.2ab - 0.9b^2$

5. Which of the following is a perfect square trinomial?

A. $x^2 + 16x + 9$
B. $x^2 - 8x - 16$
C. $25x^2 + 9$
D. $9x^2 + 12x + 4$

MP 8 Exercises 6–33: Multiply the expressions and simplify the result. Show your work.

6. $(mx + 2)(mx + 2)$

7. $(3x - 3)^2$

8. $(12c + 4)(12c - 4)$

9. $(13x + 30)(13x - 30)$

10. $(0.4a - 0.02)^2$

11. $(2x + 7)(2x - 7)$

12. $(a + 2b)^2$

13. $(xy + 5z)(xy - 5z)$

14. $(2xy + 1)^2$

15. $(3ab + 1)(3ab - 1)$

16. $\left(\frac{3}{4} + \frac{1}{3}x\right)\left(\frac{3}{4} - \frac{1}{3}x\right)$

17. $(2.1g - 3)(2.1g + 3)$

18. $(x^3 + 2)(x^3 - 2)$

19. $\left(2a - \frac{1}{3}\right)\left(2a + \frac{1}{3}\right)$

20. $2x(3x + 1)^2$

21. $(0.5x - 4y)^2$

22. $\left(\frac{2}{3}x - 2\right)^2$

23. $(1 - 4x)^2$

24. $(x^3 + 5y)^2$

25. $(2a - 3x^3)(2a + 3x^3)$

26. $(5x^2 + 3y)^2$

27. $(2x - 7y^3)^2$

28. $(x - a)^2 + (a - x)^2$

29. $x(x - 1)^2 - x(x + 1)^2$

30. $(x + 1)(x - 1)(x^2 + 1)$

31. $(a - b)(a + b)(a^2 - b^2)$

32. $(a + 2)(a - 2)(a^2 + 4)$

33. $(x^2 + 9)(x + 3)(x - 3)$

34. **MP 1, 7** The pattern of the product of the sum and difference can be used to multiply certain number pairs. Use the pattern to find the products of:

a (13)(7)
b (21)(19)
c (35)(25)
d (27)(13)
e (42)(38)
f (101)(99)

LESSON 6.6

6.6 Negative Integers as Exponents

If n is an integer and $x \neq 0$, then $x^{-n} = \frac{1}{x^n}$ and $\frac{1}{x^{-n}} = x^n$.

x^{-n} is the reciprocal of x^n. This definition means we can now write any expressions containing negative exponents without negative exponents. In other words, any algebraic expression with a negative exponent can be written as the reciprocal with a positive exponent.

To Simplify with Negative Exponents

- Subtract the exponent of the divisor from the exponent of the dividend, such as $\frac{x^3}{x^7} = x^{3-7} = x^{-4}$.
- If the exponent is negative, take the reciprocal to rewrite the expression with positive exponents, such as $x^{-4} = \frac{1}{x^4}$.

MODEL PROBLEMS

Model Problems 1–9: Perform each operation.

SOLUTION

1. $3^7 \bullet 3^{-4}$

$3^{7+(-4)} = 3^3 = 27$

2. $a^{-2} \bullet b^{-4}$

$\frac{1}{a^2} \bullet \frac{1}{b^4}$

3. $3^4 \bullet 3^{-4} \bullet 3^0$

$3^{4+(-4)} \bullet 1 = 3^0 \bullet 1 = 1 \bullet 1 = 1$

4. $\frac{1}{3^{-2}} + (10^3)^{-1}$

$3^2 + 10^{3(-1)} = 9 + 10^{-3} = 9 + \frac{1}{10^3} = 9 + \frac{1}{1{,}000}$

5. $(-5)^0 - 5^{-2}$

$1 - \frac{1}{5^2} = 1 - \frac{1}{25} = \frac{25}{25} - \frac{1}{25} = \frac{24}{25}$

6. $(a^{-4})^{-3} + (a^2)^6$

$a^{12} + a^{12} = 2a^{12}$

7. $(x^{-3})^2 \bullet (y^6)^{-1}$

$x^{-6} \bullet y^{-6} = \frac{1}{x^6} \bullet \frac{1}{y^6}$ or $\frac{1}{(xy)^6}$

8. $\left(\frac{3}{4}\right)^{-2}\left(\frac{x}{y}\right)^{-5}$

$\left(\frac{4}{3}\right)^2\left(\frac{y}{x}\right)^5 = \left(\frac{16}{9}\right)\left(\frac{y^5}{x^5}\right) = \frac{16y^5}{9x^5}$

9. $(x - y)^{-2}$

$\frac{1}{(x-y)^2}$ or $\frac{1}{x^2 - 2xy + y^2}$

PRACTICE

Exercises 1–15: Simplify. Write the variable answers with positive exponents.

1. $5^{-3} \bullet 5^5$

2. $-3b^{-3}$

3. $7 \bullet 10^{-3}$

4. $\dfrac{9}{10^{-2}}$

5. $\dfrac{5}{a^{-2}b^{-2}}$

6. $2^{-\frac{1}{2}} \bullet 2^{\frac{5}{2}} \bullet 2^0$

7. $\dfrac{xy^{-4}}{x^{-2}y}$

8. $\left(\dfrac{1}{4}\right)^{-2} + \left(\dfrac{1}{2}\right)^3$

9. $\left(\dfrac{2}{3}\right)^{-3}\left(\dfrac{3}{2}\right)^{-2}$

10. $\left((x^{-1})^{-2}\right)^{-3}$

11. $2 \bullet 3^{-1} \bullet 6^2 \bullet 12^{-1}$

12. $\dfrac{2^2 \bullet 2^{-2} \bullet 2^4}{2^{-1} \bullet 2^0 \bullet 2^{-3}}$

13. $\left(\dfrac{3}{4}\right)^0 \bullet \left(\dfrac{3}{4}\right)^{-1} \bullet \left(\dfrac{3}{4}\right)$

14. $3x^{-8}y^2 \bullet 5x^3y^{-3}$

15. $\left(2a^{-3}\right)^{-4} + \left(4x^{-4}\right)^{-2}$

16. When $x = 5$, what is the value of

$5x^0 - (5x)^0 + 5x^{-1}$?

Exercises 17–23: Find the value of x that makes each statement true.

17. $3^x \bullet 3^4 = 3^{12}$

18. $3^{-2} \bullet 3^x = 3^6$

19. $3^x \bullet 3^x = 3^{16}$

20. $3^x \bullet 3^{x-1} = 3^7$

21. $\dfrac{3^{-3}}{3^x} = 3^4$

22. MP 1, 2, 7, 8 $3^{x+2} \bullet 3^{2x-1} = 9^2$

23. MP 1, 2, 7, 8 $2^{2x+1} = 2^x \bullet 4$

6.7 Dividing Polynomials

Consider the Laws of Division for Exponents:

> For all positive integers m and n, and for every nonzero real number a, $\frac{a^m}{a^n} = a^{m-n}$.

Sometimes the division results in a positive exponent.	For example, $\frac{x^5}{x^3} = x^{5-3} = x^2$.
Sometimes the division results in a negative exponent.	For example, $\frac{y^4}{y^6}$ is $y^{4-6} = y^{-2}$, which can be written as $\frac{1}{y^2}$.
Sometimes the division results in both positive and negative exponents.	For example, $\frac{8x^4m^2}{16xm^6} = \frac{1x^{4-1}}{2m^{6-2}} = \frac{x^3}{2m^4}$.
Sometimes the division results in an exponent equal to 0.	For example, $a^0 = 1$, $6^0 = 1$, $100^0 = 1$, $(-7)^0 = 1$, $(x + y)^0 = 1$, and $(4x^2y)^0 = 1$. • 0^0 is undefined.

Dividing a Monomial by a Monomial

The rules for division follow from the fact that division is the inverse operation of multiplication.

To Divide a Monomial by Another Monomial

- Divide the numerical coefficients, using the law of signs for division.
- Divide the variable factors that have the same base using the laws of exponents, subtracting the exponent in the denominator from the exponent in the numerator.
- Simplify by multiplying the quotients that remain.
- Check the result by multiplying the divisor and the answer (or quotient). If the answer is correct, then the product should produce the original numerator.

MODEL PROBLEMS

MP 3, 7 Model Problems 1–5: Simplify each expression. Show your work.

SOLUTION

1. $\dfrac{24x^5}{-3x^2}$ $= \dfrac{24}{-3} \bullet \dfrac{x^5}{x^2} = \dfrac{8}{-1} \bullet x^{5-2} = -8x^3$

Check. $(-3x^2)\bullet(-8x^3) = 24x^5$

2. $\dfrac{-8a^3b^2}{8a^3b}$ $= \dfrac{-8}{8} \bullet \dfrac{a^3}{a^3} \bullet \dfrac{b^2}{b} = (-1)(1)b = -b$

Check. $(8a^3b)(-b) = -8a^3b^2$

3. $\dfrac{36x^2b^5}{-12x^4b^4}$ $-3x^{2-4}b^{5-4} = -3x^{-2}b$ or $\dfrac{-3b}{x^2}$

4. $\dfrac{a(a^2+1)}{a} - (a^2+1)^0$ $(a^2+1) - (a^2+1)^0 = a^2 + 1 - 1 = a^2$

5. $\dfrac{(-2a^3b^2x^4)^2}{16a^6b^4x^8}$ $\dfrac{4a^6b^4x^8}{16a^6b^4x^8} = \dfrac{4}{16} = \dfrac{1}{4}$

PRACTICE

MP 7 Exercises 1–30: Simplify. Express all answers with positive exponents. Show your work.

1. $\dfrac{a^{16}}{a^4}$

2. $\dfrac{m^5}{m}$

3. $\dfrac{x^w}{x^2}$ (where $w > 2$)

4. $\dfrac{7^y}{7^x}$ (where $x < y$)

5. $\dfrac{y^x}{y}$ (where $x > 1$)

6. $\dfrac{4^a}{4^b}$ (where $a > b$)

7. $\dfrac{a}{a^4}$

8. $\dfrac{m^x}{m}$

9. $\dfrac{1}{x^0 + 1}$

10. $\dfrac{y^{2k+1}}{y^k}$

11. $\dfrac{10^{2x+1}}{10^{x+1}}$

12. $\dfrac{8x^5}{-2x^2}$

13. $\dfrac{-0.08a^3x^2y^4}{0.2axy^2}$

14. $\dfrac{a^4b^3c^7}{a^3c^4}$

15. $\dfrac{-18r^4c^2}{-3rc}$

16. $\dfrac{0.6a^7x^2}{0.2a^2x}$

17. $\dfrac{a^m}{a^n}$ (when $m > n$)

18. $\dfrac{2^{6x}}{2^{4x}}$

19. $\dfrac{-45x^{a+5}}{9x^3}$

Practice Problems continue . . .

20. $\dfrac{48a^2x}{6x^3}$

21. $\dfrac{45a^2z^0}{-5a^4z}$

22. $\dfrac{32(xy)^mz}{8x^my^m}$

23. $\dfrac{30xy^2}{-10x^2y^3}$

24. $\dfrac{-6a^{10}m^4}{-30a^7m^5}$

25. $\dfrac{4x^my^m}{x^my^k}$ (when $m > k$)

26. $\dfrac{a^0b^n}{a^xa}$

27. $\dfrac{4(x^2)^3(y^4)^2}{2(x^2)^2(y^2)^4}$

28. $\dfrac{-9x^{3a}}{-3x^{a+3}}$

29. $\dfrac{(-5)(x^{2a})^2y^{4b-1}}{25x^{4a-1}y^{4b}}$

30. $\dfrac{x^2(1-x^2)}{x^2} - (y^2)^0$

Dividing a Polynomial by a Monomial

> In general, for all real numbers a and b, and all nonzero real numbers c, $\dfrac{a+b}{c} = \dfrac{a}{c} + \dfrac{b}{c}$ and $\dfrac{a-b}{c} = \dfrac{a}{c} - \dfrac{b}{c}$.

To Divide a Polynomial by a Monomial

- Divide each term of the polynomial by the monomial, using the distributive property.
- Combine the quotients with correct signs.
- Check by multiplying.

Lastly, we need to consider the *property of closure* with respect to polynomials. Recall that *closure* for integers means that when you add, subtract, or multiply two integers, the result is always another integer. Polynomials are also closed under addition, subtraction, or multiplication, since the sum, difference, or product of polynomials is always another polynomial. In contrast, with both integers and polynomials, the division operation is <u>not</u> closed. For instance, $\dfrac{3}{5}$ yields a non-integer result, and $\dfrac{x^5}{x^9}$ results in a negative exponent, and polynomials must have positive exponents.

MODEL PROBLEMS

Model Problems 1–3: Simplify.

SOLUTION

1. $\dfrac{6m^2 - m}{-m}$

$= \dfrac{6m^2}{-m} + \left(\dfrac{-m}{-m}\right) = -6m^{(2-1)} + 1 = -6m + 1$

Check. $-m(-6m + 1) = 6m^2 - m$

2. $\dfrac{9x^5 - 6x^3}{3x^2}$

$= \dfrac{9x^5}{3x^2} + \left(\dfrac{-6x^3}{3x^2}\right) = 3x^3 - 2x$

Check. $3x^2(3x^3 - 2x) = 9x^5 - 6x^3$

3. $\dfrac{4a^2x - 8ax + 12ax^2}{4ax}$

$= \dfrac{4a^2x}{4ax} - \dfrac{8ax}{4ax} + \dfrac{12ax^2}{4ax} = a - 2 + 3x$

Check. $4ax(a - 2 + 3x) = 4a^2x - 8ax + 12ax^2$

PRACTICE

1. Simplify: $\dfrac{6x^2 + 12x^3}{-6x^2}$

A. $1 - 2x$

B. $-1 - 2x$

C. $-x + 2x^2$

D. $2x - 1$

2. Simplify: $\dfrac{a^5x - 2a^4x^2 + a^3x^3}{a^2x}$

A. $a^5x - 2a^2x + a^3x^3$

B. $a^3x - 2a^2x^2 + ax^3$

C. $a^3 - 2a^2x + ax^2$

D. $a^2 - 2a^2x + ax$

Exercises 3–20: Simplify the following expressions by dividing by the monomial or constant.

3. $\dfrac{p + prt}{p}$

4. $\dfrac{5x^4 + 3x^2}{x^2}$

5. $\dfrac{4a^2 - a}{-a}$

6. $\dfrac{8x^3 - 6xy}{2x}$

7. $\dfrac{12x^2 - 18xy + 24y^2}{6}$

8. $\dfrac{4a^2 + 3b^2 - c^2}{-1}$

9. $\dfrac{c^2d - cd^2}{cd}$

10. $\dfrac{\pi r^2h + 4\pi rh}{\pi rh}$

11. $\dfrac{5x^3 - 4x^2 - 2x}{-x}$

12. $\dfrac{24x^3 - 12x^2 + 15x}{3x}$

13. $\dfrac{8x^3 - 14x^2 + 2x}{-2x}$

14. $\dfrac{10a^3b^3 - 5a^2b^2 + 15ab}{5ab}$

15. $\dfrac{-x^3 + 5x^4 - 6x^5}{-x^3}$

16. $\dfrac{x^a + x^y + x}{x}$

17. $\dfrac{6x^8 - 8x^6 - 2x^4}{2x^4}$

18. $\dfrac{9a^5b^3 - 27a^2b^2 + 6a^3b^5}{-3ab^2}$

19. $\dfrac{3.4a^8b^9c^{10} - 5.1a^6b^2c^8}{-1.7a^6b^2c^8}$

20. $\dfrac{5a^4 - 15a^3 + 45a^2 - 10a}{-5a}$

CHAPTER 6 REVIEW

1. If Dr. Beck has a *weekly* income of x dollars and his average *monthly* expenses are m dollars, which of the following algebraic expressions represents the amount of money he saves in one year?

A. $12(4x - 12m)$
B. $52m - 12x$
C. $52x - 12m$
D. $12m - 12x$

2. Evaluate each of the following.

a 4^{-2}
b 10^{-3}
c 2×10^{-2}
d -10^{-2}
e $(-8)^2$
f -8^2
g $\left(-\frac{1}{4}\right)^{-3}$
h $(-4)^{-3}$
i $7^0 + 7^{-2} \times 7$
j $-1^4 \times (-1)^5$

3. Simplify and express the following with positive exponents.

a $5^2 \times 5^7$
b $(8^2)^3$
c $(10 \times 10^3)^2$
d x^{-3}
e $3a^{-2}$
f $a^{-1}b^2$
g $\frac{4x^3}{y^{-2}}$
h $\frac{15x^{-1}}{3x^{-2}}$
i $(3x^{-4})^2$
j $(xy)^4 \div (xy)^3 \times (0.2)^{-3}$

4. Which expression is a perfect square trinomial?

A. $x^2 + x + 1$
B. $x^2 + 2x + 1$
C. $x^2 + 1 + y^2$
D. $x^2 - 4x - 4$

5. Which of the following equations is correct?

A. $x^a \bullet x^a = x^a + 1$
B. $(x^a)^2 \bullet (x^b) = x^{2ab}$
C. $(x^2)^3 \bullet (x^a)^2 = x^{6+2a}$
D. $(x^n)^3 \bullet (x^3)^n = x^{9n}$

6. Simplify: $2^a + 2^a + 2^a + 2^a =$

A. 2^{2+a}
B. 2^{4a}
C. 8^a
D. 8^{4a}

7. Which of the following expressions is *not equivalent* to $\frac{1}{36}$?

A. $6^{-1} \bullet 6^{-1}$
B. $6^3 \bullet 6^{-5}$
C. $6^{-2} \bullet 6^4$
D. $6^{-3} \bullet 6$

8. In each of the following:

(1) Write the polynomial in standard form.
(2) Name the coefficients of each term.
(3) State the degree of each term.
(4) State the degree of the polynomial.

a $3x - x^2 + 5x^3 - 2 + 4x^5$
b $3ab + 3ab^2 + ab^3 + b^4 + a$

Exercises 9–41: Simplify each expression.

9. $7ax - ax$

10. $2x^2 - 8a^2 + 5x^2 - 4ax - 3a^2 + 4a^2 - 5ax$

11. $3a - 4 - (-2a^2 - a)$

12. $7x^2 - 3x + 5 - (7x^2 - 5x - 5)$

13. $(mr)(mr)(-m)$

14. $(-x)^2(x^2y)(-y)^3$

15. $-3(x - y)$

16. $x(a + b - 1)$

17. $4x(x - 1)$

Chapter Review continues . . .

18. $x^3(x^4y - 2z)$

19. $3a^2(b - k - 1)$

20. $0.5ab(-8a + 2b + 5)$

21. $\pi r^2(h - 4r + 1)$

22. $10^a(10^b + 10^c)$

23. $(-3x^2y^5)^3$

24. $(-2a^2b^2)^3 + (4a^3b^3)^2$

25. $(x + 2)^2$

26. $(x - 2y)^2$

27. $(3x + 7)^2$

28. $(3x - 7)(3x + 7)$

29. $3x - 7(3x + 7)$

30. $(2n + 3)(n^2 - 4n - 1)$

31. $\frac{36a^3b^2}{-9a^2b}$

32. $\frac{7a^3b^2c^5}{-28a^2b^2c^2}$

33. $\frac{10x^{3a}}{2x^a}$

34. $\frac{2x^2 + 4x}{x}$

35. $\frac{\pi r^2 - 2\pi r}{\pi r}$

36. $\frac{2a^4 - 3a^3 - 4a^2}{-a^2}$

37. $\frac{x^2 + 7x - 8}{x + 8}$

38. $\frac{a^2 - 5a - 36}{a + 4}$

39. $6b + 2b(-3b + 2) + 5b^2$

40. $a - (a - 5)(a + 2)$

41. $2[x^2 + 3(x - 2)] - 3[x^2 + 3(x - 1)]$

42. **MP 2, 3, 7** Molina noticed that when she had three consecutive integers, such as 3, 4, 5, that $(3)(5) = 15$ and $4^2 = 16$. And, again, with 6, 7, 8, that $(6)(8) = 48$, while $7^2 = 49$. After working with both positive and negative integers, Molina offered the following conjecture: Given any three consecutive integers, starting with x, the product of the first and the third is one less than the square of the second. Clearly identify your own variables and show that, algebraically, she's right.

43. **MP 2, 3, 7** Molina's friend, Thor, said that $6^2 - 5^2$ is $36 - 25$ or 11, and that $6 + 5$ is also 11. He noticed that a similar result occurred for 9 and 10: that $10^2 - 9^2 = 100 - 81$ or 19, and that $10 + 9 = 19$. So, using those examples and many others, Thor concluded that the *positive difference* between the squares of two consecutive integers is always equal to the sum of those two integers. Show that, algebraically, he's right.

44. **MP 2** The perimeter of a rectangle is $10a + 8$ and the length is $4a + 7$.

- **a** What is the algebraic expression for the width of the rectangle? Show your work.
- **b** What is the area of the rectangle in simplest form?

45. **MP 2, 3** If n is an even number and $n + 1$ is an odd number, show algebraically that the square of an odd number is also an odd number. State your argument clearly.

46. **MP 3** The height in feet of a ball tossed in the air is given by the function $h(t) = -16t^2 + 32t + 4$, where t is time in seconds since the ball was tossed.

- **a** Find the height of the ball 1 second after it was tossed.
- **b** Find the height after 0.5 seconds and 1.5 seconds.
- **c** What conclusion can you draw from the answer to part **b**?

47. **MP 3, 7**

- **a** Use your arithmetic understanding in adding two fractions with different denominators and write a single fraction that expresses $x^{-1} + y^{-1}$.
- **b** Give a counterexample to show why $x^{-1} + y^{-1} \neq \frac{1}{x + y}$. Use your result in part **a** as another way to support your answer.

Cumulative Review for Chapters 1–6

1. **MP 7** If $x + 3$ is an even integer, then which of the following is an odd integer?

A. $(x + 3)(x + 4)$ C. $(x + 4)(x + 5)$

B. $(x + 3)^2$ D. $(x + 4)^2$

2. **MP 2, 7** Which statement is always true if the domain of the variables is the set of positive integers?

A. $\sqrt{x^2 + y^2} = x + y$

B. $xy = y$

C. $\dfrac{x + y}{z} = \dfrac{x}{z} + \dfrac{y}{z}$

D. $(x + y)^2 = x^2 + y^2$

3. Which graph represents the solution set of $|3x - 12| < 9$?

A. 

B. 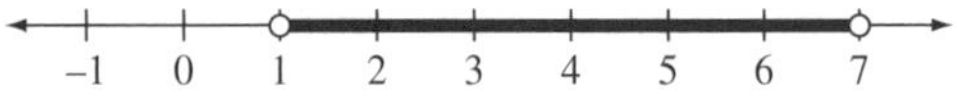

C. 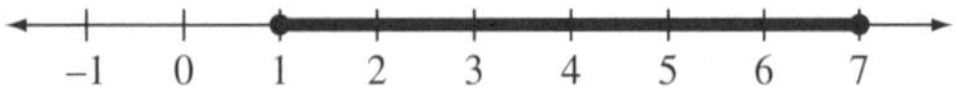

D. 

4. **MP 1, 2, 7, 8** The square on the left and the rectangle on the right have the same perimeters. What is the area of the rectangle on the right?

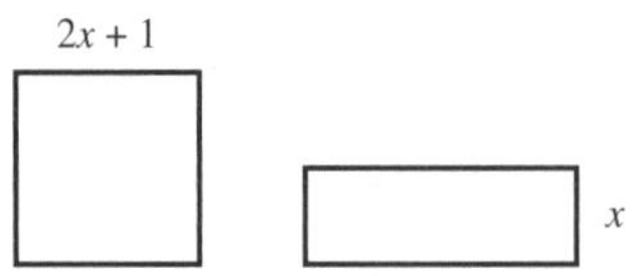

A. $4x^2 + 4x + 1$ C. $6x^2 + 4x$

B. $8x^2 + 4x$ D. $3x^2 + 2x$

5. If $g(x) = \sqrt{x - 1}$, what is the domain of values for x for which $g(x)$ is a real number?

A. $x \geq 0$ C. $0 \leq x \leq 1$

B. $x \geq 1$ D. $x \geq -1$

6. Which of the following represents the graph of the equation $x = |y - 2|$?

A. 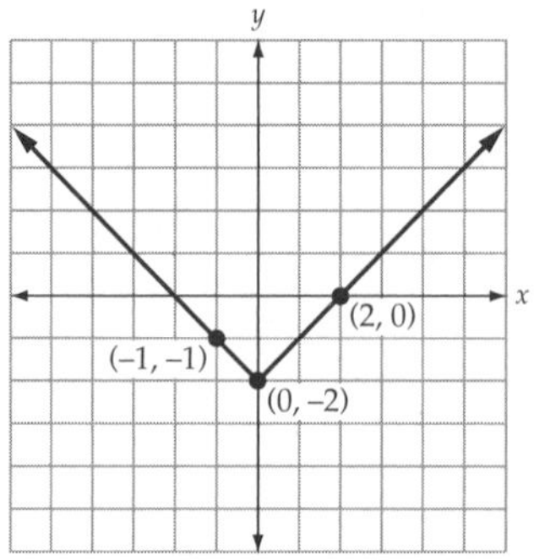

B. 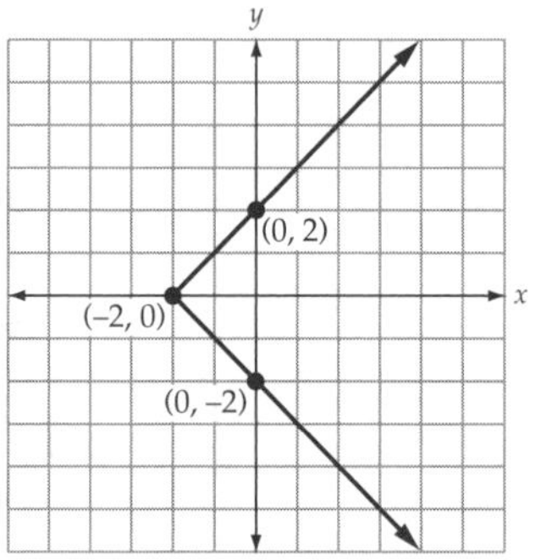

C. 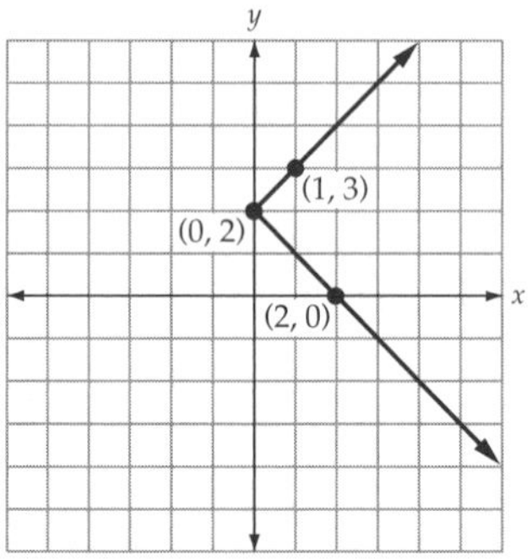

D. 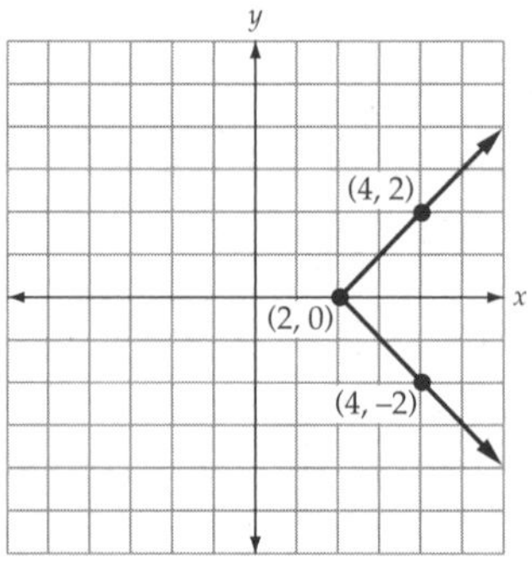

7. If $x = 4$ is the domain for both functions, where $f(x) = 3x$ and $g(x) = 3^x$, how many times larger is the value of the range for $g(x)$ than for $f(x)$?

A. They are equal.

B. 6.75

C. 5.33

D. $\frac{4}{27}$

8. Simplify:
$(2x + 3)(3x - 5) - [(1 + 2x)(1 - 2x)]$

A. $10x^2 - x - 16$

B. $10x^2 + 7x - 14$

C. $2x^2 - x - 14$

D. $2x^2 - 9x - 16$

9. Which equation is represented by the given graph?

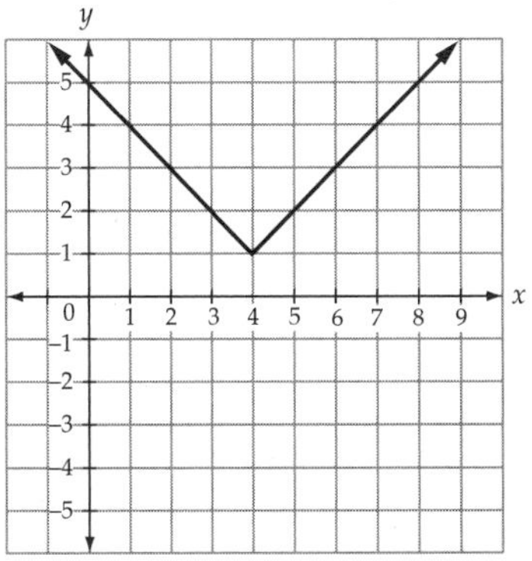

A. $y = |x| - 4$ C. $y = |x + 4| - 1$

B. $y = |x - 4| + 1$ D. $y = |x + 4| + 1$

10. If $\frac{x}{y} = \frac{2}{3}$, then $9x^2 - 4y^2$ equals

A. -4 C. 4

B. 0   D. 6

11. Classify each polynomial as a *monomial*, *binomial*, or *trinomial*. Determine the degree of the polynomial.

a $x^2 - 8$

b $-15a^3b$

c $3x + 2y - xy$

d $7x^2y^8 - 2x^2y^2$

e 219

12. Solve the following systems of linear equations algebraically. Show your work.

a $5a + b = 13$

$4a - 3b = 18$

b $x + y = 400$

$0.06x - 0.05y = 2$

c $ax = by$

$3ax - 2by = ab$

13. **MP 1, 2, 4** The length of a large rectangular garden is 5 ft longer than its width. The garden is surrounded on all sides by a 2-ft-wide blue-slate walkway. The walkway has an area of 124 ft^2.

a Write an equation using polynomials to model this situation.

b Find the dimensions of the garden.

14. **MP 7** Simplify the following products:

a $4k^2\left(\frac{k}{4} + \frac{4}{k^2}\right)$

b $10^n(10)$

c $x^{a-1}(x^{a+1})$

d $b^{1-x} \bullet b^{1+x}$

15. MP 1, 2, 4 The difference between, the actual depth of the water (d), and the measured reading (m) is given by the equation $f(d) = |d - m|$. Furthermore, the difference between the actual depth d and any measured depths m must be *less than or equal to* 5% of the actual depth.

a If a depth finder shows that clear water in a granite quarry is registering a depth of 520 feet, write a function $f(d)$ that gives the absolute difference between the actual depth and the measured depth.

b Write an inequality that can be used to find the minimum and maximum values of d, to the *nearest tenth of a foot*. State the solution set and the minimum and maximum values.

16. Using the given dimensions,

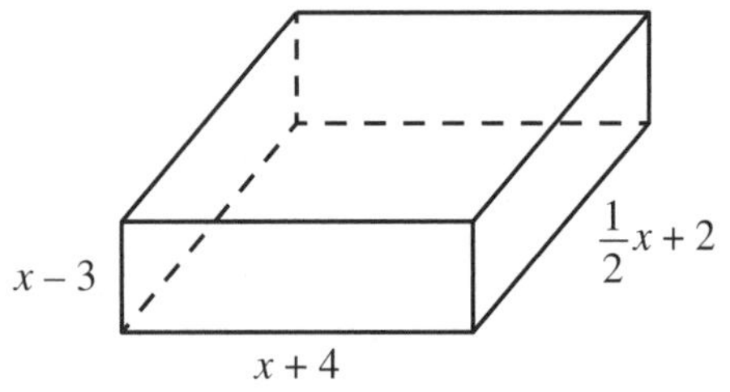

a Write a polynomial to represent the volume of the rectangular prism.

b If the value of x is 4 units, what is the numerical volume of the prism?

c What is the surface area of the rectangular prism?

17. MP 7 Simplify each of the following:

a $\dfrac{-15x^4a^3}{5x^4a}$

b $\dfrac{a^2b - a^2b^2 - 5ab^2}{-ab}$

c $\dfrac{3x^4 - 3x^3 + 3x^2}{-3x^2}$

d $\dfrac{a^x + a^y + a}{a}$

18. The water pressure P at depth d in a lake varies directly as the depth. If the pressure is 625 lb/ft^2 at a depth of 10 ft, find the formula for the pressure at any depth. Find the pressure at a depth of 16 ft.

19. If d varies directly as the square of t and $d = 144$ when $t = 3$, find d when $t = 2$.

20. If y varies directly as the cube of x, and $y = 24$ when $x = 2$, find y when $x = 3$.

21. If x varies directly as $\sqrt{m}$ and if $x = 2$ when $m = 25$, what is the value of x when $m = 100$?

22. If $\dfrac{a^x}{a^y} = a^7$ and $\dfrac{a^x \bullet a^2}{a^{3y}} = a^{19}$, solve for x and y.

23. MP 1, 2, 4, 5, 6 Dylan is a college math student who spends x hours at his part-time neighborhood lawn service getting paid \$20/hr. He spends y hours tutoring at \$30/hr. He wants to make at least \$240 a week, but he can work no more than 12 hours a week.

a Write a system of linear inequalities to represent this situation.

b Graph the solution to this system.

c Describe the range of possible combinations of hours he could work at each job and make at least \$240.

d List two possible hourly combinations that would generate more than \$240/wk.

24. For the following set of inequalities, $y > -3x + 2$ and $y \leq x - 2$:

a Graph on the same xy-plane and label the solution set A.

b State two ordered pairs within A, and one ordered pair not in the solution of either inequality.

25. If line k is the graph of $2x + ay = 6$ where a is a constant and the graph of $x + 10y = 8$ is parallel to line k, what is the value of a?

26. For what values of a and y does $(3a - 1, y) = (5a - 7, 2y - 1)$?

27. Find the inverse, f^{-1}, of each of the following functions:

a $y = 2x - 1$

b $f(x) = -\frac{2}{3}x$

28. MP 2, 4 An oil truck is loaded with 4000 gallons of gasoline and kerosene. The profit is \$0.08 on one gallon of gasoline and \$0.13 on one gallon of kerosene. Let g represent the number of gallons of gasoline and k represent the number of gallons of kerosene. If the profit is \$430, determine the number of gallons of each fuel that was loaded on the truck.

29. MP 5 A hardware company manufactures 6-inch carpenter laser levels. The company calculates its profit by finding the difference between revenue and cost. The cost function for producing x number of levels is $C(x) = 10x + 2800$. If each level sells for \$120, the revenue function for selling x levels is $R(x) = 120x$.

a How many levels must be sold to make a profit?

b How many levels must be sold to make a \$1050 profit?

30. Graph this piecewise function;

$$f(x) = \begin{cases} -1 & \text{if } x < -1 \\ -x + 2 & \text{if } x \geq -1 \end{cases}$$

31. Graph the step function $g(x) = [x] + 1$ over the given domain: $-3 \leq x < 4$.

32. MP 3, 6 Rapunzel, at some point in her study of numbers in the tower, noticed that $3^2 + 4^2 = 9 + 16 = 25$, and $4^2 + 5^2 = 16 + 25 = 41$, and $5^2 + 6^2 = 61$, etc. She said there was a pattern and that "the sum of the squares of consecutive integers is always an odd number."

Make an algebraic argument showing this conjecture is true. Clearly define your variables and identify the meaning of each term in your argument.

Chapter 7 Special Products and Factoring

Chapter Focus

In working with algebraic fractions, fractional equations, formulas, and quadratic equations, we often need to find two or more factors whose product is a given expression. This process is called *factoring*. Factoring is the reverse of distributing.

Chapter Content

Chapter Vocabulary

factoring	**greatest common factor**	**special product**
factoring by grouping	**quadratic trinomial**	**sum and product rule**
factoring completely		

Factoring

In algebra, **factoring** means breaking a polynomial into two or more parts, or its factors. When these factors are multiplied, the product is the original polynomial. Three types of factoring in algebra are:

Type 1: Factoring out the greatest common monomial

Type 2: Factoring a binomial that is the difference of two squares

Type 3: Factoring trinomials

We will use two **special products** of polynomials as shortcuts in factoring:

Special Product 1	Special Product 2
$(x + y)(x - y) = x^2 - y^2$	$(x + y)(x + y) = x^2 + 2xy + y^2$ $(x - y)(x - y) = x^2 - 2xy + y^2$

LESSON 7.1

7.1 Greatest Common Factors

The **greatest common factor** (GCF) in a polynomial is the factor that is common to each term that has the greatest possible coefficient and the greatest possible power of each variable.

> We can use the greatest common factor to factor polynomials.

We identify the greatest common factor in $4x^2 + 8x$.

- 2 is a factor of all terms.
- 4 is a factor of all terms.
- x is a factor of all terms.
- The greatest common factor is $4x$.

MODEL PROBLEMS

1. **MP 7, 8** Factor $2x^2 + 2x$. Show your work.

SOLUTION

Step 1. Examine the polynomial to find like factors that appear in each term. Look for the largest number and the variable with the highest exponent that will divide evenly into each term of the polynomial. $2, x$

Step 2. Expressed as a product, $2x$, this is the greatest common monomial factor (GCF). Write the GCF outside a pair of parentheses. $2x(\quad)$

Step 3. Divide each term by the GCF. $\frac{2x^2}{2x} = x \qquad \frac{2x^1}{2x^1} = 1$

Step 4. Write the results as a polynomial inside the parentheses. $2x(x + 1)$

Check. Multiply.

$$2x(x + 1) = (2x \bullet x) + (2x \bullet 1)$$
$$= 2x^2 + 2x \checkmark$$

Box method.

	x	$+1$
$2x$	$2x^2$	$2x$

$2x^2 + 2x$ ✓

2. Factor: $12abc^2 - 24a^2c$

SOLUTION

Step 1. Find like factors. $12, a, c$

Step 2. Set up parentheses. $12ac(\quad)$

Step 3. Divide.

$$12abc^2 \div 12ac = bc$$
$$-24a^2c \div 12ac = -2a$$

Step 4. Fill in the parentheses. $12ac(bc - 2a)$

To check factors, multiply. The product should be the given expression.

Check. Multiply.

$$12ac(bc - 2a)$$
$$= (12ac \bullet bc) + [12ac \bullet (-2a)]$$
$$= 12abc^2 + (-24a^2c)$$
$$= 12abc^2 - 24a^2c \checkmark$$

Box method.

	bc	$-2a$
$12ac$	$12abc^2$	$-24a^2c$

$12abc^2 - 24a^2c$ ✓

Here are some more examples:

Expression	Factors
$x^3y + 4xy^2$	$xy(x^2 + 4y)$
$6a^3 + 12a^2 + 3a$	$3a(2a^2 + 4a + 1)$
$15a^2x - 3x$	$3x(5a^2 - 1)$
$3x(4x - 1) + 5(4x - 1)$	$(4x - 1)(3x + 5)$
$6cy^2 - 6cx^2$	$6c(y + x)(y - x)$

PRACTICE

1. Which expression cannot be factored?

A. $x^2 + 2x$ C. $x + 1$

B. $3x^2 + 9$ D. $2x^2 + 6x - 10$

Exercises 2–3: In which case is the greatest common monomial factored out correctly?

2. $6x^3 - 9x^2 - 12x$

A. $3x^2(6x - 9 - 12)$
B. $3x(2x^2 - 3x - 4)$
C. $x(6x^2 - 9x - 12)$
D. $3(2x^3 - 3x - 4x)$

3. $5a^2bc - 5ab^2c - 5abc$

A. $5abc(abc)$
B. $5abc(a - b - 5)$
C. $5abc(a - b - 1)$
D. $5abc(a - b - c)$

4. In which case is the greatest common factor *not* a monomial expression?

A. $27x^3 - 6x^2 + 15x$
B. $x^2(a - 3b) + x^2(a - 3b)$
C. $21xz - 35ax - 3yz + 5ay$
D. $2g^2 + 2g$

MP 7 Exercises 5–15: Factor each expression. Show your work.

5. $5a - 5b$

6. $2x + 6y$

7. $ax + ab$

8. $gd - gr$

9. $ar^2 + 5a$

10. $10x^2y + 15xy^2$

11. $a(a - 7) + 9(a - 7)$

12. $x^2(x + 2) + 7(x + 2)$

13. $30x^5y^5 - 20x^3y^9 + 10x^3y^5$

14. $y(y - 1) + 2(y - 1)$

15. $8rta - 6rtb + 10rtc$

7.2 Factoring the Difference of Two Squares

A pattern can be recognized when multiplying the sum and difference of two monomials. Use the following model problems to identify a pattern.

MODEL PROBLEMS

MP 7, 8 Model Problems 1–3: Multiply and show your work.

SOLUTION

1. $(m + n)(m - n)$ $\quad (m + n)(m - n) = m^2 - mn + mn - n^2 = m^2 - n^2$

2. $(2j + k)(2j - k)$ $\quad (2j + k)(2j - k) = (2j)^2 - k^2 = 4j^2 - k^2$

3. $\left(\frac{x^3}{2} + \frac{y}{3}\right)\left(\frac{x^3}{2} - \frac{y}{3}\right)$ $\quad \left(\frac{x^3}{2} + \frac{y}{3}\right)\left(\frac{x^3}{2} - \frac{y}{3}\right) = \left(\frac{x^3}{2}\right)^2 - \left(\frac{y}{3}\right)^2 = \frac{x^6}{4} - \frac{y^2}{9}$

Certain products occur so often that you should recognize them at sight, and this product is one of them. It can be calculated using the distributive property or the FOIL method (see Chapter 6).

4. MP 7, 8 Use special product 1 to identify a pattern when multiplying the sum and difference of two monomials. Fill in the missing signs.

		SOLUTION
Special Product 1	$(x + y)(x - y) = x^2 \square y^2$	$(x + y)(x - y) = x^2 - y^2$
Examples	$(x + 6)(x \square 6) = x^2 \square 36$ $(4 \square x)(4 - x) = 16 \square x^2$	$(x + 6)(x - 6) = x^2 - 36$ $(4 + x)(4 - x) = 16 - x^2$

Special product 1 gives us an important rule:

> The product of two binomials of the form $(x + y)(x - y)$ equals the *difference of two squares*, $x^2 - y^2$.
>
> - To factor the difference of two squares, write two binomials that are the sum and difference of the square roots of the two terms.

MODEL PROBLEMS

MP 7, 8 Model Problems 1–5: Factor the following and show your work.

Check to make sure you have **factored completely**. Make sure your factored answer has all prime factors, that is, factors that cannot be further factored.

SOLUTION

1. $a^2 - b^2$ — $(\sqrt{a^2} + \sqrt{b^2})(\sqrt{a^2} - \sqrt{b^2}) = (a + b)(a - b)$

2. $16x^2 - 25$ — $(\sqrt{16x^2} + \sqrt{25})(\sqrt{16x^2} - \sqrt{25}) = (4x + 5)(4x - 5)$

3. $4y^2 - 25x^2$ — $(\sqrt{4y^2} + \sqrt{25x^2})(\sqrt{4y^2} - \sqrt{25x^2}) = (2y + 5x)(2y - 5x)$

4. $\frac{1}{4}a^2b^2 - x^4$ — $\left(\sqrt{\frac{1}{4}a^2b^2} + \sqrt{x^4}\right)\left(\sqrt{\frac{1}{4}a^2b^2} - \sqrt{x^4}\right) = \left(\frac{1}{2}ab + x^2\right)\left(\frac{1}{2}ab - x^2\right)$

5. $x^4 - 16$ — $(\sqrt{x^4} - \sqrt{16})(\sqrt{x^4} + \sqrt{16}) = (x^2 - 4)(x^2 + 4) = (x - 2)(x + 2)(x^2 + 4)$

PRACTICE

Exercises 1–2: Factor the binomial.

1. $x^2y^2 - 100 =$

A. $10xy(-10xy)$

B. $(x + y + 10)(x + y - 10)$

C. $(xy - 10)(xy - 10)$

D. $(xy + 10)(xy - 10)$

2. $\frac{9}{16}y^2 - 36 =$

A. $\left(\frac{9}{4}y + 4\right)\left(\frac{9}{4}y - 4\right)$

B. $\left(6y + \frac{3}{4}\right)\left(6y - \frac{3}{4}\right)$

C. $\left(\frac{3}{4}y + 6\right)\left(\frac{3}{4}y - 6\right)$

D. $\left(\frac{3}{4}y + 9\right)\left(\frac{3}{4}y - 9\right)$

3. Which binomial is factored correctly?

A. $\frac{x^2}{4} - \frac{y^2}{9} = \left(\frac{x}{2} + \frac{y}{3}\right)\left(\frac{y}{3} - \frac{x}{2}\right)$

B. $b^2 - 0.01 = (b - 0.1)(b - 0.1)$

C. $49 - 0.81x^2y^2 = (7 + 0.09xy)(7 - 0.09xy)$

D. $4a^6 - 9b^{10} = (2a^3 + 3b^5)(2a^3 - 3b^5)$

4. Which binomial is factored *incorrectly*?

A. $y^2 - 1 = (y + 1)(y - 1)$

B. $\frac{4}{9}a^2 - \frac{9}{25}y^2 = \left(\frac{2}{3}a + \frac{3}{5}y\right)\left(\frac{2}{3}a - \frac{3}{5}y\right)$

C. $9y^2 - 16 = (3y + 4)(3y - 4)$

D. $x^2y^2 - z^2 = (x^2y + 1)(x^2y - 1)$

MP 7, 8 Exercises 5–14: Find each product.

5. $(2m + 2n)(2m - 2n)$

6. $(0.2x + y)(0.2x - y)$

7. $(x^2 + y^2)(x^2 - y^2)$

8. $(a^2 + b^3)(a^2 - b^3)$

9. $(k + 5)(k - 5)$

10. $(4h + 3)(4h - 3)$

11. $\left(\frac{3}{4}p + \frac{2}{3}q\right)\left(\frac{3}{4}p - \frac{2}{3}q\right)$

12. $(12 + 3d)(12 - 3d)$

13. $(5f - 2g)(5f + 2g)$

14. $\left(\frac{3s^4}{t^2} - 6\right)\left(\frac{3s^4}{t^2} + 6\right)$

15. **MP 3** If you've found a shortcut for exercises 5–14, explain what it is and why it works.

Practice Problems continue . . .

MP 7 Exercises 16–31: Factor each binomial completely.

16. $a^2 - 49$

17. $m^2 - 64$

18. $49x^2 - y^2$

19. $36 - x^2$

20. $16x^2 - 1$

21. $r^2 - s^2$

22. $x^2 - y^4$

23. $a^2 - 4b^2$

24. $9a^2 - 16y^2$

25. $81x^4 - 16y^8$

26. $49 - 4m^2$

27. $25a^2 - 81b^2$

28. $y^2 - c^2d^2$

29. $s^2t^2 - k^2n^2$

30. $x^4 - 0.0016$

31. $81 - x^4$

32. What does the phrase "difference of perfect squares" mean? Give an example of an expression that is a difference of perfect squares.

33. MP 3, 7 Write an expression that is the sum of two perfect squares. Can you rewrite the expression as a product of two binomials (like you did in exercises 16–31)? Justify your answer.

LESSON 7.3

7.3 Factoring Trinomials

A third type of factoring involves trinomials. Two cases of factoring trinomials are perfect square trinomials and general quadratic trinomials.

Perfect Square Trinomials

In factoring a perfect square trinomial, we use special product 2, the square of a binomial:

Special Product 2	Examples
$(x + y)^2 = (x + y)(x + y) = x^2 + 2xy + y^2$	$(x + 6)^2 = (x + 6)(x + 6) = x^2 + 12x + 36$
$(x - y)^2 = (x - y)(x - y) = x^2 - 2xy + y^2$	$(x - 4)^2 = (x - 4)(x - 4) = x^2 - 8x + 16$

Special product 2 lets us identify a perfect square trinomial:

- The first and last terms must be perfect squares and must be positive (+).
- The middle term must be twice the product of the square roots of the first and last terms.
- The middle term can be positive (+) or negative (−). The sign of the middle term (+ or −) is the same as the sign between the terms of the squared binomial.

Methods of squaring a binomial are reviewed in Chapter 6. One method is FOIL.

Special product 2 also gives us a rule for factoring a perfect trinomial square:

- If the middle term is *positive*, the factors will be of the form $(x + y)(x + y)$.
- If the middle term is *negative*, the factors will be of the form $(x - y)(x - y)$.
- The x term in the factors is the square root of the first term in the given trinomial.
- The y term in the factors is the square root of the last term in the given trinomial.

MODEL PROBLEMS

Model Problems 1–3: Factor these perfect square trinomials:

1. $x^2 + 6x + 9$

SOLUTION

The middle term is positive, so the factors will have the form $(x + y)(x + y)$.

The x term in the factors is $\sqrt{x^2} = x$.

The y term in the factors is $\sqrt{9} = 3$.

Answer: $(x + 3)(x + 3)$ or $(x + 3)^2$

2. $x^2 - 10x + 25$

SOLUTION

The middle term is negative, so the factors will have the form $(x - y)(x - y)$.

The x term in the factors is $\sqrt{x^2} = x$.

The y term in the factors is $\sqrt{25} = 5$.

Answer: $(x - 5)(x - 5)$ or $(x - 5)^2$

3. $4x^2 + 12x + 9$

SOLUTION

The middle term is positive, so the factors will have the form $(x + y)(x + y)$.

The x term in the factors is $\sqrt{4x^2} = 2x$.

The y term in the factors is $\sqrt{9} = 3$.

Answer: $(2x + 3)(2x + 3)$ or $(2x + 3)^2$

Special Quadratic Trinomials of the Form $x^2 + bx + c$

When the *leading coefficient* (the coefficient of the term of highest degree in a polynomial expression) is 1, the coefficients of both x terms of the binomial factors are 1. In addition, the sum of the factors of the last term must equal the coefficient of the middle term. In other words, the sum of the factors of c must equal b. We call this the **sum and product rule**.

A general **quadratic trinomial** has the form $ax^2 + bx + c$. When we attempt to factor general trinomials, we always make sure we start with the trinomials in standard form.

MODEL PROBLEMS

Model Problems 1–2: Factor the following trinomials.

1. $x^2 + 10x + 24$

SOLUTION

We see that $b = 10$ and $c = 24$. Since both b and c are positive, the solution must be of the form $(x + m)(x + n)$. We list the factors of 24 and compute their sums. Stay organized. Start your list with 1 and 24 and continue with increasing whole numbers in the left column and decreasing whole numbers in the right column. Stop when the sum of the factors equals 10, the value of b.

Factors of *c*		Sum of factors
1	24	25
2	12	14
3	8	11
4	6	10

The numbers we need are 4 and 6, since the sum of the factors is equal to b, which in this case is 10.

Answer: The factors are $(x + 4)$ and $(x + 6)$.
$(x + 4)(x + 6)$ or $(x + 6)(x + 4)$ equals $x^2 + 10x + 24$
Because multiplication is commutative, the order of the factors does not matter.

2. $x^2 - 10x + 16$

SOLUTION

We see that $b < 0$ and $c > 0$. Since the constant c is positive, but b is negative, the solution must be of the form $(x - m)(x - n)$. This is the only way for the product mn to be positive, but the sum $m + n$ to be negative.

We know both binomials are differences. We list the negative factor pairs of 16, starting with -1 and -16, and stopping when the sum of the factors equals -10, the value of b.

Factors of *c*		Sum of factors
−1	−16	−17
−2	−8	−10

The numbers we need are −2 and −8. We stop here. The sum of the factors is −10, the value of b.

Answer: $(x - 2)$ and $(x - 8)$
$(x - 2)(x - 8)$ or $(x - 8)(x - 2)$ equals $x^2 - 10x + 16$

Model Problems continue . . .

Model Problems *continued*

3. $x^2 - 5x - 6$

SOLUTION

We see that $b\ (-5) < 0$ and $c\ (-6) < 0$. This is another pattern. Since both the constants c and b are negative, the solution must be of the form $(x - m)(x + n)$. The sum of the factors of the last term must equal the coefficient of the middle term. In other words, the sum of the factors of c must equal b.

We list the factor pairs of -6.

Factors of *c*		Sum of factors
−1	6	5
1	−6	−5
−2	3	1
2	−3	−1

The numbers we need are 1 and −6, since the sum of the factors is equal to *b*, which in this case is −5.

Answer: $(x + 1)$ and $(x - 6)$
$(x + 1)(x - 6)$ or $(x - 6)(x + 1)$ equals $x^2 - 5x - 6$

To Factor $x^2 + bx + c$

(1) If c is *positive,* find the factors of c that sum to $|b|$.

- If b is *positive,* both factors are positive, so the binomial factors are of the form $(x + m)(x + n)$. For example, $x^2 + 7x + 12 = (x + 3)(x + 4)$.
- If b is *negative,* both factors are negative, so the binomial factors are of the form $(x - m)(x - n)$. For example, $x^2 - 7x + 12 = (x - 3)(x - 4)$.

(2) If c is *negative,* find the factors of $|c|$ that have a difference of $|b|$. Then determine the signs of the factors. The binomial factors are of the form $(x - m)(x + n)$. For example, $x^2 + 2x - 15 = (x - 3)(x + 5)$ and $x^2 - 2x - 15 = (x + 3)(x - 5)$.

General Quadratic Trinomials of the Form $ax^2 + bx + c$, where $a \neq 1$

When factoring a general quadratic trinomial, we often use trial and error, testing all pairs of possible binomials until the product is the given trinomial. However, certain patterns help us factor more quickly. As with all of the above, the signs of the factors are determined by whether bx and c are being added or subtracted.

- If all three terms of the given trinomial are positive (+), the factored expression has the form $(dx + e)(fx + g)$ where the product of d and f is the lead coefficient a, of x^2, and the product of e and g is the constant term c. For example, $2x^2 + 8x + 6 = (2x + 2)(x + 3)$.

- If only the middle term, b, of the given trinomial is negative ($-$), the factored expression has the form $(dx - e)(fx - g)$ where the product of d and f is the lead coefficient a, of x^2, and the product of e and g is the constant term c. For example, $2x^2 - 8x + 6 = (2x - 2)(x - 3)$.

- If the last term, c, is negative, one binomial factor is the sum of two monomials $(dx + e)$ and the other binomial factor is the difference of two monomials $(fx - g)$. Again, the product of d and f is the lead coefficient a, of x^2, and the product of the positive and negative second terms is the constant term c. For example, $2x^2 + 4x - 6 = (2x - 2)(x + 3)$ and $2x^2 - 4x - 6 = (2x + 2)(x - 3)$.

MODEL PROBLEMS

MP 7 Model Problems 1–5: Factor each quadratic trinomial and show your work.

1. $x^2 + 7x + 12$

SOLUTION

Since all the signs of the given trinomial are positive, both factors will have the form $(x + y)$.

Here the coefficient of the first term is 1, so we try only factors of 12: 1 • 12, 2 • 6, and 3 • 4:

Try $(x + 1)(x + 12) = x^2 + 13x + 12$ ✗

Try $(x + 2)(x + 6) = x^2 + 8x + 12$ ✗

Try $(x + 3)(x + 4) = x^2 + 7x + 12$ ✓

Shortcut: The sum of the factors of 12 must be 7. Only one pair meets this condition: 3, 4.

2. $x^2 - 10x + 24$

SOLUTION

Only the middle term is negative, so both factors will have the form $(x - y)$.

Since the coefficient of the first term is 1, test just the factors of 24. In this case, at least one of these factors must be negative, since their sum must be -10. Because their product is $+24$, *both* must be negative. Thus, the possible factors are $-1 \bullet (-24), -2 \bullet (-12), -3 \bullet (-8)$, and $-4 \bullet (-6)$.

Only one pair (-4 and -6) gives a sum of -10.

Answer: Therefore, the factors must be $(x - 4)(x - 6)$.

3. $m^2 - m - 2$

SOLUTION

Here, the last term is negative, so the factors will have the form $(x + y)(x - y)$.

The coefficient of the first term is 1, so test only the factors of the last term. Since the last term is -2, one factor must be negative and the other positive: $1 \bullet (-2)$ or $-1 \bullet 2$.

The coefficient of the middle term is -1, and only the pair $1, -2$ will add up to -1.

Answer: The factors are $(m + 1)(m - 2)$.

Model Problems continue . . .

Model Problems *continued*

4. $x^2 + 3x - 18$

SOLUTION

The factors will have the form $(x + y)(x - y)$.

We need to test only the factors of the last term. One must be positive and the other negative. The possible factors are $1 \bullet (-18), -1 \bullet 18, 2 \bullet (-9), -2 \bullet 9, 3 \bullet (-6)$, and $-3 \bullet 6$.

Of these, only the pair $-3, 6$ will add up to the middle coefficient, 3.

Answer: The factors are $(x + 6)(x - 3)$.

5. $2x^2 + 9x - 35$

SOLUTION

The factors will have the form $(x + y)(x - y)$.

Here the coefficient of the first term is 2. Therefore, we must consider the factors of both 2 and -35.

Factors of 2: $1 \bullet 2$ and $2 \bullet 1$

Factors of -35: $1 \bullet (-35), -1 \bullet 35, 5 \bullet (-7)$, and $-5 \bullet 7$

We can eliminate $1 \bullet (-35)$ and $-1 \bullet 35$, since these would yield sums that are too great.

Use trial and error with the remaining choices, applying FOIL to check.
For example:

Try $(x - 5)(2x + 7) = 2x^2 + 7x - 10x - 35 = 2x^2 - 3x - 35$ ✗

Try $(2x - 7)(x + 5) = 2x^2 + 10x - 7x - 35 = 2x^2 + 3x - 35$ ✗

Try $(2x - 5)(x + 7) = 2x^2 + 14x - 5x - 35 = 2x^2 + 9x - 35$ ✓

Answer: $(2x - 5)(x + 7)$

With experience, you will get better and better at guessing and testing.

Factoring by Grouping

Aside from trial and error, there are other procedures you might try. A useful method is **factoring by grouping**. This method is extremely helpful when the lead coefficient is greater than 1. The procedure is best shown by example.

Factoring by Grouping	Example
Factor $ax^2 + bx + c$.	Factor $6x^2 + 19x + 15$
Find the product ac, the coefficients of the first and last terms.	$6 \bullet 15 = 90$
Find the factors of ac that sum to b, the coefficient of the middle term.	1 and 90; 91 2 and 45; 47 3 and 30; 33 5 and 18; 23 6 and 15; 21 9 and 10; 19 ✓

Rewrite the middle term, $19x$, as $10x$ plus $9x$. Group terms that have common factors. Group the first 2 terms and last 2 terms. Factor the first pair and factor the last pair.	$6x^2 + 10x + 9x + 15$ $(6x^2 + 10x) + (9x + 15)$ $2x(3x + 5) + 3(3x + 5)$
Factor out the common binomial $(3x + 5)$.	$(3x + 5)(2x + 3)$
Note: You will get the same answer if you wrote $19x$ as $9x$ plus $10x$.	$6x^2 + 9x + 10x + 15$ $(6x^2 + 9x) + (10x + 15)$ $3x(2x + 3) + 5(2x + 3)$ $(3x + 5)(2x + 3)$

Factoring by Rewriting	**Example**
Factor $p^4 + 2p^2 + 1$	Note that p^4 can be rewritten as $(p^2)(p^2) = (p^2)^2$
$(p^2)^2 + 2(p^2) + 1$	$(p^2 + 1)(p^2 + 1)$

Look for structure in problems where the trinomial exponents are greater than we see in a trinomial in standard form. Use rules for multiplying monomials with the same base.

PRACTICE

1. Which expression is a perfect trinomial square?

A. $x^2 - 5x + 4$
B. $x^2 + \frac{1}{2}x + \frac{1}{4}$
C. $4x^2 - 4x + 1$
D. $x^2 + 7x + \frac{4}{49}$

2. Factor: $7x^2 + 9x - 10$

A. $(7x + 10)(x - 1)$
B. $(7x - 5)(x + 2)$
C. $(7x + 2)(x - 5)$
D. $(7x - 1)(x + 10)$

3. Factor: $2x^2 - x - 3$

A. $(2x + 1)(x + 3)$
B. $(2x + 3)(x - 1)$
C. $(2x - 3)(x + 1)$
D. $(2x - 3)(x - 1)$

4. Which expression is prime?

A. $x^2 + 4x + 3$
B. $x^2 + 5x + 6$
C. $x^2 + 6x + 8$
D. none of the above

MP 7, 8 Exercises 5–25: Factor each trinomial, if possible. If it is not possible to factor the trinomial, justify your reasoning.

5. $x^2 - 10x + 25$

6. $x^2 - 7x + 12$

7. $x^2 + 2x - 8$

8. $x^2 - 8x - 20$

9. $11x^2 + 12x + 1$

10. $11x^2 - 12x + 1$

11. $x^2 - 5x + \frac{25}{4}$

12. $3y^2 - 4y - 4$

13. $x^2 + 2x + 1$

14. $x^2 + 3x + 2$

15. $4x^2 - 20x + 25$

16. $2x^2 + 5x + 6$

17. $16x^2 + 40x + 25$

18. $a^4 + 2a^2b^2 + b^4$

19. $6x^2 - 11x + 5$

20. $4x^2 - 39x + 81$

21. $10x^2 - 19x + 9$

22. $4x^2 + 16x + 7$

23. $k^4 - 5k^2 + 6$

24. $j^4 - 7j^2 + 12$

25. $m^6 - 11m^3 + 30$

7.4 Factoring Completely

To Factor a Polynomial Completely

(1) Find any common monomial factors.

(2) If the remaining polynomial is a binomial,

- a Check for difference of squares.
- b Check for repeated factoring, such as
  $x^4 - 16 = (x^2 - 4)(x^2 + 4) = (x - 2)(x + 2)(x^2 + 4)$.

(3) If it is a trinomial, try to factor it as the product of two binomials, using structure in the expression, if possible.

After we factor a trinomial, we must make sure the factors cannot be factored again.

MODEL PROBLEMS

Model Problems 1–4: Factor completely.

	SOLUTION
1. $ax^2 - a$	$a(x^2 - 1)$
	$a(x - 1)(x + 1)$
2. $9a^4 - 36b^4$	$9(a^4 - 4b^4)$
	$9(a^2 - 2b^2)(a^2 + 2b^2)$
3. $x^4 - 3x^3 - 40x^2$	$x^2(x^2 - 3x - 40)$
	$x^2(x - 8)(x + 5)$
4. $ax^5 - a^5x^5$	$ax^5(1 - a^4)$
	$ax^5(1 - a^2)(1 + a^2)$
	$ax^5(1 - a)(1 + a)(1 + a^2)$

PRACTICE

1. In factoring completely, the first step is:

A. Write the factors as a product.
B. Find common monomial factors.
C. Use the FOIL method.
D. Find the binomial factors.

Exercises 2–4: Factor the given expression completely.

2. $2x^2 - 72y^2$

A. $2(x + 6y)(x - 6y)$
B. $(\sqrt{2}x + 6\sqrt{2}y)(\sqrt{2}x - 6\sqrt{2}y)$
C. $2x(x - 6y)^2$
D. $2(x - 6y)^2$

3. $2x^2 - 8x - 10$

A. $2(x - 5)(x - 1)$ C. $(2x - 10)(x + 1)$
B. $2(x - 5)(x + 1)$ D. $(x - 10)(2x + 1)$

4. $x^3 - 8x^2 + 16x$

A. $(x^2 - 8)^2$ C. $x(x - 4)^2$
B. $(x - 8)(x^2 + 2)$ D. $x(x - 8)(x + 2)$

Exercises 5–24: Factor each expression completely.

5. $5x^2 - 20$

6. $ab^4 - ax^4$

7. $3x^2 + 12x + 12$

8. $9x^3 - 9x$

Practice Problems continue . . .

9. $3x^2 - 75$

10. $6a^2 - 6a^4$

11. $x^3 - x^2 - 2x$

12. $a^3 - a$

13. $x - 25x^3$

14. $ax^3 - 36ax$

15. $25x^2 - 100y^2$

16. $2a^4 - 32b^4$

17. $9x^2 + 18xy + 9y^2$

18. $5x^2 - 25x + 30$

19. $a - ar^2$

20. $x^2(x + 2) - 9(x + 2)$

21. $4x^2 + 11x + 7$

22. $8x^2 - 33x + 4$

23. $9x^2 - 31x + 12$

24. $4x^2 - 14x + 16$

25. For the expressions below,

(1) $(x + 3)(x + 7)$

(2) $2(x^2 + 10x + 21)$

(3) $x^2 + 4x - 21$

(4) $(2x^2 + 6x)(x - 7)$

a Name pairs of expressions that share exactly one factor.

b Name pairs of expressions that share exactly two factors.

CHAPTER 7 REVIEW

1. Which expression is prime?

A. $3x + 9y$
B. $x - 4$
C. $x^2 - 16$
D. $x^2 - 5x + 6$

Exercises 2–15: Find each product.

2. $3x(x - 4)$

3. $-4j(2j - 5)$

4. $(3 + d)(3 - d)$

5. $(m + 8)(m - 8)$

6. $(g + 4)(g + 2)(g - 2)$

7. $(x + 7)^2$

8. $(s - 1)(s - 1)$

9. $(y + 3)(y + 2)$

10. $(t + 8)(t - 7)$

11. $(j + 4)(2j + 1)$

12. $(3r - 5)(2r + 5)$

13. $4x^2(3 - 2x)$

14. $(4 - x)(x + 1)$

15. $(7 + m)(m + 8)$

MP 6 Exercises 16–30: Factor each expression completely. If it is not possible to factor the expression, justify your reasoning.

16. $3x^2 - 9x$

17. $2ab^2c^3 - 8abc^2$

18. $s^2 - 9$

19. $v^2 - 16c^2$

20. $a^2 + b^2$

21. $d^2 - 81$

22. $k^2 + 5k + 6$

23. $m^2 - 14m + 40$

24. $15 - 2x - x^2$

25. $x^2 - 14x + 9$

26. $2x^2 + 24x + 70$

27. $3ax^2 - 30ax + 48a$

28. $-x^2 + 3x + 28$

29. $a^4 - b^4$

30. $3r^2 - 12s^2$

Cumulative Review for Chapters 1–7

1.

Town	Number of Homes Sold in June
Springfield	26
Plainfield	49
Harborfield	53
Greenfield	12

In June, there were x more homes sold in Summit than in Plainfield and Harborfield combined. Which expression shows the number of homes sold in Summit?

A. $x + 49 + 53$

B. $x + 53 - 49$

C. $49 + 53 - x$

D. $53 - 49 - x$

2. $3.8763 \times 10^{-5} \div 5.345 \times 10^{-6}$ is approximately

A. 7.3

B. 730

C. 0.073

D. 73

3. Solve for x: $3x - 4 > -6x + 14$

A. $x < -2$

B. $x < 2$

C. $x > -2$

D. $x > 2$

4. Evaluate $(6a + 3b)(c - d)$ for $a = 2$, $b = -1$, $c = 4$, and $d = 2$.

A. 36

B. 30

C. 18

D. 10

5. For which of the following functions is $f(1) > f(2)$?

A. $f(x) = |x^2 - x|$

B. $f(x) = |x - x^2|$

C. $f(x) = \dfrac{1}{3 - x}$

D. $f(x) = \dfrac{1}{x - 3}$

6. What is the range of the function $f(x) = x^2 - \left|\dfrac{x}{2}\right|$ when the domain is $\{-2, -1, 0, 1, 2\}$?

A. $\left\{3, \dfrac{1}{2}, 0\right\}$

B. $\left\{-5, -\dfrac{3}{2}, 0\right\}$

C. $\left\{5, \dfrac{3}{2}, 0, \dfrac{1}{2}, 3\right\}$

D. $\left\{-3, -\dfrac{1}{2}, 0, \dfrac{1}{2}, 3\right\}$

7. What is the least value of x that satisfies $|x - 1| = \dfrac{3}{4}$?

A. -1.75

B. -0.75

C. 0.25

D. 1.75

8. Which of the following is the solution set for $|2x - 2| < 8$?

A. $\{x| -5 < x < 3\}$

B. $\{x| -3 < x < 5\}$

C. $\{x|\ x < -5 \text{ or } x > 3\}$

D. $\{x|\ x < -3 \text{ or } x > 5\}$

9. Replace $[(36x^6) \div (6x^6)] \div (6x^{-6})$ with an expression in which x appears only once, raised to a positive exponent.

A. x^6

B. $1296x^9$

C. x^9

D. $36x^3$

10. Write the equation of a line that passes through the points $P(1, 1)$ and $Q(-2, -7)$.

11. Write the equation of a line that passes though the point $A(3, 9)$ and is parallel to the line $y = 4x - 1$.

12. Write the equation of a line that passes through the point $(6, -1)$ and is perpendicular to the line $y = 2x + 6$.

13. Simplify:
$(5x^3 + 3x^2 - 4x + 1) + (x^3 - 2x^2 + 2)$

14. Simplify:
$(4x^3 + 4x^2 - 2x - 1) - (3x^3 - x^2 + 6x + 4)$

15. Divide $x^2 - 4x + 3$ by $x - 3$.

16. If $x = -1.5$, find the value of $f(x) = [x] - x^2 - |x|$.

17. MP 2, 3, 4 The ninth grade and the tenth grade worked on a fund-raiser together. All together, the students raised \$540. If 120 ninth-graders participated and 240 tenth-graders participated, how should the funds be divided between the grades? Draw a diagram to help explain your answer.

18. MP 7 Move the parentheses in the expression $3 - (2 \bullet 5 - 1)$ so the value of the expression is equal to 4.

19. MP 4, 5 A rock is thrown. The height of the rock is $h = -16t^2 + 54t + 7$ at any time, t, measured in seconds. The height is measured in feet.

a Approximately how high is the rock's highest point?

b Approximately when is the rock at its highest point?

c Approximately when does the rock hit the ground?

d What was the vertical distance the rock traveled?

20. MP 3, 6 Mary said an irrational number multiplied by an irrational number must be an irrational number. Ellie said she was wrong. Write an example Ellie might have used and explain your reasoning.

MP 7, 8 Exercises 21–24. Insert parentheses to make each statement true.

21. $5 - 2 \bullet 3^2 + 3 = 36$

22. $5 - 2 \bullet 3^2 + 3 = -19$

23. $5 - 2 \bullet 3^2 + 3 = -16$

24. $5 - 2 \bullet 3^2 + 3 = -10$

25. MP 4 A new playground design is illustrated in the diagram below:

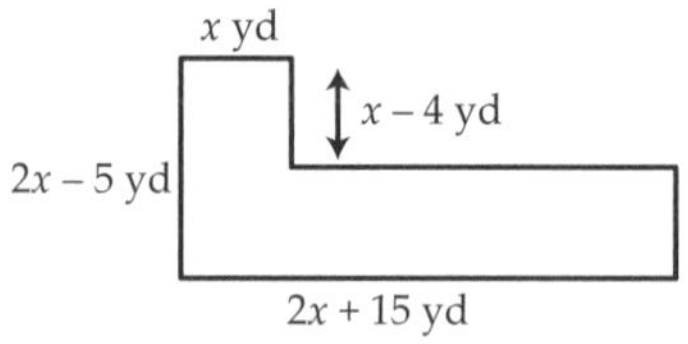

Write an expression for the area of the playground in square feet. Explain the reasoning you used to convert yards to feet.

26. MP 4, 7 The combined value of 12 coins, all either nickels or dimes, is \$1.05. How many nickels were in the mix?

27. Rewrite $\sqrt[3]{3^2}$ using fractional exponents.

28. Given the piecewise function

$$f(x) = \begin{cases} 2x - 4 & \text{if } x \leq 4 \\ 8 - x & \text{if } x > 4 \end{cases}$$

what is the value of $f(3) + f(5)$?

29. MP 2 If you drive at x miles per hour and apply your brakes, your stopping distance increases with driving velocity. Your stopping distance, in feet, is about $x + \frac{x^2}{25}$. Make a chart for the stopping distance, entering velocity values that are multiples of 10 mph, stopping at 70 mph. Graph your values. Plan a useful scale for the vertical axis.

30. MP 4, 7 Dr. Needle is planning to repave his patients' parking lot. The outline for the lot is:

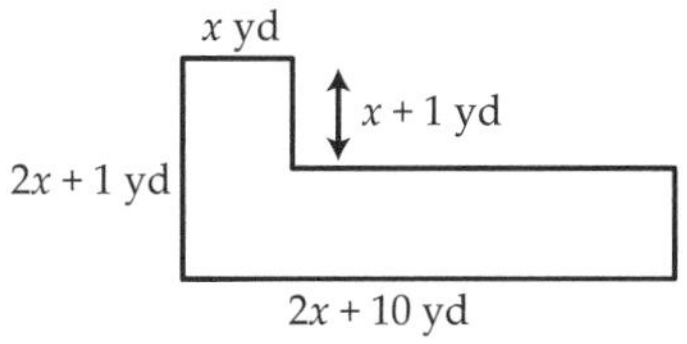

a Write an expression for the area in square feet in terms of x. Explain the reasoning you used to convert units and find the area.

b Dr. Needle has an opportunity to extend the lot by filling in the upper right section so the lot is rectangular. What is the area of the extension in terms of x?

31. MP 2, 4 The surface area of a sphere is $A = 4\pi r^2$. If the area of a circle is the same as the surface area of a sphere, find the ratio of the radius of the sphere to the radius of the circle.

32. MP 1, 2

a Which of the following correspondences are functions?

Correspondence	Yes	No
ID numbers to students		
students to ID numbers		
buildings to zip codes		
zip codes to buildings		
birthdays to first-graders		
first-graders to birthdays		
football players to heights		
heights to football players		
houses to house numbers		
house numbers to houses		

b Which functions are one-to-one?

Chapter 8 Quadratic Equations and Functions

Chapter Focus

In this chapter, we will examine strategies for solving quadratic equations, make use of the structure of quadratic equations to find solutions, and analyze the nature of the roots of equations. We will study the changes brought about by transformations of quadratic functions, and learn to express the function in a way that best suits the problem we are asked to solve. We will examine the constraints on root functions. Modeling examples will help us to appreciate the usefulness of the techniques learned.

Chapter Content

Chapter Vocabulary

completing the square	**double root**	**quadratic function**
cube root function	**incomplete quadratic equation**	**square root function**
cubic equation	**quadratic equation**	**standard form of a quadratic equation**
discriminant	**quadratic formula**	**vertex form of a quadratic function**

LESSON 8.1

8.1 Standard Form of the Quadratic Equation

A second-degree polynomial equation in one variable, such as $x^2 + 2x - 15 = 0$, is called a **quadratic equation**.

> The **standard form of a quadratic equation** is $ax^2 + bx + c = 0$ where a, b, and c are real numbers and $a \neq 0$.

Examples of quadratic equations in standard form include $x^2 + x - 6 = 0$ and $x^2 - 5 = 0$.

When a quadratic equation is written in standard form, all of the terms on one side are arranged in descending order of exponents, and the other side is zero.

MODEL PROBLEMS

Model Problems 1–6: Write in standard form:

SOLUTION

1. $x^2 + 3x = 4$ — $x^2 + 3x - 4 = 0$
2. $2x + x^2 + 1 = 0$ — $x^2 + 2x + 1 = 0$
3. $10 - 13x + 3x^2 = 0$ — $3x^2 - 13x + 10 = 0$
4. $9 + 6x + x^2 = 0$ — $x^2 + 6x + 9 = 0$
5. $x^2 + x + x + 1 = 0$ — $x^2 + 2x + 1 = 0$
6. $3x + 4 = x^2$ — $-x^2 + 3x + 4 = 0$ (Or: $x^2 - 3x - 4 = 0$)

PRACTICE

1. If $n \neq 0$, which quadratic equation is written in standard form?

A. $x + x^2 = n$

B. $-x^2 - x - n = 0$

C. $x + x^2 + n = 0$

D. $x^2 - x = n$

2. If these quadratic equations are written in standard form, in which is it true that $a = 1$, $b = 2$, and $c = 3$?

A. $2x + x^2 = 3$

B. $3 + 2x = -x^2$

C. $2x = 3 + x^2$

D. $1 + 2x + 3x^2 = 0$

3. Which sentence represents a quadratic equation that can be expressed in standard form?

A. A number squared is equal to the sum of zero and the same number squared.

B. There are three consecutive even integers such that one-third the sum of the greater two is equal to the least of the three.

C. The square of the difference between a number and one is thirty-six.

D. One divided by a number is equal to one divided by the sum of twice the number and one.

4. Which of the following can be written as a quadratic equation in standard form?

A. $x^2 + 3x - 5 = x^2 + x + 7$

B. $x(x + 3) = 5x(1 - x^2)$

C. $x^2 - 9 = \frac{1}{x}$

D. $3(x^2 + 1) = (x + 5)(x - 5)$

Exercises 5–9: Write each quadratic equation in standard form.

5. $x(x + 2) = 8$

6. $x^2 = 35 - x - 15$

7. $x(x - 5) = 24$

8. $x^2 - 7x = -2x + 6$

9. $x(2x - 7) = 3x^2 - 8$

10. MP 3 The following examples *cannot* be written as quadratic equations in standard form. For each, explain why not.

a $(x + 1)(x - 1) = x^2$

b $x(x + 1)(x - 1) = 0$

c $x + 1 = 5x - 5$

LESSON 8.2

8.2 Solving Quadratic Equations Algebraically

Solving Quadratic Equations Using the Zero Product Property

Second-degree polynomial expressions can often be factored to get two first-degree, or linear, expressions. This gives us a strategy for solving quadratic equations.

> Remember that linear expressions are expressions in which the highest power of x is 1.

Suppose that the product of two expressions is 0. Using the zero product property of multiplication, we know that *at least one* of these expressions equals zero:

If a and b are real numbers, then $ab = 0$ if and only if $a = 0$ or $b = 0$.

To Solve Quadratic Equations Using the Zero Product Property

(1) Write the quadratic equation in standard form.	$x^2 + x - 6 = 0$	
(2) Factor the quadratic expression.	$(x + 3)(x - 2) = 0$	
(3) Set each factor equal to 0 (by the zero product property).	$x + 3 = 0$	$x - 2 = 0$
(4) Solve each equation to find the solution set, or roots.	$x = -3$	$x = 2$
(5) Check each root in the original quadratic equation.	$x^2 + x - 6 = 0$ $(-3)^2 + (-3) - 6 = 0$ $9 + (-3) - 6 = 0$ $0 = 0$ ✓	$x^2 + x - 6 = 0$ $(2)^2 + (2) - 6 = 0$ $4 + 2 - 6 = 0$ $0 = 0$ ✓

If the leading coefficient is 1, we can factor the trinomial using the sum and product method learned in chapter 7.

MODEL PROBLEMS

Model Problems 1–3: Solve each quadratic equation and check your solution.

1. $x^2 + 5x + 4 = 0$

SOLUTION

Write the quadratic equation in standard form. $x^2 + 5x + 4 = 0$

Factor the equation. $(x + 1)(x + 4) = 0$

Set each factor equal to 0. $(x + 4) = 0$ $(x + 1) = 0$

Solve each equation. $(x + 4) = 0$ $(x + 1) = 0$

$x = -4$ $x = -1$

Check.

$x = -4$	$x = -1$
$x^2 + 5x + 4 = 0$ $(-4)^2 + 5(-4) + 4 = 0$ $16 - 20 + 4 = 0$ $0 = 0$ ✓	$x^2 + 5x + 4 = 0$ $(-1)^2 + 5(-1) + 4 = 0$ $1 - 5 + 4 = 0$ $0 = 0$ ✓

Answer: $x = -4$ or $x = -1$. The solution set is $\{-4, -1\}$.

Model Problems continue . . .

Model Problems *continued*

2. $x^2 - 8x + 16 = 0$

SOLUTION

Factor the left side of the equation. $x^2 - 8x + 16 = (x - 4)(x - 4) = 0$

Set each factor equal to zero and solve: $(x - 4) = 0$ $\quad$ $(x - 4) = 0$

$x = 4$ $\quad$ $x = 4$

Check.

$x = 4$
$x^2 - 8x + 16 = 0$ $(4)^2 - 8(4) + 16 = 0$ $16 - 32 + 16 = 0$ $0 = 0$ ✓

Answer: $x = 4$. The solution set is $\{4\}$.

While every quadratic equation has two roots, in this case both roots are the same. The **double root** is written only once. Trinomials with two identical factors are called *perfect square trinomials.*

3. $3x^2 + 8x + 4 = 0$

SOLUTION

Factor the left side of the equation. $3x^2 + 8x + 4 = (3x + 2)(x + 2) = 0$

At least one factor must equal zero. $3x + 2 = 0$ or $x + 2 = 0$

Solve both equations. $x = -\frac{2}{3}$ $\quad$ $x = -2$

Check.

$x = -\frac{2}{3}$	$x = -2$
$3x^2 + 8x + 4 = 0$ $3\left(-\frac{2}{3}\right)^2 + 8\left(-\frac{2}{3}\right) + 4 = 0$ $3\left(\frac{4}{9}\right) - \frac{16}{3} + 4 = 0$ $\frac{4}{3} - \frac{16}{3} + 4 = 0$ $-\frac{12}{3} + 4 = 0$ $-4 + 4 = 0$ $0 = 0$ ✓	$3x^2 + 8x + 4 = 0$ $3(-2)^2 + 8(-2) + 4 = 0$ $3(4) - 16 + 4 = 0$ $12 - 16 + 4 = 0$ $-4 + 4 = 0$ $0 = 0$ ✓

Answer: $x = -\frac{2}{3}$ or $x = -2$. The solution set is $\left\{-\frac{2}{3}, -2\right\}$.

Model Problems continue . . .

Model Problems *continued*

4. One root of the equation $x^2 + 3x + k = 0$ is -1.

a Find the value of k.

b Find the second root.

SOLUTION

a The value $x = -1$ makes the equation true, so substitute -1 for x:

$$(-1)^2 + 3(-1) + k = 0$$
$$1 - 3 + k = 0$$
$$-2 + k = 0$$
$$k = 2$$

Answer: The value of k is 2.

b Substitute 2 for k in the given equation. $x^2 + 3x + 2 = 0$

Factor. $(x + 2)(x + 1) = 0$

Set each factor equal to zero. $x + 2 = 0 \quad x + 1 = 0$

Solve each equation. $x = -2 \quad x = -1$

Check the second root.

$x = -2$
$x^2 + 3x + 2 = 0$
$(-2)^2 + 3(-2) + 2 = 0$
$4 + (-6) + 2 = 0$
$0 = 0$ ✓

Answer: The second root is -2.

5. **MP 4, 5** Jose throws a ball into the air with an initial velocity of 48 feet per second, from a height of 5 feet above the ground. If the function $h(t) = -16t^2 + 48t + 5$ represents the height, $h(t)$, in feet, and t, the time in seconds, after how many seconds is the ball at a height of 37 feet?

SOLUTION

Since the height $h(t)$ is 37 feet, then $37 = -16t^2 + 48t + 5$

Subtract 37 and rewrite the equation in standard form. $0 = -16t^2 + 48t - 32$

Multiply every term of the trinomial by -1. $0 = 16t^2 - 48t + 32$

Divide every term by 16. $0 = t^2 - 3t + 2$

Factor the trinomial. $0 = (t - 1)(t - 2)$

Set each factor equal to zero and solve each equation. $t - 1 = 0 \quad t - 2 = 0$

$t = 1 \quad t = 2$

Check.

$t = 1$	$t = 2$
$37 = -16(1)^2 + 48(1) = 5$ $37 = -16 + 48 + 5$ $37 = 37$ ✓	$37 = -16(2)^2 + 48(2) + 5$ $37 = -16(4) + 96 + 5$ $37 = -64 + 96 + 5$ $37 = 37$ ✓

Answer: The ball is at a height of 37 feet after 1 second as it rises and after 2 seconds as it falls.

ALTERNATE SOLUTION

Use a graphing calculator and set the WINDOW to $-5 \le x \le 10$ and $-5 \le y \le 50$ (scale 2) or anything similar.

Press [Y=] [(-)] [1] [6] [X,T,Θ,n] [x²] [+] [4] [8] [X,T,Θ,n] [+] [5] [ENTER] [3] [7] [GRAPH].

To find the coordinates of the first intersection, move the cursor near the intersection and press [2nd] [CALC] [5] [ENTER] [ENTER] [ENTER]. Move the cursor near the second intersection and repeat the keystrokes.

Model Problems continue . . .

Model Problems *continued*

6. Write an equation of the form $ax^2 + bx + c = 0$ such that the roots, or solution set, will be $\{-2, 7\}$.

SOLUTION

Work backward.	Let $x = -2$ and $x = 7$
Rewrite the equations.	$x + 2 = 0$ and $x - 7 = 0$
Write the expressions on the left as factors, in parentheses, and set the product equal to 0.	$(x + 2)(x - 7) = 0$
Multiply, using FOIL.	$x^2 - 5x - 14 = 0$

Check.

$x = -2$	$x = 7$
$x^2 - 5x - 14 = 0$	$x^2 - 5x - 14 = 0$
$(-2)^2 - 5(-2) - 14 = 0$	$7^2 - 5(7) - 14 = 0$
$4 + 10 - 14 = 0$	$49 - 35 - 14 = 0$
$0 = 0$ ✓	$0 = 0$ ✓

ALTERNATE SOLUTION

Sum and Product of the Roots

If a quadratic equation has two integer roots, then we can write the quadratic with $a = 1$, so that $x^2 + bx + c = 0$.

The *sum* of the roots is equal to $-b$. The *product* of the roots is equal to c.

$$\begin{aligned}(x - root_1)(x - root_2) &= x^2 + (-1)(root_2 + root_1)x + (root_1)(root_2)\\ &= x^2 + (-1)(-b)x + c\\ &= x^2 + bx + c\end{aligned}$$

Identify the roots. The two roots are -2 and 7.

Find the sum of the roots.

$$-b = -2 + 7$$
$$-b = 5$$
$$b = -5$$

Find the product of the roots.

$$c = (-2)(7)$$
$$c = -14$$

By substitution, write the equation. $x^2 + bx + c = 0$

$$x^2 + (-5)x + (-14) = 0$$
$$x^2 - 5x - 14 = 0$$

Solving Cubic Equations Algebraically

In some cases, factoring can be used to find the roots of higher-order polynomial functions. A cubic, or third degree function, can sometimes be factored as the product of a common monomial or binomial expression factor of degree one and a quadratic expression factor of degree two.

> The degree of the polynomial, the largest exponent, tells us the maximum number of roots the polynomial function may have. A factorable cubic equation has three real roots.

The standard form of a **cubic equation** is $ax^3 + bx^2 + cx + d = 0$ where a, b, c, and d are real numbers and $a \neq 0$.

MODEL PROBLEM

Solve, and check your solution: $a^3 = 4a^2 + 5a$

SOLUTION

Write the cubic equation in standard form. $a^3 - 4a^2 - 5a = 0$

Factor the left side to get a monomial and a quadratic expression. $a(a^2 - 4a - 5) = 0$

Then factor completely. $a(a - 5)(a + 1) = 0$

Set each factor equal to zero. $a = 0$ $a - 5 = 0$ $a + 1 = 0$

Solve the resulting equations. $a = 0$ $a = 5$ $a = -1$

Answer: $a = 0$, $a = 5$, or $a = -1$. The solution set is $\{0, 5, -1\}$.

Check.

$a = 0$	$a = 5$	$a = -1$
$a^3 = 4a^2 + 5a$	$a^3 = 4a^2 + 5a$	$a^3 = 4a^2 + 5a$
$0^3 = 4(0^2) + 5(0)$	$5^3 = 4(5^2) + 5(5)$	$(-1)^3 = 4(-1)^2 + 5(-1)$
$0 = 0 + 0$ ✓	$125 = 4(25) + 25$	$-1 = 4(1) + (-5)$
	$125 = 100 + 25 = 125$ ✓	$-1 = 4 - 5 = -1$ ✓

PRACTICE

1. Solve: $x^2 - 13x - 30 = 0$

A. $\{-15, -2\}$
B. $\{-15, 2\}$
C. $\{15, -2\}$
D. $\{15, 2\}$

2. Solve: $x^2 + 5x = 6$

A. $\{-1, 6\}$
B. $\{1, -6\}$
C. $\{2, -3\}$
D. $\{2, 3\}$

Practice Problems continue . . .

3. For which equation is the solution set {3, 4}?

A. $x^2 + 3x + 4 = 0$
B. $x^2 - 7x + 12 = 0$
C. $x^2 + 12x + 7 = 0$
D. $x^2 - 9x = 16$

4. For which equation is the solution set {−8, 2}?

A. $x^2 + 6x - 16 = 0$
B. $x^2 - 6x - 10 = 0$
C. $x^2 - 12x - 64 = 0$
D. $x^2 - 16x + 6 = 0$

Exercises 5–13: Solve each equation and check your solution.

5. $x^2 - 10x + 25 = 0$

6. $x^2 + 22x + 57 = 0$

7. $x^2 + 14x + 40 = 0$

8. $x^2 - 11x + 18 = 0$

9. $2x^2 + 9x + 7 = 0$

10. $5x^2 - 26x + 5 = 0$

11. $3x^2 + 8x + 5 = 0$

12. $2x^2 + 32x - 114 = 0$

13. $3x^2 + 14x + 8 = 0$

Exercises 14–17: In these problems, solution sets are given. For each solution set, write an equation of the form $ax^2 + bx + c = 0$.

14. {4, −2}

15. {5, 8}

16. {−3}

17. {−11, 3}

Exercises 18–20: In each of these problems, an equation and one of its roots are given. Find:

a the value of k
b the second root

18. 5 is a root of $x^2 - 7x + k = 0$

19. 5 is a root of $x^2 - 3x + k = 0$

20. 7 is a root of $x^2 - 3x = -k$

21. A ball is thrown into the air with an initial velocity of 24 feet per second from a height of 6 feet above the ground. The equation that models the motion is $h(t) = -16t^2 + 24t + 6$, where t is the time, in seconds, that the ball has been in the air, and $h(t)$ is the ball's height at time t, in feet. After how many seconds is the ball at a height of 14 feet?

22. Three positive consecutive odd integers are represented by x, $x + 2$, and $x + 4$. If 19 is subtracted from twice the square of the smallest number, the result is equal to the product of the other two integers. Find the three positive consecutive odd integers.

23. A baseball is thrown upward from the surface of a certain moon in the solar system. If the height of the ball is modeled by the equation $y = -2t^2 + 38t + 10$, where t is the time, in seconds, and y is the height, in feet, for what value of t is the ball exactly 150 feet above the surface?

24. MP 1, 2, 7 In the figure below, the area of rectangle *LAND* is 154 square inches, and the side of square *S* is x. Using the information in the figure below, what is the length of side x?

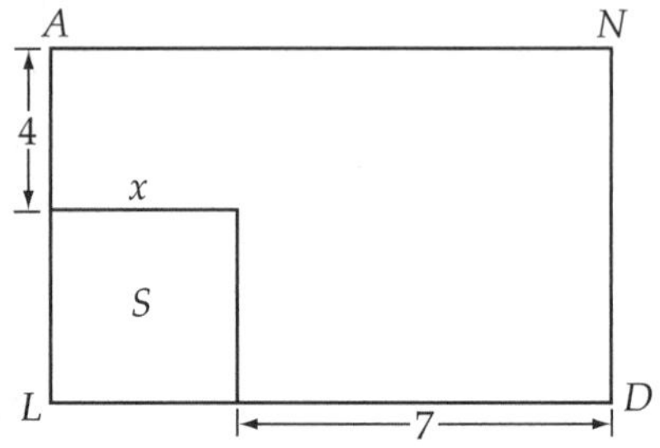

25. MP 2, 4, 5, 7 A ball is thrown upward at an initial speed of 72 feet per second from a platform 50 feet high. If the height above the ground, in feet, is given by the equation $h(t) = -16t^2 + 72t + 50$, where t is time in seconds, when will the ball hit the ground? Use a calculator.

Incomplete Quadratic Equations

An **incomplete quadratic equation** is a quadratic equation in which $b = 0$ or $c = 0$, or both $b = 0$ and $c = 0$.

	Incomplete Form	Standard Form
Constant is missing.	$ax^2 + bx = 0$	$ax^2 + bx + 0 = 0$
Linear term is missing.	$ax^2 + c = 0$	$ax^2 + 0x + c = 0$
Constant and linear term are missing.	$ax^2 = 0$	$ax^2 + 0x + 0 = 0$

Each type of incomplete quadratic equation can be written in standard ("complete") form.

To Solve Incomplete Quadratic Equations

(1) Rewrite the equation, if necessary, so that all terms with the unknown are on one side of the equal sign, leaving zero on the other side.

(2) Combine like terms, if any.

(3) Factor completely.

(4) Set each factor equal to zero and solve the resulting equations.

(5) Check both solutions.

MODEL PROBLEMS

1. Solve and check your solution: $x^2 = 6x$

SOLUTION

Rewrite. $x^2 - 6x = 0$

Factor. $x(x - 6) = 0$

Set each factor equal to zero and solve. $x = 0$ $\quad x - 6 = 0$

$x = 0$ $\quad x = 6$

Check.

$x = 0$	$x = 6$
$x^2 = 6x$	$x^2 = 6x$
$0^2 = 6(0)$	$6^2 = 6(6)$
$0 = 0$ ✓	$36 = 36$ ✓

Answer: $x = 0$ or $x = 6$. The solution set is $\{0, 6\}$.

Model Problems continue . . .

Model Problems *continued*

2. **MP 7** Solve for x and check: $ax^2 + bx = 0$

SOLUTION

Factor. $x(ax + b) = 0$

Set each factor equal to zero and solve. $x = 0 \quad ax + b = 0$

$$ax = -b$$

$$x = \frac{-b}{a} \text{ or } -\frac{b}{a}$$

Check.

$x = 0$	$x = -\frac{b}{a}$
$ax^2 + bx = 0$ $a(0^2) + b(0) = 0$ $0 + 0 = 0$ $0 = 0$ ✓	$ax^2 + bx = 0$ $a\left(-\frac{b}{a}\right)^2 + b\left(-\frac{b}{a}\right) = 0$ $a\left(\frac{b^2}{a^2}\right) + b\left(-\frac{b}{a}\right) = 0$ $\frac{b^2}{a} + \left(-\frac{b^2}{a}\right) = 0$ $0 = 0$ ✓

Answer: $x = 0$ or $x = -\frac{b}{a}$. The solution set is $\left\{0, -\frac{b}{a}\right\}$.

3. Solve and check your solution: $4x^2 - 27 = x^2$

SOLUTION

Rewrite. $4x^2 - x^2 = 27$

Combine like terms. $3x^2 = 27$

Divide both sides by 3. $x^2 = 9$

Take the square root of both sides and simplify. $\sqrt{x^2} = \pm\sqrt{9}$

$$x = \pm 3$$

Check.

$x = 3$	$x = -3$
$4x^2 - 27 = x^2$ $4(3)^2 - 27 = (3)^2$ $4(9) - 27 = 9$ $36 - 27 = 9$ $9 = 9$ ✓	$4x^2 - 27 = x^2$ $4(-3)^2 - 27 = (-3)^2$ $4(9) - 27 = 9$ $36 - 27 = 9$ $9 = 9$ ✓

Model Problems continue . . .

Answer: $x = 3$ or $x = -3$

Model Problems continued

4. Solve and check: $4x^2 = 49$

SOLUTION

Divide both sides by 4. $x^2 = \frac{49}{4}$

Take the square root of both sides and simplify. $x = \pm\sqrt{\frac{49}{4}} = \pm\frac{7}{2}$

Check.

$x = \frac{7}{2}$	$x = -\frac{7}{2}$
$4x^2 = 49$	$4x^2 = 49$
$4\left(\frac{7}{2}\right)^2 = 49$	$4\left(-\frac{7}{2}\right)^2 = 49$
$4\left(\frac{49}{4}\right) = 49$	$4\left(\frac{49}{4}\right) = 49$
$49 = 49$ ✓	$49 = 49$ ✓

Answer: $x = \frac{7}{2}$ or $x = -\frac{7}{2}$.

The solution set is $\left\{\frac{7}{2}, -\frac{7}{2}\right\}$.

5. Solve for x and check: $9x^2 - m^2 = 0$

SOLUTION

Rewrite. $9x^2 = m^2$

Divide by 9. $x^2 = \frac{m^2}{9}$

Take the square root of both sides and simplify. $x = \pm\sqrt{\frac{m^2}{9}} = \pm\frac{m}{3}$

Check.

$x = \frac{m}{3}$	$x = -\frac{m}{3}$
$9x^2 - m^2 = 0$	$9x^2 - m^2 = 0$
$9\left(\frac{m}{3}\right)^2 - m^2 = 0$	$9\left(-\frac{m}{3}\right)^2 - m^2 = 0$
$9\left(\frac{m^2}{9}\right) - m^2 = 0$	$9\left(\frac{m^2}{9}\right) - m^2 = 0$
$m^2 - m^2 = 0$ $0 = 0$ ✓	$m^2 - m^2 = 0$ $0 = 0$ ✓

Answer: $x = \frac{m}{3}$ or $x = -\frac{m}{3}$. The solution set is $\left\{\frac{m}{3}, -\frac{m}{3}\right\}$.

PRACTICE

1. Solve: $x^2 - 4x = 5x$

A. $\{-5, 0, 1\}$
B. $\{-5, 1\}$
C. $\{0, 9\}$
D. $\{-9, 0, 9\}$

2. Solve: $\frac{x}{2} = \frac{2}{x}$

A. $\{2\}$
B. $\{0, 2\}$
C. $\{-2, 2\}$
D. $\{-2, 0, 2\}$

3. For which equation is the solution set $\{0, 1\}$?

A. $x^2 - x = 0$
B. $x^3 - x = 0$
C. $x^2 - 1 = 0$
D. $x - 1 = 0$

4. For which equation is the solution set $\left\{-\frac{6}{5}, \frac{6}{5}\right\}$?

A. $\frac{12}{5x} = \frac{x}{60}$

B. $\frac{6 - x}{4} = \frac{5}{6 + x}$

C. $\frac{6}{x} = \frac{25x}{6}$

D. $5x^2 + 6x = 0$

Exercises 5–19: Solve and check. Explain how you arrived at the solution.

5. $x^2 + 2x = 0$

6. $x^2 = 5x$

7. $4x^2 = 28x$

8. $3x^2 = -5x$

9. $8a^2 = 2a$

10. $3x^2 - 4x = 5x$

11. $\frac{x^2}{5} = \frac{x}{15}$

12. $5x(x - 6) - 8x = 2x$

13. $3x^2 + 25 = 25 - 15x$

14. $3x^2 = 6ax$ for x

15. $\frac{2x^2}{25} = 18$

16. $16x^2 - 400 = 0$

17. $x^2 - 16 = 48$

18. $(x - 6)(x + 6) = 28$

19. $a^2x^2 = 49$ for x

20. Solve each formula for the variable indicated.

a $A = \pi r^2$ for r

b $S = at^2$ for t

c $A = 4\pi r^2$ for r

d $E = mc^2$ for c

e $K = \frac{1}{2}mv^2$ for v

f $F = \frac{mv^2}{r}$ for v

g $s = \frac{1}{2}gt^2$ for t

h $V = \pi r^2 h$ for r

21. **MP 1, 2, 4, 5, 7** Janie and Norbert want to sod a portion of their backyard and build the largest square concrete patio that they can afford. The area to be covered is 70 feet by 70 feet. They will do all the work themselves. The cost of sod is \$0.20 per square foot. The cost of concrete is \$2.00 per square foot. They have a budget of \$1700. How large can the patio be?

Fractional Quadratic Equations

To Solve a Fractional Quadratic Equation

- Cross multiply only if there is just one fraction on each side of the equal sign.
- For any other fractional equation, clear the fractions by multiplying each term by the lowest common denominator (LCD).
- Rewrite the equation in standard form, with all terms on one side of the equal sign: $ax^2 + bx + c = 0$.
- Factor and solve.
- Check your solution set.

MODEL PROBLEMS

1. Solve and check your solution: $\dfrac{x+5}{3} = \dfrac{10}{x-8}$

SOLUTION

Cross multiply. $(x + 5)(x - 8) = 30$

Use FOIL. $x^2 - 8x + 5x - 40 = 30$

Combine terms and write the equation in standard form. $x^2 - 3x - 70 = 0$

Factor. $(x + 7)(x - 10) = 0$

Solve. $x + 7 = 0 \quad x - 10 = 0$

$x = -7 \qquad x = 10$

> Using the LCD and cross multiplying are related procedures.
>
> For example, $\dfrac{x}{a} = \dfrac{y}{b}$ has a common denominator of *ab*.
>
> Multiply both sides by the LCD, *ab*, to get $bx = ay$. This is the same result as cross multiplying.
>
> In this example, the LCD is $3(x - 8)$.

Check. The check must be done with the *original* equation.

$x = -7$	$x = 10$
$\dfrac{x+5}{3} = \dfrac{10}{x-8}$	$\dfrac{x+5}{3} = \dfrac{10}{x-8}$
$\dfrac{-7+5}{3} = \dfrac{10}{-7-8}$	$\dfrac{10+5}{3} = \dfrac{10}{10-8}$
$\dfrac{-2}{3} = \dfrac{10}{-15}$ or $-\dfrac{2}{3} = -\dfrac{10}{15}$	$\dfrac{15}{3} = \dfrac{10}{2}$
$-\dfrac{2}{3} = -\dfrac{2}{3}$ ✓	$5 = 5$ ✓

Answer: $x = -7$ or $x = 10$. The solution set is $\{-7, 10\}$.

Model Problems continue . . .

Model Problems *continued*

2. Solve and check your solution: $2 + \frac{5}{n} = \frac{12}{n^2}$

SOLUTION

Multiply each term by the LCD, n^2.	$2(n^2) + \frac{5}{n}(n^2) = \frac{12}{n^2}(n^2)$
Simplify.	$2n^2 + 5n = 12$
Write in standard form.	$2n^2 + 5n - 12 = 0$
Factor.	$(2n - 3)(n + 4) = 0$
Solve.	$2n - 3 = 0 \quad n + 4 = 0$
	$n = \frac{3}{2} \quad n = -4$

Check.

$n = \frac{3}{2}$	$n = -4$
$2 + \frac{5}{n} = \frac{12}{n^2}$	$2 + \frac{5}{n} = \frac{12}{n^2}$
$2 + \left(5 \div \frac{3}{2}\right) = 12 \div \left(\frac{3}{2}\right)^2$	$2 + \frac{5}{-4} = \frac{12}{(-4)^2}$
$2 + \frac{10}{3} = \frac{48}{9}$	$\frac{8}{4} - \frac{5}{4} = \frac{12}{16}$
$\frac{16}{3} = \frac{16}{3}$ ✓	$\frac{3}{4} = \frac{3}{4}$ ✓

In checking, decimal equivalents can also be used.

Answer: $n = \frac{3}{2}$ or $n = -4$. The solution set is $\left\{\frac{3}{2}, -4\right\}$.

PRACTICE

1. In which case will cross multiplying result in a quadratic equation?

A. $\frac{x}{7} = \frac{4}{x - 3}$

B. $\frac{x}{7} = \frac{x - 3}{4}$

C. $\frac{x}{x - 3} = \frac{4}{7}$

D. $\frac{7}{x} = \frac{4}{x - 3}$

2. In which case do we need to use the LCD?

A. $\frac{2x}{3} = \frac{6}{x}$

B. $\frac{x}{2} - 2 = \frac{6}{x}$

C. $\frac{x}{2} - \frac{8}{x} = 0$

D. each of the above

Practice Problems continue . . .

3. Find the solution set: $\frac{2x+3}{6x+1} = \frac{1}{2x}$

A. $\left\{\frac{1}{2}, -\frac{1}{2}\right\}$

B. $\{2, -2\}$

C. $\{1, -1\}$

D. $\left\{\frac{1}{3}, -\frac{1}{3}\right\}$

4. Find the solution set: $\frac{2}{x} = \frac{3}{x^2 - 1}$

A. $\left\{-\frac{1}{2}, 2\right\}$

B. $\left\{\frac{1}{2}, -2\right\}$

C. $\left\{\frac{1}{2}, -\frac{1}{2}\right\}$

D. $\{1, -1\}$

Exercises 5–20: Solve and check. Explain how you arrived at the solution.

5. $\frac{x}{5} = \frac{3}{x+2}$

6. $\frac{8}{x} = \frac{x+2}{3}$

7. $\frac{3x}{4} = \frac{x^2}{8}$

8. $\frac{7x}{3} = \frac{x^2}{6}$

9. $\frac{x+2}{2} = \frac{1}{x+3}$

10. $\frac{x+4}{3} = \frac{3}{x+4}$

11. $\frac{x-2}{2} = \frac{3}{x+3}$

12. $\frac{x-1}{4} = \frac{12}{x+1}$

13. $\frac{x+2}{3} = \frac{4}{x-2}$

14. $\frac{3x+4}{3} = \frac{3}{3x-4}$

15. $\frac{5x+2}{8} = \frac{4}{5x-2}$

16. $\frac{2x^2-3}{2} = \frac{x^2-3}{3}$

17. $\frac{x+3}{2} = \frac{8}{x-3}$

18. $\frac{4+x}{2x} = \frac{x}{4-x}$

19. $\frac{4x^2-5}{3} = \frac{2x^2-3}{2}$

20. $\frac{3x-2}{x} = \frac{3x+3}{x+2}$

LESSON 8.3

8.3 Solving Quadratic Equations by Completing the Square

For all trinomials, we can rewrite the equation as a perfect square trinomial on the left equal to a constant on the right.

All quadratic equations we have solved so far have been factorable from standard form. Other equations can be solved by a process known as **completing the square**.

For all perfect square trinomials, such as $x^2 + 6x + 9 = 0$, written in standard form, $x^2 + bx + c = 0$, there is a pattern, $c = \left(\frac{b}{2}\right)^2$. In this example, $9 = \left(\frac{6}{2}\right)^2$.

Procedure for Completing the Square	Example
Start with a quadratic equation in standard form.	$2x^2 + 12x + 14 = 0$
Rewrite the equation in the form $x^2 + bx = -c$ and simplify, if possible.	$2x^2 + 12x + 14 - 14 = 0 - 14$ $2x^2 + 12x = -14$ $x^2 + 6x = -7$
Add $\left(\frac{b}{2}\right)^2$ to each side. Simplify the constant terms.	$x^2 + 6x + \left(\frac{6}{2}\right)^2 = -7 + \left(\frac{6}{2}\right)^2$ $x^2 + 6x + 9 = -7 + 9$ $x^2 + 6x + 9 = 2$
The left side is now a perfect square trinomial. Write it as a binomial term squared.	$(x + 3)^2 = 2$
Take the square root of each side.	$x + 3 = \pm\sqrt{2}$
Solve for x.	$x = -3 \pm\sqrt{2}$
Write the two solutions.	$x = -3 + \sqrt{2}$ or $x = -3 - \sqrt{2}$

MODEL PROBLEMS

1. **MP 7** What constant added to $x^2 - 8x$ makes the resulting trinomial a perfect square?

SOLUTION

Find half the coefficient of x. half the coefficient of x is -4

Square it. $(-4)^2 = 16$

Add the constant to the binomial. $x^2 - 8x + 16$

Check.

$$(x - 4)^2 = (x - 4)(x - 4)$$
$$= x^2 - 4x - 4x + (-4)^2$$
$$= x^2 - 8x + 16$$

Answer: 16

2. **MP 7** What constant added to $x^2 - 11x$ makes the resulting trinomial a perfect square?

SOLUTION

Find half the coefficient of x. half the coefficient of x is $-\frac{11}{2}$

Square it. $\left(-\frac{11}{2}\right)^2 = \frac{121}{4}$

Add the constant to the binomial. $x^2 - 11x + \frac{121}{4}$

Answer: $\frac{121}{4}$

Model Problems continue . . .

3. Solve $x^2 + 12x - 13 = 0$

SOLUTION

Given. $x^2 + 12x - 13 = 0$

Subtract the constant term from both sides of the equation. $x^2 + 12x = 13$

Complete the square.

$$\left(\frac{12}{2}\right)^2 = \frac{144}{4} = 36$$

$$x^2 + 12x + 36 = 13 + 36$$

$$x^2 + 12x + 36 = 49$$

Write as a binomial term squared. $(x + 6)^2 = 49$

Take the square root of each side. $\sqrt{(x + 6)^2} = \pm\sqrt{49}$

$$x + 6 = \pm 7$$

Solve for x. $x = -6 \pm 7$

Answer: $x = 1$ or $x = -13$

4. Solve $2x^2 + 4x + 1 = 0$

SOLUTION

Given. $2x^2 + 4x + 1 = 0$

Subtract the constant term from both sides of the equation. $2x^2 + 4x = -1$

Divide both sides by 2, the coefficient of x^2. $\frac{2x^2}{2} + \frac{4x}{2} = -\frac{1}{2}$

Simplify. $x^2 + 2x = -\frac{1}{2}$

Complete the square. $\left(\frac{2}{2}\right)^2 = 1$

$$x^2 + 2x + 1 = -\frac{1}{2} + 1$$

Simplify. $x^2 + 2x + 1 = 0.5$

Write as a binomial term squared. $(x + 1)^2 = 0.5$

Take the square root of each side. $x + 1 = \pm\sqrt{0.5}$

Solve for x. $x = -1 \pm \sqrt{0.5}$

Answer: $x = -1 + \sqrt{0.5}$ or $x = -1 - \sqrt{0.5}$

PRACTICE

Exercises 1–4: Rewrite the standard form quadratic expressions as perfect squares.

1. $x^2 + 14x + 49$

2. $x^2 - 18x + 81$

3. $x^2 + \frac{2}{3}x + \frac{1}{9}$

4. $x^2 - \frac{3}{2}x + \frac{9}{16}$

5. MP 7 Find an expression equivalent to $x^2 + x + \frac{1}{2}$ that *includes* a perfect square trinomial.

Exercises 6–15: Rewrite each expression by completing the square.

6. $x^2 - 2x - 1$

7. $j^2 - 6j + 6$

8. $m^2 - 3m - 3$

9. $z^2 - 0.4z + 1$

10. $k^2 - \frac{3}{5}k + 2$

11. $x^2 - 0.2x + 3$

12. $x^2 + bx + c$

13. $\frac{1}{2}x^2 - 6x + 12$

14. $\frac{1}{4}x^2 - 2x + 10$

15. $-8x^2 + 8x + 1$

Exercises 16–19: Use completing the square to find the roots of the equations.

16. $x^2 - 4x - 8 = 0$

17. $-2x^2 + 4x + 8 = 0$

18. $\frac{1}{2}x^2 - 6x = 8$

19. $-x^2 + 8x = -6$

20. MP 3 Name two different methods of solving the quadratic equation, $x^2 + 22x + 120 = 0$. Which is easiest? Explain.

LESSON 8.4

8.4 Solving Quadratic Equations from the Graph

We have found solutions for quadratic equations by the method of factoring and using the zero product property and by completing the square. The solutions, or roots, of a quadratic equation can also be found by graphing the equation and looking at the x-intercepts of the graph.

To Solve a Quadratic Equation Graphically

- Write an equation in the form $y = ax^2 + bx + c$.
- Graph the parabola $y = ax^2 + bx + c$ using a suitable table of values.
- Identify where the parabola crosses the x-axis (where $y = 0$). These are the roots, or solutions, to the quadratic equation.

A quadratic equation can have two, one, or zero real solutions. The real solutions are where the graph crosses the x-axis (twice) or where it touches the x-axis (once). There is no solution where the graph does not meet the x-axis at all.

CASE I: Parabola Intersects the x-Axis at Two Distinct Points

We solve $y = x^2 - 4$ graphically.

Make a table of values.

x	$x^2 - 4$	y
-3	$(-3)^2 - 4$	5
-2	$(-2)^2 - 4$	0
-1	$(-1)^2 - 4$	-3
0	$(0)^2 - 4$	-4
1	$(1)^2 - 4$	-3
2	$(2)^2 - 4$	0
3	$(3)^2 - 4$	5

Using the table, graph $y = x^2 - 4$.

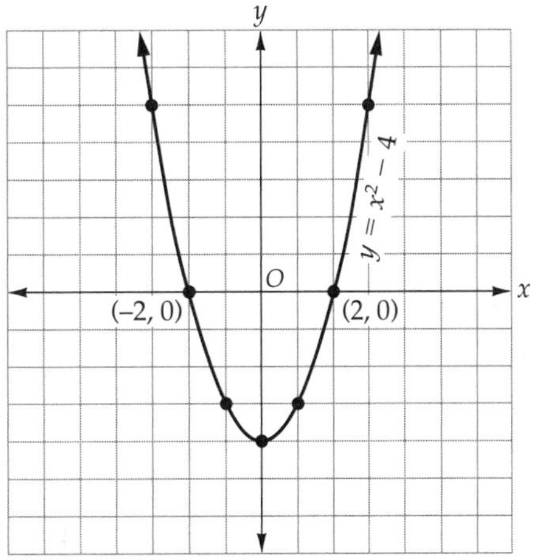

If the graph crosses the x-axis at two distinct points, the roots are real and unequal.

The x-intercepts of the graph are $(-2, 0)$ and $(2, 0)$. The roots of the equation are -2 and 2.

CHECK: We check the roots by solving the equation algebraically.

$$x^2 - 4 = 0$$

$$(x + 2)(x - 2) = 0$$

$$x + 2 = 0 \qquad x - 2 = 0$$

$$x = -2 \checkmark \qquad x = 2 \checkmark$$

The solution set is $\{2, -2\}$.

CASE II: Parabola Touches the x-Axis at Exactly One Point

We solve $y = x^2 + 4x + 4$ graphically.

Make a table of values.

x	$x^2 + 4x + 4$	y
-5	$(-5)^2 + 4(-5) + 4$	9
-4	$(-4)^2 + 4(-4) + 4$	4
-3	$(-3)^2 + 4(-3) + 4$	1
-2	$(-2)^2 + 4(-2) + 4$	0
-1	$(-1)^2 + 4(-1) + 4$	1
0	$(0)^2 + 4(0) + 4$	4
1	$(1)^2 + 4(1) + 4$	9

Using the table, graph $y = x^2 + 4x + 4$ around the axis of symmetry.

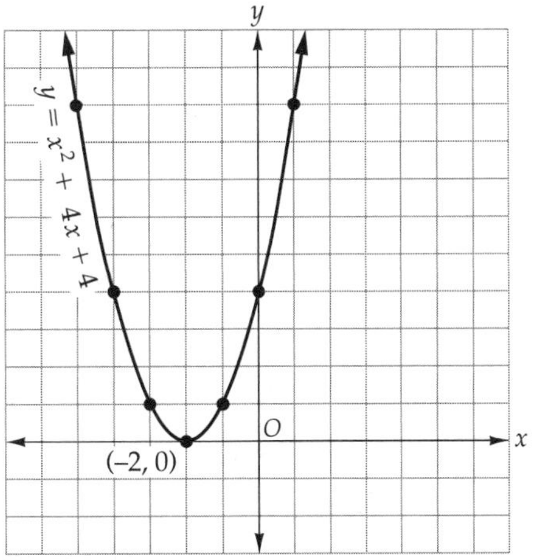

Since the graph touches the x-axis at exactly one point, the roots are real and equal. This is a double root.

CASE II: continues . . .

The x-intercept of the graph is the point $(-2, 0)$, which is also the turning point of the parabola. The solution set is $\{-2\}$.

CHECK: We check the roots by solving the equation algebraically.

$$x^2 + 4x + 4 = 0$$

$$(x + 2)(x + 2) = 0$$

$$x + 2 = 0 \quad x + 2 = 0$$

$x = -2$ ✓ $x = -2$ ✓ The roots of the equation are *both* -2.

CASE III: Parabola Does Not Meet the x-Axis

An example is the graph of $y = x^2 - 2x + 2$.

x	$x^2 - 2x + 2$	y
-2	$(-2)^2 - 2(-2) + 2$	10
-1	$(-1)^2 - 2(-1) + 2$	5
0	$(0)^2 - 2(0) + 2$	2
1	$(1)^2 - 2(1) + 2$	1
2	$(2)^2 - 2(2) + 2$	2
3	$(3)^2 - 2(3) + 2$	5
4	$(4)^2 - 2(4) + 2$	10

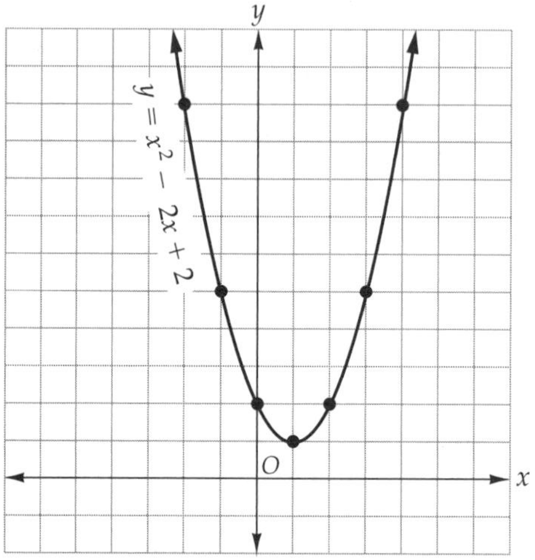

Since the graph does not touch the x-axis, the equation has no real roots.

MODEL PROBLEM

The graph is of $f(x) = x^2 + x - 12$. Use the graph to solve the equation $0 = x^2 + x - 12$.

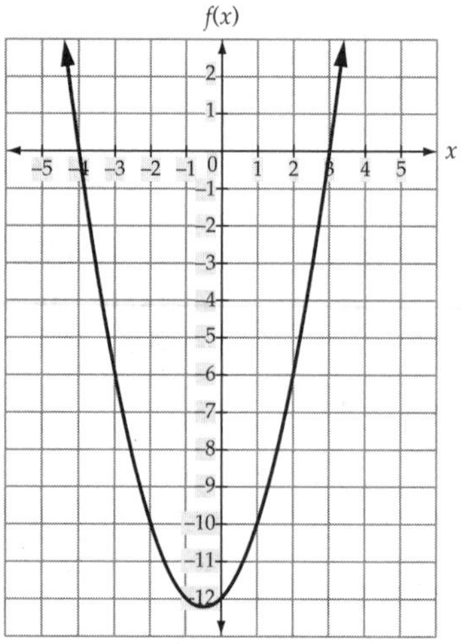

SOLUTION

There are two points where the parabola crosses the x-axis, so there are two solutions for the equation $0 = x^2 + x - 12$.

Answer: $x = -4, x = 3$

Check.

$x^2 + x - 12 = 0$	
$x = -4$	$x = 3$
$(-4)^2 + (-4) - 12 = 0$	$(3)^2 + (3) - 12 = 0$
$16 + (-4) - 12 = 0$	$9 + (3) - 12 = 0$
$0 = 0$ ✓	$0 = 0$ ✓

PRACTICE

1. How many x-intercepts does the graph of $x^2 + x + 5 = 0$ have?

A. 0
B. 1
C. 2
D. an infinite number of intercepts

2. What is the largest root of $x^2 + 5x - 6 = 0$?

A. 6
B. 5
C. 3
D. 1

3.

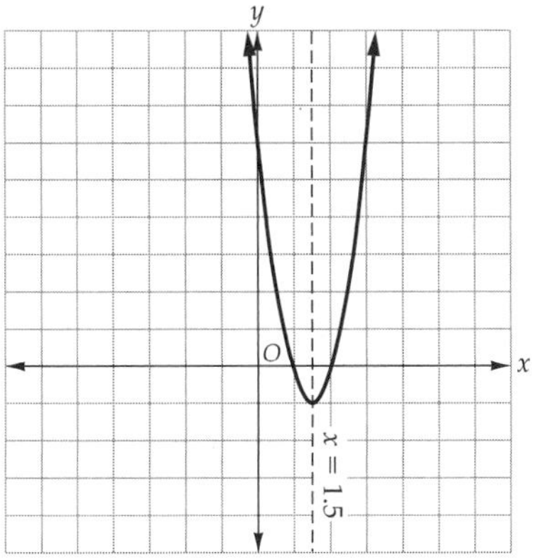

From this graph of $3x^2 - 9x + 6 = 0$, we can conclude that the equation has

A. no roots
B. one root at 6
C. one root at 1.5
D. two roots, one at 1 and one at 2

4. The single solution of $x^2 + 7x + 12.25 = 0$ lies between what two integer values of x?

A. -6 and -5
B. -4 and -3
C. 3 and 4
D. 5 and 6

Exercises 5–20: Solve the quadratic equations by graphing and labeling the roots. Identify whether the roots are real and unequal, real and the same (double roots), or no real roots.

5. $x^2 - x - 6 = 0$

6. $x^2 + 2x = 0$

7. $x^2 - 1 = 0$

8. $x^2 - 6x + 9 = 0$

9. $x^2 + 8x + 16 = 0$

10. $-x^2 + 6x - 27 = 0$

11. $x^2 + 3x = 0$

12. $x^2 - 4x - 21 = 0$

13. $0 = x^2 - 2x - 3$

14. $0 = x^2 - 12x + 36$

15. $0 = -x^2 + 4x + 12$

16. $0 = x^2 + 2x + 5$

17. $x^2 - 10x = -25$

18. $x^2 - x + 4 = 0$

19. $x^2 + 9 = 0$

20. $2x^2 - 18 = 0$

8.5 Graphing Quadratic Functions

Key Features of the Graph

We will look at the key features of graphs of parabolic functions of the form, $f(x) = ax^2 + bx + c$.

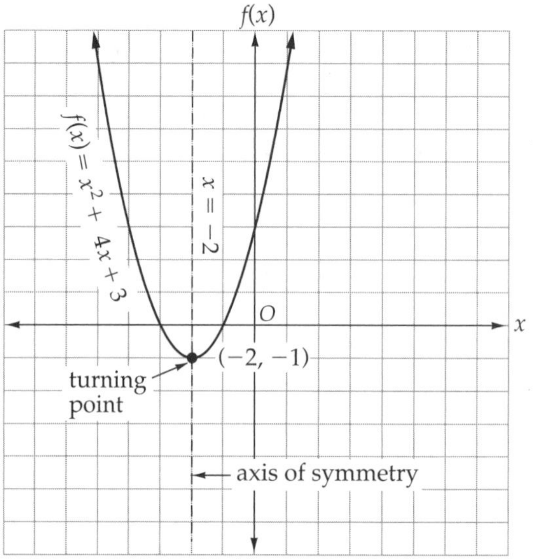

$f(x) = ax^2 + bx + c$ is the standard form of a **quadratic function.**

1. **axis of symmetry:** The axis of symmetry is a line that passes through the vertex and is parallel to the y-axis. It divides the parabola into mirror images.

   The axis of symmetry can be found algebraically by using the formula $x = \frac{-b}{2a}$. In the graph of $f(x) = x^2 + 4x + 3$, we substitute for a and b to get the axis of symmetry, $x = \frac{-4}{2(1)} = -2$, or the vertical line $x = -2$.

The axis of symmetry is an equation of a line, not just a number.

2. **vertex**, or **turning point:** The vertex is either a minimum point (the graph curves up) or a maximum point (the graph curves down). The x-coordinate of the turning point is $\frac{-b}{2a}$. In the graph of $f(x) = x^2 + 4x + 3$, the x-coordinate is $\frac{-b}{2a} = \frac{-(4)}{2(1)} = -2$. The y-coordinate of this point is found

   by substituting the x-value at the turning point into the original equation, so $y = x^2 + 4x + 3 = (-2)^2 + 4(-2) + 3 = 4 - 8 + 3 = -1$. The turning point is $(-2, -1)$.

3. **end behavior of the graph:** Quadratic functions either open up or open down. The coefficient of the x^2 term, a, determines the direction.

   - If a is positive, the graph opens up. The vertex is the minimum and the y-values increase as x changes in either direction. Both ends of the function extend to positive infinity. In the graph of $f(x) = x^2 + 4x + 3$, a is positive, so the graph opens up.
   - If a is negative, the graph opens down. The vertex is the maximum and the y-values decrease as x changes in either direction. Both ends of the function extend to negative infinity.

4. ***y*-intercept:** The y-intercept is where $x = 0$. Simply substitute 0 for x into the original equation, so $f(x) = (0)^2 + 4(0) + 3 = 3$. The y-intercept is (0, 3).

5. ***x*-intercept** or ***x*-intercepts:** The roots or zeros (since $f(x) = 0$ at these points) are the x-values or x-intercepts of the equation. The graph of $f(x) = x^2 + 4x + 3$ crosses the x-axis twice at $x = -3$ and $x = -1$. The roots are -3 and -1, so we can say that the x-intercepts are $(-3, 0)$ and $(-1, 0)$.

   - If the quadratic can be factored, we can use the zero product property to find the zeros. In this case, the quadratic function $f(x) = x^2 + 4x + 3 = (x + 3)(x + 1)$. Using the zero product property, we find that $x = -3$ and $x = -1$. This quadratic has two zeros, but that need not be the case. If the quadratic were shifted vertically, it might have no x-intercepts, and no zeros.
   - If the quadratic cannot be factored, we will use the quadratic formula, which we explain later.

6. **average rate of change:** We analyze the average rate of change between $-2 \le x \le 2$. To find the average rate of change, we calculate the slope of a line between those points. For example, the average rate of change over the interval is $\frac{y_2 - y_1}{x_2 - x_1}$ or $\frac{f(x_2) - f(x_1)}{x_2 - x_1}$. In the example graph, the average rate of change from the vertex $(-2, -1)$ to the point $(-1, 0)$ is $\frac{y_2 - y_1}{x_2 - x_1} = \frac{0 - (-1)}{-1 - (-2)} = \frac{1}{1} = 1$.

The slope is constantly changing on any curve. With a curve, such as a quadratic, we are limited to finding the average rate of change between two points.

x	*f*(*x*)
−2	−1
−1	0
0	3
1	8
2	15

Average Rate of Change
1
3
5
7

The average rate of change is increasing incrementally (1, 3, 5, 7). This is a pattern that can be used to graph the rest of the parabola. We can confirm this increase by looking at the graph; you can see it is becoming steeper as we move farther from the vertex.

Graphing Quadratic Functions of the Form $f(x) = ax^2 + bx + c$

To Graph a Quadratic Function of the Form $f(x) = ax^2 + bx + c$

- Plot the vertex.
- Determine the direction of the parabola (up or down).
- Calculate and plot the y-intercept, and then use the axis of symmetry to plot a symmetrical point.
- Plot the zeros, or x-intercepts, of the function. If the quadratic equation can be factored, use the zero product property to find the zeros. If the quadratic equation cannot be factored, use the quadratic formula (which we discuss later) to find the zeros.
- Use the pattern found from analyzing the average rate of change to graph additional points on the parabola.

To Graph a Quadratic Function Using a Graphing Calculator

- Enter the function on the [Y=] screen of your calculator.
- Choose an appropriate window.
- Graph the function.
- Press [2nd] [CALC] [2] to find the zeros or roots.
- Enter left and right bounds for each zero.

To Find the Turning Point, or Vertex, Using a Graphing Calculator

- Graph the function.
- Look at the graph to determine whether the turning point is a maximum or a minimum.
- Press [2nd] [CALC] [3] to find the minimum or [2nd] [CALC] [4] to find the maximum.
- Enter left and right bounds for the minimum or maximum.

MODEL PROBLEM

MP 6 Graph the function $f(x) = x^2 - 2x - 8$. Label the vertex, axis of symmetry, and zeros of the function. Find the average rate of change from the vertex to the y-intercept.

SOLUTION

Axis of symmetry: The axis of symmetry is the line $x = 1$.

Plot the vertex: The x-coordinate of the vertex can be found using $\frac{-b}{2a}$, so that $\frac{-(-2)}{2(1)} = 1$. To find the y-value of the vertex, we substitute 1 into the expression $x^2 - 2x - 8$ and find the y-coordinate of the vertex is $1^2 - 2(1) - 8 = -9$. The vertex is $(1, -9)$.

Determine the direction of the parabola: a is positive, since $a = 1$, so the graph opens up.

Plot the y-intercept and symmetrical point: The y-intercept is found by setting x equal to 0 in the expression, $0^2 - 2(0) - 8 = -8$. The y-intercept is $(0,-8)$. The point across the axis of symmetry from the y-intercept is $(2,-8)$.

Plot the zeros of the function: The function, in factored form, is $f(x) = (x + 2)(x - 4)$. From the zero product property, we can tell that the zeros of this function are -2 and 4. The x-intercepts are $(-2, 0)$ and $(4, 0)$.

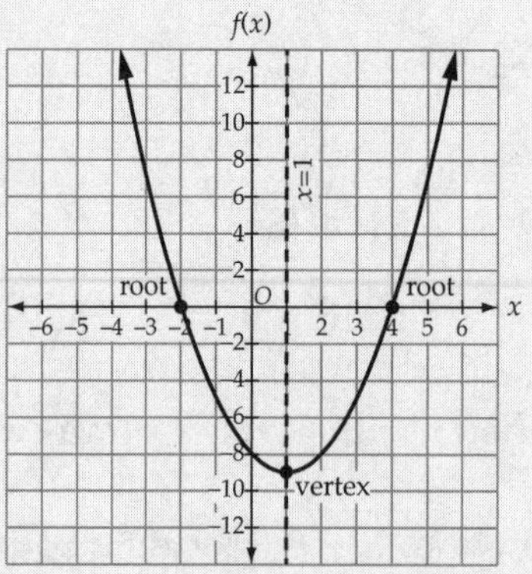

Average rate of change: The average rate of change between the vertex $(1,-9)$ and the y-intercept $(0, -8)$ is $\frac{y_2 - y_1}{x_2 - x_1} = \frac{-8 - (-9)}{0 - 1} = \frac{1}{-1} = -1$.

PRACTICE

1. What is the equation of the axis of symmetry for $f(x) = x^2 - 4x$?

A. $x = 2$

B. $x = -\frac{1}{8}$

C. $y = \frac{1}{8}$

D. $y = -2$

2. Identify the turning point of $f(x) = -x^2 - 2x$.

A. (4, 8)
B. (1, −3)
C. (−1, 1)
D. (−4, −8)

3. Which equation does the parabola in the graph represent?

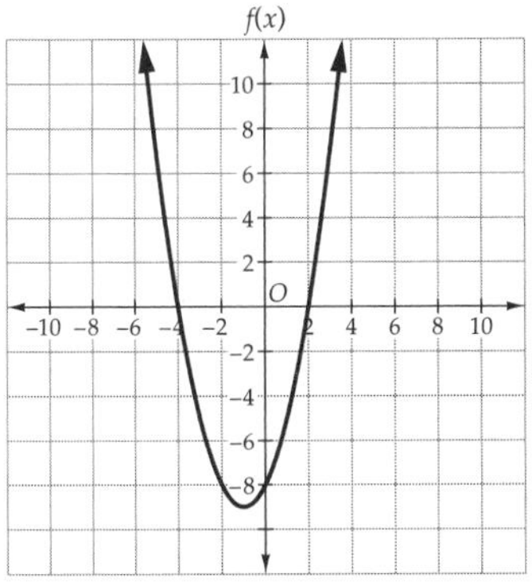

A. $f(x) = x^2 + 2x + 8$
B. $f(x) = x^2 + 2x - 8$
C. $f(x) = x^2 - 2x - 8$
D. $f(x) = x^2 - 2x + 8$

4. Which parabola is the graph of the equation $f(x) = -x^2 + 4x - 3$?

A.
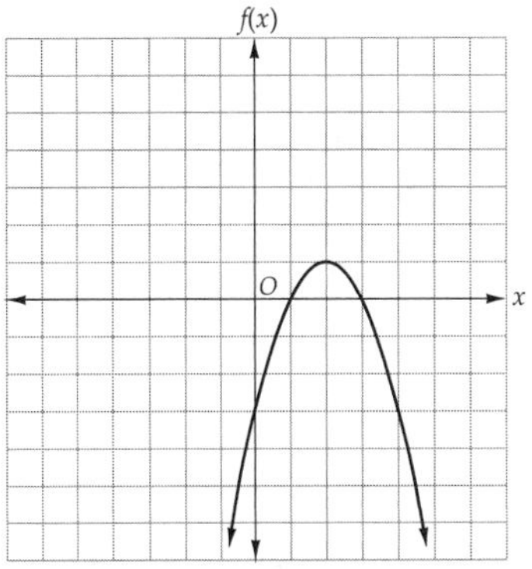

B.
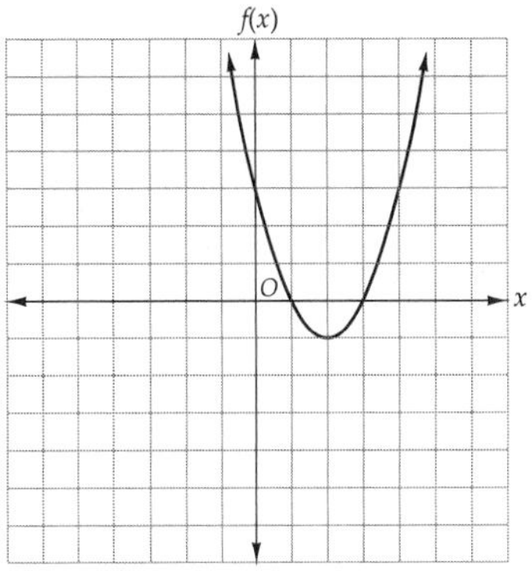

C.
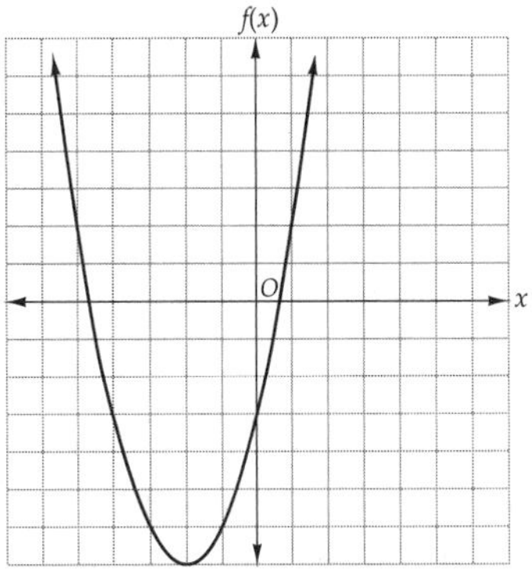

D.
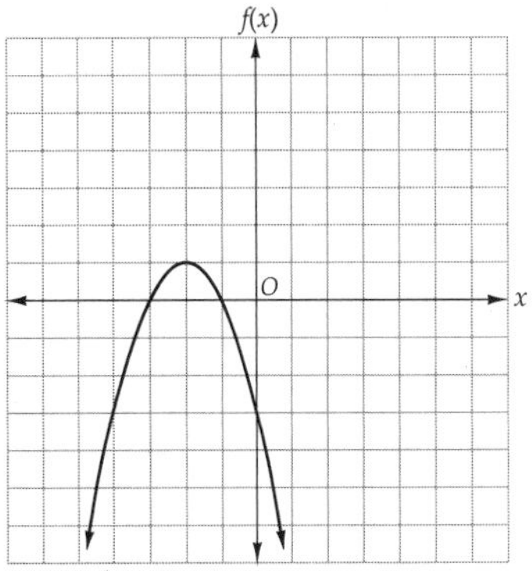

Practice Problems continue . . .

Exercises 5–9: What are the coordinates of the vertex of each of the following? Identify the vertex as a maximum or a minimum.

5. $f(x) = -x^2 + 6x + 10$

6. $f(x) = x^2 - 10x - 14$

7. $f(x) = 4x^2 + 8x - 11$

8. $f(x) = -x^2 - 6$

9. $f(x) = 2x^2 - 7x$

Exercises 10–15: Using the domain indicated in the parentheses, prepare a table of values and graph the quadratic function. Find the equation of the axis of symmetry and the turning point. Identify the turning point as a maximum or a minimum.

10. $f(x) = x^2 - 6x - 7$ $(0 \le x \le 6)$

11. $f(x) = -2x^2$ $(-3 \le x \le 3)$

12. $f(x) = x^2 + 2$ $(-3 \le x \le 3)$

13. $f(x) = x^2 - 3x - 4$ $(-1 \le x \le 5)$

14. $f(x) = 2(x^2 - 1)$ $(-3 \le x \le 3)$

15. $f(x) = -x^2 + 4x - 1$ $(1 \le x \le 5)$

Exercises 16–20: For each of the functions below,

- **a** Find the vertex and axis of symmetry.
- **b** Determine the direction of the parabola.
- **c** Find the y-intercept and use the y-intercept to find another point across the axis of symmetry.
- **d** Find the zero(s).
- **e** Sketch the graph.
- **f** Describe the end behavior of the graph.
- **g** State increasing and decreasing intervals graphed.
- **h** Find the average rate of change from the vertex to the smallest x-intercept.
- **i** Find the average rate of change from the vertex to the largest x-intercept.

16. $f(x) = x^2 + 4x + 3$

17. $f(x) = x^2 - 4x + 3$

18. $f(x) = 2x^2 - 8x$

19. $f(x) = -(x^2 - 2x - 8)$

20. $f(x) = -x^2 + 4x + 21$

Exercises 21–22: Find the x-intercepts and the y-intercept.

21. $f(x) = (x^2 - 4)(x + 1)$

22. $f(x) = (x - 1)(x^2 + x - 6)$

23. **MP 2, 3** For a linear function the rate of change is the slope. Why is $\frac{y_2 - y_1}{x_2 - x_1}$ not a good measure of change for a quadratic function?

24. **MP 1, 2, 3** If you know two zeros (x-intercepts) for a quadratic function, is that enough information to find the function? Explain your answer.

25. The point $(2, -1)$ is the vertex of a quadratic function below. The points $(4, 3)$ and $(1, 0)$ also fall on the graph of the function.

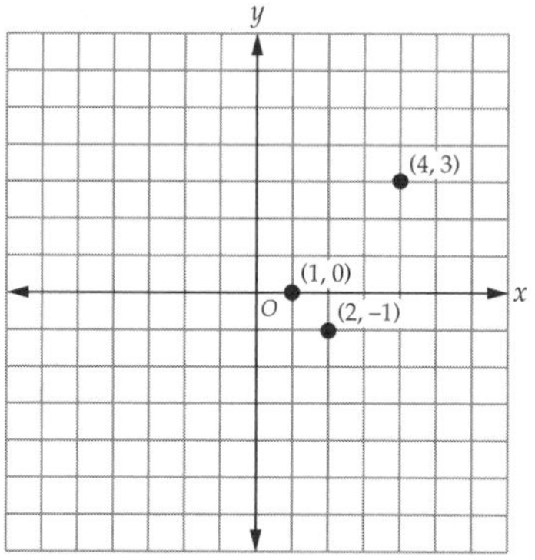

- **a** Complete the graph of this quadratic function. You do not need to complete any algebraic calculations.
- **b** Find the y-intercept.
- **c** Find the x-intercepts.
- **d** Find the values on the graph for which the function is always increasing.
- **e** Find the values on the graph for which the function is always decreasing.

Practice Problems continue . . .

MP 2, 3, 6 Exercises 26–30: A portion of the graph of quadratic function $f(x)$ is shown in the diagram to the right. The table below shows some values for linear function $g(x)$.

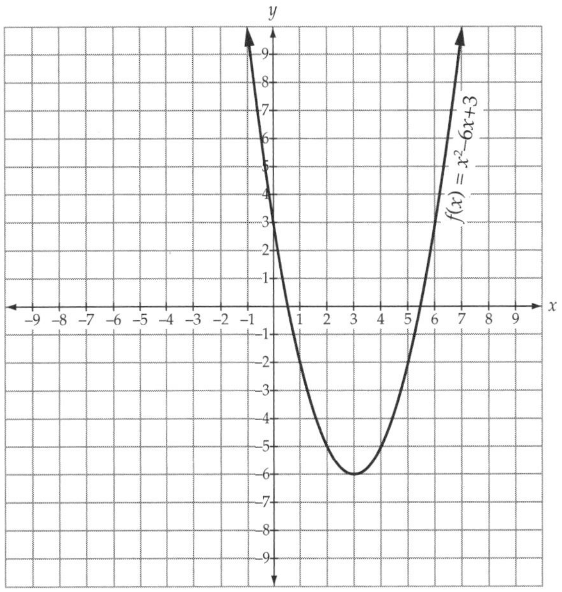

x	$g(x)$
−3	6
0	3
3	0
6	−3

In each box, write either

$<$ (less than), $=$(equal to) , or $>$(greater than)

26. The y-coordinate of the y-intercept of $f(x)$ ☐ The y-coordinate of the y-intercept of $g(x)$

27. $f(3)$ ☐ $g(3)$

28. The maximum value of $f(x)$ on the interval $-3 \leq x \leq 3$ ☐ The maximum value of $g(x)$ on the interval $-3 \leq x \leq 3$

29. The average rate of change for $f(x)$, $0 \leq x \leq 3$ ☐ The average rate of change for $g(x)$, $0 \leq x \leq 3$

30. The largest zero of $f(x)$ ☐ The zero of $g(x)$

LESSON 8.6

8.6 Quadratic Functions in Vertex Form

As we have seen, the vertex of the parabola is an important point. If we know the vertex, we know the minimum or maximum value of the function.

We can use the completing the square procedure to rearrange the standard form of a quadratic function $f(x) = ax^2 + bx + c$ to the **vertex form**, $f(x) = a(x - h)^2 + k$. The vertex form highlights the vertex (h, k).

We show the graph of $f(x) = x^2 + 6x + 5$, which is written as $f(x) = (x + 3)^2 - 4$ in vertex form. Notice that the function contains a vertex at $(-3, -4)$.

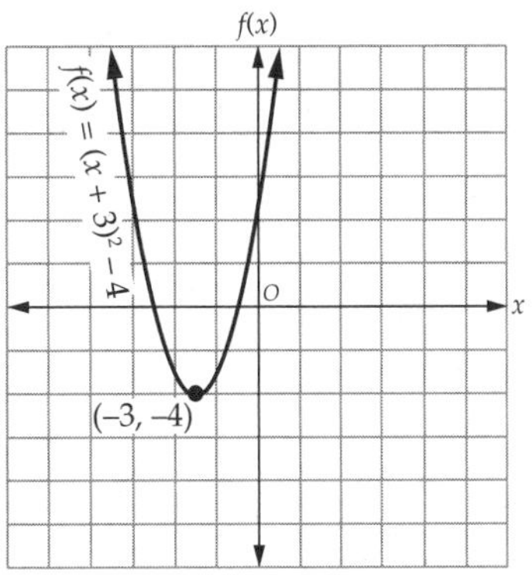

Earlier, completing the square was used to solve quadratic equations. In this section, completing the square is used to define the vertex, an essential point for constructing a quadratic graph.

To Write a Quadratic Function in Vertex Form

Given.	$f(x) = x^2 + 6x + 5$
Complete the square. • Rewrite the function in the form $x^2 + bx = -c$ and simplify, if possible.	$f(x) - 5 = x^2 + 6x + 5 - 5$ $f(x) - 5 = x^2 + 6x$
• Add $\left(\frac{b}{2}\right)^2$ to each side. Simplify the constant terms.	$f(x) - 5 + \left(\frac{6}{2}\right)^2 = x^2 + 6x + \left(\frac{6}{2}\right)^2$ $f(x) - 5 + 9 = x^2 + 6x + 9$ $f(x) + 4 = x^2 + 6x + 9$
• The right side is now a perfect square trinomial. Write it as a binomial term squared.	$f(x) + 4 = (x + 3)^2$
Subtract the constant from both sides of the equation and simplify. The function is now in vertex form.	$f(x) + 4 - 4 = (x + 3)^2 - 4$ $f(x) = (x + 3)^2 - 4$
Use the structure of the vertex form of the function $f(x) = a(x - h)^2 + k$ to determine the vertex.	$-h = 3$ or $h = -3$ $k = -4$ The vertex is $(-3, -4)$. It is a minimum since a equals positive 1 and the parabola opens up.

MODEL PROBLEMS

1. **MP 7** Rewrite $f(x) = x^2 - 4x - 3$ in vertex form and state the vertex.

SOLUTION

Given. $f(x) = x^2 - 4x - 3$

Complete the square. $f(x) + 3 = x^2 - 4x$

$f(x) + 3 + (-2)^2 = x^2 - 4x + (-2)^2$

$f(x) + 7 = (x - 2)^2$

Write in vertex form. $f(x) = (x - 2)^2 - 7$

$f(x) = (x - h)^2 + k$

$f(x) = (x - (2))^2 + (-7)$

$h = 2, k = -7$

Vertex. $(2, -7)$

Model Problems continue . . .

Model Problems *continued*

2. **MP 7** Identify the vertex of $f(x) = 3x^2 + 2x + 3$.

SOLUTION

The original equation is in standard form. We will rewrite it in vertex form by completing the square.	$f(x) = 3x^2 + 2x + 3$
Subtract the constant term from both sides	$f(x) - 3 = 3x^2 + 2x$
Factor out the lead coefficient from the right side and leave space to complete the square.	$f(x) - 3 = 3\left(x^2 + \frac{2}{3}x + \quad\right)$
Complete the square. Note that on the right side we added 3 times the quantity $\frac{1}{9}$, since $\frac{1}{9}$ is in the parentheses. We must add that same quantity to the left side of the equation.	$f(x) - 3 + 3\left(\frac{1}{9}\right) = 3\left(x^2 + \frac{2}{3}x + \frac{1}{9}\right)$ $\left(\frac{1}{2} \times \frac{2}{3}\right)^2 = \left(\frac{1}{3}\right)^2 = \frac{1}{9}$
Simplify the constant on the left by combining like terms.	$f(x) - 2\frac{2}{3} = 3\left(x^2 + \frac{2}{3}x + \frac{1}{9}\right)$
Rewrite the parentheses as a binomial squared.	$f(x) - 2\frac{2}{3} = 3\left(x + \frac{1}{3}\right)^2$
Add the constant to both sides of the equation.	$f(x) = 3\left(x + \frac{1}{3}\right)^2 + 2\frac{2}{3}$
Use the structure of the vertex form of the equation $f(x) = a(x - h)^2 + k$ to determine the vertex.	$-h = \frac{1}{3}$ or $h = -\frac{1}{3}$ $\quad k = 2\frac{2}{3}$ The vertex is $\left(-\frac{1}{3}, 2\frac{2}{3}\right)$. It is a minimum since a equals positive 3 and the parabola opens up.

PRACTICE

Exercises 1–8: Identify the vertex of each quadratic function.

1. $f(x) = x^2 + 2x + 2$

2. $f(x) = x^2 - 5x - 3$

3. $f(x) = 2x^2 - 4x - 3$

4. $f(x) = -4x^2 - x - 6$

5. $f(x) = -16x^2 + 4x + 10$

6. $f(x) = \frac{1}{2}x^2 - 4x - 4$

7. $f(x) = \frac{1}{4}x^2 - 8x + 5$

8. $f(x) = 0.5x^2 + 4x - 3$

8.7 Transformations of Quadratic Functions

As we continue to observe patterns in functions, we will examine transformations of the most basic quadratic parent function, $f(x) = x^2$, compared to the vertex form $f(x) = a(x - h)^2 + k$.

1. **Reflection about the x-axis:** If $a < 0$, the graph is reflected over the horizontal line containing the vertex. The graph curves down, as in the graph of $g(x) = -x^2$. The vertex remains the same, but is now the maximum.

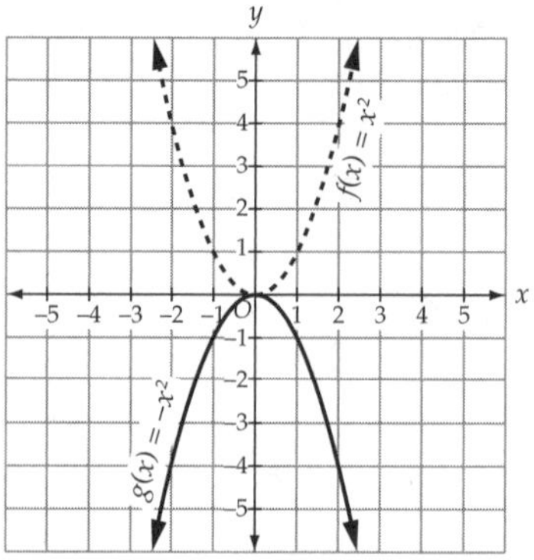

2. **Vertical stretching:** If $|a| > 1$, the graph is steeper (or narrower) than the parent function, as is the case in both $g(x) = 2x^2$ and $h(x) = 4x^2$. The vertex remains the same. The graph looks narrower and its average rate of change is greater (it's steeper).

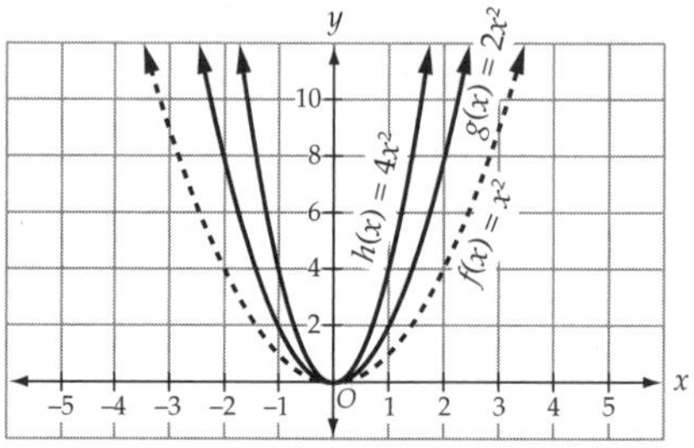

3. **Vertical shrinking:** If $0 < |a| < 1$, the graph is wider (less steep) than the parent function, as is the case in both $g(x) = \frac{1}{2}x^2$ and $h(x) = \frac{1}{4}x^2$. The vertex remains the same.

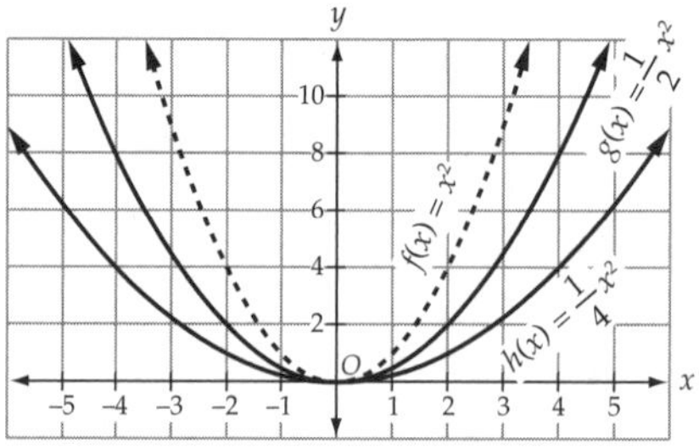

4. **Vertical translation:** If $f(x) = x^2 + k$, as in the graph of $g(x) = x^2 + 2$, then the parent function shifts up k units. If $f(x) = x^2 - k$, as in the graph of $h(x) = x^2 - 2$, then the parent function shifts down k units. This is true for all functions, including quadratic functions.

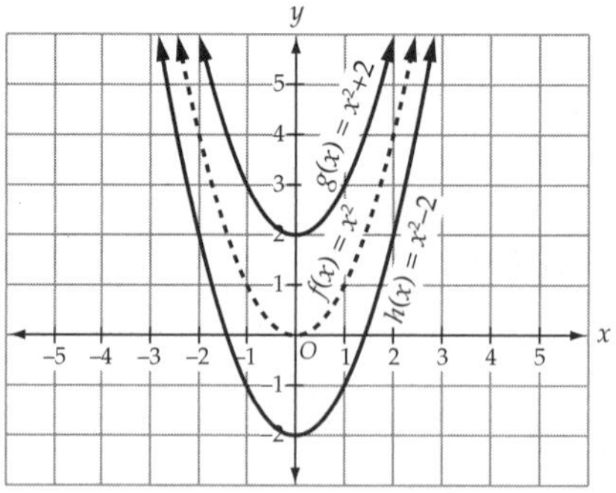

5. **Horizontal translation:** If $f(x) = (x + h)^2$, as in the graph of $h(x) = (x + 2)^2$, then the parent function shifts to the left h units. If $f(x) = (x - h)^2$, as in the graph of $g(x) = (x - 2)^2$, then the parent function shifts to the right h units. This is true for all functions, including quadratic functions.

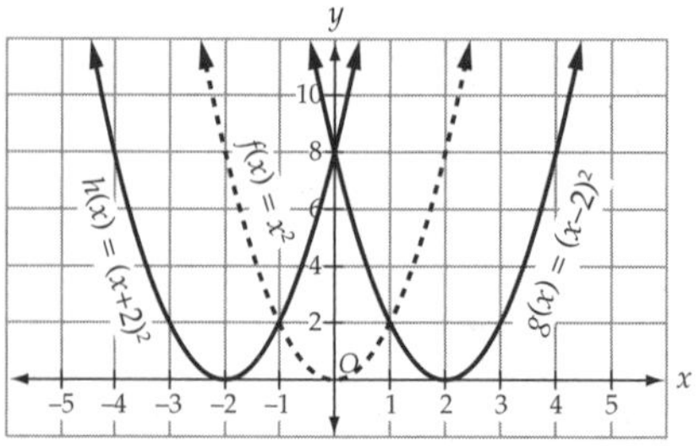

MODEL PROBLEM

Describe changes of the function $f(x) = -2(x + 3)^2 + 4$ from the parent function $f(x) = x^2$. Confirm your description by graphing the function and parent function.

SOLUTION

Reflection about the x-axis: The function $f(x) = -2(x + 3)^2 + 4$ will be a parabola facing downward, as opposed to the parent function, because a is negative.

Vertical stretch: The function $f(x) = -2(x + 3)^2 + 4$ will be stretched vertically compared to the parent function, because the absolute value of a is greater than 1.

Vertical translation: The vertex of the function will be shifted up 4 units compared to the parent function because $k = 4$.

Horizontal translation: The vertex of the function will be shifted to the left 3 units compared to the parent function because $h = -3$.

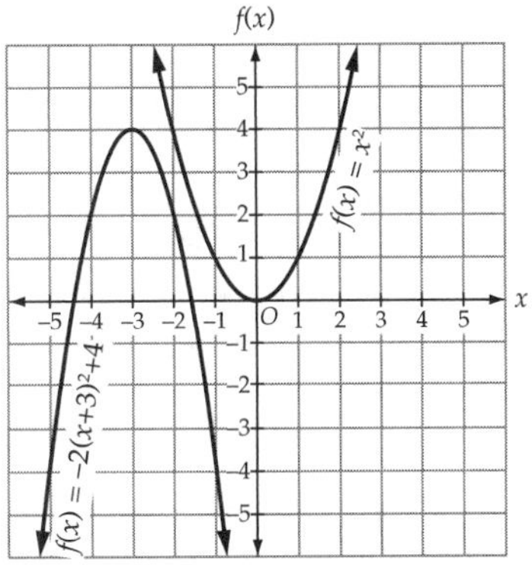

PRACTICE

Exercises 1–13: Sketch a graph of the function and describe the changes from the parent function $f(x) = x^2$.

1. $g(x) = x^2 + 5$
2. $g(x) = x^2 - 5$
3. $g(x) = (x - 3)^2$
4. $g(x) = (x + 3)^2 + 2$
5. $g(x) = 2x^2 - 3$
6. $g(x) = 0.5x^2$
7. $g(x) = (3x)^2$
8. $g(x) = \left(\frac{x}{2}\right)^2$
9. $g(x) = (-3x)^2$
10. $g(x) = \left(-\frac{x}{2}\right)^2$
11. $g(x) = 2(x - 3)^2$
12. $g(x) = -2(x - 3)^2$
13. $g(x) = -2(x - 3)^2 + 2$

Exercises 14–16: Refer to transformations of the function $g(x) = x^2$.

14. Write a set of instructions you would use to transform $g(x)$ to $h(x) = -3(x + 1)^2 + 2$.
15. For which transformations to $g(x)$ does the vertex remain the same?
16. The graph of $h(x)$ opens down. How can you change the graph so that it opens up, has the same vertex, and has the same shape?
17. Compare the average rate of change of the functions $f(x) = 2x^2$ and $g(x) = (2x)^2$ in the interval $0 \le x \le 2$.

18. Compare the average rate of change of the functions $f(x)$, $g(x)$, and $h(x)$ over the interval $0 \le x \le 2$.

$f(x) = 3x^2$

x	$g(x)$
0	21
1	1
2	3
3	5

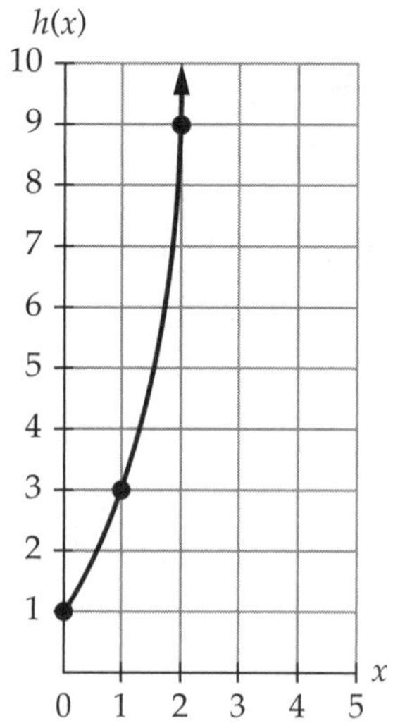

19. MP 2, 3, 7, 8 The function $f(x)$ is a quadratic function with vertex (x, y). Describe changes to the vertex x- and y-coordinates of the function for $h(x) = 2f(x) - 1$. Use a graphing calculator to test your hypothesis for 3 different possible $f(x)$ quadratics to see if the changes are consistent with your explanation.

20. MP 5, 8 For the functions $f(x) = x^2$, $g(x) = 2x^2$, and $h(x) = 3x^2$, find a pattern in the rate of change as x moves one unit away from the vertex, two units away from the vertex, and three units away from the vertex. How does a change in the coefficient affect the rates of change in the function?

LESSON 8.8

8.8 The Quadratic Formula and the Discriminant

Quadratic Formula

Any quadratic equation written in standard form can be solved by using the quadratic formula. We derive the quadratic formula by applying the completing the square method to a generic quadratic equation in standard form.

> We use the quadratic formula for quadratic equations that are not easily factorable.

The **quadratic formula** is defined as $x = \dfrac{-b \pm \sqrt{b^2 - 4ac}}{2a}$.

The two roots are $x = \dfrac{-b + \sqrt{b^2 - 4ac}}{2a}$ and $x = \dfrac{-b - \sqrt{b^2 - 4ac}}{2a}$.

Derivation of the Quadratic Formula	Example
Start with a quadratic equation in standard form.	$ax^2 + bx + c = 0$
Rewrite the equation in the form $x^2 + b'x = -c'$.	$ax^2 + bx = -c$ $x^2 + \frac{b}{a}x = -\frac{c}{a}$
Add $\left(\frac{b}{2a}\right)^2$ to each side.	$x^2 + \frac{b}{a}x + \left(\frac{b}{2a}\right)^2 = -\frac{c}{a} + \left(\frac{b}{2a}\right)^2$
The left side is now a perfect square trinomial. Write it as the binomial squared. Simplify and rearrange the right side terms.	$\left(x + \frac{b}{2a}\right)^2 = \left(\frac{b}{2a}\right)^2 - \frac{c}{a} = \frac{b^2}{4a^2} - \frac{c}{a}$
$4a^2$ is the least common denominator on the right-hand side.	$\left(x + \frac{b}{2a}\right)^2 = \frac{b^2 - 4ac}{4a^2}$
Take the square root of each side.	$x + \frac{b}{2a} = \pm\sqrt{\frac{b^2 - 4ac}{4a^2}}$
Simplify.	$x + \frac{b}{2a} = \frac{\pm\sqrt{b^2 - 4ac}}{\sqrt{4a^2}} = \frac{\pm\sqrt{b^2 - 4ac}}{2a}$
Subtract $\frac{b}{2a}$ from each side.	$x + \frac{b}{2a} - \frac{b}{2a} = \frac{\pm\sqrt{b^2 - 4ac}}{2a} - \frac{b}{2a}$
Combine terms.	$x = \frac{-b \pm \sqrt{b^2 - 4ac}}{2a}$
Write the two solutions.	$x = \frac{-b + \sqrt{b^2 - 4ac}}{2a}$ and $x = \frac{-b - \sqrt{b^2 - 4ac}}{2a}$

In order to avoid careless mistakes when solving quadratic equations with the quadratic formula, use the following guidelines:

(1) Write the equation in standard form.

(2) Write the values of a, b, and c ($a =, b =, c =$).

(3) Write the quadratic formula symbolically.

(4) Substitute a, b, and c. Be careful about negative signs.

(5) Perform the calculations.

It is very important to follow directions for showing answers. You may be asked to show your answers in simplest radical form or as a decimal expression rounded to a specific place value. In real-world modeling problems, you may have to reject a root that is outside the domain of the problem.

MODEL PROBLEM

Solve $3x^2 + 2x = 1$ using the quadratic formula. Show your work.

SOLUTION

Write the equation in standard form. $3x^2 + 2x = 1$ is expressed as $3x^2 + 2x - 1 = 0$

Write the values of a, b, and c. $a = 3,\ b = 2,\ c = -1$

Write the quadratic formula symbolically. $x = \dfrac{-b \pm \sqrt{b^2 - 4ac}}{2a}$

Substitute a, b, and c. $x = \dfrac{-2 \pm \sqrt{2^2 - 4(3)(-1)}}{(2)(3)}$

Simplify. $x = \dfrac{-2 \pm \sqrt{4 + 12}}{6} = \dfrac{-2 \pm \sqrt{16}}{6} = \dfrac{-2 \pm 4}{6}$

Add and subtract. $x = \dfrac{-2 + 4}{6} = \dfrac{2}{6} = \dfrac{1}{3}$ and $x = \dfrac{-2 - 4}{6} = \dfrac{-6}{6} = -1$

Answer: $x = \dfrac{1}{3}$ and $x = -1$

Check.

Write the equation in standard form. $3x^2 + 2x = 1$ is expressed as $3x^2 + 2x - 1 = 0$

Factor. $(3x - 1)(x + 1) = 0$

Solve. $3x - 1 = 0$ $\quad x + 1 = 0$

$3x = 1$ $\quad x = -1$ ✓

$x = \dfrac{1}{3}$ ✓

You can check your answer using the factored form of the equation. If the roots are $\frac{1}{3}$ and -1, the factored equation is $(3x - 1)(x + 1) = 0$ for this example.

The Discriminant

> The **discriminant** is the radicand, $b^2 - 4ac$, the value under the radical sign in the quadratic formula. It is the square of the value following the $\pm$ sign.

Looking at the quadratic formula, we see that the discriminant tells us the *nature of the roots.*

	Value of Discriminant	Nature of Roots	Number of x-intercepts	Example Graph
If the discriminant is a perfect square, such as 9, the expression $\sqrt{9}$ can be simplified without a radical sign. It is a rational number. There are two rational solutions.	$b^2 - 4ac$ is a positive perfect square	2 rational roots	2	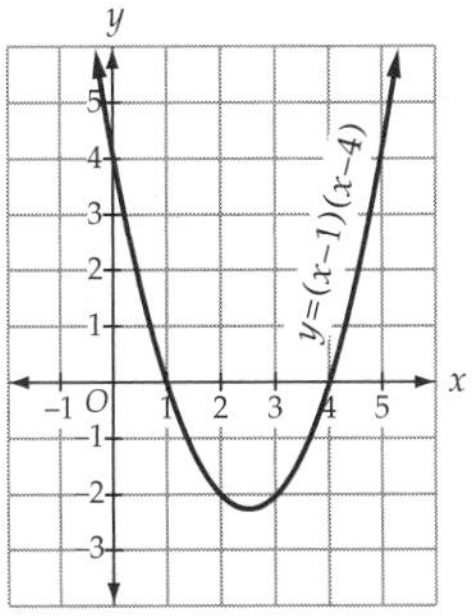
If the discriminant is positive, but not a perfect square, the exact solutions are real, but cannot be written as a rational number. For instance, if the discriminant is 12, the radical, $\sqrt{12}$, will not drop out. There are two solutions, but both are irrational.	$b^2 - 4ac$ is positive, not a perfect square	2 irrational roots	2	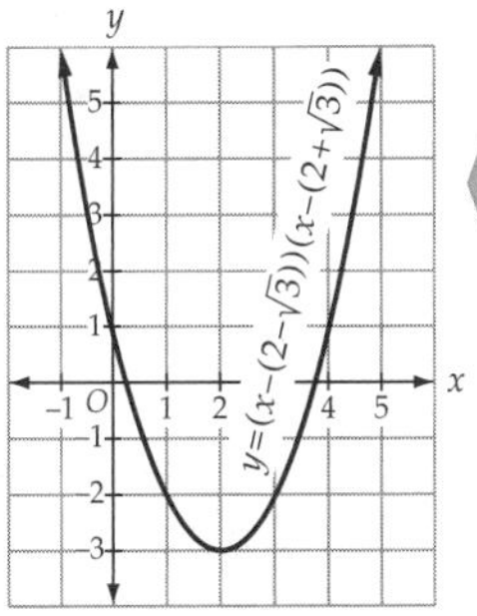
If the discriminant is 0, adding and subtracting 0 results in the same value. The graph has only one value when $y = 0$. The minimum or maximum value is the x-intercept.	$b^2 - 4ac$ is 0 (zero)	double root	1	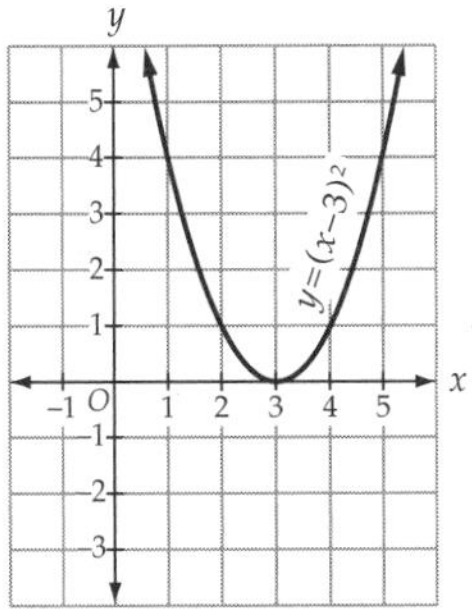
If the discriminant is negative, such as -4, then the roots are not real numbers. The square root of a negative number is an imaginary number. The roots are in the set of complex numbers. What does this mean for the graph? The graph is a parabola, but never intercepts the x-axis.	$b^2 - 4ac$ is negative	no real roots (complex roots)	0	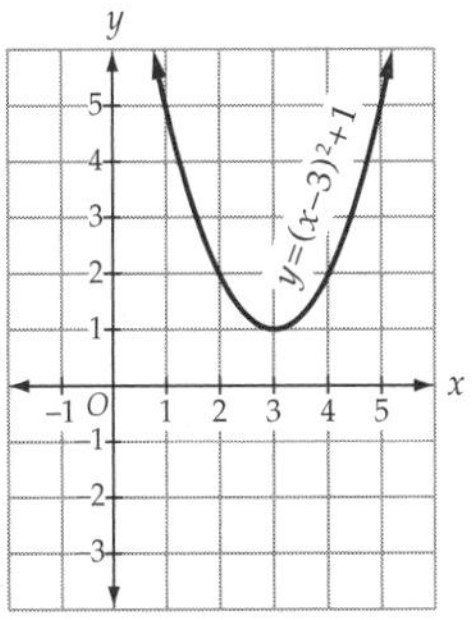

Whether the positive radicand is a perfect square or not, the graph shows two roots. Addition and subtraction of the discriminant result in two different solutions. The x-axis is crossed twice.

Remember, double roots mean the solutions, or roots, of the equation are the same.

MODEL PROBLEMS

MP 3 Model Problems 1–4: Describe the nature of the roots for the equations below:

1. $x^2 - 6x + 9 = 0$

SOLUTION

$a = 1, b = -6, c = 9 \quad b^2 - 4ac = (-6)^2 - 4(1)(9) = 36 - 36 = 0$

This equation has one solution because there is one x-intercept. The x-intercept is a double root.

2. $x^2 - 3x - 10 = 0$

SOLUTION

$a = 1, b = -3, c = -10 \quad b^2 - 4ac = (-3)^2 - 4(1)(-10) = 9 + 40 = 49$

This has two rational solutions because there are two rational x-intercepts. Since 49 is a perfect square, there are two rational roots.

3. $x^2 - 3x + 10 = 0$

SOLUTION

$a = 1, b = -3, c = 10 \quad b^2 - 4ac = (-3)^2 - 4(1)(10) = 9 - 40 = -31$

There is no solution because the graph does not intercept the x-axis. Since the function does not intercept the x-axis, there are no solutions and no real roots.

4. $x^2 - 5x + 5 = 0$

SOLUTION

$a = 1, b = -5, c = 5 \quad b^2 - 4ac = (-5)^2 - 4(1)(5) = 25 - 20 = 5$

This equation has two irrational solutions because there are two irrational x-intercepts. The x-intercepts come from the roots. Since 5 is not a perfect square, there are two irrational roots.

PRACTICE

Exercises 1–9: For each equation,

- **a** Find the discriminant and describe the nature of the roots.
- **b** If the roots are real, solve each quadratic equation. State rational roots in simplest form, and round irrational roots to the nearest thousandth.

1. $x^2 - 5x - 3 = 0$

2. $x^2 - 2x - 8 = 0$

3. $x^2 + 4x + 4 = 0$

4. $x^2 + 6x + 6 = 0$

5. $4x^2 - 1 = 0$

6. $3x^2 - 6 = 0$

7. $x^2 + 3x + 9 = 0$

8. $3x^2 - 12x = 0$

9. $x^2 + 6x + 10 = 0$

10. Find all values of b so that $x^2 - bx + 9 = 0$ has a double root.

11. **MP 3, 5, 7** Which of the following does not have any real solutions? How can you tell?

- **a** $0 = x^2 - 4x$
- **b** $0 = x^2 - 4x + 4$
- **c** $0 = x^2 + 4x + 4$
- **d** $0 = x^2 + 4x + 16$

8.9 Modeling with Quadratic Equations

> Quadratic equations often apply to real-world problems, such as number exercises, physics problems, puzzles, and geometric applications.

Physics Applications

We use quadratic equations in solving physics problems dealing with projectiles. A projectile is an object whose motion is determined by its initial velocity and its acceleration.

Projectile problems involving the height of an object thrown up in the air or simply dropped all have similar-looking formulas. The formulas describe functions in which the rate of change is not constant, but changes in a prescribed way. The general formula for the height of an object as a function of time t is given by:

height $= -16t^2 +$ (initial velocity)(t) $+$ initial height, or $h(t) = -16t^2 + vt + h$

- The coefficient of t^2 tells us how the velocity changes, which is also known as acceleration. In fact, the coefficient of t^2 is exactly half the acceleration. The unit for acceleration is $\frac{\text{distance}}{\text{time}^2}$, such as feet per second squared, or $\frac{\text{feet}}{\text{second}^2}$.
- The coefficient of t is the initial value of the velocity, or rate of change.
- The initial velocity, v, can be positive, negative, or zero. It depends on whether the object was thrown upward, thrown downward, or simply dropped. The unit for velocity is $\frac{\text{feet}}{\text{second}}$.
- The constant term, h, is the height of the ball, in feet, at the beginning of the throw or drop.

Business Applications

We use quadratic equations to find the number of items we should produce and sell to make the most profit. The following terms are used in business applications:

Unit Price: The price per item that a business charges.

Quantity: The number of items sold.

Revenue: The total income based upon sales.

Production Cost or Unit Cost: The cost of producing one item.

Profit: The amount of money a business makes from the sales.
Profit = Total Revenue − Total Production Cost
Profit = quantity · unit price − quantity · unit cost

MODEL PROBLEMS

1. **MP 2, 4** At exactly 6 P.M. a football is kicked upward from ground level with an initial velocity of 32 feet per second. The function $h(t) = -16t^2 + 32t$ gives the height of the ball in feet after t seconds.

a What is the maximum height reached by the football?

b After how many seconds does the ball touch the ground?

c At exactly what time does the ball touch the ground?

SOLUTION

a Axis of symmetry of $y = -16t^2 + 32t$ is $t = \frac{-b}{2a} = \frac{-32}{2(-16)} = \frac{-32}{-32} = 1.$

Substitute 1 for t and solve for y. $y = -16t^2 + 32t = -16(1)^2 + 32(1) = -16 + 32 = 16$
The maximum height is the turning point. The turning point is (1, 16).
Therefore, in 1 second, the football reached a maximum height of 16 feet.

b Since the ball touches the ground at 0 feet, set $-16t^2 + 32t = 0$ and solve for t.

Factor. $t(-16t + 32) = 0$

Set each factor to 0. $t = 0$ sec (as it was kicked) and $-16t + 32 = 0$, so that $-16t = -32$ and $t = 2$, which means 2 seconds (after it was kicked).

c The time is exactly 2 seconds after 6 P.M.

2. **MP 2, 3, 4, 6, 7** An object is launched straight up in the air with an initial velocity of 48 feet per second from a stage 10 feet high. Use the function $h(t) = -16t^2 + vt + h$.

a After how many seconds will it reach the maximum height? Explain your answer.

b What will be the maximum height? Explain your answer.

c When will it hit the ground?

d Choose an appropriate scale and create a graph of the situation. Label the initial height, vertex, and root(s).

e Where does the velocity change from positive to negative?

SOLUTION

To find the function for the situation, we substitute in the initial velocity, 48 ft/sec for v, and 10 feet for h. We then can use the function $h(t) = -16t^2 + 48t + 10$.

a The x-coordinate of the vertex is $\frac{-b}{2a} = \frac{-48}{2(-16)} = \frac{-48}{-32} = 1.5$ seconds.

b The vertex is the maximum in the formula, since the parabola opens down. We can substitute 1.5 for t to find the maximum height. $h(t) = -16(1.5)^2 + 48(1.5) + 10 = 46$ feet

Model Problems continue . . .

ALTERNATE SOLUTION FOR a AND b

The vertex form will also tell us when it reaches its maximum height. $h(t) = -16t^2 + 48t + 10$

Simplify and complete the square. $h(t) = -16(t^2 - \frac{48}{16}t \quad) + 10$

$$h(t) = -16\left(t^2 - 3t + \left(-\frac{3}{2}\right)^2\right) + 10 + 16\left(-\frac{3}{2}\right)^2$$

$$h(t) = -16(t - \frac{3}{2})^2 + 10 + 36$$

$$h(t) = -16(t - \frac{3}{2})^2 + 46$$

The vertex is $(\frac{3}{2}, 46)$.

c The height will be zero when it hits the ground, so $0 = -16t^2 + 48t + 10$. Since it can't be factored, we will use the quadratic formula. You could simplify the equation first by dividing by 2 and use the new values. Either way, you will get the same answer, since they are equivalent equations.

$$0 = -16t^2 + 48t + 10$$

$$t = \frac{-b \pm \sqrt{b^2 - 4ac}}{2a}$$

$$t = \frac{-48 \pm \sqrt{48^2 - 4(-16)10}}{2(-16)}$$

$$t = \frac{-48 + \sqrt{2944}}{-32} \text{ or } t = \frac{-48 - \sqrt{2944}}{-32}$$

$$t = -0.20 \text{ or } t = 3.2$$

The object will hit the ground at 3.2 seconds. $t = -0.20$ is not a possible solution to this problem, since time must be positive in this case.

d

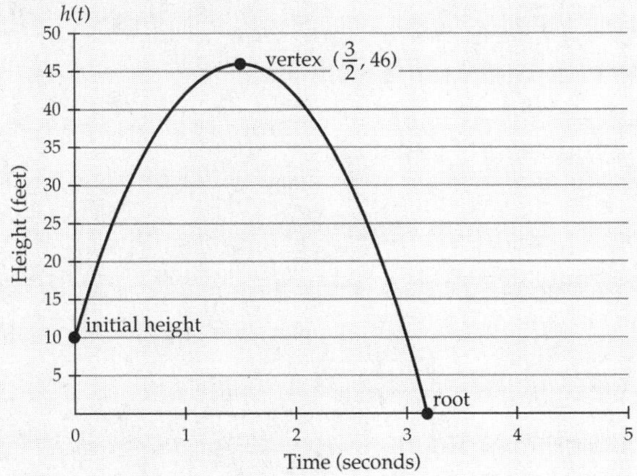

e The velocity changes from positive to negative at the turning point.

Model Problems continue . . .

3. **MP 2, 4, 6, 7** A small craft store knows that the higher the price they charge for an item, the fewer the items sold. They can produce a window decoration for \$2. Unsure about a selling price, they experimented with different prices, each for the same period of time. They charted their data:

Selling Price (s)	Quantity Sold (q)
\$5	70
\$10	60
\$15	50

a Use the table to determine a linear expression to represent the quantity sold (q).

b Find the selling price that would result in the highest profit.

c Choose an appropriate scale and create a graph of the situation. Label the vertex.

d Estimate the selling price needed to create a profit.

SOLUTION

a Using the first 2 rows, the slope, m, of the line $= \dfrac{y_2 - y_1}{x_2 - x_1} = \dfrac{60 - 70}{10 - 5} = \dfrac{-10}{2} = -2.$

Substitute values into $y = mx + b$ to find the y-intercept.

$$70 = -2(5) + b$$
$$70 = -10 + b$$
$$b = 80$$
$$q = -2s + 80$$

b The profit P = quantity (q) • unit price (s) − quantity (q) • unit cost (\$2).

Write profit as a function of selling price (s).

$$P(s) = qs - 2q$$
$$P(s) = (-2s + 80) \bullet s - 2(-2s + 80)$$
$$P(s) = -2s^2 + 80s + 4s - 160$$

Complete the square to transform the formula into vertex form. Note that $21^2 = 441$.

$$P(s) = -2s^2 + 84s \qquad -160 +$$
$$P(s) = -2(s^2 - 42s \quad) \qquad -160 +$$
$$P(s) = -2(s^2 - 42s + 21^2) \qquad -160 + 2(441)$$
$$P(s) = -2(s - 21)^2 + 722$$

The vertex (21, 722) is a maximum value.

Answer: A selling price of \$21 would result in the maximum profit of \$722.

c

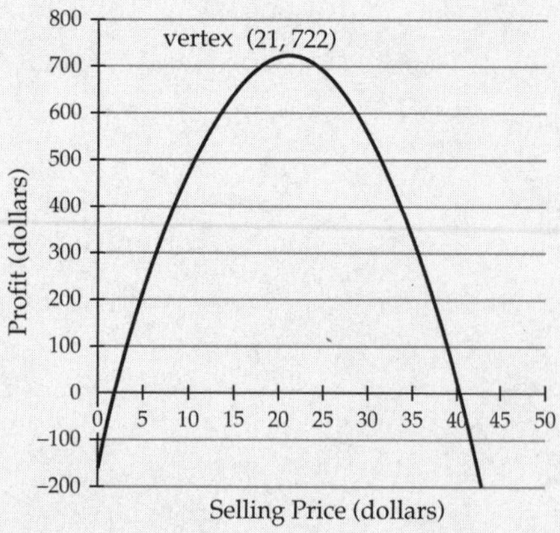

d The company will make a profit when the selling price is between $\$2 < x < \$40$. The company loses money when the selling price is less than \$2 or more than \$40.

Model Problems continue . . .

Model Problems *continued*

4. The graph of a quadratic function includes the points $(0, -6)$, $(2, 0)$, and $(-4, 6)$. Find the function.

SOLUTION

Since we know the y–intercept and two other points for a quadratic, we can form a system of linear equations to determine the standard form of the quadratic function.

> **It takes only three points to determine a quadratic function.**

The y-intercept tells us that when $x = 0$, $y = -6$. We substitute those values for x and y and find c.

$$f(x) = ax^2 + bx + c$$
$$(-6) = a(0)^2 + b(0) + c$$
$$-6 = c$$

We can now form a system of two linear equations in two unknowns, a and b.

$$(2, 0)\quad a(2)^2 + b(2) - 6 = 0 \qquad (-4, 6)\quad a(-4)^2 + b(-4) - 6 = 6$$
$$4a + 2b - 6 = 0 \qquad 16a - 4b - 6 = 6$$

Use the elimination method.

- Multiply the left equation by 2:

$$2(4a + 2b - 6) = 0$$
$$8a + 4b - 12 = 0$$

- Add the equations and simplify to solve for a.

$$8a + 4b - 12 = 0$$
$$+\ 16a - 4b - 6 = 6$$
$$24a - 18 = 6$$
$$+18 = +18$$
$$24a = 24$$
$$a = 1$$

Substitute the value of a into one of the equations and solve for b.

$$4a + 2b - 6 = 0$$
$$4(1) + 2b - 6 = 0$$
$$-2 + 2b = 0$$
$$+2 \qquad = +2$$
$$2b = 2$$
$$b = 1$$

Check in the second equation.

$$16a - 4b - 6 = 6$$
$$16(1) - 4(1) - 6 = 6$$
$$6 = 6$$
$$a = 1,\ b = 1,\ c = -6$$
$$f(x) = x^2 + x - 6$$

Finally, check all three points in the equation for $f(x)$.

$$(0, -6):\quad -6 = 0^2 + 0 - 6 = -6$$
$$(2, 0):\quad 0 = 2^2 + 2 - 6 = 4 + 2 - 6 = 0$$
$$(-4, 6):\quad 6 = (-4)^2 + (-4) - 6 = 16 - 4 - 6 = 6$$

Answer: $f(x) = x^2 + x - 6$

PRACTICE

1. Twice the square of an integer is 3 less than 7 times the integer. Find the integer.

A. -3
B. -1
C. 1
D. 3

2. The square of a number increased by 3 times the number equals 4. Find all possible solutions.

A. $\{1, -4\}$
B. $\{-1, -5\}$
C. $\{1\}$
D. $\{0, -3\}$

3. The sum of the squares of two consecutive odd integers is 202. Find the integers.

A. $\{11, 9\}$ or $\{-9, -11\}$
B. $\{11, 9\}$
C. $\{5, 7\}$ or $\{-7, -5\}$
D. $\{-11, -13\}$ or $\{9, 11\}$

4. When a number is decreased by its reciprocal, the result is $2\frac{1}{10}$. Find the number.

A. $2\frac{1}{2}$

B. $\frac{2}{5}$

C. $2\frac{1}{2}$ or $-\frac{2}{5}$

D. $2\frac{1}{2}$ or $-2\frac{1}{2}$

5. Six times the square of a number decreased by 5 times the number equals 1. Find the negative solution.

6. Find two pairs of consecutive odd integers whose product is 63.

7. The sum of the squares of two consecutive even integers is 164. Find the integers.

8. The square of a number is 12 more than the number. Find the number.

9. The square of a number decreased by 3 times the number is 18. Find the number.

10. The product of a number and 5 less than the number is 24. Find the number.

11. The product of two consecutive integers is 42. Find the integers.

12. The square of 1 more than a number is equal to 4 more than 4 times the number. Find the number.

13. The sum of two numbers is 14 and their product is 48. Find the numbers.

14. One number is 3 less than another number. Their product is 40. Find the numbers.

15. The sum of 3 times the square of a number and 6 times the number is equal to twice the square of that number, decreased by 8. Find the number.

16. If the square of a number is increased by 4 times the number, the result is 12. Find the number.

17. The difference of the squares of a number and one-half the number is 27. Find the number.

18. Two numbers are consecutive integers. The square of the lesser added to twice the greater is 37. Find the numbers.

19. The sum of a number and its reciprocal is $2\frac{1}{6}$. Find all solutions.

20. If 4 is added to 7 times a number, the result is twice the square of the number. Find the number.

21. **MP 2, 4** Lee has 40 feet of fencing material to enclose a rectangular garden that has a brick wall along one side. If the width of the garden is x, then we can represent the length of the garden as $40 - 2x$. What is the maximum area of the garden that can be enclosed by the 40 feet of fencing?

22. **MP 2** Robert plans to build a deck against his house. He decides to fence in the three other sides first with 120 feet of wooden fencing. What is the maximum area of the deck he can build based on the amount of fencing he has?

Practice Problems continue . . .

23. Alice tosses a volleyball in the air. The function $h(t) = -16t^2 + 8t + 8$ represents the distance, in feet, that the ball is from the ground at any time t.

a What is the maximum height of the ball?

b After how many seconds is the ball at maximum height?

c After how many seconds does the ball touch the ground?

24. Karen is on the beach and throws a seashell straight up. The equation that models that flight is $h(t) = -16t^2 + 96t$, where t is the time in seconds, and $h(t)$ is the height.

a What is the maximum height of the seashell?

b How many seconds does it take for the seashell to reach maximum height?

c For how many seconds is the seashell in the air?

25. The height of a baseball $h(t)$ at time t, where $t \geq 0$ and where the ball is struck initially at 4 feet above ground, is modeled by the equation $h(t) = -16t^2 + 64t + 4$.

a After how many seconds is the ball at maximum height?

b What is the maximum height of the baseball?

c After how many seconds is the ball at a height of *exactly* 52 feet?

26. MP 2, 4, 6 As a science experiment, students tried to package raw eggs so they could be dropped from the roof and not break. The height as a function of time is $h(t) = -16t^2 + 40$.

a What do the terms stand for? Why is there no t term?

b Choose an appropriate scale and create a graph of the situation. Label key features of the graph, including the vertex, initial height, and roots.

c Describe the velocity of the egg.

27. A local jeweler is marketing a piece of jewelry. She has collected data on sales and prices for the past few years. When the selling price of the product went up, the number of sales went down. The cost of producing a single item is $10.

a Use the table to write a linear equation representing the quantity sold (q) as a function of price (s).

Selling Price (s)	Quantity Sold (q)
$25	25
$30	20
$35	15

b Revenue is defined as prices times quantity sold. Write an equation describing the revenue in terms of the selling price (s).

c Write an equation describing the cost in terms of selling price (s).

d Profit is defined as revenue minus cost. Write an equation describing the profit in terms of the selling price (s). Graph this function.

e Find the new selling price that would result in the highest profit. What is the profit at this price?

28. A manufacturer produces a small electronic device for $20. For several months, the company tried selling the device at higher and higher prices, trying to increase profit. Unfortunately, with every increase in price, sales declined. The table below shows the data.

a Determine a linear model to represent quantity sold (q) as a function of the selling price (s).

Selling Price (s)	Quantity Sold (q)
$30	1000
$40	800
$50	600

b Find the selling price that would result in the highest profit.

Practice Problems continue . . .

Exercises 29–31: Find the quadratic function whose graph passes through the points shown.

29. $(0, -10)$, $(4, -8)$, and $(-2, 0)$

30. $(0, -1)$, $(-2, 9)$, and $(2, 5)$

31. $(0, 2)$, $(2, -2)$, $(-3, -7)$

32. A weight is dropped from a tower. The table shows the height of the weight in feet, t seconds after it is dropped. Determine a quadratic function that models the data.

Time (t)	0	1	2	3	4	5
Height $h(t)$	500	484	436	356	244	100

33. The relationship between the measure of a side of an equilateral triangle and its area is shown below. Find the function that describes this relationship using an algebraic model and using a geometric model. Were the two answers the same?

Side Length	1	2	3	4
Area	$\frac{\sqrt{3}}{4}$	$\sqrt{3}$	$\frac{9\sqrt{3}}{4}$	$4\sqrt{3}$

LESSON 8.10

8.10 Solving Quadratic-Linear Systems of Equations

Graphic Solutions to Quadratic-Linear Systems

The graphic solution of a quadratic-linear system consists of finding the intersection or intersections of the graph of the quadratic function and the graph of the linear function. The idea can be extended to systems including a quadratic function and an absolute value function or a quadratic function and a piecewise function.

To Solve Quadratic-Linear Systems Graphically

- Draw the graphs of both functions on the same coordinate plane.
- Find the common solutions by reading the points of intersection of the two graphs.
- Write the solutions as ordered pairs.
- Check the solutions in both original equations.

The solution set to a quadratic-linear pair may consist of two points, one point, or no points.

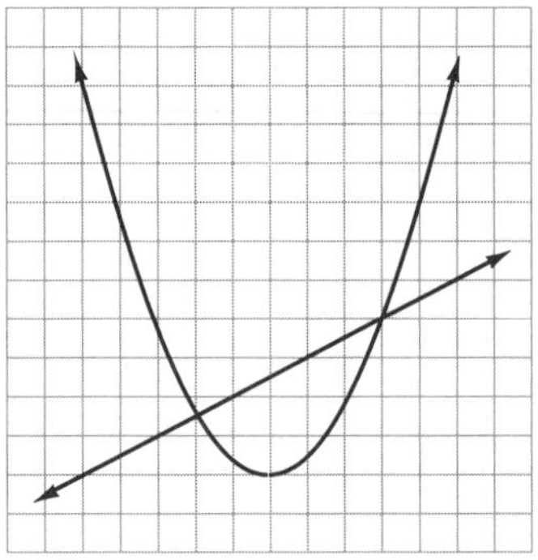

Two Solutions

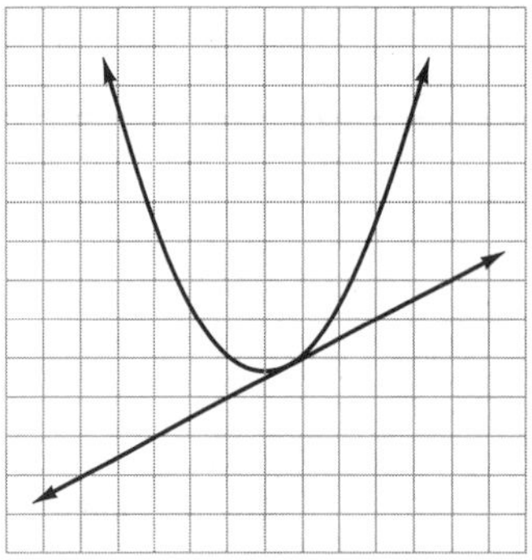

One Solution

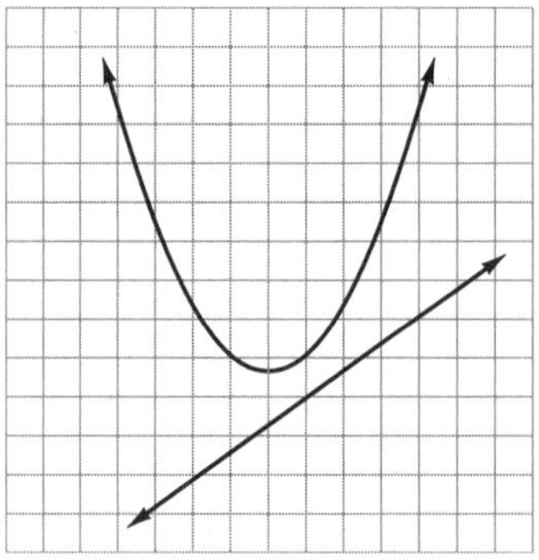

No Solution

MODEL PROBLEMS

1. Find the solution set for

$y = x^2 - 2x + 1$
$y = -x + 3$

SOLUTION

For $y = x^2 - 2x + 1$, the equation of the axis of symmetry is $x = \frac{-b}{2a} = \frac{-(-2)}{2(1)} = 1$.

Create a table centered on $x = 1$.

x	$x^2 - 2x + 1$	y
-2	$(-2)^2 - 2(-2) + 1$	9
-1	$(-1)^2 - 2(-1) + 1$	4
0	$(0)^2 - 2(0) + 1$	1
1	$(1)^2 - 2(1) + 1$	0
2	$(2)^2 - 2(2) + 1$	1
3	$(3)^2 - 2(3) + 1$	4
4	$(4)^2 - 2(4) + 1$	9

Plot the points and draw the parabola. The line $y = -x + 3$ is already in slope-intercept form. The y-intercept is 3 and the slope is -1. Graph the line.

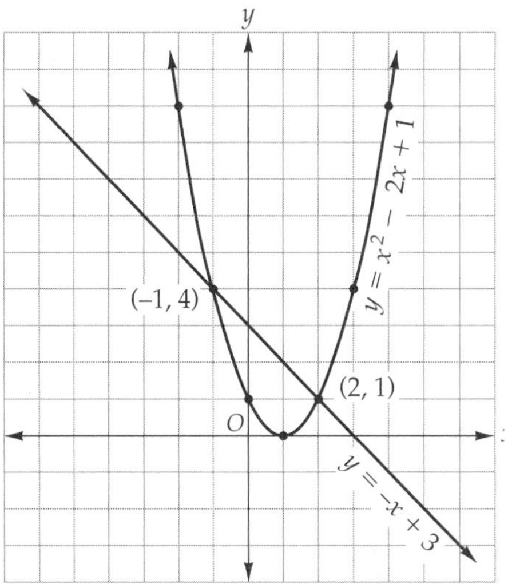

The graphs intersect at the two points $(-1, 4)$ and $(2, 1)$. The solution set is $\{(-1, 4), (2, 1)\}$.

Check for $(-1, 4)$:

$y = x^2 - 2x + 1$
$4 = (-1)^2 - 2(-1) + 1$
$4 = 1 + 2 + 1$
$4 = 4$ ✓

$y = -x + 3$
$4 = -(-1) + 3$
$4 = 1 + 3$
$4 = 4$ ✓

Check for $(2, 1)$:

$y = x^2 - 2x + 1$
$1 = (2)^2 - 2(2) + 1$
$1 = 4 - 4 + 1$
$1 = 1$ ✓

$y = -x + 3$
$1 = -(2) + 3$
$1 = 1$ ✓

Model Problems continue . . .

Model Problems *continued*

2. Find the solution set for

$y = x^2 - 2x + 1$

$y = -2x + 1$

SOLUTION

The parabola is copied from the example above. For the line $y = -2x + 1$, the slope is -2 and the y-intercept is 1.
The graphs intercept at only one point (0, 1). The solution set is $\{(0, 1)\}$.

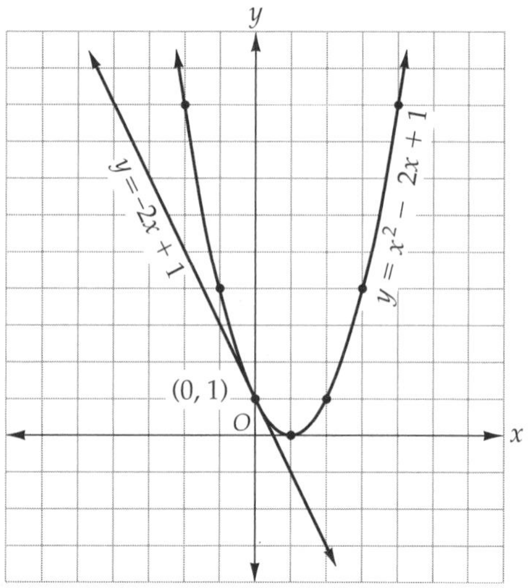

Check for (0, 1):

$y = x^2 - 2x + 1$	$y = -2x + 1$
$1 = (0)^2 - 2(0) + 1$	$1 = -(0) + 1$
$1 = 1$ ✓	$1 = 1$ ✓

3. Find the solution set for

$y = x^2 - 2x + 1$

$y = -x - 3$

SOLUTION

Again, the parabola is copied from the example above. For the line $y = -x - 3$, the slope is -1 and the y-intercept is -3.

The graphs do not intersect. The solution is the empty set, $\varnothing$.

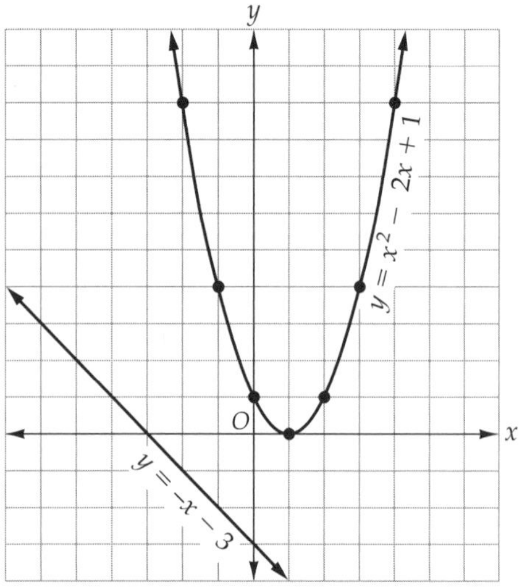

4. Find the solution set for

$y = x^2 - 2x + 1$

$y = |x - 1|$

SOLUTION

Again, the parabola is copied from the example above. The line $y = |x - 1|$ intersects at three points: (0, 1), (1, 0), and (2, 1).

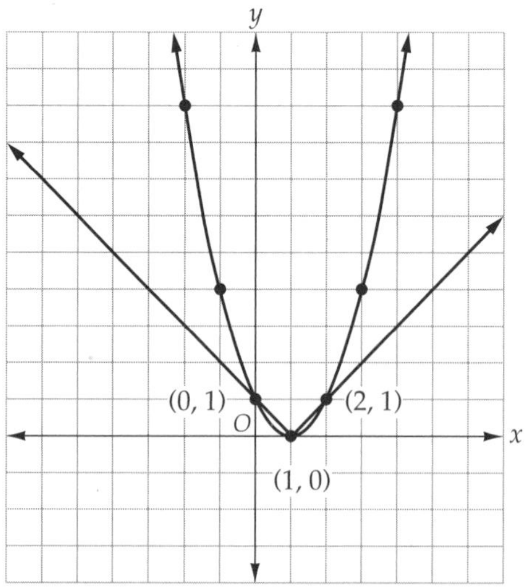

PRACTICE

1. Which graph shows the solution to the system $y = x - 2$ and $y = x^2 - 6x + 4$?

A.

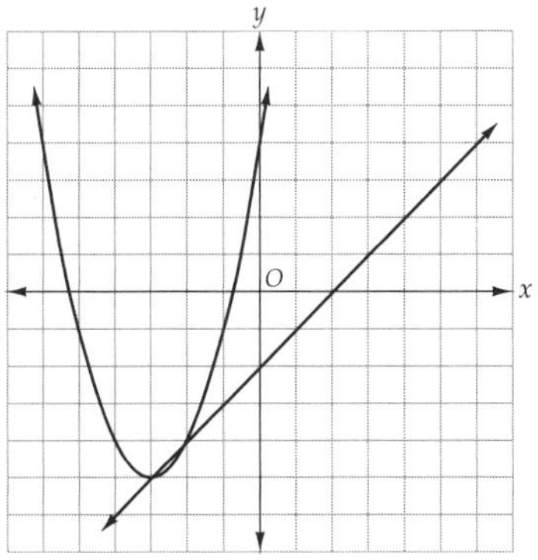

B.

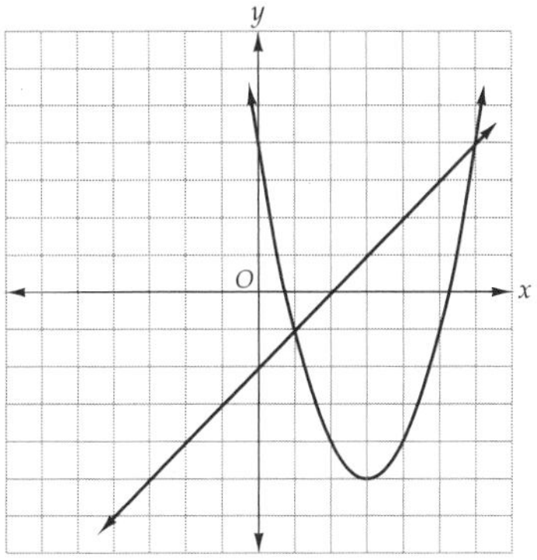

C.

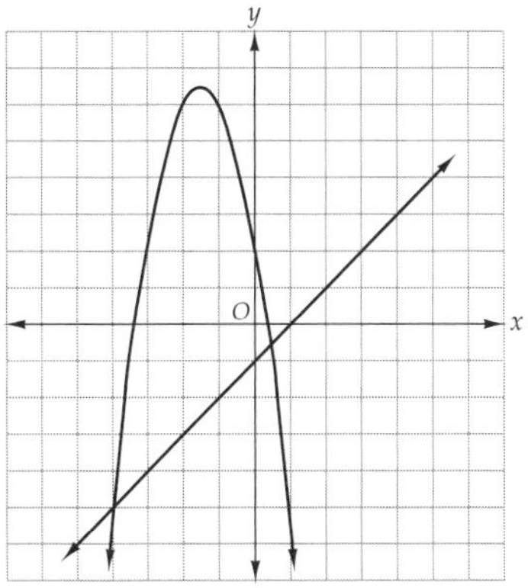

D.

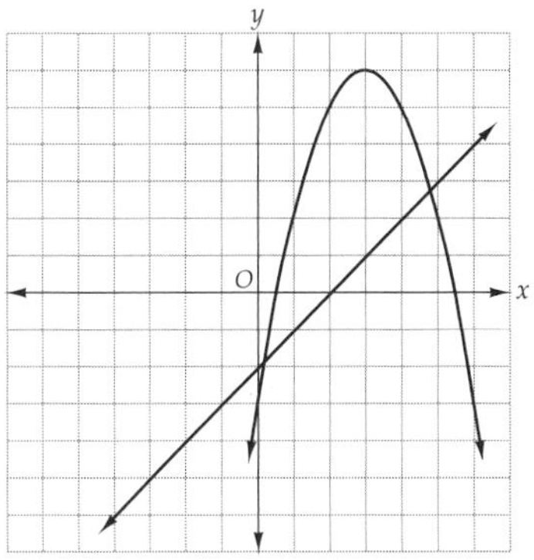

2. Which graph shows the solution set of $y = -\frac{1}{2}x - 4$ and $y = x^2 - 4$?

A.

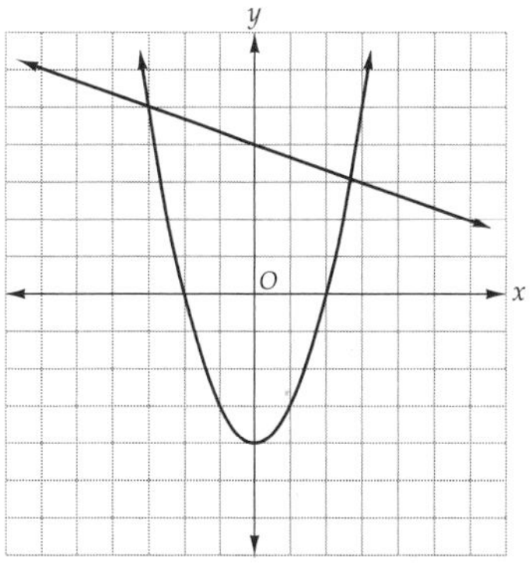

B.

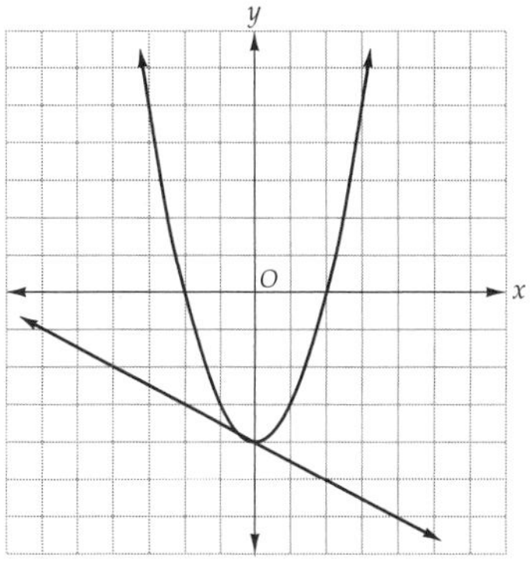

C.

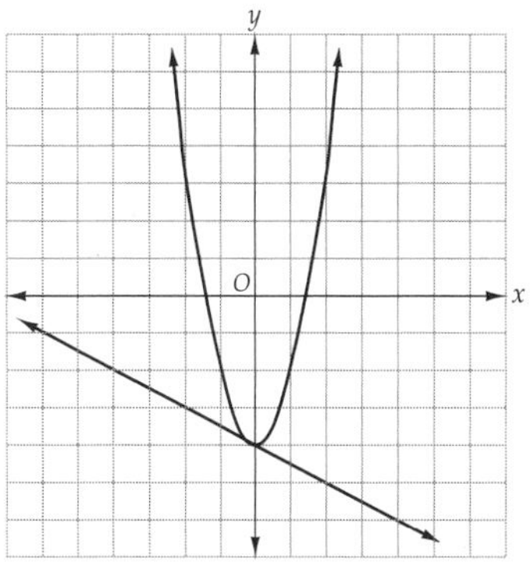

D.

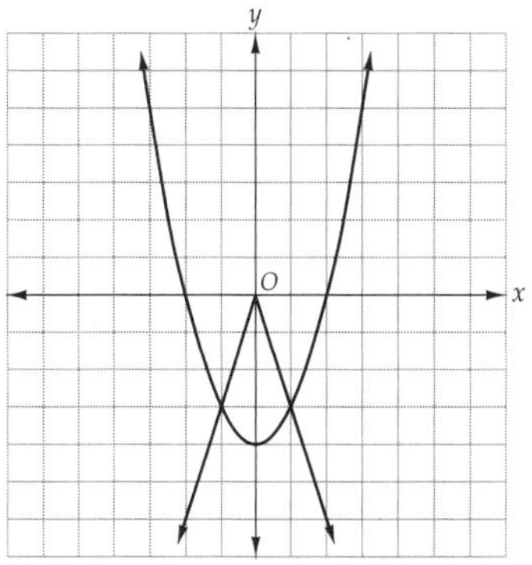

Practice Problems continue . . .

3. Which set of equations describes the graphs?

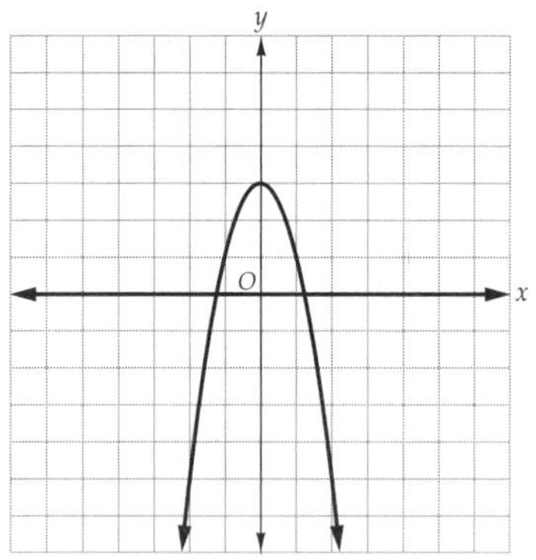

A. $x = 0$ and $y = -2x^2 + 3$
B. $x = 0$ and $y = 2x^2 + 3$
C. $y = 0$ and $y = 2x^2 + 3$
D. $y = 0$ and $y = -2x^2 + 3$

4. Which set of equations describes the graphs?

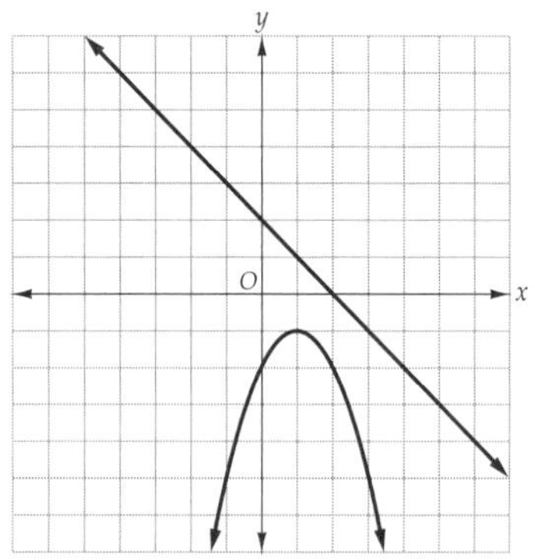

A. $y = x + 2$ and $(x - 1)^2 + (y + 1) = 0$
B. $y = x + 2$ and $(x - 1)^2 - (y + 1) = 0$
C. $x + y = 2$ and $-(x - 1)^2 + (y + 1) = 0$
D. $x + y = 2$ and $(x - 1)^2 + (y + 1) = 0$

Exercises 5–20: Solve each system of equations graphically and check. If there is no solution, write "no solution."

5. $y = x - 6$
$y = x^2 - 6$

6. $y = x^2 - 2x$
$y = x + 4$

7. $y = -x^2 + 4x + 1$
$y = x - 3$

8. $(x - 3)^2 + (y + 2) = 4$
$y = -2$

9. $y = x^2 + 2$
$y = x + 4$

10. $y = x^2 + 4x + 4$
$y = -2x - 5$

11. $y = -x^2 + 6x - 4$
$y = 2x$

12. $y = 2x^2$
$y = -2x + 4$

13. $2x^2 + 2y = 18$
$x = 3$

14. $y = x^2$
$y = -3$

15. $y = x^2 - 4x + 9$
$y = 2x + 1$

16. $y = x^2 - 5x + 4$
$y = -2$

17. $y = x^2 + x - 6$
$y = 6$

18. $y = 2x^2 + 4x - 2$
$x = 3$

19. $y = x^2 - 4x + 4$
$y = |x - 2|$

20. $y = x^2 + 4$
$y = |x|$

Solving Quadratic-Linear Pairs Algebraically

To Solve Quadratic-Linear Pairs Using the Substitution Method

(1) Solve the linear equation for one of the variables, x or y. Solving for either variable will work.
(2) Substitute this expression for the appropriate variable in the quadratic equation.
(3) Solve the quadratic equation.
(4) Substitute the solutions found in step 3 in the linear equation and solve.
(5) Check by substituting the ordered pairs in both given equations.

The algebraic solutions to a quadratic-linear system are handled the same way as solutions to linear-linear systems. Depending on the problem, the substitution method or the elimination method can be used.

MODEL PROBLEM

Solve by the substitution method: $y = x^2 - 4x + 4$; $2y = x + 4$

SOLUTION

Since the x term is squared in the quadratic equation, we solve the linear equation for y.

$$2y = x + 4$$
$$y = \frac{1}{2}x + 2$$

Substitute this expression for y in the quadratic equation.

$$y = x^2 - 4x + 4$$
$$\frac{1}{2}x + 2 = x^2 - 4x + 4$$

To clear the fraction, multiply each term by 2. Then write in standard form.

$$x + 4 = 2x^2 - 8x + 8$$
$$0 = 2x^2 - 9x + 4$$

Solve by factoring.

$$2x^2 - 9x + 4 = (2x - 1)(x - 4) = 0$$
$$2x - 1 = 0 \quad x - 4 = 0$$
$$x = \frac{1}{2} \qquad x = 4$$

Substitute both x-values in the linear equation to find the corresponding y-values.

$x = \frac{1}{2}$	$x = 4$
$2y = x + 4$	$2y = x + 4$
$2y = \frac{1}{2} + 4 = 4\frac{1}{2} = \frac{9}{2}$	$2y = 4 + 4$
	$2y = 8$
$y = \frac{9}{2} \div 2 = \frac{9}{4}$	$y = 4$

Check. Substitute both ordered pairs in both given equations.

$(x, y) = \left(\frac{1}{2}, \frac{9}{4}\right)$		$(x, y) = (4, 4)$	
$y = x^2 - 4x + 4$	$2y = x + 4$	$y = x^2 - 4x + 4$	$2y = x + 4$
$\frac{9}{4} = \left(\frac{1}{2}\right)^2 - 4\left(\frac{1}{2}\right) + 4$	$2\left(\frac{9}{4}\right) = \frac{1}{2} + 4$	$4 = 4^2 - (4 \bullet 4) + 4$	$2(4) = 4 + 4$
$\frac{9}{4} = \frac{1}{4} - 2 + 4$	$\frac{18}{4} = 4\frac{1}{2}$	$4 = 16 - 16 + 4$	$8 = 8$ ✓
$2\frac{1}{4} = 2\frac{1}{4}$ ✓	$4\frac{1}{2} = 4\frac{1}{2}$ ✓	$4 = 4$ ✓	

Answer: $(x, y) = \left(\frac{1}{2}, \frac{9}{4}\right)$ or $(4, 4)$

To Solve Quadratic-Linear Pairs Using the Addition (or Elimination) Method

(1) Add the two equations to eliminate one variable, y. You may need to add an opposite (subtract). If necessary, first write an equivalent equation for one or both of the original equations.

(2) The sum will be a quadratic equation in one variable, x. Solve it.

(3) Substitute the solutions in the original linear equation and solve.

(4) Check by substituting the ordered pairs in the given equations.

> **When the y term is the same or equivalent in both equations, set the two expressions equal to each other, simplify (write in standard form), and solve.**

MODEL PROBLEM

Solve by the addition (elimination) method: $y = x^2 - 4x + 4$
$2y = x + 4$

SOLUTION

To eliminate y, multiply all terms in the quadratic equation by 2. Multiply the linear equation by -1 and add.

$$\begin{array}{lcrcl} y = x^2 - 4x + 4 & \rightarrow & 2y &=& 2x^2 - 8x + 8 \\ 2y = x + 4 & \rightarrow & -2y &=& \quad - x - 4 \\ \hline & & 0 &=& 2x^2 - 9x + 4 \end{array}$$

Now proceed as in the Model Problem on the previous page: Solve this quadratic equation, substitute the values of x in the linear equation to solve it, and check the ordered pairs by substitution in the given equations.

PRACTICE

1. Solve:

$y = 3 - x^2$

$y = -x - 3$

A. $(x, y) = (-3, 0)$ or $(2, -5)$
B. $(x, y) = (-1, 4)$ or $(6, -9)$
C. $(x, y) = (-2, -1)$ or $(3, -6)$
D. $(x, y) = (0, -3)$ or $(1, -4)$

2. Solve:

$y = x^2 - 8x + 7$

$y = -x - 3$

A. $(x, y) = (-5, -2)$ or $(-2, 1)$
B. $(x, y) = (-2, 1)$ or $(4, -7)$
C. $(x, y) = (1, -4)$ or $(7, 10)$
D. $(x, y) = (2, -5)$ or $(5, -8)$

3. If $7x - y = 10$ and $y = x^2 + 3x - 10$, which is a possible value for x?

A. $x = \frac{10}{7}$
B. $x = 2$
C. $x = 4$
D. $x = 5$

4. If $x^2 - y = 15$ and $x + y = 15$, which is a possible value for x?

A. $x = 0$
B. $x = 5$
C. $x = 10$
D. $x = 15$

Practice Problems continue . . .

5. When Alice and Valerie tried to solve the following system of equations, Alice said there were an infinite number of real solutions and Valerie said there were no real solutions. Which student, if either, is correct? Explain.

$y = 2x^2 - 2x + 3$
$y = -2x - 3$

Exercises 6–25: Solve each system and check your solution.

6. $y = 4x^2$
$y = 8x$

7. $x^2 + 3 = y$
$x + y = 5$

8. $y = x^2$
$y = -2x + 8$

9. $y = x^2 - 4$
$y = x + 2$

10. $y^2 = 4x$
$x - y = -4$

11. $x^2 - 4x - 5 = y$
$y = 3x - 11$

12. $2y = x - 10$
$y = x^2 + 2x - 15$

13. $y = -x^2 - 4x + 1$
$y = 2x + 10$

14. $y = -\frac{1}{2}x^2 + 3x$
$2y - x = 0$

15. $y = -x^2 + 6x - 1$
$y = x + 3$

16. $y = \frac{1}{2}x^2 + 3x - 2$
$2y = 8x - 1$

17. $y = -\frac{1}{2}x^2 + 3x - \frac{1}{2}$
$y = \frac{5}{4}x - 6$

18. $y = \frac{1}{2}x^2 - 5x + 2$
$x - 2y = 24$

19. $x^2 + y^2 = 10$
$x + y = 4$

20. $x^2 + y^2 = 20$
$3x + y = 2$

21. $x^2 + y^2 = 16$
$y^2 - 2x = -8$

22. $x^2 + y^2 = 25$
$x + 2y = 10$

23. $2x^2 - y^2 = 14$
$x - y = 1$

24. $x^2 + 1 = 4y$
$3x - 2y = 2$

25. $y - 2x = 1$
$x^2 - 3xy + y^2 = -1$

26. The length of a rectangular garage is 2 yards more than its width. The area is 80 square yards. What are the dimensions of the garage?

27. The area of Janina's rectangular garden is 45 square meters. The length of the garden is 4 meters more than the width. What are the dimensions of the garden?

28. The area of a rectangle is 70 square inches. The width is 3 inches less than the length. What are the dimensions?

29. A rectangular minipark is 16 yards long and 40 yards wide. The town adds the same amount to the length and the width, increasing the area by 305 square yards. How much is added to each dimension?

30. Two opposite sides of a square are each increased by 6 inches. The other two opposite sides are each decreased by 1 inch. The result is a rectangle that is twice the area of the square. What is the length of a side of the square?

31. The perimeter of a rectangle is 22 feet, and the area is 24 square feet. Find the length and the width.

Practice Problems continue . . .

32. The perimeter of a rectangular walk-in closet is 26 feet. If the length is increased by 4 feet and the width is increased by 3 feet, the area of the new closet will be 96 square feet. Find the dimensions of the new closet.

33. One side of a rectangular garden plot is the bank of a stream. The other 3 sides are enclosed by 12 yards of fencing. The area is 16 square yards. Find the possible dimensions of the garden.

34. A rectangle is 3 times as long as it is wide. If the width is increased by 6 feet and the length is decreased by 3 feet, the area is doubled. Find the dimensions of the original rectangle.

35. The length of a rectangle exceeds its width by 7 inches. The length of the rectangle is decreased by 2 inches, and the width is increased by 3 inches. The resulting new rectangle has an area 1 square inch less than twice the area of the original rectangle. Find the dimensions of the original rectangle.

LESSON 8.11

8.11 Graphing Cubic and Root Functions

Graphing Cubic Functions

We show a graph of the parent function $f(x) = x^3$ and compare it to $g(x) = -x^3$. In the graph of $f(x) = ax^3$, where a is positive,

- As the x-values move toward negative infinity, the values of $f(x)$ also move toward negative infinity.
- As the x-values move toward positive infinity, the values of $f(x)$ also move toward positive infinity.

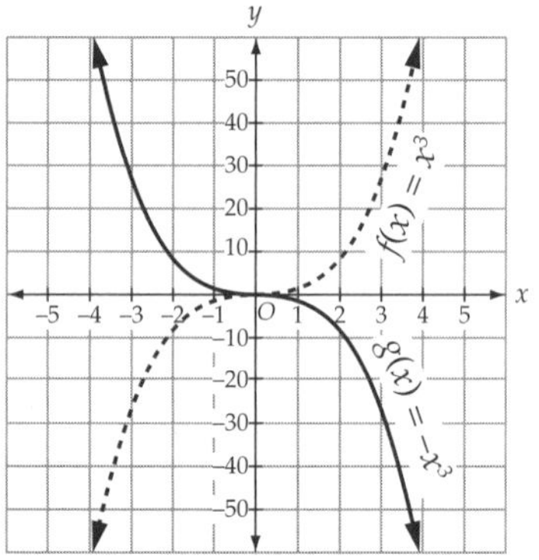

The graph of every cubic function has the same basic shape.

If a is negative, such as in $g(x) = -x^3$, then the reverse is true.

- As the x-values move toward negative infinity, the values of $g(x)$ move toward positive infinity.
- As the x-values move toward positive infinity, the values of $g(x)$ move toward negative infinity. Just like in other functions, if a is negative, the graph is reflected about the x-axis.

In both $f(x) = x^3$ and $g(x) = -x^3$, the graph crosses the x-axis at $x = 0$. The one root for both $f(x) = x^3$ and $g(x) = -x^3$ is $x = 0$.

We show two graphs of cubic polynomial functions, $h(x) = x^3 - x^2 - 4x + 4$ and $k(x) = -(x^3 - x^2 - 4x + 4)$.

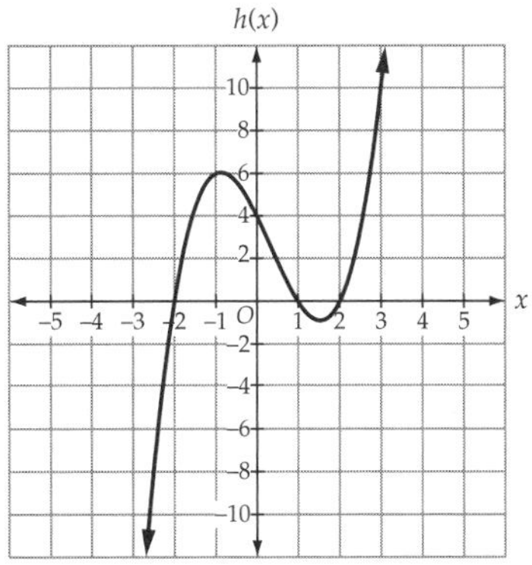

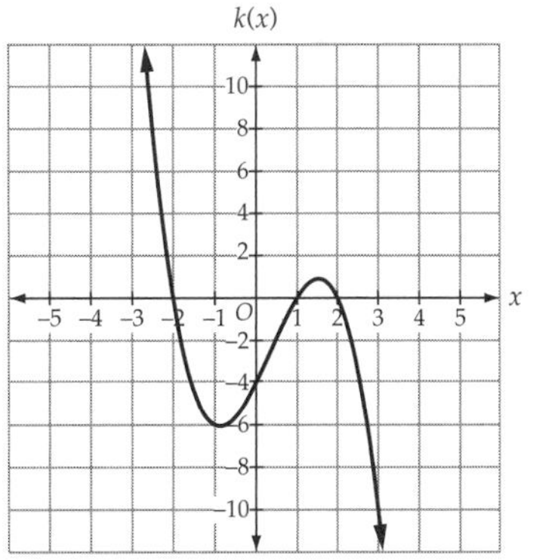

- We can use the graphs of cubic polynomial functions to find the zeros and write a polynomial in factored form. Both $h(x) = x^3 - x^2 - 4x + 4$ and $k(x) = -(x^3 - x^2 - 4x + 4)$ have zeros at $x = -2$, $x = 1$, and $x = 2$.
- We know the sign of a by observing the end behavior of the graph. For $h(x) = x^3 - x^2 - 4x + 4$ as x approaches negative infinity, the value of $h(x)$ also approaches negative infinity. As x approaches positive infinity, the value of $h(x)$ also approaches positive infinity. The opposite end behavior is true for $k(x) = -(x^3 - x^2 - 4x + 4)$.
- The factored form of $h(x) = x^3 - x^2 - 4x + 4$ is $h(x) = (x - 1)(x - 2)(x + 2)$. The factored form of $k(x) = -(x^3 - x^2 - 4x + 4)$ is $k(x) = -(x - 1)(x - 2)(x + 2)$.

To Graph a Cubic Function of the Form $f(x) = k(x + a)(x + b)(x + c)$

- Determine the direction of the end behavior.
- Calculate and plot the y-intercept.
- Plot the zeros or x-intercepts of the function. Use the zero product property to find the zeros.

MODEL PROBLEM

Sketch the graph of $f(x) = (x^2 - 4x + 3)(x + 3)$.

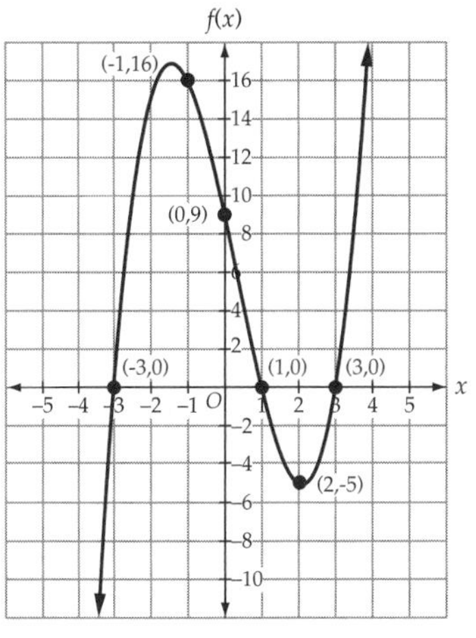

SOLUTION

Rewrite the function in completely factored form: $f(x) = (x - 1)(x - 3)(x + 3)$.

Since the coefficient of x^3 is positive in this case, the end behavior of the function goes from negative infinity to positive infinity.

From the zero product property, we can tell that the zeros of this function are -3, 1, and 3.

The x-intercepts are (1, 0), (3, 0), and (−3, 0). The y-intercept, found by setting x equal to 0, is (0, 9). The graph is a curve through these points. We don't know the x- or y-values of the points where the graph reverses direction. However, we can make an approximation by evaluating the expression for x-values between the zeros.

Graphing Square Root Functions

The parent **square root function** is $f(x) = \sqrt{x}$, the principal square root of x. The domain of this function is all non-negative real numbers, since the square root of a negative number does not exist in the set of real numbers. The range of a square root function is also all non-negative real numbers.

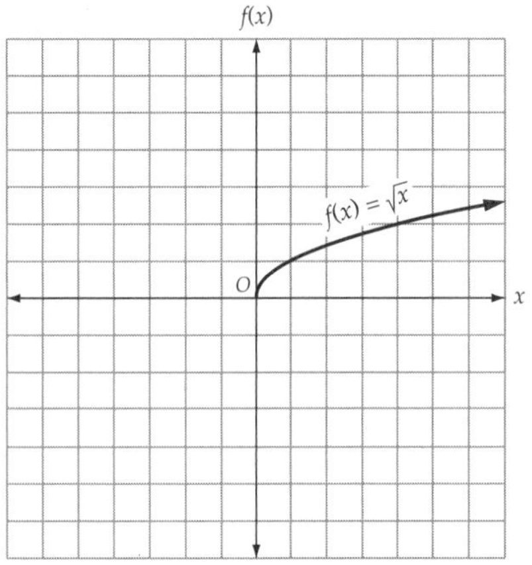

Looking at the graph of $f(x) = \sqrt{x}$, we see that the graph begins at the origin and that the values of $f(x)$ increase as x increases. However, as x increases, the rate of change of $f(x)$ decreases.

The relation $y = \pm\sqrt{x}$ is the inverse of the quadratic function $g(x) = x^2$. However, $y = \pm\sqrt{x}$ fails the vertical line test and is not a function. The inverse of the quadratic function $g(x) = x^2, x \geq 0$, is the function $f(x) = \sqrt{x}$.

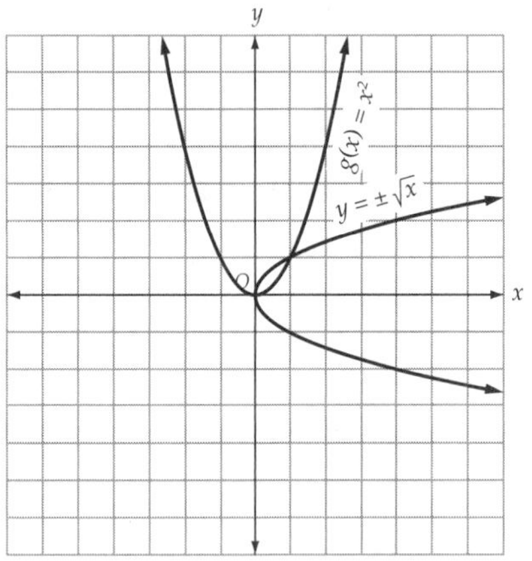

Graphing Cube Root Functions

The parent **cube root function** is $f(x) = \sqrt[3]{x}$. Since we can find the cube root of any real number, positive or negative, the domain of this function is all real numbers.

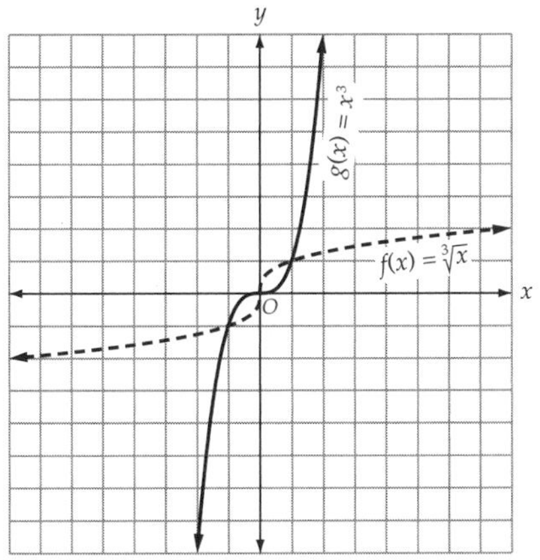

The graph is strictly increasing without an upper or lower boundary. Therefore, the range is also the set of all real numbers. As the graph shows, the closer the domain value is to zero, the greater the rate of change. If we shift the graph of $f(x) = \sqrt[3]{x}$ left, right, up, or down, or if we change the amplitude or scale, the domain and range remain the set of all real numbers. While the rate of change increases as domain values move farther from the origin for $g(x) = x^3$, the rate of change decreases as domain values move farther from the origin for $f(x) = \sqrt[3]{x}$.

MODEL PROBLEMS

1. Find the domain and range of the function $f(x) = \sqrt{x} + 2$.

SOLUTION

The domain is determined by the radicand and is therefore all non-negative real numbers.

Either plot points or use your calculator to graph $y = \sqrt{x} + 2$ to find the range. The graph remains strictly increasing. The minimum value occurs when $x = 0$. That value is 2. The range is all real numbers greater than or equal to 2.

2. Find the domain and range of the function $f(x) = \sqrt{x - 4} + 1$.

SOLUTION

The radicand expression is non-negative when $x \geq 4$. Therefore, the domain is the set of all real numbers greater than or equal to 4. The graph remains strictly increasing, with a minimum value when the radical expression is zero. When $\sqrt{x - 4} = 0$, the value of $f(x) = \sqrt{x - 4} + 1$ is 1. Thus, the range of the function is all real numbers greater than or equal to 1.

PRACTICE

1. Describe the relationship between the graphs of $g(x) = x^2$ and $f(x) = \sqrt{x}$.

2. Find the domain and the range of the function $f(x) = \sqrt{x} - 1$.

3. Find the domain and the range of the function $f(x) = \sqrt{3x}$.

4. Find the domain and range of the function $f(x) = \sqrt{\frac{x}{3}}$.

5. Find the domain and range of the function $f(x) = 3\sqrt{x}$.

6. Find the domain and range of the function $f(x) = \sqrt{x + 1}$.

7. Is $y = -\sqrt{x}$ a function? Explain your answer.

8. Describe the relationship between the graphs of $y = x^3$ and $y = \sqrt[3]{x}$. How are they alike? How are they different? Specifically, compare the average rates of change in three intervals: before zero, near zero, and after zero.

9. Is the domain of $y = \frac{1}{\sqrt[3]{x}}$ the same as the domain of $y = \sqrt[3]{x}$? Explain your answer.

10. For what value(s) of x is $\sqrt{x} = \sqrt[3]{x}$ true?

11. For what values of x is $\sqrt[3]{x} > \sqrt{x}$ true?

12. For all positive odd values of n, what are the domain and range of $\sqrt[n]{x}$?

CHAPTER 8 REVIEW

1. Solve for x: $64x^2 = 9m^2$

A. $\{24m, -24m\}$ C. $\left\{\frac{3}{8}m\right\}$

B. $\left\{2\frac{2}{3}m\right\}$ D. $\left\{-\frac{3}{8}m, \frac{3}{8}m\right\}$

2. One root of $x^2 - 10x + k = 0$ is 5. Find k and the other root.

A. $k = 25$ and the other root is 5

B. $k = -25$ and the other root is 5

C. $k = 25$ and the other root is -5

D. $k = -25$ and the other root is -5

3. Solve: $\frac{x + 7}{9} = \frac{3}{x + 1}$

A. $\{-2, 10\}$ C. $\{2, 10\}$

B. $\{-10, 2\}$ D. $\{10, 2\}$

4. Three numbers are consecutive integers. The square of the second number is 8 more than the sum of the other two numbers. Which of the following is a solution?

A. 0, 1, 2 C. 2, 3, 4

B. 1, 2, 3 D. 3, 4, 5

5. Which of the following states the vertex and axis of symmetry for the quadratic function $y = x^2 + 2x - 3$?

A. $(1, 0)$; $x = 1$ C. $(-1, -6)$; $x = -1$

B. $(-1, -4)$; $x = -1$ D. $(2, 5)$; $x = 2$

6. A small rectangular garden 6 feet by 10 feet has a brick path of uniform width, x, placed around it. If the entire area of both the garden and the walkway equals 140 square feet, which of the following equations can be used to find the uniform width, x?

A. $x^2 + 16x - 20 = 0$ C. $x^2 + 8x - 20 = 0$

B. $x^2 + 16x - 80 = 0$ D. $x^2 + 8x - 80 = 0$

Chapter Review continues . . .

Exercises 7–16: Solve each quadratic equation algebraically and check your solutions.

7. $x^2 - 12 = 11x$

8. $4x^2 + 28x = 0$

9. $5x^2 + 4x - 1 = 0$

10. $2x^2 - 7x - 15 = 0$

11. $(x + 8)^2 = 25$

12. $\dfrac{x + 3}{5} = \dfrac{6}{x + 4}$

13. $2a^2 + 5a = 3$

14. $x^2 + 16 = 8x$

15. $(2x - 1)^2 = 9$

16. $(x + 1)^2 - 5x = 71$

Exercises 17–21: Solve and leave your answers in simplest radical form.

17. $x^2 - 24 = 0$

18. $x^2 + x - 4 = 0$

19. $x^2 - 2x - 1 = 0$

20. $2x^2 - x - 2 = 0$

21. $x^2 + 2x - 2 = 0$

Exercises 22–25: Use the roots given below to write a quadratic equation.

22. $\{2, 7\}$

23. $\{-2, -5\}$

24. $\{-1, 9\}$

25. $\{-6, -6\}$

26. If one root of $x^2 - 8x + k = 0$ is -3, what is

a the value of k?

b the other root?

Exercises 27–31: For each of the given functions,

a Write the equation of the axis of symmetry.

b Find the coordinates of the turning point and identify it as the maximum or minimum.

c Graph the quadratic equation and determine the roots of the equation.

d Check the solution set by solving algebraically.

27. $y = x^2 - 7x + 10$

28. $y = x^2 - 12x + 35$

29. $y = -2x^2 - 4x + 1$

30. $y = 2x^2 - 4x$

31. $y = x^2 - 2x + 1$

Exercises 32–35: Karen graphed $f(x) = x^2 - 2x - 3$. Compare and contrast Karen's graph with the functions given below.

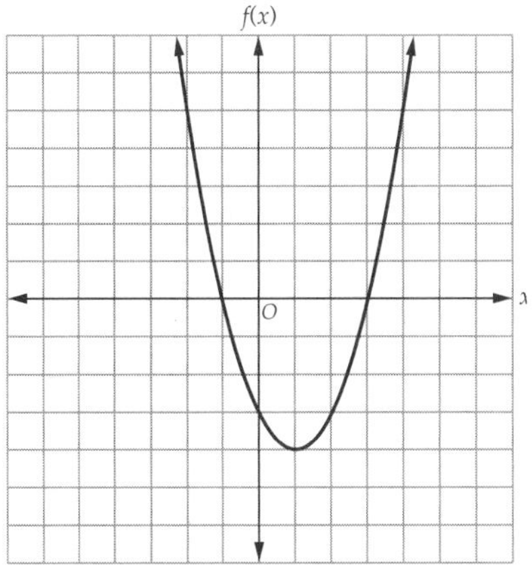

32. Sketch the graph of $f(x) + 1$.

33. Sketch the graph of $f(x - 2)$.

34. Sketch the graph of $f(0.5x)$.

35. Sketch the graph of $-f(x)$.

Exercises 36–39: Describe the nature of the roots.

36. $y = 2x^2 - 3x - 10$

37. $y = 3x^2 + 6x + 5$

38. $y = x^2 - 4x + 4$

39. $y = 2x^2 + 5x - 12$

Chapter Review continues . . .

MP 6 Exercises 40–41: In the following systems of quadratic-linear pairs, use both algebra and graphic methods to find the solution sets. Justify your solutions.

40. $y = x^2 - 6x + 5$

$y = 2x - 10$

41. $3x - y = 9$

$x^2 = 2y + 10$

42. Solve the following system of equations algebraically.

$xy = 6$

$x + y = 5$

43. The perimeter of a rectangle is 42 inches and the area is 98 square inches. Find the dimensions of the rectangle.

44. MP 4 A rectangular sheet of copper is twice as long as it is wide. From each corner a 3-inch square is cut out, and the ends are then turned up to form a tray. If the volume of the tray is 324 cubic inches, what were the original dimensions of the sheet of copper?

45. A cement walkway of uniform width has been built around an in-ground rectangular pool. The area of the walkway is 1,344 square feet. The pool itself is 80 feet long by 20 feet wide. What is the width of the walkway?

46. The height (in feet) of a golf ball hit into the air is given by $h = 64t - 16t^2$, where t is the number of seconds elapsed since the ball was hit.

a Graph the height of the ball versus time for the first 4 seconds.

b What is the maximum height of the ball during the first 4 seconds?

c How long will it take for the ball to reach its maximum height?

d Describe the velocity of the ball starting at $t = 0$ until it lands.

47. During a tropical storm, an antenna broke loose from the roof of a building 144 feet high. Its height h above the ground after t seconds is given by $h = -16t^2 + 144$. Graph the height of the antenna with respect to time until it hits the ground.

48. When an arrow is shot into the air, its height h (in feet) above the ground is given by $h = -16t^2 + 32t + 5$, where t is the time elapsed in seconds. If the arrow hit a target after 0.75 seconds, what was the maximum height of the arrow?

Cumulative Review for Chapters 1–8

1. Three girls practiced for a marathon run. The chart below shows the average speed each girl recorded for the final week of practice. Rank the girls from fastest to slowest.

Rebecca	10 miles per hour
Rita	1350 yards per minute
Rosa	12 feet per second

A. Rebecca, Rita, Rosa

B. Rosa, Rita, Rebecca

C. Rita, Rebecca, Rosa

D. Rita, Rosa, Rebecca

2. The sun is approximately 1.5×10^8 km from Earth. The sun is approximately 1.4×10^9 km from Saturn. The distance from the sun to Saturn is about how many times the distance from the sun to Earth?

A. 1.1×10^0

B. 1.1×10^1

C. 9.3×10^0

D. 9.3×10^1

3. Margie's recipe for banana bread calls for $1\frac{1}{2}$ cups of flour and 3 bananas. She wanted to use 4 bananas. How much additional flour does she need?

A. 2 cups

B. $1\frac{1}{2}$ cups

C. $\frac{1}{3}$ cup

D. $\frac{1}{2}$ cup

4. Find the equation of the line perpendicular to $y = 2x - \frac{1}{4}$ containing the point $(-2, 6)$.

A. $y = -\frac{1}{2}x + 5$

B. $y = -2x + 2$

C. $y = 4x + 10$

D. $y = -4x - 2$

5. Skip is practicing tennis serves against a wall. The distance between Skip and the tennis ball, in feet, at any time t, measured in seconds, is $d(t) = -1.5|t - 8| + 9$. Which analysis of the formula is true?

A. Skip is 9 feet from the wall and the ball will return to him in 1.5 seconds.

B. Skip is 9 feet from the wall and the ball will return to him in 12 seconds.

C. Skip is 8 feet from the wall and the ball will return to him in 1.5 seconds.

D. Skip is 8 feet from the wall and the ball will return to him in 9 seconds.

6. Find the solution for these equations.

$4x + 3y = 6; -5x - y = 9$

A. $x = 3, y = -6$

B. $x = -5, y = -3$

C. $x = -3, y = 9$

D. $x = -3, y = 6$

7. Find the product:

$(1 - x)(x + 1) =$

A. $x^2 - 1$

B. $1 - x^2$

C. $x^2 - 2x - 1$

D. $-x^2 + 2x - 1$

8. Find the nature of the roots for $f(x) = 2x^2 - 3x - 4$.

A. 2 complex roots

B. equal roots

C. 2 rational roots

D. 2 irrational roots

9. Choose the domain for $g(x) = \frac{1}{\sqrt{x-3}}$.

A. All real numbers

B. All real numbers greater than or equal to 3

C. All real numbers greater than 3

D. All real numbers greater than 0

10. The width of a rectangular plot of land is $\frac{2}{3}$ the length. The area of the plot is 384 square yards. Find the perimeter of the plot.

11. The Care Club is baking sugar cookies and oatmeal cookies with raisins. They sell the cookies in zippered bags and are confident they can sell all they make. As they plan for the week, they realize they have constraints on their baking project:

Flour:	1 bag of sugar cookies requires 1.6 pounds of flour. 1 bag of oatmeal cookies requires 1.2 pounds of flour. They have 48 pounds of flour.
Raisins	1 bag of oatmeal cookies requires 0.2 pounds of raisins. They have 15 pounds of raisins.
Time:	Each type of cookie takes about 15 minutes to bake. They have 8 hours to complete the task.

Let x = number of bags of sugar cookies and y = number of bags of oatmeal cookies. Write three inequalities to help you find how much of each cookie the Care Club can bake.

12. Express $\frac{12x^5yz^3}{3x^6y^2z^3}$ in simplest form with all positive exponents.

13. Solve the system by graphing.

$2x + 3y = 3;\ 5x - 8 = 1 - 6y$

14. A rectangle has length represented by the expression $4x^2 + 3x - 1$ and width represented by the expression $2x^2 + 4$. Write expressions for the perimeter and the area of the rectangle.

15. Write $f(x) = -3x^2 + 66x - 375$ in vertex form.

16. MP 1, 7 An art gallery charges $25 for a poster, $35 for a small lithograph, and $50 for an original still life. Last month, the gallery sold 6 posters and 3 original still-life pictures. The salesperson lost the receipt envelope for small lithographs. She knew she took in $545. How many small lithographs did she sell?

17. Solve the inequality and graph the solution: $6x + 2 < 8x - 4$

18. Rewrite using exponents and simplify:

$$\frac{\sqrt{x}\,\sqrt[3]{x}}{\sqrt[6]{x}}$$

19. Graph and compare $f(x) = 3x^2$ and $g(x) = (3x)^2$. Describe the vertices and average rate of change.

20. Write the compound inequality shown by the graph.

21. Simplify $\frac{\sqrt{98} - \sqrt{72}}{\sqrt{18}}$.

22. Express in simplest form: $\frac{4x}{2x-5} + \frac{10}{5-2x}$

23. What is the solution set for $x^2 - 4x - 12 < 0$?

24. **MP 7** Write the equation of the graphed parabola in standard form. Find two different ways to write the equation.

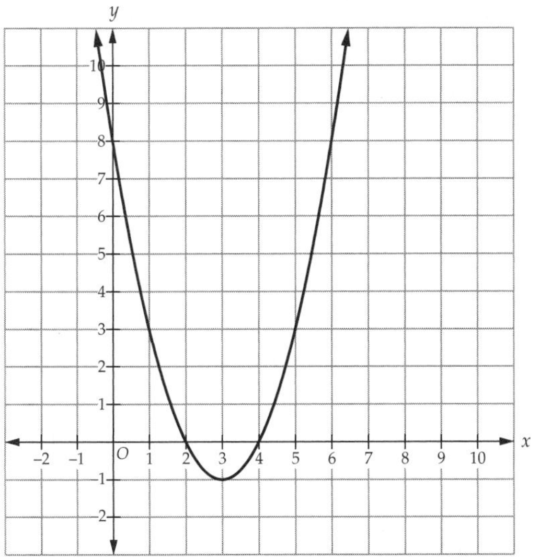

25. Write $\frac{3}{3 - \sqrt{7}}$ as a fraction with a rational denominator.

26. **MP 1, 2, 4** The Community Arena has 1000 seats. The prices for seats are \$100 for the orchestra, \$75 for the center, and \$50 for the side rows. There are twice as many center seats as side-row seats. When the theater is full, the money taken in from ticket sales is \$76,000. How many seats are there in each category?

27. **MP 3** Juanita designed a square area rug. Each side is $x + 4$ feet long. Her sister Margaret suggested she make the rug a rectangle with a length 1 foot longer than the side of the square and a width 1 foot shorter than the side of the square. Margaret said the area would be the same. Juanita said the area would be different. Who do you agree with? Why?

28. **MP 4, 6** Wendy babysits for the Crest family every Saturday night. She charges \$10 per hour for the first 4 hours and 50% more for time after the first 4 hours. She is paid the full hourly rate for any part of an hour she works. Wendy's parents do not let her babysit for more than 8 hours. Draw a graph showing how much money Wendy can earn.

29. **MP 1, 2, 4** Clare's home, her school, and the library are on the same rural road. At 3:00 P.M. her mother picked her up at school and drove her to the library. Her mother drove for 10 minutes at 30 mph. Clare spent 15 minutes in the library. She remembered Jonny was coming to her house to study, so they left the library and drove home at a constant speed of 36 mph and arrived home at 3:30 P.M.

Draw a graph to show the distance Clare's mother's car drove with respect to elapsed time. Choose appropriate labels for your axes.

Chapter 9 Exponents and Exponential Functions

Chapter Focus

In this chapter, we will extend our understanding of positive and negative exponents and examine the relationship of powers and roots. We will study exponential functions and their graphs. We will see that exponential growth and decay functions provide a basic mathematical model of phenomena that change over time. These exponential functions have useful applications in fields such as banking, medicine, nuclear energy, engineering, and the social sciences. We will also study arithmetic and geometric sequences.

Chapter Content

	Lessons	Standards
9.1	**Rational Exponents and Radicals**	N-RN.1; N-RN.2; N-RN.3
9.2	**Graphing Exponential Functions** Key Features of the Graph Transformations of Exponential Functions	A-SSE.3c; A-REI.10; F-IF.6; F-IF.7e; F-IF.8b; F-IF.9; F-BF.3; F-LE.1a; F-LE.1c; F-LE.3
9.3	**Modeling Exponential Growth and Decay**	N-Q.3; A-SSE.1b; A-SSE.3c; A-CED.2; A-CED.3; A-REI.11; F-IF.4; F-IF.5; F-IF.6; F-IF.7e; F-IF.8b; F-LE.5
9.4	**Sequences and Arithmetic Sequences** Sequences Recursive Formula for Arithmetic Sequences General Rule for Arithmetic Sequences	F-IF.3; F-BF.1a; F-BF.2; F-LE.2
9.5	**Geometric Sequences** Recursive Formula for Geometric Sequences General Rule for Geometric Sequences	F-IF.3; F-BF.1a; F-BF.2; F-LE.1a; F-LE.1c; F-LE.2

CHAPTER 9 REVIEW

Cumulative Review for Chapters 1–9

Chapter Vocabulary

arithmetic sequence
asymptote
common difference
common ratio
explicit
explicit formula
exponential decay
exponential decay model
exponential function
exponential growth
exponential growth model
general rule
geometric sequence
recursive
sequence

LESSON 9.1

9.1 Rational Exponents and Radicals

Exponential expressions with rational exponents, such as $8^{\frac{2}{3}}$ and $x^{\frac{1}{4}}$, can be evaluated or simplified. The radical sign $\sqrt{\ }$ acts in the same way as the rational exponent $\frac{1}{2}$. In other words, raising a number to the $\frac{1}{2}$ power is the same as taking its square root.

We show how exponential expressions and radical expressions are equivalent:

	Exponential Expression	**Radical Expression**
Given.	The square of $3^{\frac{1}{2}} = \left(3^{\frac{1}{2}}\right)^2$	The square root of 3 squared $= (\sqrt{3})^2$
Simplify.	$\left(3^{\frac{1}{2}}\right)^2 = 3^1 = 3$	$(\sqrt{3})^2 = \sqrt{3} \bullet \sqrt{3} = \sqrt{9} = 3$
Use the substitution property to set equations equal to each other.	$\left(3^{\frac{1}{2}}\right)^2 = (\sqrt{3})^2$	
We can conclude that the two expressions in the parentheses are equivalent.	$3^{\frac{1}{2}} = \sqrt{3}$	

To Simplify Radicals

- In converting from exponential form to radical form, the denominator of the fraction becomes the *index*, or *root*. For example, $8^{\frac{1}{3}} = \sqrt[3]{8}$ and $16^{\frac{1}{4}} = \sqrt[4]{16}$.
- The *numerator* of the fraction will remain the power.

Use the rules of exponents to help you simplify exponential expressions:

Power of zero	$x^0 = 1$, for all $x \neq 0$
Product of powers	$x^a \bullet x^b = x^{a+b}$
Power of a product	$(xy)^a = x^a y^a$
Power of a power	$(x^a)^b = x^{ab}$
Quotient of a power	For all $x \neq 0$, $\frac{x^a}{x^b} = x^{a-b}$.
Power of a quotient	For all $y \neq 0$, $\left(\frac{x}{y}\right)^a = \frac{x^a}{y^a}$.
Negative powers	For all $x \neq 0$, $x^{-n} = \frac{1}{x^n}$ and $\frac{1}{x^{-n}} = x^n$.

Consider the rational numbers represented by $\frac{a}{b}$ and $\frac{c}{d}$, where a, b , c, and d are integers:

$\frac{a}{b} + \frac{c}{d} = \frac{ad + bc}{bd}$	The sum always results in another rational number.
$\frac{a}{b} \cdot \frac{c}{d} = \frac{ac}{bd}$	The product always results in another rational number.

Similar rules exist for the sums and products of irrational numbers.

The sum or product of two rational numbers is always rational. The sum or product of two irrational numbers is sometimes rational.

MODEL PROBLEMS

1. Evaluate the expression, $8^{\frac{2}{3}}$, in two ways.

SOLUTION

METHOD 1

$8^{\frac{2}{3}} = (\sqrt[3]{8})^2 = 2^2 = 4$

METHOD 2

$8^{\frac{2}{3}} = (\sqrt[3]{8^2}) = \sqrt[3]{64} = 4$

2. Evaluate $125^{\frac{2}{3}}$.

SOLUTION

$125^{\frac{2}{3}} = (\sqrt[3]{125})^2 = (5)^2 = 25$

3. Evaluate $4^{-\frac{5}{2}}$.

SOLUTION

$4^{-\frac{5}{2}} = \frac{1}{4^{\frac{5}{2}}} = \frac{1}{(\sqrt{4})^5} = \frac{1}{(2)^5} = \frac{1}{32}$

4. Simplify $\frac{\sqrt{a} \bullet \sqrt[3]{a}}{\sqrt[6]{a^5}}$.

SOLUTION

Rewrite the expression using exponents and then simplify.

$\frac{\sqrt{a} \bullet \sqrt[3]{a}}{\sqrt[6]{a^5}} = \frac{a^{\frac{1}{2}} \bullet a^{\frac{1}{3}}}{a^{\frac{5}{6}}} = \frac{a^{\frac{1}{2}+\frac{1}{3}}}{a^{\frac{5}{6}}} = \frac{a^{\frac{5}{6}}}{a^{\frac{5}{6}}} = 1$

Model Problems continue . . .

Model Problems *continued*

5. Simplify $\sqrt{x^7} \bullet \sqrt[3]{x}$.

SOLUTION

$\sqrt{x^7} \bullet \sqrt[3]{x} = (x^7)^{\frac{1}{2}} \bullet (x)^{\frac{1}{3}} = x^{\frac{7}{2}} \bullet x^{\frac{1}{3}} = x^{\frac{7}{2}+\frac{1}{3}} = x^{\frac{23}{6}}$

Since $\frac{23}{6}$ is an improper fraction, it can be rewritten in radical form as $\sqrt[6]{x^{23}} = x^3\sqrt[6]{x^5}$.

$\sqrt[6]{x^{23}} = \sqrt[6]{(x \bullet x \bullet x \bullet x \bullet x \bullet x) \bullet (x \bullet x \bullet x \bullet x \bullet x \bullet x) \bullet (x \bullet x \bullet x \bullet x \bullet x \bullet x) \bullet x \bullet x \bullet x \bullet x \bullet x}$

$= x^3 \bullet \sqrt[6]{x^5}$

6. Rewrite each of the following as radicals in simplified form.

SOLUTION

a $x^{\frac{3}{2}}$ — $x^{\frac{3}{2}} = \sqrt{x^3} = x\sqrt{x}$

b $x^{\frac{5}{2}}$ — $x^{\frac{5}{2}} = \sqrt{x^5} = x^2\sqrt{x}$. An alternate method is to divide 5 by 2. The answer, 2 remainder 1, means x^2 is out in front of the radical sign and x^1 is under the radical sign as the radicand.

c $x^{\frac{9}{2}}$ — Dividing 9 by 2, we have 4 remainder 1. Thus, $x^{\frac{9}{2}} = x^4\sqrt{x}$.

d $x^{\frac{7}{3}}$ — Dividing 7 by 3, we have 2 remainder 1.Thus, $x^{\frac{7}{3}} = x^2\sqrt[3]{x}$.

7. Examine the completed addition and multiplication of irrational number problems shown below. What conclusions about the sums and products of irrational numbers can you draw? Explain how you know your reasoning is correct.

		SOLUTION
a	$\sqrt{2} + (1 - \sqrt{2})$	$\sqrt{2} + (1 - \sqrt{2}) = 1$ (rational)
b	$\sqrt{6} + 2\sqrt{6}$	$\sqrt{6} + 2\sqrt{6} = 3\sqrt{6}$ (irrational)
c	$\sqrt{2} \cdot \sqrt{2}$	$\sqrt{2} \cdot \sqrt{2} = \sqrt{4} = 2$ (rational)
d	$\sqrt{2} \cdot \sqrt{3}$	$\sqrt{2} \cdot \sqrt{3} = \sqrt{6}$ (irrational)
e	$(2 + \sqrt{3})(2 - \sqrt{3})$	$(2 + \sqrt{3})(2 - \sqrt{3}) = 4 - 2\sqrt{3} + 2\sqrt{3} - \sqrt{9}) = 4 - 3 = 1$ (rational)

PRACTICE

Exercises 1–10: Simplify. Write all answers in positive rational form. Identify if the answer is rational or irrational.

1. $27^{\frac{1}{3}}$

2. $8^{-\frac{1}{3}}$

3. $8^{\frac{1}{3}} \bullet 8^{-\frac{5}{3}}$

4. $16^{\frac{3}{4}}$

5. $9^{\frac{1}{2}} \bullet 9^{-\frac{3}{2}}$

6. $8^{-\frac{4}{3}}$

7. $64^{\frac{4}{3}}$

8. $125^{-\frac{2}{3}}$

9. $10^{-\frac{3}{2}} \bullet 10^{\frac{7}{2}}$

10. $\left(\frac{1}{16}\right)^{\frac{1}{2}}\left(\frac{1}{16}\right)^{-\frac{1}{4}}$

Practice Problems continue . . .

Exercises 11–20: Simplify. Write all answers in positive rational form.

11. $(8x^9)^{\frac{2}{3}}$

12. $(16x^6)^{\frac{3}{2}}$

13. $(216x^{-12})^{-\frac{1}{3}}$

14. $(8x^9)^{-\frac{2}{3}}$

15. $\left(\dfrac{a^{-\frac{1}{4}}}{m^{\frac{3}{4}}}\right)^{12}$

16. $(x^4y^{-8})^{-\frac{3}{4}}$

17. $\left(\dfrac{9x^2}{y^8}\right)^{-\frac{1}{2}}$

18. Simplify the radicals.

a $\sqrt[3]{2} \bullet \sqrt[3]{4}$

b $(3\sqrt{2})^2$

c $\sqrt{16^3}$

d $\sqrt{9^3}$

e $\sqrt[4]{8} \bullet \sqrt[4]{2}$

f $\sqrt{81a^8d^2}$

19. Write the following in rational exponential form.

a $\sqrt[4]{x^3}$

b $\sqrt[3]{x^2}$

c $(\sqrt[5]{x})^4$

d $\sqrt[11]{a^7}$

20. Simplify but leave the answer in radical form.

a $\sqrt{x^5} \bullet \sqrt[3]{x^2}$

b $\dfrac{\sqrt{x}}{\sqrt[4]{x}}$

c $(\sqrt[3]{a})^7$

d $\sqrt[3]{\dfrac{8x^6}{m^9}}$

21. Provide a counterexample to prove that the following statements are not true. Then, correct the statements so they are true, and explain why each of the statements is true after being corrected.

a The sum of two irrational numbers always results in an irrational number.

b The sum of two irrational numbers always results in a rational number.

c The product of two irrational numbers always results in an irrational number.

d The product of two irrational numbers always results in a rational number.

LESSON 9.2

9.2 Graphing Exponential Functions

Key Features of the Graph

A function that contains a variable in the place of a numerical exponent is called an **exponential function**. The form of that function can be described by the equation $f(x) = b^x$ where $b > 0$, $b \neq 1$, and the variable x is a real number.

> $g(x) = \left(\dfrac{1}{2}\right)^x$ is the same as saying $g(x) = 2^{-x}$.

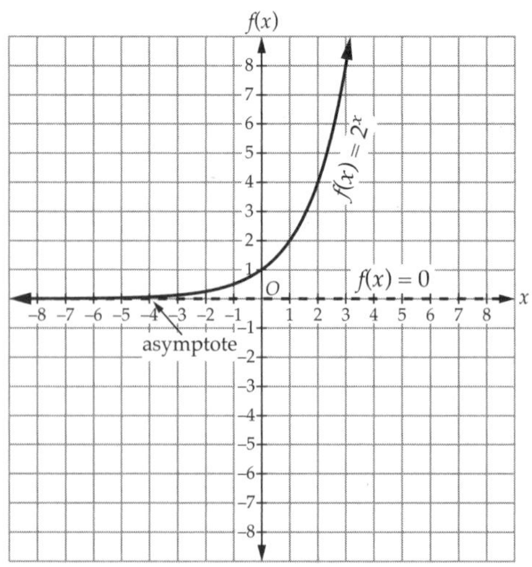

An exponential function can increase, as with $f(x) = 2^x$.

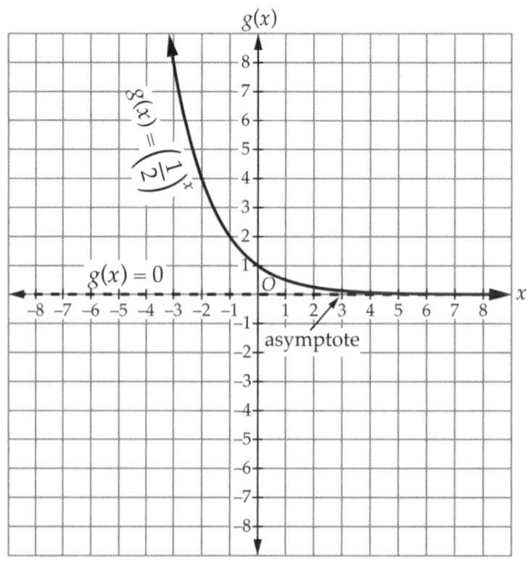

An exponential function can also decrease, as with $g(x) = \left(\dfrac{1}{2}\right)^x$.

1. **asymptote:** An **asymptote** is the line toward which the graph of a function continuously approaches but never touches. The x-axis (or $y = 0$) is the *horizontal asymptote* for an exponential function.

2. **end behavior of the graph:** The end behaviors of exponential functions are predictable: one end of the graph will be seeking the asymptote (whether increasing or decreasing) and the other end will be seeking infinity, either positive infinity ($+\infty$) or negative infinity ($-\infty$).

   - Exponential functions in the x-direction extend from ($-\infty$) to ($+\infty$). The domain of exponential functions is all real numbers.
   - Exponential functions in the y-direction extend from the asymptote to positive or negative infinity. The range of an exponential function is either all positive real numbers, $y > 0$, or all negative real numbers, $y < 0$.

3. **y-intercept:** The graphs of the functions $f(x) = 2^x$ and $g(x) = \left(\frac{1}{2}\right)^x$ both have a y-intercept at the point (0, 1).

4. **x-intercept:** The graphs of the functions $f(x) = 2^x$ and $g(x) = \left(\frac{1}{2}\right)^x$ do not cross the x-axis, so they do not have an x-intercept.

5. **average rate of change:** Exponential functions are curved. Just as with quadratic functions, we are limited to finding the average rate of change between two points. Remember that we can find the average rate of change between two points by calculating the slope between the two points.

   We compare the average rate of change of the exponential function $f(x) = 2^x$:

   - We can see that the average rates of change between points (−2, 0.25) and (−1, 0.5), (−1, 0.5) and (0, 1), (0, 1) and (1, 2), and (1, 2) and (2, 4) are *increasing* exponentially as the function goes toward positive infinity.

x	$f(x)$
−2	0.25
−1	0.5
0	1
1	2
2	4

Average Rate of Change
0.25
0.5
1
2

This is an *increasing function* that illustrates **exponential growth.**

We compare the average rate of change of the exponential function $g(x) = \left(\frac{1}{2}\right)^x$:

- We can see that the absolute value of the average rates of change between points (−2, 4) and (−1, 2), (−1, 2) and (0, 1), (0, 1) and (1, 0.5), and (1, 0.5) and (2, 0.25) are *decreasing* exponentially as the function goes toward positive infinity.

x	$g(x)$
−2	4
−1	2
0	1
1	0.5
2	0.25

Average Rate of Change	Absolute Value of Average Rate of Change
−2	2
−1	1
−0.5	0.5
−0.25	0.25

This is a *decreasing function* that illustrates **exponential decay.**

Transformations of Exponential Functions

We look at the exponential parent function $f(x) = b^x$ compared to the general form $f(x) = ab^{(x-h)} + k$.

1. **Reflection about the x-axis:** The coefficient tells us about reflection about the x-axis compared to the parent function. If $a < 0$, the coefficient is negative and the function is reflected across the x-axis and moves downward toward $(-\infty)$. The *asymptote* for both functions is still the x-axis, or $y = 0$.

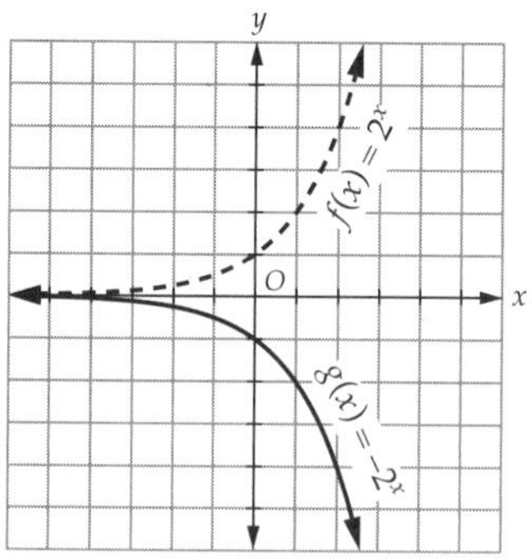

2. **Reflection about the y-axis:** If $a > 0$ and $0 < b < 1$, the function is reflected across the y-axis. The *asymptote* for both functions is still the x-axis, or $y = 0$.

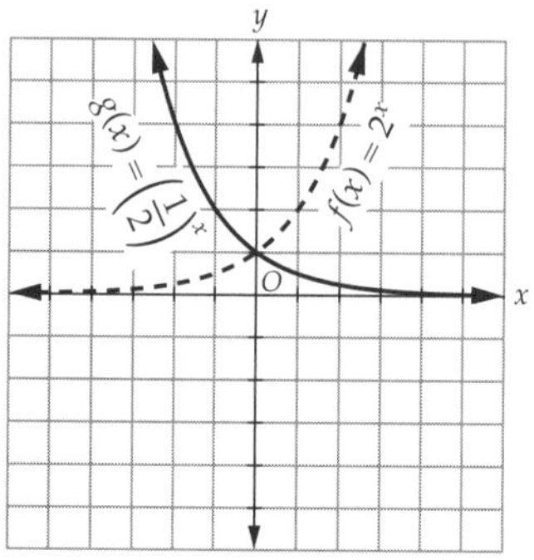

3. **Comparing y-intercepts:** The y-intercept is $(0, a)$.
   - We can write the parent function in the form $f(x) = ab^x$ as $f(x) = 2^x = (1)(2^x)$. The y-intercept is $(0, 1)$.
   - The coefficient of the function $g(x) = (2)(2^x)$ is 2, so the y-intercept is $(0, 2)$.

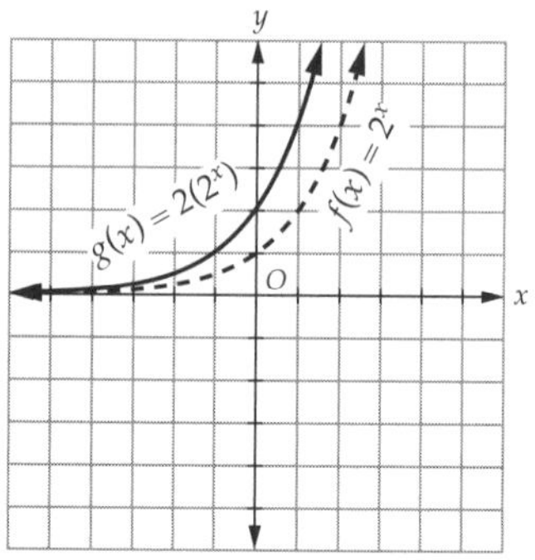

4. **Vertical stretching:** If $|a| > 1$, then the graph is steeper compared to the parent function. The graph of $g(x) = 3(2^x)$ is steeper than the parent function $f(x) = 2^x$.

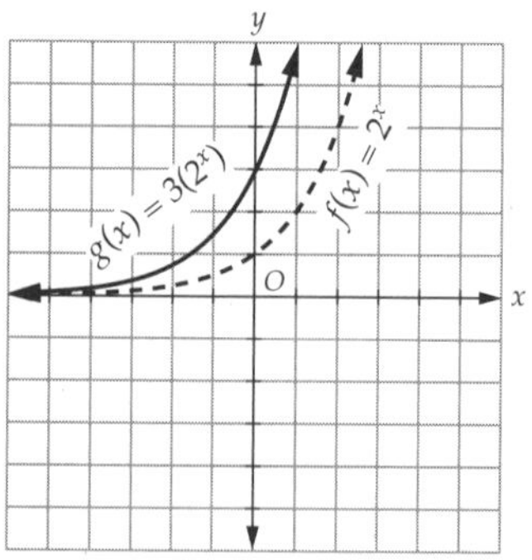

5. **Vertical shrinking:** If $0 < |a| < 1$, then the graph is less steep than the original parent function. The graph of $g(x) = \frac{1}{2}(2^x)$ is less steep compared to $f(x) = 2^x$.

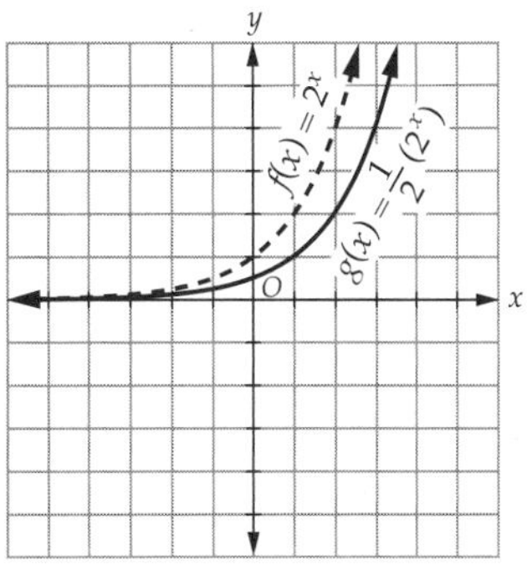

6. **Vertical translation:** If $f(x) = ab^x + k$, as in the graph of $g(x) = 2^x + 2$, then the parent function translates, or shifts, up k units. If $f(x) = ab^x - k$, as in the graph of $h(x) = 2^x - 3$, then the parent function shifts down k units.

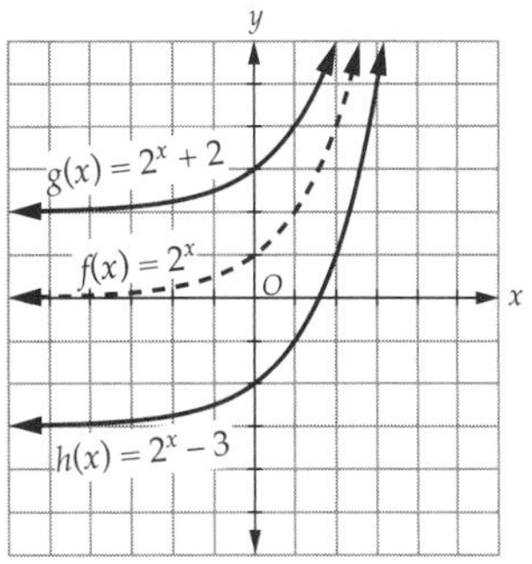

- The constant k identifies the asymptote. For $f(x) = 2^x$ the asymptote is $y = 0$. For $g(x) = 2^x + 2$ the asymptote is $y = 2$, and for $h(x) = 2^x - 3$ the asymptote is $y = -3$.
- The y-intercepts are each 1 more than the asymptote. For $f(x) = 2^x$ the y-intercept is 1, $(0 + 1)$; for $g(x) = 2^x + 2$ the y-intercept is 3, $(2 + 1)$; for $h(x) = 2^x - 3$ the y-intercept is -2, $(-3 + 1)$.

The same rules for translating functions apply to other functions, such as linear, absolute value, and quadratic functions.

7. **Horizontal translation:** If $f(x) = ab^{x+h}$, as in the graph of $g(x) = 2^{x+1}$, then the parent function shifts to the left h units. If $f(x) = ab^{x-h}$, as in the graph of $h(x) = 2^{x-2}$, then the parent function shifts to the right h units.

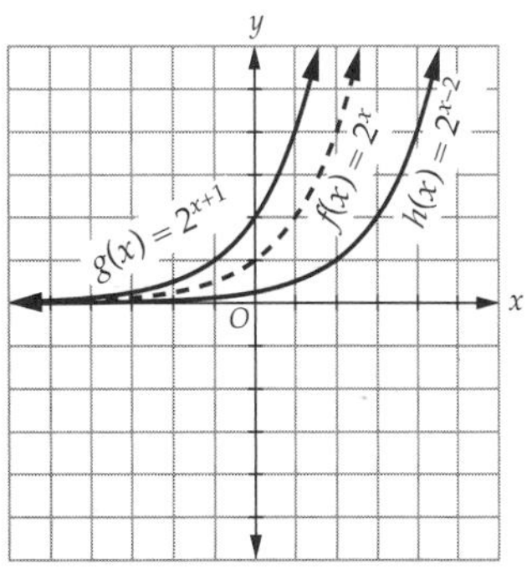

- The asymptotes are all $y = 0$.
- The y-intercepts have changed. For $f(x) = 2^x$ the y-intercept is still $(0, 1)$; for $g(x) = 2^{x+1}$ the y-intercept is at $(0, 2)$; for $h(x) = 2^{x-2}$ the y-intercept is at $(0, 0.25)$.

MODEL PROBLEMS

1. Compare and contrast the graphs of two functions $g(x) = y = 2^{x+1} - 3$ and $h(x) = y = 2^{x-3} + 1$ against the parent function $f(x) = y = 2^x$ using a, h, and k.

SOLUTION

The graphs indicate that $g(x) = 2^{x+1} - 3$ has been horizontally shifted left 1 unit and vertically shifted down 3 units, while $h(x) = 2^{x-3} + 1$ indicates a horizontal shift 3 units to the right and vertical shift 1 unit up.

We can specify the asymptotes and the y-intercepts: for $f(x)$ the asymptote is $y = 0$ and y-intercept is $(0, 1)$; for $g(x)$ the asymptote is $y = -3$ and y-intercept $(0, -1)$; for $h(x)$ the asymptote is $y = 1$ and y-intercept $(0, 1.125)$.

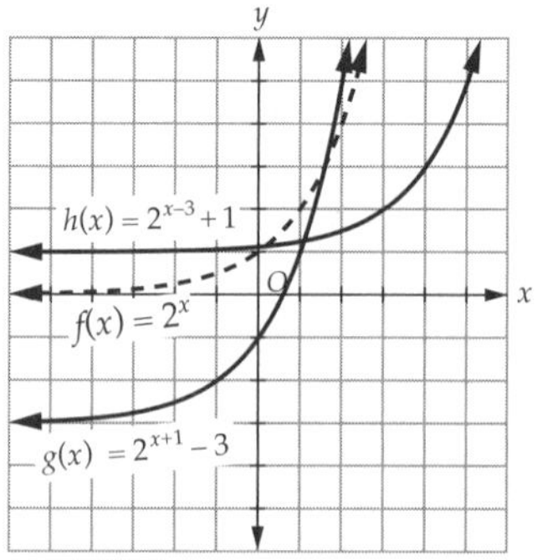

2. For each of the given functions, $f(x) = 2^x$, $g(x) = 2^x + 3$, $h(x) = 2^{x+3}$, and $m(x) = 2^{x-1} - 2$

a State the transformation that applies to the parent function $f(x)$ in order to generate the functions $g(x)$, $h(x)$, and $m(x)$.

b Identify the asymptote.

c Identify the y-intercept.

SOLUTION

a Transformations: for $g(x)$, the function is vertically shifted up 3 units; for $h(x)$, the function is horizontally shifted to the left 3 units; for $m(x)$, the function is horizontally shifted to the right 1 unit and vertically shifted down 2 units.

b Asymptotes: for $f(x)$, $y = 0$; for $g(x)$, $y = 3$; for $h(x)$, $y = 0$; for $m(x)$, $y = -2$

c y-intercepts: for $f(x)$, $(0, 1)$; for $g(x)$, $(0, 4)$; for $h(x)$, $(0, 8)$; for $m(x)$, $(0, -1.5)$

3. Graph $y = \left(\frac{1}{2}\right)^x$ and its reflection about the x-axis. Provide a table of values. Show the algebra that identifies this function.

SOLUTION

The reflection of a function about the x-axis follows the rule of keeping the x and taking the opposite of y.

$y = \left(\frac{1}{2}\right)^x$ becomes $-y = \left(\frac{1}{2}\right)^x$ and (solving for y) we have $y = -\left(\frac{1}{2}\right)^x$.

x	−3	−2	−1	0	1	2	3
$\left(\frac{1}{2}\right)^x$	8	4	2	1	$\frac{1}{2}$	$\frac{1}{4}$	$\frac{1}{8}$

x	−3	−2	−1	0	1	2	3
$-\left(\frac{1}{2}\right)^x$	−8	−4	−2	−1	$-\frac{1}{2}$	$-\frac{1}{4}$	$-\frac{1}{8}$

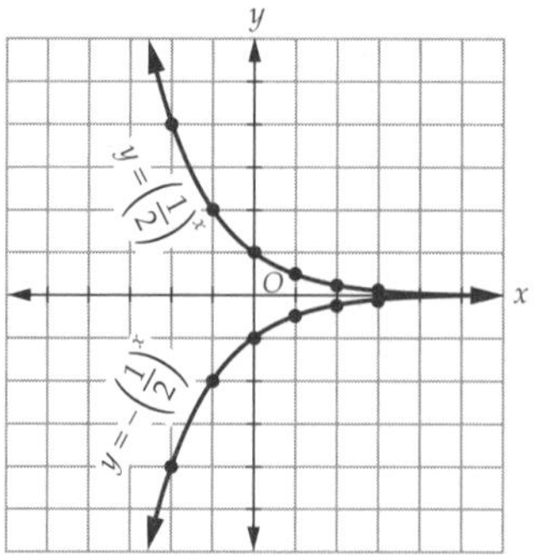

Model Problems continue . . .

Model Problems *continued*

4. **MP 1, 7** Graph the functions, identify the type of functions, and compare the domains, ranges, asymptotes and average rates of change of: $y = 2x$ and $y = 2^x$. If there are solutions to the system, identify them.

SOLUTION

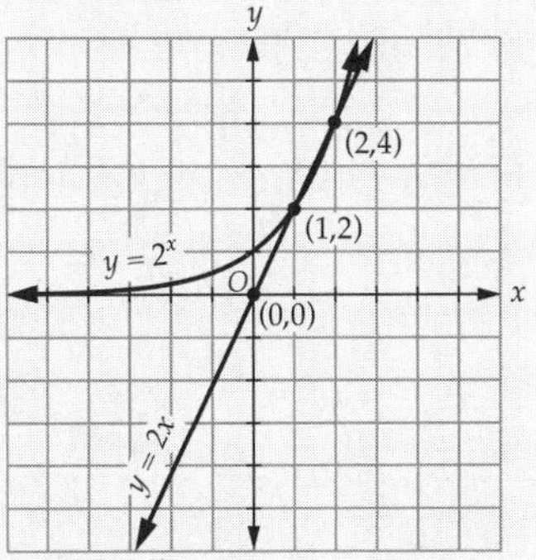

Type of function: $y = 2x$ is a linear function, and $y = 2^x$ is an exponential function.

Domain: all real numbers for both functions, $-\infty < x < \infty$

Range: for $y = 2x$ all real numbers; for $y = 2^x$, $0 < y < \infty$

Asymptote: Only the exponential function has an asymptote. It is $y = 0$.

Average rate of change: The average rate of change for $y = 2x$ is the constant slope $m = 2$. For linear functions the graph always grows by equal differences. The average rate of change for $y = 2^x$ is not constant since it increases by a factor of 2 from one x interval to the next.

Solutions to system: $y = 2x$ and $y = 2^x$ cross at two points, so there are two solutions to the system. The solutions are at (2, 4) and (1, 2) since both points satisfy both equations.

5. **MP 2** Given the graph of $y = x^2$ and $y = 2^x$, compare the average rates of change of the functions over the intervals

a $-3 \le x \le -1$

b $1 \le x \le 3$

c $3 \le x \le 5$

SOLUTION

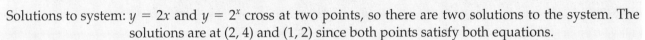

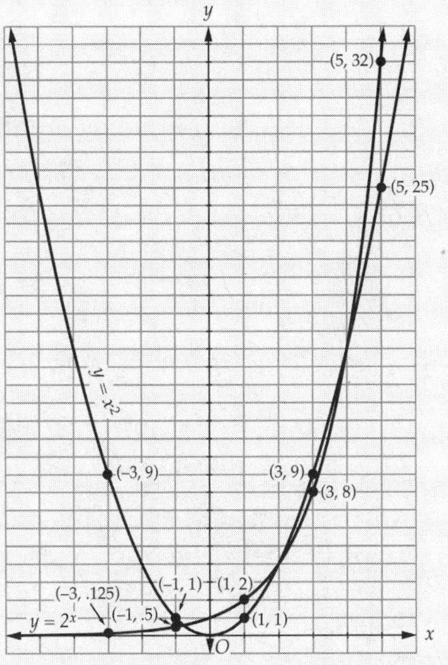

$y = x^2$

x	y
−3	9
−1	1
1	1
3	9
5	25

Average Rate of Change
−4
0
4
8

$y = 2^x$

x	y
−3	0.125
−1	0.5
1	2
3	8
5	32

Average Rate of Change
0.1875
0.75
3
12

a The average rate of change for $y = 2^x$ is positive and for $y = x^2$ is negative, but the absolute value of the rate of change for $y = x^2$ is greater than the rate of change for $y = 2^x$.

b The average rates of change of both equations are positive, but the parabola's rate of change is greater.

c The average rates of change are both positive, but the rate of change for $y = 2^x$ is greater.

Model Problems continue . . .

Model Problems *continued*

6. **MP 1, 4** Snail A moves at the pace shown in the table below, with positions in centimeters and time in seconds. Snail B starts at 5 centimeters and moves at 3 centimeters per second. Snail C moves according to the function $C(t) = 1.5^t$.

- **a** Graph the situation.
- **b** Which snail will be the farthest from the zero position at 6 seconds?
- **c** Which one will eventually move the farthest from zero?

Snail A:

Time	0	1	2	3	4	5	6	7	8	9	10
Position	0	0.5	2	4.5	8	12.5	18	24.5	32	40.5	50

SOLUTION

a

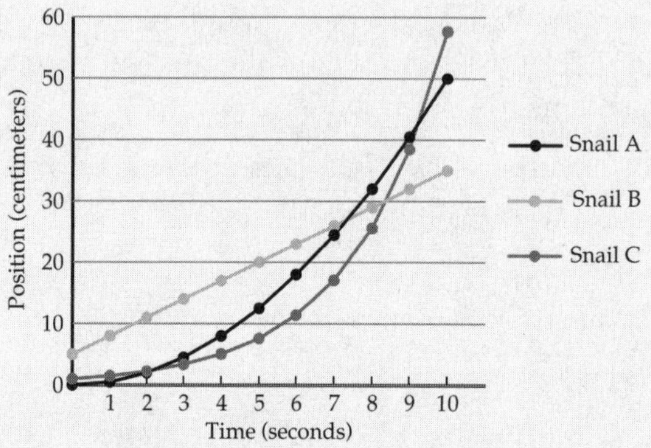

To graph Snail A: Use the information in the table above to graph Snail A. The graph of Snail A is a quadratic function.

To graph Snail B: To write a function for Snail B, $B(t)$, that describes its movement, we identify its initial position, 5 centimeters, and rate of movement, 3 centimeters per second. The function is written as $B(t) = 5 + 3t$. The graph of Snail B is a linear function.

To graph Snail C: Graph the function $C(t) = 1.5^t$. The graph of Snail C is an exponential function.

b At 6 seconds, the graph of Snail B, the linear snail, has the greatest output value. The linear snail is the farthest from zero.

c An exponential term will eventually be the greatest. At around 10 seconds, the exponential graph of Snail C has the greatest value, and it continues to grow faster than either of the other functions. Snail C, the exponential snail, will eventually be the one that has moved the greatest distance.

PRACTICE

1. Which is the equation of the graph?

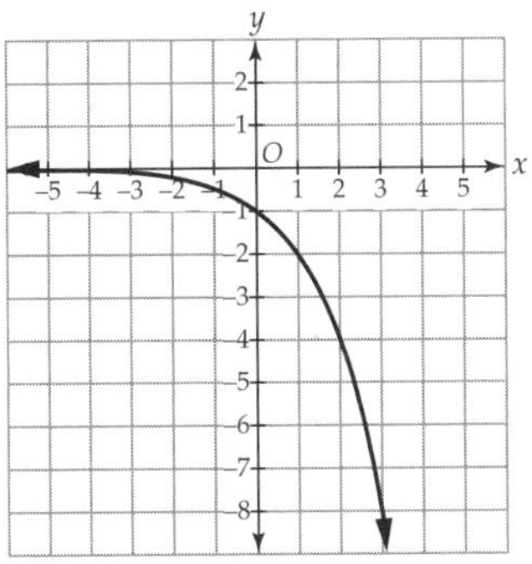

A. $y = 2^{-x}$ C. $y = 2^{x}$

B. $y = -2x$ D. $y = -2^{x}$

2. The graph of $f(x) = b^x$, where $b > 0$, contains the point

A. $(-1, 0)$ C. $(0, 1)$

B. $(0, 0)$ D. $(1, 0)$

3. Which statement describes the graph of $y = 6^x$?

A. It is an increasing function that lies entirely in quadrants I and IV.

B. It is an increasing function that lies entirely in quadrants I and II.

C. It is a decreasing function that lies entirely in quadrants I and II.

D. It is a decreasing function that lies entirely in quadrants I and IV.

4. The graph of $y = \left(\frac{1}{3}\right)^x$ lies in which two quadrants?

A. I and II

B. II and III

C. III and IV

D. I and IV

5. The graph of the equation $y = 3^x$ intersects

A. the x-axis and the y-axis

B. the y-axis only

C. the x-axis only

D. neither the x-axis nor the y-axis

6. Which of the following is the graph of the given equation: $y = 4^{-x}$?

A.

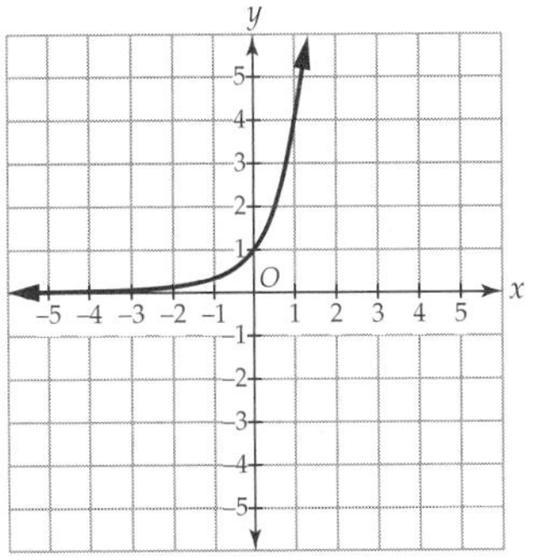

B.

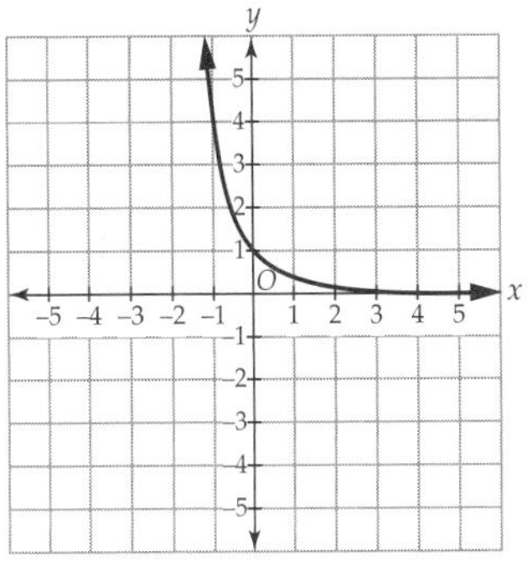

C.

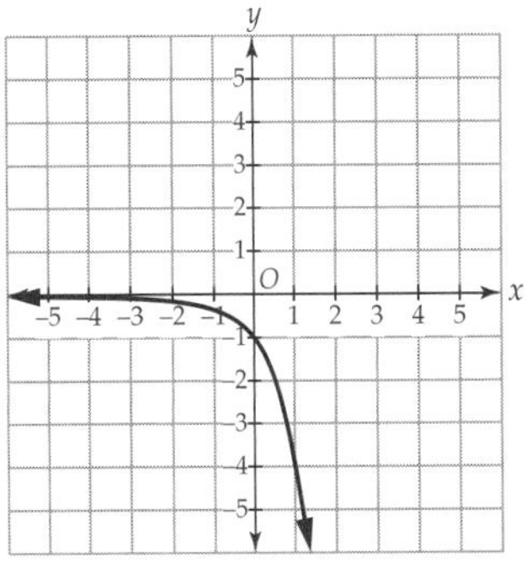

D.

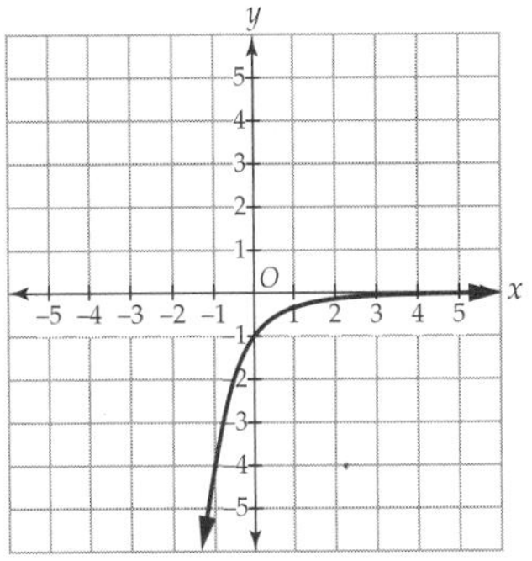

Practice Problems continue . . .

7. Given the following graph, which function represents that graph?

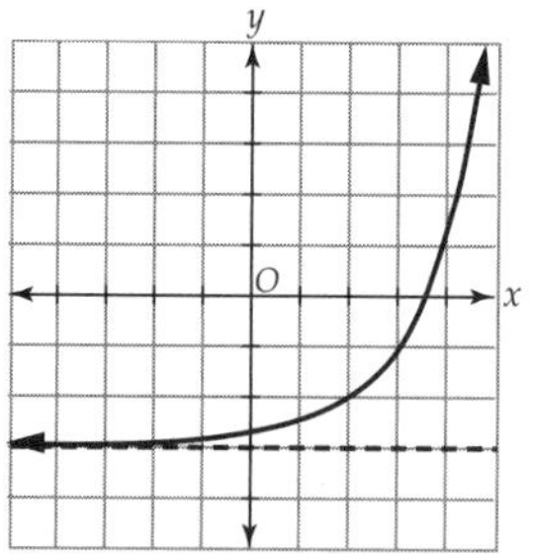

A. $y = 2^{x-2} - 2$ C. $y = 2^{x+2} - 2$

B. $y = 2^{x-2} - 3$ D. $y = 2^{x+2} - 3$

8. Given the following graph, which function represents that graph?

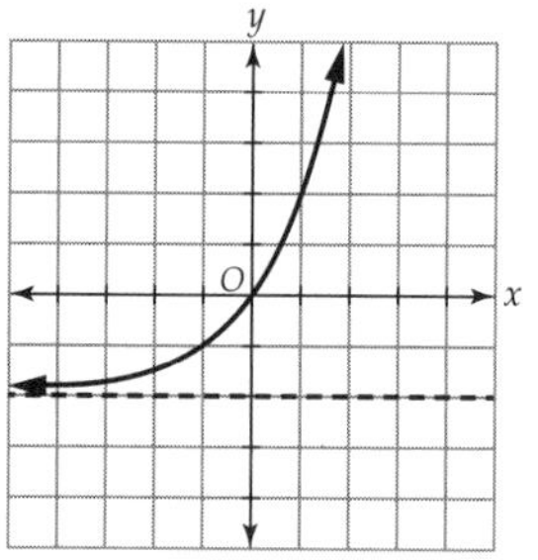

A. $y = 2^{x+1} - 1$ C. $y = 2^{x} + 2$

B. $y = 2^{x-1} + 1$ D. $y = 2^{x+1} - 2$

9. Given the following graph, which function represents that graph?

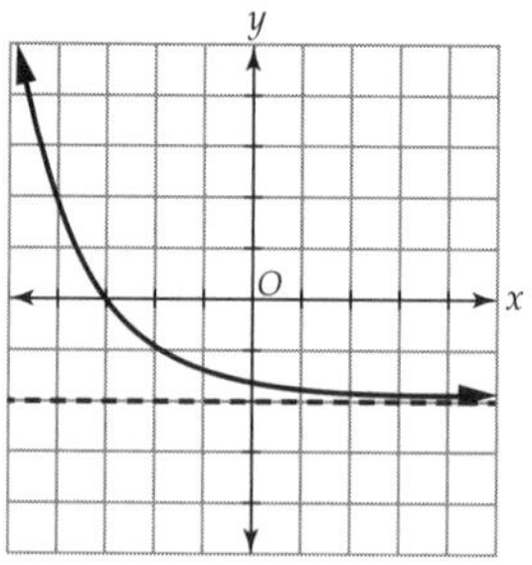

A. $y = \left(\frac{1}{2}\right)^{x+2} - 2$ C. $y = \left(\frac{1}{2}\right)^{x-2} - 1$

B. $y = \left(\frac{1}{2}\right)^{x-2} - 2$ D. $y = \left(\frac{1}{2}\right)^{x+2} - 1$

10. Given the following graph, which function represents that graph?

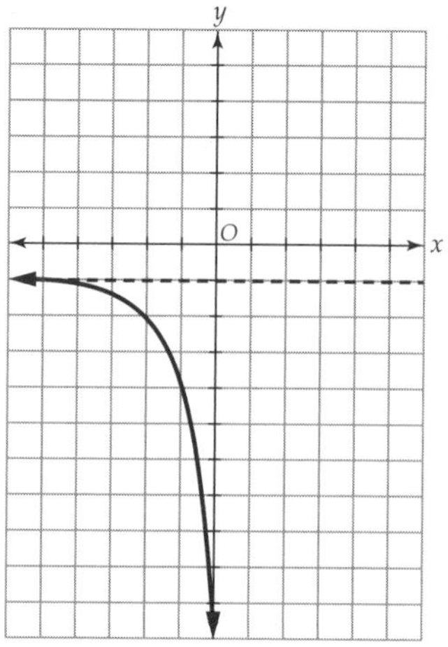

A. $y = -3^{x+2}$

B. $y = -3^{x-2} - 1$

C. $y = -3^{x+2} - 1$

D. $y = -3^{x+1} - 1$

11. Identify each of the following as functions of exponential growth or exponential decay. Justify your reasoning.

a $y = 4(0.75)^x$
b $y = 3(2.1)^x$
c $y = \frac{3}{4}(1.01)^x$
d $y = 0.25(0.25)^x$
e $f(n) = 0.05(1.50)^n$
f $f(t) = 0.1(0.1)^t$

Exercises 12–13: Complete the following tables.

12. $y = 10^x$

x	−3	−2	−1	0	0.5	1	1.5	2	3
y	0.001								

13. $f(x) = \left(\frac{1}{3}\right)^x$

x	−3	−2	−1	0	1	2	3	4	5
$f(x)$	27								

Practice Problems continue . . .

14. Match each curve with the correct equation listed below.

(1) $y = b^x; b > 1$

(2) $y = b^{x-3} - 3; b > 1$

(3) $y = b^x; 0 < b < 1$

(4) $y = b^x - 3; b > 1$

A.

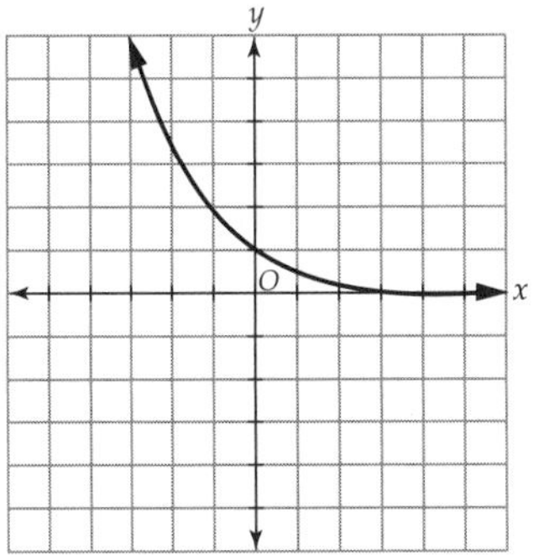

B.

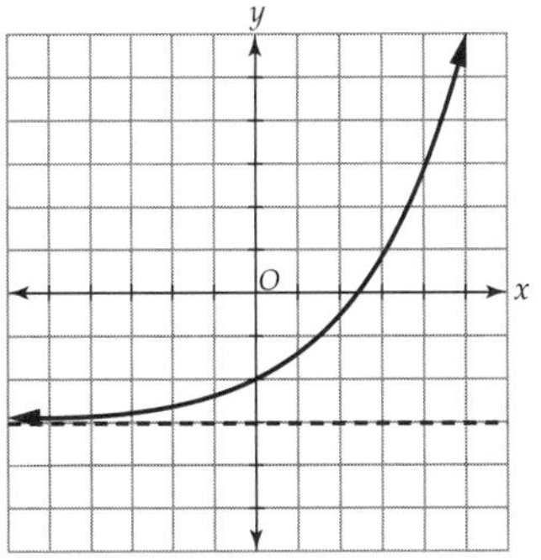

C.

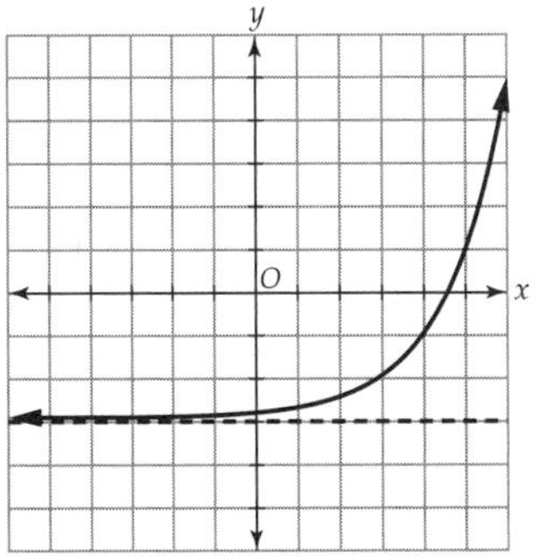

D.

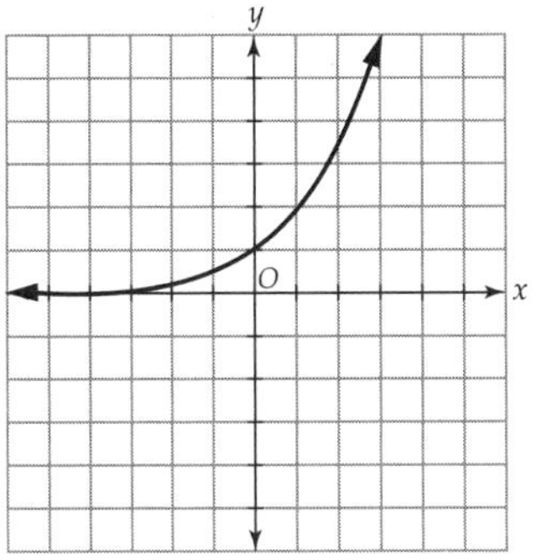

15. a Graph the function $y = 2^x + 1$.

b Graph the reflection of $y = 2^x + 1$ about the x-axis. Write the equation of that new graph.

16. MP 2, 3 On the same plane, graph the exponential function $f(x)$, and then sketch the graph of the $g(x)$ function. Identify any horizontal asymptotes. Describe the relationship of the two graphs.

$$f(x) = 4^x; g(x) = -(4^x)$$

17. MP 3 On the same plane and over the interval $-3 \leq x \leq 0$, graph the pair of functions and describe the relationship.

$$f(x) = 3^{x+2} + 1; g(x) = -3^{x+2} + 1$$

18. MP 3 On the same plane, graph the exponential function $f(x)$, and then sketch the graph of $g(x)$. Identify any horizontal asymptotes. Describe the relationship of the two graphs.

$$f(x) = 5^x; g(x) = \left(\frac{1}{5}\right)^x$$

19. MP 3 Using a short table of values, and on the same plane, graph the exponential function $f(x)$, and then sketch the graphs of $g(x)$ and $h(x)$. Identify any horizontal asymptotes. Describe the relationship of the three graphs.

$$f(x) = 3^x; g(x) = \frac{1}{3}(3^x); h(x) = 3(3^x)$$

20. In each comparison set, explain clearly what changes have occurred to the given function.

a Compare $f(x) = 2^x$ with the following:
- i. $h(x) = 2^x - 1$
- ii. $n(x) = 2^x + 2$
- iii. $g(x) = 2^{x+1}$

b Compare $f(x) = 3^x$ with the following:
- i. $g(x) = 3^{x+1}$
- ii. $m(x) = 3^{x-3}$
- iii. $h(x) = 3^{x-1} - 1$

Practice Problems continue . . .

21. MP 6 Given the parent function $f(x) = 2^x$, write the equation with the given description.

a Asymptote is -3 and is translated 3 units to the right.
b Asymptote is $+1$ and is horizontally shifted 2 units to the left.
c Vertical shift is down 4 units and horizontal shift is 5 units left.
d Vertical shift is 2 units up and horizontal translation is 3 units to the right.

22. What graphic transformation has been applied to $g(x) = 2^x$ to create each of the four new functions given below?

a $h(x) = 2^{x+5} - 4$

b $f(x) = 2^{x-4} + 5$

c $m(x) = 3(2^{x+1}) - 1$

d $t(x) = \frac{1}{4}(2^x) + 2$

23. a Given the graph of $f(x) = 2^{x+1} - 3$, what would be the equation of this same graph if it was translated left one unit and incurred a vertical shift of 2 units as well as stretched by a factor of 4?

b Given the graph of $g(x) = 3^{x-1} + 2$, what would be the equation of this same graph if it was shifted vertically -2 units, translated horizontally left 1 unit and shrunk by a factor of 0.5?

24. a Given the graph of $g(x) = 4^{x-4} + 1$, what would be the equation of the same graph if it was translated right 2 units and down 2 units?

b Given the graph of $h(x) = 3^{x+1} - 2$, what would be the equation of the same graph shifted 3 units to the right and stretched by a factor of 2.5?

25. MP 2, 5

a Graph $y = 2(0.4)^x$ and $y = 0.25(2)^x$.
b Find the intersection of the two graphs.

26. Graph $y = 2^x - 2^{-x}$ on the interval $[-2, 2]$.

LESSON 9.3

9.3 Modeling Exponential Growth and Decay

Many real-world problems involve a quantity (some value) growing or decaying exponentially over a period of time. Typically, *exponential growth* focuses on populations, financial investments, or biological entities growing in size, while *exponential decay* is often found in the diminishing price of a product (as in the yearly loss of the value of a car, called *depreciation*), or the steady decrease in a population, or the radioactive decay of isotopes.

> In general, these exponential functions are in the form $f(t) = ab^t$, where a and b are real numbers, and where $a \neq 0$, and $b \neq 1$, and t represents time.
>
> Initially $t = 0$, $f(0) = ab^0 = a(1) = a$, so the quantity a is called the *initial value* and b is called the *growth factor*.

$f(t) = ab^t$ is another way of representing $f(x) = ab^x$.

Exponential Growth and Decay

If $b > 1$, then there is exponential growth. To calculate exponential growth, we use the **exponential growth model**.

$$A = a(1 + r)^t$$
A = future value
a = initial value
r = growth rate
b is $(1 + r)$ = growth factor
t = time

If $0 < b < 1$, then there is exponential decay. To calculate exponential decay, we use the **exponential decay model**.

$$A = a(1 - r)^t$$
A = future value
a = initial value
r = decay rate
b is $(1 - r)$ = decay factor
t = time

MODEL PROBLEMS

1. MP 2, 4, 6 If the population of a small village in Maine is 100 and grows by approximately 6% a year, how large will the population be in 20 years?

a Identify the variables.

b Substitute the values in the growth equation and calculate the result.

SOLUTION

a The future value, A, is unknown. The growth rate, r, is 6%, which equals 0.06. $t = 20$. The initial value, a, is 100.

b After 20 years the approximate population will be $100(1 + 0.06)^{20} = 320.71$, or about 321 people.

Model Problems continue . . .

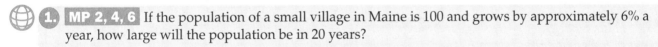

Model Problems *continued*

2. **MP 2, 4, 7** Radioactive decay is a typical example of an exponential function where the amount of radioactive material is reduced by one-half over every certain period of time. This period is called the "half-life" of the given material. Material *M* has a half-life of 100 years, which means that after one hundred years only half of the original material remains, and after another 100 years half of that material remains. If there are 600 grams of radioactive material *M*, then how much of this material would remain radioactive after 200 years, 300 years, *n* years? Graph the results.

SOLUTION

We could calculate $600 \times \frac{1}{2} = 300$ and then $300 \times \frac{1}{2} = 150$ and we would have the answer to what remains after 200 years. After 300 years, $150 \times \frac{1}{2} = 75$ grams remain. We could also write $600 \times \frac{1}{2} \times \frac{1}{2} \times \frac{1}{2}$ or $600 \times \left(\frac{1}{2}\right)^3$ to find the amount of radioactive material after 300 years. Instead, we can use the exponential decay model.

Using the exponential decay equation, we would get $f(0) = 600$ and $f(x) = 600(0.5)^x$, where x equals the number of 100-year periods. The decay rate is 50%, or 0.5. The initial value is 600 grams. The decay factor is 0.5.

Let $x = 2$ (representing 200 years), so that $f(2) = 600(0.5)^x = 600(0.5)^2 = 600(0.25) = 150$ grams remaining. The following table and graph represent such exponential decay over a period of 500 years.

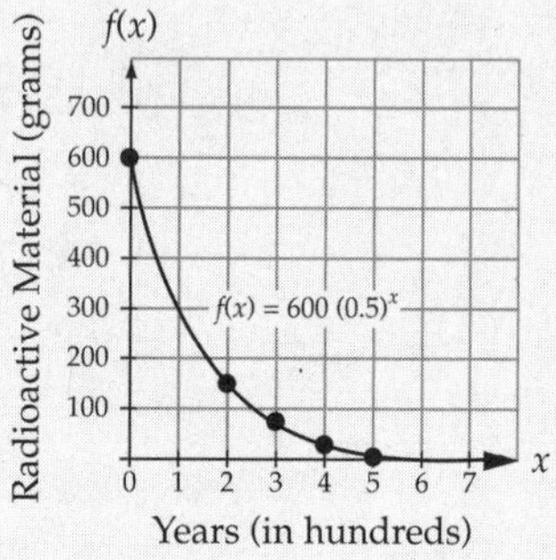

x (years in hundreds)	1	2	3	4	5
y (radioactive grams)	300	150	75	37.5	18.75

3. **MP 4** The number of bacteria in a controlled laboratory environment increases at a rate that doubles every hour. Initially, there are 100 bacteria in the culture. The function $f(x) = 100(2)^x$ provides the relationship between the time x in hours and the number of bacteria in the culture, $f(x)$.

a Set up a table and graph the function over the first 4 hours.

b Use the results to estimate when the culture will reach 1000 bacteria.

SOLUTION

a

x	0	1	2	3	4
y	100	200	400	800	1600

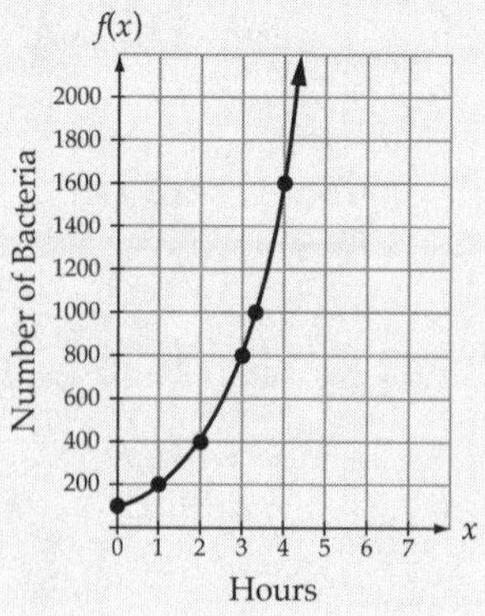

b The bacteria reaches 1000 sometime between 3 and 4 hours. We locate the intersection of $y = 1000$ with $y = 100(2)^x$ and the result is 3.322 hours, or 3 hours and 19 minutes.

Model Problems continue . . .

4. **MP 4, 6** A bank offers a savings account annual interest rate of 4.5% *compounded monthly*.

If 4.5% were simply being applied as an annual rate, we would use the exponential growth formula for *compound interest*:

$$A = P(1 + r)^t$$

A = future value

P = principal, or initial, value

r = annual interest rate

t = number of years

However, if we applied the bank's offer of 4.5% *compounded monthly*, we would have to use this formula:

$$A = P\left(1 + \frac{r}{n}\right)^{nt}$$

A = future value

P = principal, or initial, value

r = annual interest rate

t = number of years

n = the number of times the interest rate is applied per year

nt = the total number of times the interest rate is compounded

a If \$5,000 is deposited in the account and no money is withdrawn, and we used compound interest (i.e., once a year), how much money (to the nearest dollar) would be in that account after two years?

b Using the monthly compound interest on \$5,000, how much would be in the account after two years?

c Explain the difference between the anually compounded and the monthly compounded values.

SOLUTION

a $A = \$5{,}000 \times (1 + 0.045)^2 = \$5{,}460.13$ and the two-year interest return would be \$460.13.

b To compound monthly, we must first convert the annual rate to a monthly rate. Divide the annual rate by $n = 12$ (the number of months in a year).

$$\frac{r}{n} = \frac{4.5\%}{12} = \frac{0.045}{12} = 0.00375 \text{ per month}$$

Find the value of nt.

Since the compounding is occurring every month for two years, the exponent $nt = 12(2)$, or 24 months.

Use the formula $A = P\left(1 + \frac{r}{n}\right)^{nt}$ and substitute.

$$A = P\left(1 + \frac{r}{n}\right)^{nt}$$

$$A = 5{,}000 \times (1 + 0.00375)^{24}$$

$$= 5{,}000 \times (1.00375)^{24}$$

$$= 5{,}469.9506 \approx \$5{,}469.95$$

c The increase of \$9.82 is a result of compounding the interest more frequently. The extra amount can be thought of as additional "interest on interest."

Model Problems continue . . .

5. **MP 4, 5** The growth of a certain strain of bacteria is modeled by the equation $Y = B(1 + r)^x$, where Y represents the final number of bacteria, B is the initial number of bacteria, x is the time in hours, and r is the rate of growth per hour.

a If there were 12 bacteria specimens, and the rate of growth is 80%, how many bacteria specimens will there be after 11 hours? Round to the nearest hundred.

b After how many hours will the bacterial population reach 100,000?

SOLUTION

a Substitute 12 for B, 11 for x, and 0.8 for r in the growth equation.

$Y = 12(1 + 0.8)^{11} = 12(1.8)^{11} = 12(642.684) = 7{,}712.2$, or 7,700

b Since we are asked to find the time it would take to produce a Y-value of 100,000, we substitute the known values and solve for x using a graphing calculator.

Graph $y = 12(1.8)^x$ in Y_1 and $y = 100{,}000$ in Y_2.

Find the intersection of the two graphs: press [2nd] [TRACE] and [5]: Intersect.

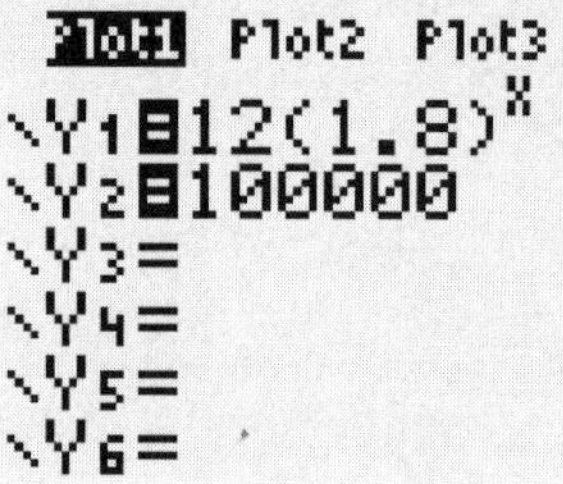

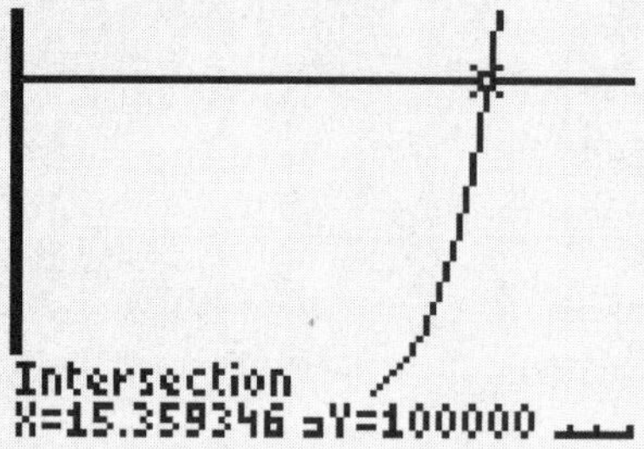

$x \approx 15.359$ hours

PRACTICE

1. A stockbroker finds a bank stock that turns his \$10,000 investment into approximately \$12,000 in 2 years. Over the two years, what was the annual rate of return on his initial investment?

A. 9%

B. 9.5%

C. 10.1%

D. 10.5%

2. Find the value of a \$6500 investment paying 6% interest compounded quarterly, at the end of 5 years. Use the formula $A = P\left(1 + \frac{r}{n}\right)^{nt}$.

3. An Impressionist painting increases in value at an average rate of 9% a year. If the original cost of the painting to the Museum of Art was \$1500, what was the value of the painting (to the nearest dollar) at the end of a 20-year holding period?

4. The cost C for maintenance on a new hybrid car increases each year by 10%. If Frank paid \$400 this year for maintenance, then the cost x years from now can be given by the function $C(x) = 400(n)^x$.

a What is the value of n?

b What is the cost in 6 years?

c In how many years will the cost be approximately twice what he paid this year?

Practice Problems continue . . .

5. What is the value, after 12 years, of \$2500 invested at 8% interest compounded quarterly?

6. MP 1, 2, 4, 6 Phil needs \$2000, including sales tax, to buy the flatscreen TV he wants. He has \$1800 in a savings account. It earns 5% interest compounded quarterly. Phil thinks he will have enough money in 2 years. Is Phil right or wrong? Justify your reasoning.

7. MP 1, 2, 4, 6 Three years ago, Mark paid \$125 for a signed Ken Griffey Jr. rookie baseball card. The value of the card grew by 10% a year.

a What is the value of the card now?

b What can he expect the value to be at the end of three more years at a new rate of 20% a year?

c If he sells it at the end of the next 3 years, what percent profit will he make on the baseball card?

8. MP 7, 8 The number of bacteria in a petri dish over a period of hours is modeled by the function $N(t) = 50(2^{2t})$ where t represents time, in hours.

a According to the model, what is the number of bacteria in the dish when

(1) $t = 0$?

(2) $t = 1$?

(3) $t = 3$?

b What would be an equivalent way of expressing $N(t) = 50(2^{2t})$?

9. The population of Small Town in 1850 was 250, and it has increased by 60% every 25 years.

a Identify the function that models the growth of population in this small town.

b To the nearest 100, what will the population be in the year 2025?

10. Depreciation can be determined by the formula $V = c(1 - r)^t$, where V represents the value of the car after t years, c is the original cost of the car, and r is the rate of depreciation. If the car cost \$25,000 when new and the rate of depreciation is 8%, what is the value of the car after 4.5 years?

11. Karen needs to replace her car. The price of the new car is \$28,400. If she leases it, she expects to pay \$510 a month for 2 years. At the end of 2 years, she has the buyout option of purchasing the car for \$20,855. If the car depreciates at 18% a year, how will the depreciated value of the car compare to the buyout price of the lease?

12. A tank contains 774 gallons of oil. One-third of the oil is released each time the valve is opened. How much oil (to the nearest tenth gallon) will remain in the tank after the valve is opened 7 times?

13. MP 1, 2, 4, 5 If a rubber ball is dropped from a height of 81 meters and rebounds on each bounce two-thirds of the distance from which it fell, how many meters does it fall on its 7th descent (downward trip)?

14. Find the number of bacteria present after 3 hours when $f(k) = n(2^k)$ models the growth of bacteria. Note: $n = 100$ bacteria to begin with, and k is the number of replications occurring in a given time frame. In this case, replication occurs every 10 minutes for 3 hours.

15. In the following problems, the given amount of money, P, is invested at the given annual rate, r, and compounded monthly.

a Write the formula for the value of the investment.

b What is the value of each of the following investments after 2 years?

(1) \$2500 at 6.3%

(2) \$4000 at 3%

(3) \$5000 at 7.5%

Practice Problems continue . . .

16. MP 2, 3, 4, 5 A man wants to purchase a new upright piano for his family. The piano costs \$4500. He deposits \$4000 in a savings account that pays 3.6% annual interest compounded yearly. Will there be enough money in the account after 3 years? Justify your reasoning.

17. A bacteria culture is doubling every 15 minutes. After one and one-quarter hours there were approximately 16,000 bacteria present.

a What was the initial amount?

b How many bacteria will be present after 3 hours?

c State the exponential function that models the data.

d Complete the table. Then graph the result.

Number of quarter-hour units (x)	1	2	4	5	6	8	10	12
Number of bacteria (y)								

18. If we have 500 grams of radioactive material:

a With a half-life of 30 seconds, how much remains in 4 minutes?

b With a half-life of 30 minutes, how much remains in 3 hours?

c With a half-life of one month, how much remains radioactive after one year?

d With a half-life of one year, how many grams were radioactive

(1) one year ago?

(2) two years ago?

(3) 6 months ago?

19. The concentration of a certain medication in a person's bloodstream decreases exponentially. The given medication loses 20% of its concentration every hour, and the concentration $f(x)$ is modeled by the equation $f(x) = (1.5)(0.80)^t$ where t is time in hours and 1.5 mg/L represents peak concentration.

a Graph the equation over 6 hours.

b What is the approximate time when *one-half* the peak concentration of medication remains?

c After how many hours is the concentration less than 0.5 mg/L?

20. The number of computers in Jericho High School has grown exponentially. In the year 2000, there were 240 computers. In 2001, there were 288 computers.

a Approximately how many computers were in the system by the year 2004?

b Approximately how many computers were there by the year 2011?

c After how many years will they have four times as many computers as they started with in 2000?

21. A new desktop computer costs \$2800 and its value decreases over time. A model for the decreasing value, V, (in dollars) of the computer after n years is given by $V = 2800(0.80)^n$.

a Based on the formula model, what is the decay rate?

b When the value of the computer is less than \$1000 the company will purchase a replacement. Check the values at 4 and 5 years and decide if and when new computers should be purchased.

LESSON 9.4

9.4 Sequences and Arithmetic Sequences

Sequences

A **sequence** is a list written in a given order. If we recorded the day of the month for birthdays of students seated in the first row of a class, we might get a list such as 1, 10, 29, 6, 11. We could chart the results in a table:

Student Seat Number	1	2	3	4	5
Day	1	10	29	6	11

Sequences are special types of functions. The set of position places, $\{1, 2, 3, \ldots, n\}$, is the domain of the function. The set of values associated with these position places {1, 10, 29, 6, 11} is the range. The ordered pairs for this function are {(1, 1), (2, 10), (3, 29), (4, 6),(5, 11)}.

The terms in the range of a sequence are usually designated as $a_1, a_2, a_3, \ldots, a_n$. Since a sequence is a function, $f(1) = a_1, f(2) = a_2, \ldots, f(n) = a_n$.

We will define sequences **recursively**, where the value in any position can be found if we know the value of the position preceding it. We will also define sequences **explicitly**, where the definition is derived from a general rule, dependent upon the position in the sequence.

Most sequences are related by a pattern that can be described numerically. After this brief introduction to sequences, we will concentrate on sequences that can be described by simple rules.

MODEL PROBLEM

Predict the next term in the sequence 4, 9, 19, 39, ... Explain your reasoning.

SOLUTION

The first term in the sequence is 4, which we define as $a_1 = 4$.

The second term in the sequence can be found by $a_2 = 2\,a_1 + 1 = 2(4) + 1 = 9$.

The third term in the sequence can be found by $a_3 = 2\,a_2 + 1 = 2(9) + 1 = 19$

The fourth term in the sequence can be found by $a_4 = 2\,a_3 + 1 = 2(19) + 1 = 39$.

The fifth term in the sequence will be $a_5 = 2\,a_4 + 1 = 2(39) + 1 = 79$.

Answer: The next term in the sequence is 79.

PRACTICE

Exercises 1–4: Describe the pattern in words for each sequence and predict the next term in the sequence.

1. 3, 6, 9, 12, . . .

2. 2, 7, 12, 17, . . .

3. 1.2, 2.3, 3.4, 4.5, . . .

4. 1, 8, 27, 64, 125, . . .

5. The sequence 1, 1, 2, 3, 5, 8, 13, . . . is a famous sequence called the Fibonacci sequence. Describe the pattern in words and find the next two terms in the sequence.

Recursive Formula for Arithmetic Sequences

In an **arithmetic sequence**, each term equals the sum of the preceding term and a constant called the **common difference**. For instance: 2, 5, 8, 11, 14 is an arithmetic sequence. It starts with 2, and each term that follows is the result of adding the constant 3 to the prior term. The common difference for this sequence is 3.

Sequence	2		5		8		11		14
Common difference		3		3		3		3	

We can define the sequence above recursively. A recursive definition defines the value in position 1 and defines the pattern that calculates the value in any position after position 1 from the prior position. For example,

$a_1 = 2$

$a_n = a_{n-1} + 3$

Any arithmetic sequence can be written *recursively* using the format:

$a_n = a_{n-1} + d$

where a_n = general term

a_{n-1} = term before a_n

d = common difference

MODEL PROBLEMS

1. The sixth term of an arithmetic sequence is 11, and the common difference is -2. What is the seventh term?

SOLUTION

We start with the formula that defines an arithmetic sequence. $a_n = a_{n-1} + d$

The question asks for a_7, the seventh term, and we are told the sixth term and d. We substitute, replacing the subscripts with the indices stated in the problem. $a_7 = a_6 + d$

We substitute again, replacing a_6 with 11 since we are told 11 is the sixth term. We also replace d with the stated common difference, -2. $a_7 = 11 + (-2)$

We add to get the seventh term, 9. $a_7 = 11 + (-2) = 9$

Model Problems continue . . .

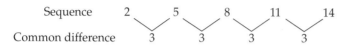

Model Problems *continued*

2. What is the common difference for the arithmetic sequence 10, 7, 4, 1, −2,...?

SOLUTION

We calculate the common difference of the infinite arithmetic sequence that begins 10, 7, 4,...

We state a formula for the common difference d. The common difference is calculated by subtracting any term from the term that follows it. $d = a_n - a_{n-1}$

We decide to subtract the first term, a_1, from the second term, a_2. $d = a_2 - a_1$

We substitute, replacing the variables with the values of the terms. $d = 7 - 10$

We subtract. The common difference is −3. $d = -3$

3. If the first four terms of an arithmetic sequence are 13, 9, 5, and 1, what is a_6?

SOLUTION

We are asked for the sixth term in an arithmetic sequence. We will start by calculating d, the common difference.

Calculate common difference.

$d = a_2 - a_1$

$d = 9 - 13$

$d = -4$

Definition of arithmetic sequence. $a_n = a_{n-1} + d$

To calculate a_6, first calculate a_5.

$a_5 = a_4 + d$

$a_5 = 1 + (-4)$

$a_5 = -3$

Add d to calculate a_6.

$a_6 = a_5 + d$

$a_6 = -3 + (-4)$

$a_6 = -7$

General Rule for Arithmetic Sequences

Although you could calculate any term in an arithmetic sequence by starting with the first term and repeatedly adding the common difference, there is a way to calculate a term directly. To provide an informal derivation, we calculate the first four terms of an arithmetic sequence to find a pattern.

the first term $= a_1$

the second term $a_2 = a_1 + d$

the third term $a_3 = a_1 + d + d = a_1 + 2d$

the fourth term $a_4 = a_1 + d + d + d = a_1 + 3d$

the fifth term $a_5 = a_1 + 4d$

the sixth term $a_6 = a_1 + 5d$

In general, any arithmetic sequence can be written in the **general rule**:

$$a_n = a_1 + (n - 1)d$$

where a_n = general term

a_1 = first term

n = term number

d = common difference

> The difference, *d*, should remind you of the slope, *m*, in the slope-intercept formula $y = mx + b$ because $d = \frac{\Delta a_n}{\Delta n} = \frac{\text{change in } a_n}{\text{change in } n}$.

Given the recursive form and the general rule of an arithmetic sequence, we have a choice about which to use. Often, the general rule is more useful.

MODEL PROBLEMS

1. **a** Given the 3rd term = 3.2 and $d = -0.4$ in an arithmetic sequence, find the second term.

b Find the term a_5 in the arithmetic sequence of 3, 1.7, 0.4,...

SOLUTION

a Since $a_3 = a_2 + d$, by substitution we have $3.2 = a_2 + -0.4$.

So, $a_2 = 3.2 + 0.4 = 3.6$

Answer: $a_2 = 3.6$

b The common difference $d = a_2 - a_1 = 1.7 - 3 = -1.3$

Since the general rule gives us $a_5 = a_1 + d(n - 1)$, by substituting we can write $a_5 = 3 + (-1.3)(5 - 1)$ and $a_5 = 3 + (-1.3)(4) = 3 + (-5.2) = -2.2$

Answer: $a_5 = -2.2$

2. Consider the arithmetic sequence 6, 9, 12, 15.

a Use the general rule to write the explicit formula and simplify.

b Find the 9th and 27th terms of this sequence.

SOLUTION

a Using the general rule $a_n = a_1 + (n - 1)d$ we will substitute 6 for a_1 and 3 for d.

We now have $a_n = 6 + (n - 1)3$ and, by simplifying, $a_n = 6 + 3n - 3$, so that the rule is $a_n = 3 + 3n$.

> The simplified form, derived from the general rule, is referred to as the **explicit formula.**

Answer: $a_n = 3 + 3n$

b Using the explicit formula the 9th term is $a_9 = 3 + 3(9) = 30$.

The 27th term is $a_{27} = 3 + 3(27) = 84$.

Answer: 30 and 84

Model Problems continue . . .

Model Problems *continued*

3. If an arithmetic sequence is defined recursively as $a_1 = 6$ and $a_n = a_{n-1} + 5$,

a Find the common difference.

b Write the general rule and simplify to the explicit formula.

c Find the 14th term.

SOLUTION

a If $a_n = a_{n-1} + 5$ then $a_n - a_{n-1} = 5$, so the common difference $d = 5$.

b Using the general rule $a_n = a_1 + (n - 1)d$, $a_n = 6 + (n - 1)5 = 6 + 5n - 5$, so that $a_n = 1 + 5n$.

c Using the answer to **b**, $a_{14} = 1 + 5(14) = 71$.

Answer: **a** $d = 5$ **b** $a_n = 1 + 5n$ **c** $a_{14} = 71$

4. In an arithmetic sequence with a first term of 24 and a common difference of 30, what number term is 174?

SOLUTION

Use the general rule.	$a_n = a_1 + (n - 1)d$
Substitute 174 for a_n, 24 for a_1, and 30 for d.	$174 = 24 + (n - 1)30$
Simplify and solve for n.	$150 = 30n - 30$
	$180 = 30n$
	$n = 6$

Answer: 174 is the 6th term.

5. Write out the first four terms of an arithmetic sequence in which the 8th term is 24 and the 15th term is 10.

SOLUTION

Since $a_8 = 24$ and $a_{15} = 10$, we can find the common difference d by keeping in mind that d is equivalent to describing m (slope). We can state that the common difference

$$d = \frac{\Delta a_n}{\Delta n} = \frac{\text{change in } a_n}{\text{change in } n} = \frac{a_{15} - a_8}{15 - 8} = \frac{10 - 24}{7} = \frac{-14}{7} = -2.$$

So $d = -2$.

Now use the general rule $a_n = a_1 + (n - 1)d$ to find a_1, the first term.

Substitute in (-2) for d and 24 for a_8.

If $a_8 = a_1 + (8 - 1)(-2)$, then $24 = a_1 + 7(-2)$ and $24 = a_1 - 14$.

Lastly, $a_1 = 38$. If we add the difference (-2) three times, we will find the first four terms to be 38, 36, 34, and 32.

Answer: 38, 36, 34, 32

Model Problems continue . . .

6. **MP 2, 4, 7** Andy's grandparents open a college savings account for him on his thirteenth birthday. They deposit \$500, and every month thereafter they deposit \$100. The following table describes the growth of money (ignoring the interest) in his account over 7 months.

Month	n	1	2	3	4	5	6	7
Account Balance	$f(n)$	500	600	700	800	900	1000	1100

a Write the general rule and simplify to show the explicit formula in function notation.

b Graph the function.

SOLUTION

a The common difference d is \$100. The general rule is $a_n = a_1 + d(n - 1)$, or in function notation $f(n) = f(1) + d(n - 1) = 500 + 100(n - 1)$ where $n \geq 1$. Simplified to the explicit formula $f(n) = 100n + 400$.

b If we plot the points on the same coordinate plane, (1, 500), (2, 600), (3, 700), ...(7, 1100), we see that this arithmetic sequence forms a discrete linear function. That is, $f(n) = 100(n - 1) + 500$ where $n \geq 1$, and by observation we note that the slope m equals the common difference d.

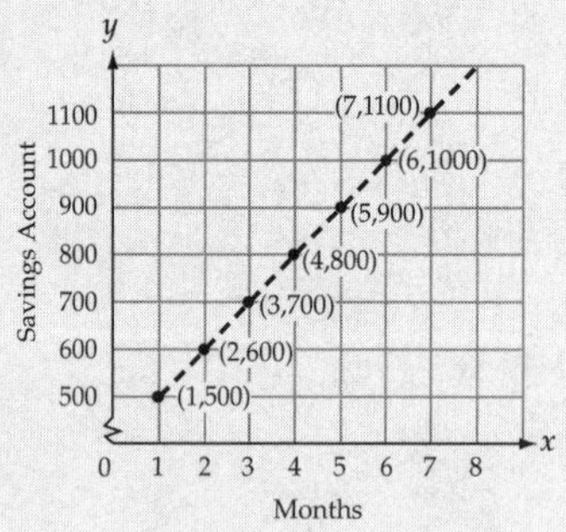

Note that if we were to draw a line through the points, we could write a function in the form $y = mx + b$.

PRACTICE

1. Which of these are arithmetic sequences?

I. 9, 15, 21, 27, 33, . . .
II. 18, 10, 2, −6, −14, . . .
III. 7, 11, 16, 22, 29, . . .
IV. 1, −2, 3, −4, 5, −6, 7, −8, 9, . . .

A. I only
B. I and II only
C. I, II, and III only
D. I, II, III, and IV

2. Which is the correct formula for a_n in the given sequence: 2, 5, 10, 17, . . . ?

A. $a_n = 2^n + 1$
B. $a_n = n^2 + 1$
C. $a_n = 2n + 1$
D. $a_n = 3n - 1$

3. What is the formula for the nth term of the sequence 10, 12, 14, 16, . . . ?

A. $a_n = 10(2)^n$
B. $a_n = 10(2)^{n-1}$
C. $a_n = 8 + 2n$
D. $a_n = 10 + 2n$

4. If $a_5 = 100$ and $a_{11} = 10$ are two terms of an arithmetic sequence, then what is the value of a_9?

A. 15
B. 40
C. 70
D. 85

Practice Problems continue . . .

5. For each of the following arithmetic sequences, write out the first five terms.

a If the first term is 4 and the common difference is 3.

b If the first term is 5 and the common difference is −3.

c If the first term is 9 and the common difference is $-\frac{1}{2}$.

6. a Find the 6th term in the arithmetic sequence of 5, 2.6, 0.2, −2.2, . . .

b Find a_5 in the arithmetic sequence 6, 7.3, 8.6, . . .

c If $a_1 = 8$ in an arithmetic sequence where the common difference is −1.1, what is the fifth term?

7. For each of the following sequences, find the common difference, *d*, and find the general rule and simplify to the explicit formula.

a 2, 7, 12, 17, . . .

b 8, 3, −2, −7, . . .

c 6.0, 7.2, 8.4, . . .

8. If $a_1 = 4$ and $a_n = a_{n-1} - 3$,

a Find the common difference.

b Find the general rule for a_n and simplify to the explicit formula.

c Find the 15th term.

9. If $a_{11} = 5$ and $a_{14} = 68$,

a Find *d*, the common difference.

b Find the first term a_1.

c Find the general rule for a_n and simplify to the explicit formula.

10. Find the specific indicated term of each arithmetic sequence.

a Find the 30th term of an arithmetic sequence with a 1st term of −1 and a common difference of 4.

b Find the 25th term with a first term of 4 and a common difference of $-\frac{1}{3}$.

c Find the 50th term of the arithmetic sequence:

3, 7, 11, 15, 19, 23, . . .

11. For each of the following, use the data given to identify the specific number of the term. In other words, solve for *n* in the general rule $a_n = a_1 + (n - 1)d$.

a Which term of this arithmetic sequence (9, 13, 17,…) will be 225?

b Find what number term −35 is in an arithmetic sequence that has a first term of 7 and a common difference of −3.

c In an arithmetic sequence with a first term of 13 and a common difference of 7, what number term is 251?

12. A contest offers 25 prizes. The first prize is $40,000 and each successive prize is $1200 less than the preceding prize. What is the value of the 25th-place prize?

13. A large half-circle theatre has 50 seats in the first curved row, 58 seats in the second row, 66 seats in the third row, and so on, in an increasing arithmetic sequence. How many seats are in the last row of the theatre if there are 20 rows?

14. Prove that for any arithmetic sequence $a_7 + a_{10} = a_8 + a_9$.

15. If $x - 5$, $2x$, and $4x + 6$ are the first three terms of an arithmetic sequence, find *x* and the values of the three terms.

16. If $x - 7$, $2x - 6$, and $x + 1$ are the first three terms of an arithmetic sequence, find the value for *x* and the values for each of the three terms.

17. MP 2, 4 Ava is trying to get into shape for her European walking tour. She is beginning her exercise routine by walking on the treadmill for 3 minutes on the first day. She is adding 2 minutes to each day until she leaves for her tour.

a Derive the explicit formula for the *n*th term in the sequence and simplify.

b How many minutes will she be walking on the treadmill on the 16th day?

18. MP 2, 4 The bottom step of a brick staircase uses 43 bricks. The second step has 39 bricks, and the third step has 35 bricks.

a Derive the explicit formula for the *n*th term in the sequence and simplify.

b If this pattern continues up to the 8th step, how many bricks does the 8th step contain?

Practice Problems continue . . .

19. A contest offers 20 prizes, with the first prize worth \$12,000 and each successive prize worth \$400 less than the preceding prize.

a Write the equation for the nth-place prize.

b Find the 20th term of the sequence.

20. For the arithmetic sequence {2, 7, 12, 17, 22, . . .},

a Find the value of c, given the explicit formula $a_n = dn + c$.

b State the explicit formula.

c Find the 20th term using the explicit formula.

d Find the 20th term using the general rule $a_n = a_1 + d(n - 1)$.

LESSON 9.5

9.5 Geometric Sequences

Recursive Formula for Geometric Sequences

In a **geometric sequence**, each term equals the product of the preceding term and a constant called the **common ratio**, r, where $r \neq 0$ and $r \neq 1$. For instance, 3, 12, 48, 192 is a geometric sequence. It starts with 3, and each term that follows is formed by multiplying the prior term by 4, which is the common ratio for this sequence.

Sequence	3		12		48		192
Common ratio		4		4		4	

The recursive form for the nth term of a geometric sequence is defined by the function:

$$a_n = a_{n-1} \bullet r$$

where a_n = general term

a_{n-1} = term before a_n

r = common ratio

General Rule for Geometric Sequences

The general rule for the nth term of a geometric sequence, with a first term of a_1 and a common ratio of r, is the exponential function:

$$a_n = a_1 r^{n-1}$$

where a_n = general term

a_1 = first term

r = common ratio

n = term number

MODEL PROBLEMS

1. For the following geometric sequence, 2, 6, 18, 54, . . .

a Find r, the common ratio.

b Find the explicit formula and simplify.

c Find the 10th term.

SOLUTION

a The common ratio $r = \frac{6}{2} = 3$.

b Using the formula $a_n = a_1(r^{n-1})$, the explicit formula for the nth term is $a_n = 2 \bullet 3^{n-1}$.

c Substituting 10 for n, we have $a_{10} = 2 \bullet 3^{10-1} = 2(3^9) = 39{,}366$.

2. In the following geometric sequence, 12, −6, 3, . . .

a Find the common ratio.

b Find the explicit formula and simplify.

c Find the 6th term.

SOLUTION

a The common ratio $r = \frac{-6}{12} = -\frac{1}{2}$.

b Since $a_1 = 12$ and $r = -\frac{1}{2}$, the explicit formula $a_n = 12\left(-\frac{1}{2}\right)^{n-1}$.

c For the 6th term, $a_6 = 12\left(-\frac{1}{2}\right)^{n-1} = 12\left(-\frac{1}{2}\right)^5 = 12\left(-\frac{1}{32}\right) = -\frac{3}{8}$ or −0.375.

Answer: a $-\frac{1}{2}$ b $a_n = 12\left(-\frac{1}{2}\right)^{n-1}$ c −0.375

3. In the geometric sequence –7, x_2, x_3, 189, . . .

a Find r, the common ratio.

b Find the missing terms x_2 and x_3.

c Find the 5th term.

SOLUTION

a Since 189 is the 4th term, $189 = x_1 r^{n-1} = -7(r^3)$. Dividing by −7, we have $r^3 = -27$ and $r = -3$ (the common ratio).

b $x_2 = -7(-3) = 21$ and $x_3 = -7(-3)^2 = -63$

c To find the 5th term we have two choices:

First, we could use the recursive formula $x_5 = x_4 r$, which equals $189(-3) = -567$. Second, we could use the explicit formula $a_n = a_1(r^{n-1})$, such that $x_5 = x_1 r^{n-1}$ and $(-7)(-3)^4 = -7(81) = -567$.

Answer: a $r = -3$ b $x_2 = 21, x_3 = -63$ c $x_5 = -567$

Model Problems continue . . .

Model Problems *continued*

4. **MP 4** On the first swing, the length of the arc through which a pendulum swings is 24 inches. The length of each successive swing is $\frac{7}{8}$ of the preceding swing. Find the length of the arc on the fifth swing. (Round your answer to the nearest tenth.)

SOLUTION

We will use the general rule of a geometric sequence $a_n = a_1(r^{n-1})$, where $a_1 = 24$, $r = \frac{7}{8}$, and $n = 5$ and simplify to the explicit formula.

$$a_5 = 24\left(\frac{7}{8}\right)^{5-1} = 24\left(\frac{7}{8}\right)^4 = 24 \times \frac{2401}{4096} = 14.068 \approx 14.1 \text{ inches}$$

Answer: The length of the fifth-swing arc is 14.1 inches.

5. **MP 4, 7, 8** A ball is dropped from 8 feet. When it bounces, it rises to 50% of the height from which it was dropped.

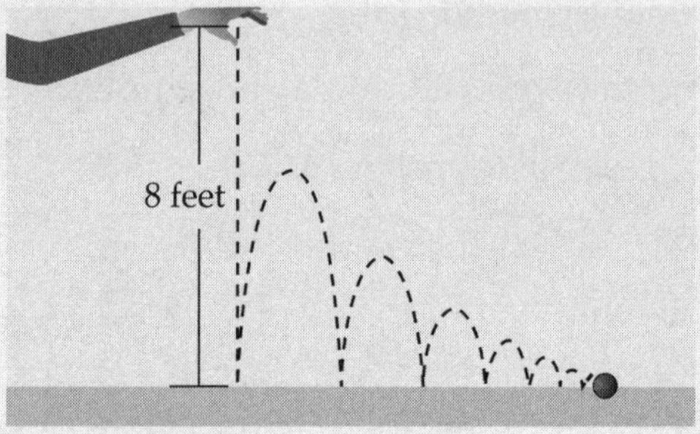

a Graph the height at which it starts and then the height to which it rises for its first 6 bounces.

b Describe a limitation of this model.

SOLUTION

a The problem says each time the ball rises to 50% of the height from which it was dropped. That means the common ratio is 0.5, so $r = 0.5$.

The ball starts at 8 feet.

Each time, the ball rises to 50% of the height of the prior bounce. These are the peaks. We can calculate each term by multiplying the prior term by 0.5 or $\frac{1}{2}$. This means we are calculating a geometric sequence, since there is a common ratio.

Peaks	Height
0	8
1	8 • 0.5 = 4
2	4 • 0.5 = 2
3	1
4	0.5
5	0.25
6	0.125

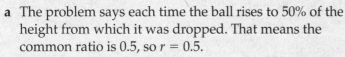

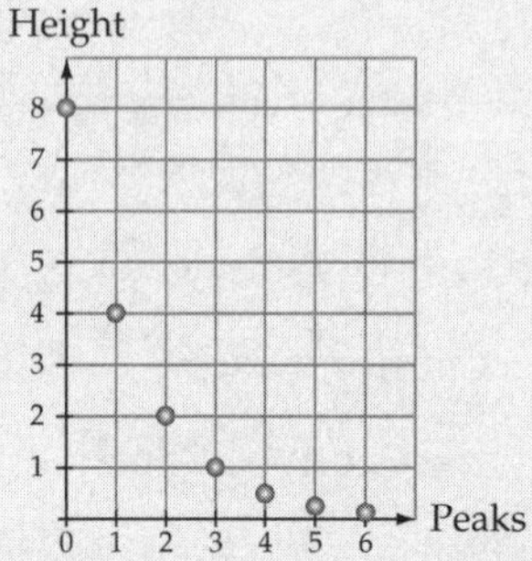

The graph of height versus peak number in the model problem, where the common ratio is greater than 0 but less than 1, can be described as exponential decay.

b The exponential function approaches zero, but never reaches it. This would mean that the ball never stops bouncing, but in reality, it does.

In summary,

- Each sequence is a function: an arithmetic sequence is a linear function, and a geometric sequence is an exponential function.
- One similarity between the arithmetic and geometric sequences is the use of a *common difference d* in arithmetic sequences and the use of a *common ratio r* in geometric sequences.
- One essential difference is in the recursive formula for each: in the arithmetic sequence the common difference d is *added to* a_{n-1}, while in the geometric sequence the common ratio r is used to *multiply* a_{n-1}.

PRACTICE

1. Write the first 5 terms of a geometric sequence in which a_1 and r are given:

a $a_1 = 2, r = 5$

b $a_1 = -3, r = 2$

c $a_1 = 8, r = \frac{1}{2}$

d $a_1 = 4, r = -3$

e $a_1 = \frac{1}{2}, r = 2$

f $a_1 = 6, r = -\frac{1}{2}$

2. a If the geometric sequence is $15, 5, \frac{5}{3}, \frac{5}{9}, \ldots,$ what is the common ratio?

b If the geometric sequences is $88, -44, 22, \ldots,$ what are the 4th and 5th terms?

c Given the geometric sequence 42, 16.8, 6.72, . . . , find the next term. Do not round.

3. Write the first 4 terms of a geometric sequence in which a_4 and r are given:

a $a_4 = 512, r = 2$

b $a_4 = 3, r = \frac{1}{2}$

4. In each of the following geometric sequences, find the common ratio, find the nth term, and find the 6th term.

a $9, 3, 1, \frac{1}{3}, \ldots$

b $1, -2, 4, \ldots$

c $81, 54, 36, 24, 16, \ldots$

d $1, -1, 1, \ldots$

e $\sqrt{3}, 3, 3\sqrt{3}, 9, \ldots$

f $1, x, x^2, x^3, \ldots$

5. Determine which of the following sequences are geometric. If the sequence is geometric, then state the explicit formula.

a $1, 3, 9, 15, 45, \ldots$

b $3, 6, 12, 24, 48, \ldots$

c $2, 4, 16, 256, \ldots$

d $2, 4, 8, 16, \ldots$

e $7, -7, 7, -7, 7, \ldots$

6. If the nth term of a geometric sequence is given as $\frac{2^{n+1}}{3^n}$,

a What are the first, second, and third terms?

b Find the common ratio.

Practice Problems continue . . .

7. If the 4th term of a geometric sequence is 15 and the 7th term is 405, find the common ratio and all the missing terms, first through seventh.

8. In the geometric sequence 3, x_2, x_3, -24, . . . which of the following are the values of the missing terms x_2 and x_3?

A. 6, 12

B. 6, -12

C. -6, 12

D. -6, -12

9. In the geometric sequence 2, x_2, x_3, 250, . . . which of the following are the values for the missing terms x_2 and x_3?

A. 10, -50

B. 10, 50

C. 5, 25

D. 25, 125

10. In the geometric sequence 2, x_2, x_3, $\frac{1}{4}$, . . . , which of the following are the values of the missing terms x_2 and x_3?

A. $1, \frac{1}{2}$

B. $\frac{1}{2}, \frac{1}{8}$

C. $\frac{3}{4}, -\frac{1}{2}$

D. $-1, -\frac{1}{2}$

11. The formula $a_n = -5(3)^{n-1}$ describes a geometric sequence. Which formula also describes this sequence?

A. $a_1 = 1; a_n = -15a_{n-1}$

B. $a_1 = 3; a_n = -5a_{n-1}$

C. $a_1 = -5; a_n = 3a_{n-1}$

D. $a_1 = -5; a_n = 15a_{n-1}$

12. Write the nth term in the form $a_1 r^{n-1}$ for the geometric sequence defined by $a_n = \left(\frac{1}{2}\right)^{2n}$ and find the value of a_1 and r.

Exercises 13–26: Write the explicit formula to be used in addressing each of the following problems. Use the formulas to solve the problems.

13. **MP 2, 3, 4** A salesman offered to sell David a new $48,000 car for 15 monthly payments. He said the first payment would be $3 and would then double each month for the 15 months. If David accepts this seemingly great deal, what would his 12th payment be? What would his last payment be? Should he accept the deal? Explain.

14. A large snowfall of 45 inches fell on Buffalo. If one-third of the snow melts each day, how much snow will remain

a After 2 days?

b After 3 days?

c After 5 days, will there be more or less than an inch of snow on the ground?

15. The Ballantines' house cost $135,000 in 2004. If the value of the house increased at an annual rate of 5%,

a What is its value 6 years later, in 2010?

b What is it worth in the year 2015?

16. A pearl was purchased for $1000. If its value V increases by 7% each year,

a State the value of the pearl for each of the next five years.

b What is its value V after n years?

c What is the constant ratio?

17. With the common ratio of the half-life of a radioactive substance represented by (0.5), how much radioactive material remains after 4 hours from an 800 mg sample with a half-life of one hour?

Practice Problems continue . . .

18. If a secure lab has 6.4 ounces of a certain radioactive material with a half-life of 10 minutes, how much of the radioactive material remains after one hour?

19. In a lab culture, there are 24 bacteria of a certain strain that doubles its number every hour. How many bacteria will be present

a at the end of 5 hours?

b at the end of 10 hours?

20. If a certain bacteria strain doubles its number every half-hour and there are 3 bacteria to begin with, represent how many bacteria will be present after 24 hours.

21. A ball is dropped from a height of 100 feet and bounces up nine-tenths of its previous height after each bounce. After the 8th bounce, the height of the ball will be approximately how many feet?

22. A handball is dropped from a height of 5 yards and loses 20% of its height on each bounce.

a What is the height of the ball after 5 bounces?

b after n bounces?

23. Three numbers whose common difference is 5 are in an arithmetic sequence. If the first number is left unchanged, and 1 is subtracted from the second, and 2 is added to the third, the resulting three numbers are in a geometric sequence. Find the three original numbers and the geometric sequence.

24. A geometric sequence consisting of positive numbers has $a_1 = 18$ and $a_5 = \frac{32}{9}$. Find the common ratio r.

25. If $x - 3$, $x - 1$, and $2x + 1$ are the first three terms in a geometric sequence,

a Find x.

b Find the three terms, and state the explicit formula for $f(n)$. (Hint: There should be two sets of answers.)

26. If the height of a rosemary bush is 1 foot tall and it grows at the rate of 5% each month,

a Write the explicit formula and generate the geometric sequence of growth for the first 5 months.

b What is the height after 10 months?

27. Write the explicit formula for the nth term of the geometric sequence that has two known terms, $a_4 = 4$ and $a_7 = 32$, and simplify.

CHAPTER 9 REVIEW

1. Which of the following is equivalent to $a^{\frac{5}{3}}$?

A. $a\sqrt[3]{a^2}$ C. $\sqrt[5]{a^3}$

B. $a^2\sqrt[3]{a}$ D. $a\sqrt[5]{a^2}$

2. Which of these is equivalent to $\sqrt[6]{27x^{12}}$?

A. $3x^2$ C. $x^2\sqrt{3}$

B. $x\sqrt{3}$ D. $\sqrt{3x^3}$

3. The expression $\sqrt[3]{64x^{16}}$ is equivalent to

A. $4x\sqrt[3]{x^5}$ C. $8x^4$

B. $4x^5\sqrt[3]{x}$ D. $8x^8$

4. The expression $(a^2 - 1)^{-\frac{2}{3}}$ is equivalent to

A. $\sqrt[3]{(a^2 - 1)^2}$ C. $\dfrac{1}{\sqrt[3]{(a^2 - 1)^2}}$

B. $\sqrt{(a^2 - 1)^3}$ D. $\dfrac{1}{\sqrt{(a^2 - 1)^3}}$

Chapter Review continues . . .

5. If the graphs of $y = 3^x$ and $y = x$ are drawn on the same set of axes, they will intersect when x is equal to

A. 0

B. 1

C. 3

D. They will never intersect.

6. If the graphs of $y = 2^x$ and $y = 2x$ are drawn on the same set of axes, they will intersect when x is equal to

A. 1

B. 2

C. 1 and 2

D. They will never intersect.

7. The graph of $y = \left(\frac{1}{b}\right)^x$ for $b > 0$ is a reflection of the graph of $y = b^x$ about the

A. x-axis

B. y-axis

C. line $y = x$

D. line $y = -x$

8. The asymptote for $y = 2^{(x+1)} - 2$ is

A. $y = -2$

B. $y = -1$

C. $y = 0$

D. $y = 1$

9. Which could *not* be described as an exponential function?

A. the number of bacteria in a culture that increases 7.3% every hour

B. the amount of a person's salary if he gets a \$3500 raise every year

C. the medication remaining in the body t hours after it is injected

D. the amount of money in a bank account compounded monthly

10. A population increases from 13,000 at an annual rate of 4% a year. Which function would model this?

A. $P(t) = 13{,}000(0.04)^t$

B. $P(t) = 13{,}000(0.4)^t$

C. $P(t) = 13{,}000(1.04)^t$

D. $P(t) = 13{,}000(1.4)^t$

11. A population decreases from 13,000 at an annual rate of 4% a year. Which function would model this?

A. $P(t) = 13{,}000(-0.4)^t$

B. $P(t) = 13{,}000(-0.04)^t$

C. $P(t) = 13{,}000(0.6)^t$

D. $P(t) = 13{,}000(0.96)^t$

12. The half-life of an unstable isotope G is approximately 3 seconds. Which of the following best represents the amount of a 15-gram sample of isotope G that would remain after t seconds?

A. $15 \bullet \left(\frac{1}{2}\right)^t$

B. $15 \bullet \left(\sqrt[3]{\frac{1}{2}}\right)^t$

C. $\sqrt[3]{15} \bullet \left(\frac{1}{2}\right)^t$

D. $15 \bullet \left(\frac{1}{8}\right)^t$

13. Which formula can be used to find the nth term in the geometric sequence 96, 72, 54, . . .?

A. $a_n = 96\left(\frac{4}{3}\right)^{n-1}$

B. $a_n = 96\left(\frac{3}{4}\right)^{n-1}$

C. $a_n = 96\left(\frac{4}{3}\right)^{n}$

D. $a_n = 96\left(\frac{3}{4}\right)^{n}$

14. Which of the following sequences is arithmetic?

A. 7, 9, 11, 14

B. −7, −1, 5, 11

C. $1\frac{1}{3}, 1\frac{2}{3}, 2\frac{1}{3}, 3$

D. 12, 5, −3, −10

15. Which of the following would give you the 20th term of the arithmetic sequence 6, 13, 20, 27, . . . ?

A. $20 \bullet 6$

B. $6 + 20 \bullet 7$

C. $20 \bullet 7$

D. $6 + 19 \bullet 7$

Chapter Review continues . . .

16. Which of the following would *not* be a term of this geometric sequence?

3, 6, 12, 24, . . .

A. 48 C. 96

B. 64 D. 192

17. Given the geometric sequence 12, −4, $\frac{4}{3}$, . . . , which of the following is the value of a_8?

A. $-\frac{4}{729}$

B. $-\frac{4}{2187}$

C. $-\frac{4}{6561}$

D. $\frac{4}{729}$

18. a Graph the following three functions on the same coordinate system.

$f(x) = -2^x$, $f(x) = 2^{-x}$, and $f(x) = -x$

b How many solutions are there to the system?

19. MP 2, 6 On the same coordinate system and for the interval $-3 \le x \le 3$, sketch each of the three graphs.

(1) $y = 2^x$ (2) $y = \left(\frac{2}{3}\right)^x$ (3) $y = x + 1$

Compare the results.

a Are the graphs increasing or decreasing?

b How many solutions are there to the system?

c Identify the x- and y-intercepts.

d For domain and range use interval notation to describe their end behavior.

e Are there any horizontal or vertical asymptotes?

20. Graph the function $f(x) = 0.25(2)^x$ for the given values of x: $\{-2, -1, 0, 1, 2, 3, 4, 5\}$. Does the graph illustrate exponential growth or decay?

21. a Sketch the graph of $y = \left(\frac{1}{3}\right)^x$ and $y = x + 4$ in the interval $-2 \le x \le 2$ on the same coordinate plane.

b Identify the solutions to the system.

22. If $f(x) = 2^x$ is the parent function, write an equation based on the given description that would represent the correct transformation of that parent function.

a A vertical rise of 3 units and a horizontal shift to the right of 5 units.

b The asymptote is $y = -2$ and the horizontal shift is 2 units to the left.

c The graph is reflected about the x-axis and the vertical shift is 3 units up.

23. Given the population function $f(t) = 30(1.15)^t$, where $f(t)$ is the population (in thousands) in a town t years after 2008,

a What was the initial population of the town?

b At what rate is the population growing?

24. Graph each function in the same xy-coordinate plane. Identify the asymptote and y-intercept.

a $y = 2^{x-1} + 3$ over interval $-3 \le x \le 3$

b $y = 2^x - 3$ over interval $-3 \le x \le 3$

c $y = 2^{x-3} + 3$ over interval $-1 \le x \le 5$

d $y = -2^{x+1}$ over interval $-3 \le x \le 2$

25. How much money would you have after one year, if you put \$600 in a savings account that earned 3% compound interest annually? How much money would you have after 2 years? 5 years? Write an expression for the amount of money you would have after t years.

26. To the nearest dollar, find the value after 10 years of \$3500 invested at 5% and compounded quarterly.

Chapter Review continues . . .

27. A container originally held 4,000 grams of pressured air. However, at some point, it began leaking 5% of its air every day. After losing air for 8 days, how many grams of air remained?

28. The number of bacteria in a culture triples every four hours. If 1,000 bacteria are present initially, how many bacteria will be present at the end of 24 hours?

29. A computer system's value depreciates annually at a rate of 30%. If its initial value is $100,000, what is its value at the end of the eighth year?

30. MP 1, 2, 4 The formula, $S(t) = A(1 + r)^t$, links salary growth to rates of inflation.

If Kate's current salary is $45,000 and the rate of inflation is 3%:

a Explain the meaning of each term in the formula.

b What is her expected salary in three years?

c What is her expected salary in 10 years?

d Can she expect to double her salary in 20 years?

31. A specially designed sewing machine costs $5,200 and depreciates one-tenth its value every year.

a Write an equation to model this situation in order to determine the value of the machine after 5 years.

b To the nearest dollar, how much will the machine be worth at the end of the fifth year?

32. The population of a town is now 6,000 and has an expected increase of 10% a year for the next 5 years.

a Write an equation to be used to find (to the nearest integer) the total population after 5 years and find that population.

b What is the percent increase over those 5 years?

c In how many years will the population reach 20,000?

33. Find the first four terms and the 10th term of each sequence.

a $a_n = 3n - 1$

b $a_n = n^2 + 1$

c $a_n = \frac{n}{n + 1}$

d $a_n = 3^n - 1$

e $a_n = 5n + 11$

f $a_n = \frac{n - 1}{2}$

34. Find the first 5 terms of the sequence defined by $f(1) = 6$ and $f(n) = \frac{3}{f(n - 1)}$ for $n > 1$.

35. For each of the following arithmetic sequences, find the common difference, d, and write out the first four terms if

a the 10th term is 12 and the 14th term is 32

b the 7th term is 6 and the 17th term is 46

c $a_{92} = 1234$ and $a_{25} = 1904$

36. What is the 26th term if 30 is the first term in an arithmetic sequence and the common difference is -10?

37. What is the 51st term of an arithmetic sequence if the common difference is 1.2 and the first term is 2.5?

38. What number term is -29 if the first term in an arithmetic sequence is 3 and the common difference is -4.

39. If the 5th term in an arithmetic sequence is 8 and the 11th term is 26, what are the 6th through the 10th?

40. In an arithmetic sequence, the 4th term is -13 and the 20th term is 35. Find the common difference for the sequence. What are the first three terms? What are the 17th through 20th terms?

Chapter Review continues . . .

41. If the first four terms of an arithmetic sequence are 2, 8, 14, 20, and the 21st term is 122, what is the value of the 20th term?

42. MP 2, 4 On the first day of the viral outbreak, the emergency clinic at Columbia County Medical took in 13 patients. On each successive day the number of new patients increased by eight. Write and use an arithmetic sequence to specify the number of new patients that came in for treatment on the tenth day.

43. Given the infinite geometric sequence $\left\{1, -\frac{2}{3}, \frac{4}{9}, \ldots\right\}$

a Find the common ratio.

b Find the general term.

c Find the value of a_8.

44. For the geometric sequence a, ar, find

a the 3rd term

b the 5th term

c the nth term

45. If 3, 9, 27, . . . are the first three terms of a geometric sequence, what is the 8th term?

46. In the geometric sequence $-2, 8, -32, \ldots,$ what is the value of a_7?

47. Given the sequence $-9, x, -3,$

a Find the value of x when this sequence is arithmetic.

b Find the value of x when this sequence is geometric.

48. Given these formulas, write the first seven terms of the sequence:

$a_1 = 1, a_2 = 3,$ and $a_{n+1} = a_n + a_{n-1}$

49. Given this arithmetic sequence 2, 7, 12, 17, . . .

a Find the explicit formula for a_n and simplify.

b Find the recursive formula for the $(n + 1)$th term.

50. Given the arithmetic sequence 11, 10, 9, 8, 7, . . .

a Find the explicit formula for a_n and simplify.

b Find the recursive formula for a_{n+1} and simplify.

c Find the value of a_{100}.

51. Three positive numbers are in the ratio of 1 : 7 : 25. If 4 is added to each number, the resulting numbers form a geometric sequence. Find the original three numbers and the geometric progression. What is the explicit formula for this geometric sequence?

52. MP 2, 3, 4 Below are population estimates collected from the census for two different cities.

City	1960	1970	1980	1990	2000	2010
Bonneville	355,000	400,000	460,000	509,000	549,000	600,000
Astor	4,800	5,660	6,800	8,300	10,000	11,800

a Determine if the population data for each city can be best modeled by a linear or exponential function. Graphing the data will help you make a determination. Explain your reasoning.

b If you found a model for the city's population, what predictions could you make for the future population? Do you think the projections would be accurate? Explain why or why not.

Cumulative Review for Chapters 1–9

1. A mail-order card company charges 60 cents for each greeting card plus a handling fee of \$1.80. Which equation could be used to find the number (n) of cards ordered, if the total charge was \$9?

   A. $(0.6 + 1.8)n = 9$

   B. $0.6n + 1.8 = 9$

   C. $0.60n + 1.80n = 9$

   D. $60n + 1.80 = 9$

2. Let A = area of a circle as a function of the radius where $A(r) = \pi r^2$.

   Which expression represents the area of a circle whose radius is increased by 10%?

   A. $0.10A(r)$

   B. $A(r + 0.10)$

   C. $A(0.10r)$

   D. $A(1.1r)$

3. If $2 < |x| < 5$ and $3 < |y| < 6$, which of the following must be true?

   A. $y < x$

   B. $x < y$

   C. $xy > 0$

   D. $|xy| > 6$

4. The temperature in the science lab does not deviate from 23°C by more than 5°C. If T is the acceptable temperature range (in degrees Celsius) in the science lab, which of the following represents all possible values of T?

   A. $|T - 5| \leq 23$

   B. $|T - 5| \geq 23$

   C. $|T - 23| \leq 5$

   D. $|T - 23| \geq 5$

5. If $x < -3$ or $x > 3$, which of the following must be true?

   (a) $x^2 > 3$

   (b) $|x| > 3$

   (c) $x^3 > 3$

   A. (c) only

   B. (a) and (b) only

   C. (a) and (c) only

   D. (a), (b), and (c)

6.

x	1	2	3	4	5	6
$f(x)$	1	5	9	13	17	21

   The table above represents a relationship between x and $f(x)$. Which of the following linear equations describes that relationship?

   A. $f(x) = x + 3$

   B. $f(x) = 3x - 1$

   C. $f(x) = 2x + 1$

   D. $f(x) = 4x - 3$

7. If $f(x) = x^2$ and $m(x) = f(x - 3)$, then for what value of x is it true that $f(x) = m(x)$?

   A. 0   C. $\frac{3}{2}$

   B. $\frac{2}{3}$ D. 3

8. In which quadrants does the solution lie for this system of inequalities?

   $y > -x + 3$ and $y < x - 3$

   A. I, II   C. I, II, III

   B. I, IV   D. II, III

9. If the point (a, b) lies on the graph of $y = f(x)$, then the graph of $y = f^{-1}(x)$ must contain which point?

A. $(-a, -b)$ C. $(-a, b)$

B. $(-b, -a)$ D. (b, a)

10. In the equation $ax^2 + 6x - 9 = 0$, no real roots will be generated if

A. $a < -1$ C. $a > -1$, only

B. $a < 1$, only D. $-1 < a < 1$

11. If $0.005 \leq x \leq 0.5$ and $0.01 \leq y \leq 0.10$, then what is the largest value of $\frac{x}{y}$?

A. 0.05 C. 5

B. 0.5 D. 50

12. Which of these equations has no solution?

A. $|x - 2| - 3 = -1$

B. $|2 - x| - 3 = -1$

C. $-3|x - 5| + 8 = 14$

D. $|x + 3| - 2 = -1$

13. If the equation of line l is $x + 4y = 12$, which of the following is the equation of a line perpendicular to line l?

A. $y = -4x + 3$

B. $y = 4x - 3$

C. $y = \frac{1}{4}x + 3$

D. $y = -\frac{1}{4}x - 3$

14. The number of tadpoles in a certain pond during a summer period of 92 days can be modeled by the function

$g(n) = \frac{n^2}{3} - 10n + k$, where k is a constant

and $g(n)$ stands for the number of tadpoles on a given numbered day n. On what numbered day, n, was the number of tadpoles the same as it was on day 12?

A. 3 C. 15

B. 6 D. 18

15. A picture is 3 inches longer than it is wide. The picture is surrounded by a white mat 2 inches wide. The total area of the mat is 120 square inches. If w is the width of the picture, which equation states a correct relationship?

A. $(w + 4)(w + 7) + w(w + 3) = 120$

B. $(w + 2)(w + 5) - w(w + 3) = 120$

C. $(w + 4)(w + 7) - w(w + 3) = 120$

D. $(w + 2)(w + 5) + w(w + 3) = 120$

16. Given the function defined by $|2 - 4x| < 4$, which of the following is an interval that does not contain a solution for x?

A. $-1 < x < 0.5$

B. $-1 < x < -\frac{2}{3}$

C. $-0.5 < x < 2$

D. $0.75 < x < 1.25$

17. Which function best represents this graph?

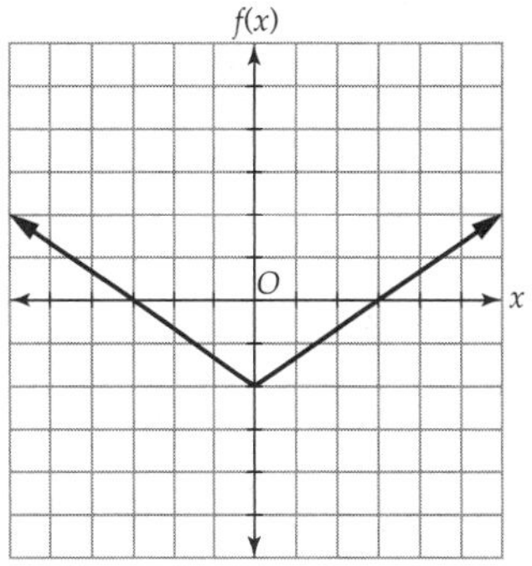

A. $f(x) = \frac{2}{3}|x - 2|$

B. $f(x) = \left|\frac{2}{3}\right| x - 2$

C. $f(x) = \left|\frac{2}{3}x\right| - 2$

D. $f(x) = \left|\frac{2}{3}x - 2\right|$

18. If the first term of an arithmetic sequence is -3 and the fifth term is 15, what is the 51st term?

A. 153 C. 225

B. 222 D. 228

19. Which of the following functions has a *range* of all real numbers?

A. $y = -x^2 + 5$

B. $y = |x| - 4$

C. $y = x^3$

D. $y = (x - 3)^2$

20. Given the geometric sequence $10, -5, \frac{5}{2}, -\frac{5}{4}, \ldots$, what is the value of the 10th term?

A. $-\frac{5}{256}$ C. $\frac{5}{256}$

B. $-\frac{5}{128}$ D. $\frac{5}{128}$

21. Evaluate each of the following. Identify if the answer is rational or irrational.

a $3^{-1} + 4^{-1}$

b $5^{-1} \div 5^0$

c $\left(\frac{3}{4}\right)^{-1} \bullet \left(\frac{4}{3}\right)^{-1} \bullet (-1)^3$

d $\sqrt[3]{64} + \sqrt{64} + 64^0$

22. Find the value in simplest form. Identify if the answer is rational or irrational.

a $16^{-\frac{1}{4}}$

b $81^{-\frac{3}{4}}$

c $\sqrt{8} + \sqrt{50}$

d $(\sqrt{27})^3$

23. Given $f(x) = |2x - 15|$

a Identify all the values for which $f(x) < x$.

b List the set of integer values for which $f(x) < x$.

24. a To the nearest tenth, convert 25 miles/hr to ft/sec.

b Change 88 ft/sec to miles per hour. Show your work.

25. **MP 1, 4, 6** For the years 2005 to 2020, the function, $S(p) = 0.115p + 3000$, expresses the expected number of students in a large city school district in terms of the actual population, p, of the district. If the district population was 350,000 in 2005 and is expected to increase to 410,000 by 2020,

a What would be the expected increase in new students?

b What is the approximate percent increase (to the nearest hundredth) in the new student population in this district?

26. Two straight lines are given by the following equations:

$y = m_1x + b_1$ and $y = m_2x + b_2$ where m_1, m_2, b_1, and b_2 are constants.

a What are the conditions for m_1, m_2, b_1, and b_2, if the two straight lines have no points in common?

b What are the conditions for m_1, m_2, b_1, and b_2, if the two straight lines have all their points in common?

c What are the conditions for m_1, m_2, b_1, and b_2, if the two straight lines have exactly one point in common?

d What are the conditions for m_1, m_2, b_1, and b_2, if the two straight lines are perpendicular to each other?

e What are the conditions for m_1, m_2, b_1, and b_2, if the two straight lines have exactly two points in common?

27. A board-game manufacturer produces a game called Multiple Choice at a cost of \$3 and can sell it for \$9. The overhead or daily fixed cost for this game's production is \$150.

If the total daily cost is given by the function $C(g) = 150 + 3g$ where g represents the number of games produced,

a Write an equation to represent the number of games that must be sold in a day to break even. Find that number of games.

b During a five-day week, how much money must be brought in to break even?

c What is the least number of Multiple Choice games that must be sold in order to make a profit for the week?

28. a Find the discriminant of $-3x^2 + x + 10 = 0$.

b How many roots are there? Describe the nature of those roots.

29. a If the equation of the axis of symmetry of $y = 2x^2 - px + 7$ is $x = 3$, what is the value of p?

b If the parabola $y = x^2 - 6x + k$ has its turning point on the x-axis, what is the value of k?

c If the roots of the equation $ax^2 + 6x = -3$ are real, rational, and equal, what is the value of a?

30. Graph the piecewise function:

$$f(x) = \begin{cases} x^2 & \text{if } x \le 0 \\ \sqrt{x} & \text{if } 0 < x \le 4 \\ \dfrac{3x}{4} & \text{if } x > 4 \end{cases}$$

31. MP 2

a If a, b, and c form an arithmetic sequence, express c in terms of a and b.

b If a, b, and c form a geometric sequence, express c in terms of a and b.

32. Find the solution set for each of the following.

a $\left|\dfrac{x+3}{2}\right| = 5$

b $\left|\dfrac{x+1}{4}\right| < 4$

c $\left|\dfrac{x-3}{5}\right| \ge -1$

33. Graph each of the three absolute-value functions on the xy-plane:

$y = |x + 3|$, $y = |x| - 3$, and $y = |x - 3| - 3$

34. In the figure given, part of the graph of $y = f(x)$ is shown. If f is a quadratic function, such that $f(x) = a - x^2$, what is the greatest possible value of $f(x)$?

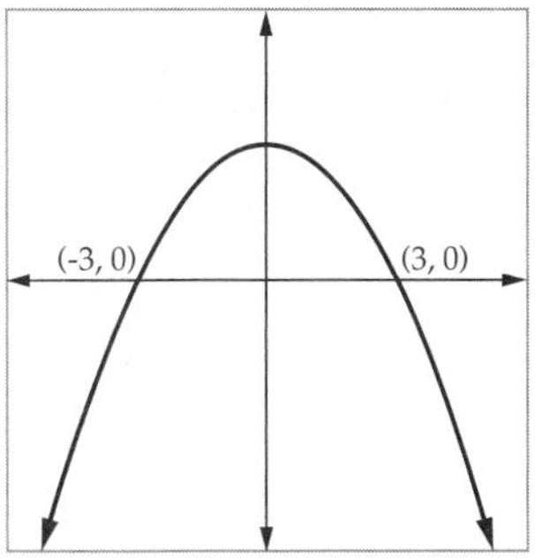

35. In each of the following, use the information given to produce the first 5 terms of a geometric sequence.

a $a_1 = 2$ and $r = 3$

b $a_1 = 1$ and $a_{n+1} = 7a_n$

c $a_1 = 64$ and $a_{n+1} = \dfrac{3}{4}a_n$

d $a_1 = 4$ and $a_2 = 20$

36. Simplify each of the following.

a $9^{-\frac{3}{2}} \bullet 9^{\frac{7}{2}}$

b $\left(\dfrac{1}{9}\right)^{\frac{1}{2}}\left(\dfrac{1}{9}\right)^{-\frac{1}{2}}$

37. MP 1, 7 The accrued balance of an amount A with a given rate r after one year, two years, three years, four years, etc. . . . , is expressed by the following geometric sequence: $A(1 + r)$, $A(1 + r)^2$, $A(1 + r)^3$, $A(1 + r)^4$, ... Find the accrued balance to the nearest dollar after 10 years for an annual compound interest rate of 5% on a principal amount of $10,000.

38. A given radioactive substance has a half-life of 3.5 years.

a How much of a 6-ounce sample remains after 17.5 years?

b What percent of the radioactive material has been lost over that time?

39. The half-life of radium is approximately 1600 years. If, initially, 24 ounces of radium was present in the lab,

a How much would be left after 200 years?

b after 2000 years?

40. **MP 4, 5, 8** In the 2010–2011 academic year, the average cost for one year at a four-year private college was $27,000, which was an increase of 3.5% from the previous year. Assume this trend continues.

a Write a function $C(x)$ that can be used to model the cost of a college education x years from now.

b Find $C(4)$.

c How much should parents expect to pay for their new baby's first year of college? Assume the child will enter college in 18 years.

d When will one year at a private college cost an average of $100,000?

41. a The first of three numbers is x. The second number is 9 less than 3 times the first. The third is 6 less than 3 times the first. If twice the third is decreased by the second, the result is 39. Find the three numbers.

b In the given sequence, $\{a, b, 13, \ldots\}$, the first term is a, and each term after the first is found by subtracting 3 from twice the preceding term. What is the value of a?

42. a If $0 < n < 1$, which of the following lists the numbers from least to greatest?

A. $n^2, \sqrt{n}, n$ C. $\sqrt{n}, n, n^2$

B. $n^2, n, \sqrt{n}$ D. $x, \sqrt{n}, n^2$

b If $x = \frac{1}{4}$, which of the following is less than x?

A. $\sqrt{x}$ C. $\frac{1}{x}$

B. x^2 D. $\frac{x}{1-x}$

c If n is an integer greater than 1, and if $x = n + \frac{1}{n}$, which of the following is false?

A. $x \neq n$ C. $xn > n^2$

B. $n \bullet \frac{1}{n} < x$ D. x is an integer

43. Alice deposited a total of $6000 in two different banks. One bank paid 4% interest and the other 6%. The interest on the account that pays 4% was $35 more than the interest on the account that pays 6%. If x is the amount invested at 4% and y is the amount invested at 6%,

a Write a system of equations that will determine the amount of money invested in each account.

b Solve that system and state the amount of money invested in each account.

44. a Solve for x and state your answer as a compound inequality: $|6x - 5| \leq 8$

b Graph the solution set of $|3x - 2| > -2$. How many integers are in your answer? Explain.

45. Solve for x.

a For all numbers x, where $x \neq 5$, let $f(x) = \dfrac{x + 11}{5 - x}$. If $f(x) = \dfrac{5}{2}$, what is the value of x?

b If $100^x = 0.001$, find the value of x.

c $a(x - 1) + b(1 - x) = x(a + b)$

d $n = \dfrac{a - x}{b - x}$

46. a A ball is tossed up at an initial velocity of 56 ft/sec. The height of the ball, t seconds after it is thrown, is given in feet by the formula $h(t) = 56t - 16t^2$. How many seconds after the ball is thrown will it return to the ground?

b When a batter hits a baseball, the height of the ball $h(t)$ in feet, at time t, where $t \geq 0$, is determined by the equation $h(t) = -16t^2 + 64t + 3$. For what interval of time is the height of the ball ≥ 51 feet?

47. Write the piecewise function rules for these two graphs:

a

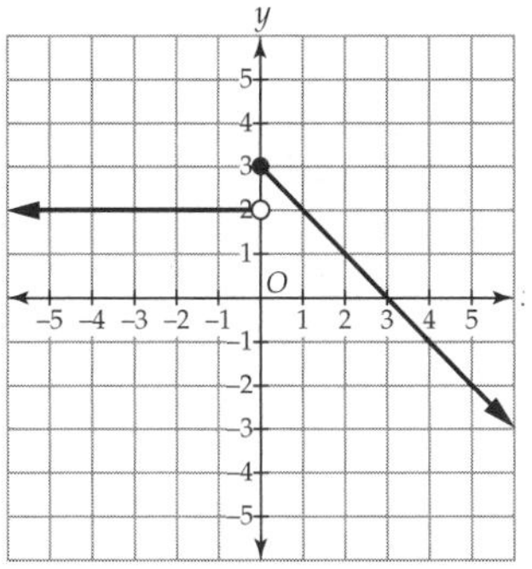

b

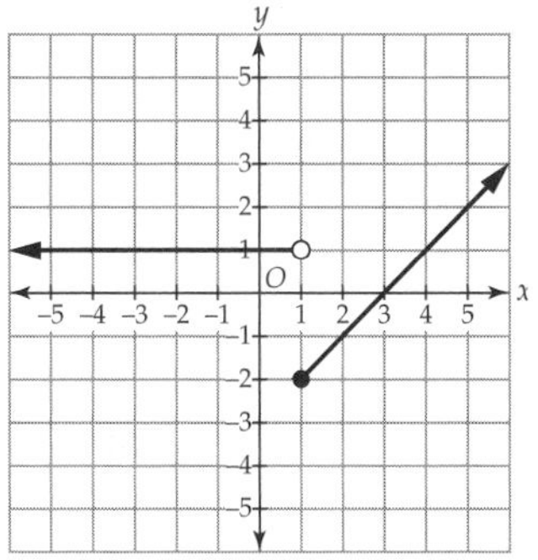

48. Chuck rides his bike to the store at the rate of 10 mph. His mother decides later to drive her car to the same store and travels at 30 mph. After 10 minutes of driving, his mother passes the same signpost that her son passed 30 minutes before.

a How far is the signpost from their home?

b In how many more minutes after passing the signpost will his mother catch up to him?

c What was the actual distance from the signpost to the place where she waved at him and passed him on the road?

d If the store is still 5 miles away when she passes him, how long will his mother have been in the store when he gets there?

49. If $2n$ is an even integer, show that the difference of the squares of two consecutive odd integers is a multiple of eight.

50. **MP 3** Explain how this area diagram can be used to show that $(a + b)^2 \neq a^2 + b^2$.

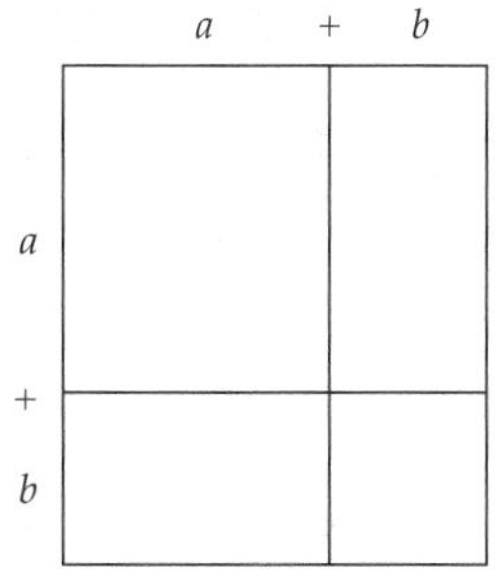

51. **MP 3, 6** If you multiply a rational number by an irrational number, will you always, sometimes, or never get a rational number for an answer? The ratios represent rational numbers. z represents an irrational number. Is it possible that $\dfrac{a}{b} \bullet z = \dfrac{c}{d}$?

52. **MP 3, 6** If you add a rational number and an irrational number, will you always, sometimes, or never get a rational number for an answer? The ratios represent rational numbers. z represents an irrational number. Is it possible that $\dfrac{a}{b} + z = \dfrac{c}{d}$?

Chapter 10 Interpreting Quantitative and Categorical Data

Chapter Focus

Statistics is a problem-solving process consisting of formulating questions that can be answered with data. This process includes designing and implementing a plan to collect relevant bias-free data, analyzing the data, and interpreting the results in the context of the original question. Topics of study include graphs and data distribution, properties of distribution, and bivariate data, including residuals.

Chapter Content

Chapter Vocabulary

association	**frequency**	**median**
bias	**histogram**	**mode**
box-and-whisker plot	**interquartile range**	**outlier**
coefficient of determination	**joint frequency**	**regression**
conditional frequency	**joint relative frequency**	**relative frequency table**
conditional relative frequency	**line of best fit**	**residual**
correlation	**marginal frequency**	**scatter plot**
correlation coefficient	**marginal relative frequency**	**standard deviation**
dot plot	**mean**	**two-way frequency table**
extrapolate		

LESSON 10.1

10.1 Simple Single-Count Statistics

Data collected by means of surveys, observation, or research is often summarized by graphs. Data refers to the raw information, the information you want to analyze and understand.

Let's look at the data from people who estimated the number of hours of television they watched in the past week. The table below shows the results. The **frequency** is the number of people that answered in the same way. For instance, the frequency of people answering one hour is two people.

Number of Hours	Number of Responders
0	1
1	2
2	4
3	4
4	8
5	8
6	6
7	10
8	10
9	7

Number of Hours	Number of Responders
10	15
11	12
12	16
13	4
14	10
15	15
16	18
17	18
18	15
19	12

Number of Hours	Number of Responders
20	10
21	8
22	10
23	6
24	7
25	5
26	0
27	0
28	1
29	1

Histograms

We can graph this data using a **histogram**. The widths of the bars are equal, representing equal intervals. In this histogram, the data is grouped in intervals of three hours. The frequency of each interval is represented by the height of the bar. There are no gaps between intervals, or bars.

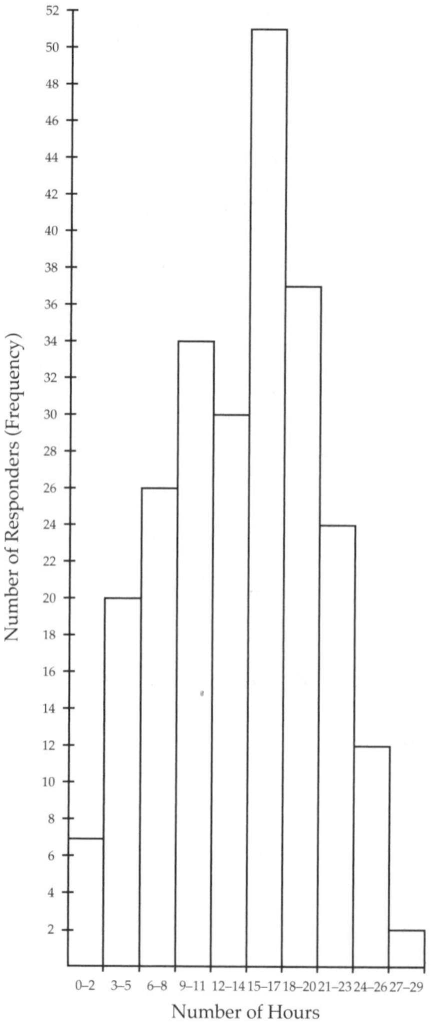

Dot Plots

While histograms are used for grouping data, **dot plots** are not grouped. Every piece of data collected is displayed. We use the same data on the number of responders versus hours of TV-watching to create a dot plot.

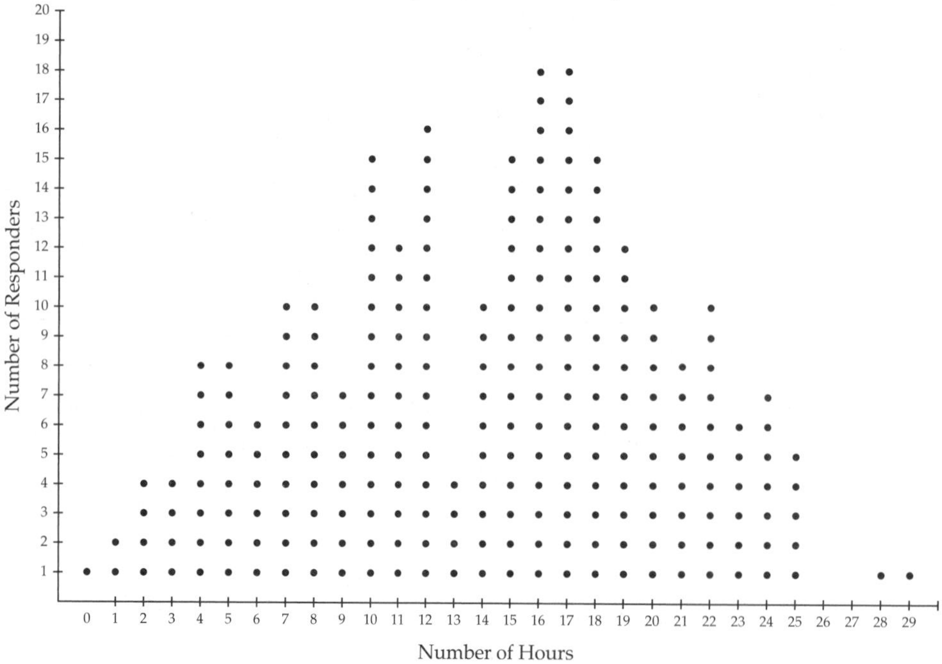

If a plot shows the data in each column to be about the same, the data can be said to have a *uniform distribution*. If the data centers around one value, it can be said to be *symmetric*. The other plots show the data to one side or the other, and they are said to be *skewed* left or right.

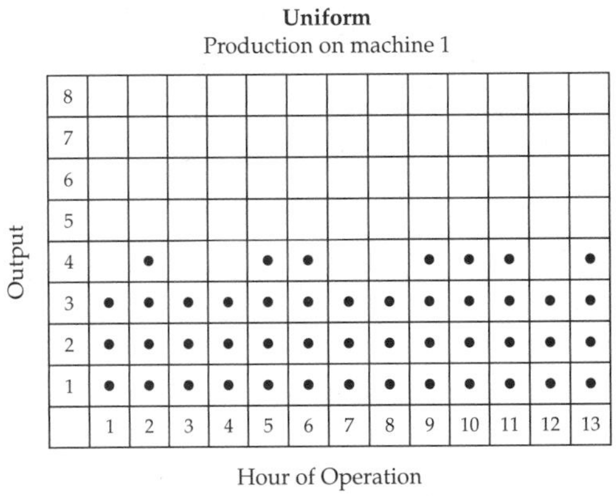

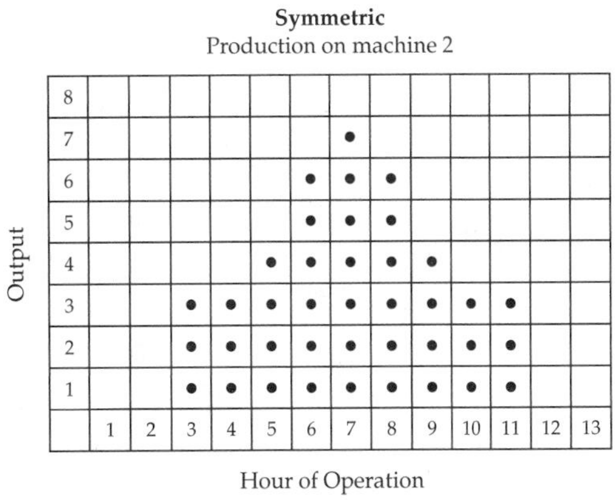

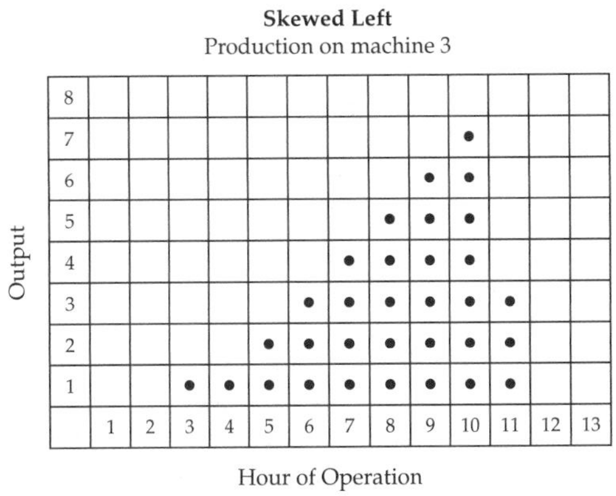

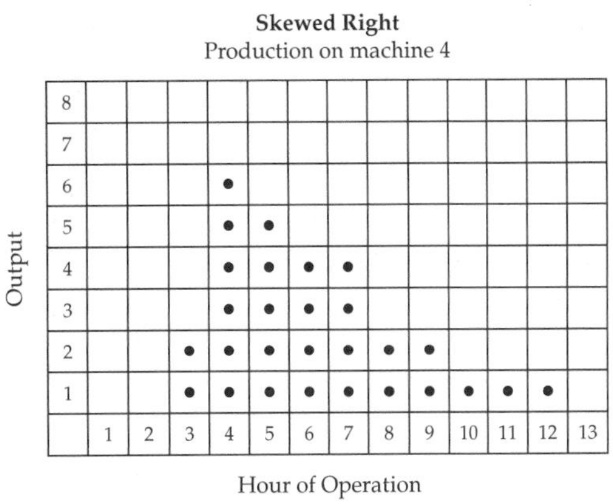

Different charts and graphs are good for showing different relationships. Dot plots and histograms both show frequency of occurrence. A dot plot counts the frequency of occurrence for some small number of events. In the dot plot below, you see the number of trees of different types in a small park in Germany.

When the number of events increases, a histogram is a more convenient way to show frequency. In the histogram below, you see the heights of 12-year-old children in a small city in China. There are over 500 children, so drawing a dot plot would be tedious. The heights of the children are shown in 5-centimeter intervals.

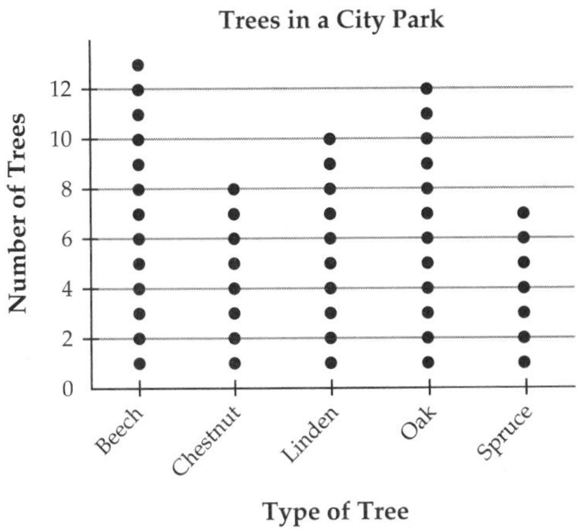

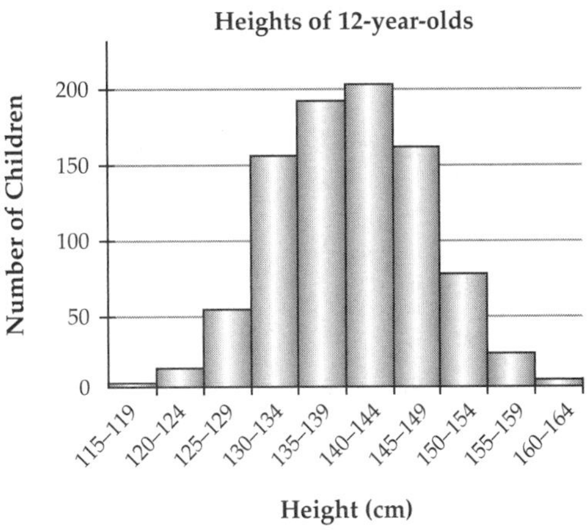

MODEL PROBLEM

MP 2, 3, 5 Construct a dot plot to show the heights, in inches, of the students listed below. Describe the shape of the data.

Charlie	62	Harry	59	Dawn	60	Eric	61
Jay	60	Alexandra	60	Quinn	60	Wendy	60
Ross	58	Joshua	61	Piper	62	Andrew	62
Jordan	59	Kyle	68	Reagan	63	Cortney	60
Sophia	58	Juan	61	Sam	59	Anna	59

SOLUTION

The smallest value is 58 and the largest value is 68. An easy way to make the dot plot is to use graph paper. However, any carefully constructed sketch is fine.

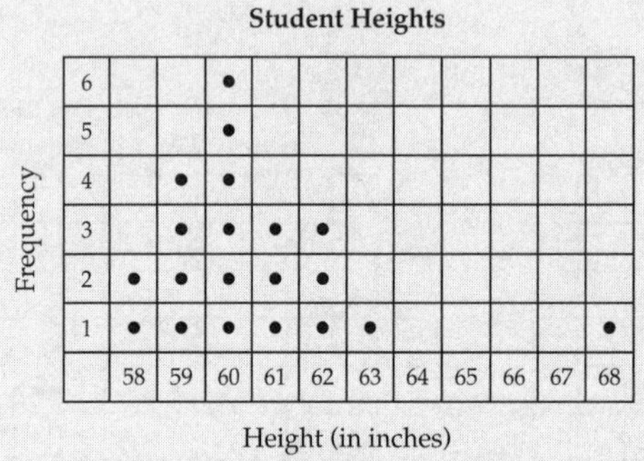

An **outlier** is a data point that is numerically far from the bulk of data points.

Answer: The heights are clustered between 58 inches and 63 inches and are fairly symmetric around 60 inches. There is a gap between these heights and one value of 68. This value is called an *outlier*.

PRACTICE

1. The heights of a group of 36 people are measured to the nearest inch. The heights range from 47 inches to 76 inches. To construct a histogram showing 10 intervals, the length of each interval should be

A. 2 inches

B. 3 inches

C. 4 inches

D. 5 inches

Exercises 2–4: Use the following test grades for 18 students to complete each exercise.

72, 86, 95, 75, 100, 85, 87, 100, 81, 84, 78, 94, 96, 80, 100, 98, 96, 91

2. Complete the frequency table.

Interval	Frequency
96–100	
91–95	
86–90	
81–85	
76–80	
71–75	
Total Frequency =	

Practice Problems continue . . .

3. Draw a frequency histogram.

4. How many students had grades less than 81?

Exercises 5–6: The heights of 15 students, in inches, are given.

65, 60, 64, 70, 71, 68, 65, 77, 69, 67, 66, 65, 61, 67, 70

5. Construct a frequency table for the data, using intervals of 5 inches.

6. Draw a frequency histogram for the data with 5-inch intervals.

Exercises 7–10: Use the following test grades of 24 students to complete each exercise.

88, 82, 86, 86, 87, 89, 88, 90, 87, 89, 89, 88, 86, 85, 83, 89, 85, 84, 87, 88, 87, 88, 89, 88

7. Construct a frequency table for the data, using intervals of 1.

8. Draw a histogram for the data with intervals of 5.

9. Construct a dot plot for the data.

10. Use the graphs constructed to describe the shape of the data values.

11. Refer to the table below:

Soda Cans Collected by Ms. Sepe's Class					
Ava	0	Lois	20	Virginia	20
Barbara	80	Marc	20	Wendy	20
Charlie	10	Nancy	10	Zoe	30
Dawn	10	Olivia	0	Cort	10
Eric	10	Pauline	10	Andrew	10
Falynn	70	Quinn	80	Sean	20
George	0	Ross	20	Karen	30
Hayley	20	Sara	20	Jim	20
Ira	20	Teddy	10	Stephen	20
Jordan	60	Uri	60	Danielle	50

a Construct a dot plot for the data.

b Describe the shape of the data.

12. MP 3, 4 The scores on a test in Ms. Abidor's three Algebra classes were graphed on the histogram below.

a How would you describe the distribution of scores in her classes?

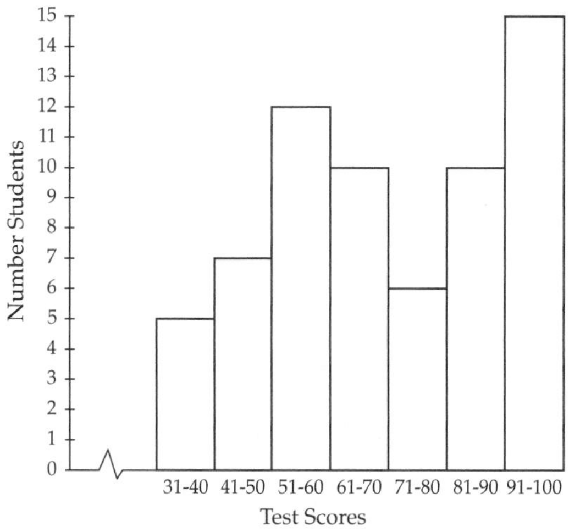

b The data was graphed again using intervals of 25. The graph is shown below. How is the interpretation of the information lost by selecting wider intervals?

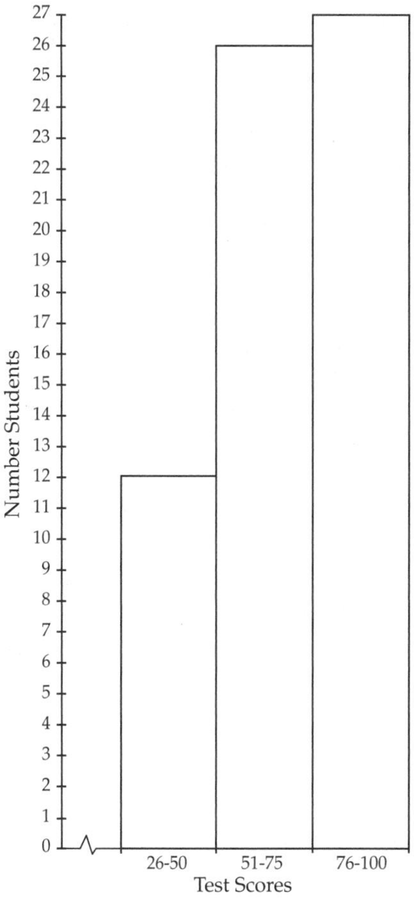

10.2 Measures of Central Tendency

The **mean** (or average), represented by $\bar{x}$, of a set of numbers is found by adding the numbers and then dividing the sum by the number of data items in the set, often called the *count*. For example, if Matthew's grades are 80, 92, 85, 91, 95, and 88, the mean is found using the formula:

$$\bar{x} = \frac{\text{sum}}{\text{number of items}} = \frac{80 + 92 + 85 + 91 + 95 + 88}{6} = \frac{531}{6} = 88.5$$

The **median** is the middle value when a set of numbers is arranged in order from least to greatest (or from greatest to least).

- If there is an *odd* number of items, the median is the middle number. For the numbers 2, 5, 7, 19, 20, the median is 7.
- If there is an *even* number of items, the median is the average of the two middle numbers. For the numbers 3, 4, 6, 7, 8, 9, the median is $\frac{6 + 7}{2} = \frac{13}{2} = 6.5$.

The median is not necessarily a number in the data set.

The **mode** is the value or values that appear most often in a set. A set of values may have *no mode* (if each value appears the same number of times), *one mode*, or *more than one mode*. For the numbers 3, 7, 5, 3, 2, 5, 8, the modes are 3 and 5.

MODEL PROBLEMS

1. MP 2, 3, 4 As part of a statistics project, Dr. Feeney asked students to anonymously provide their weekly allowance. Dr. Feeney posted the following chart showing allowances to the nearest dollar. Larry, Lauren, and Lindsay were triplets in Dr. Feeney's class. Each received \$5.00 allowance each week.

Allowance	Frequency
\$5.00	3
\$10.00	8
\$15.00	7
\$20.00	6
\$100.00	1

Each sibling tested a different measure of central tendency to try to convince Mom and Dad that a higher allowance would be reasonable. Larry found the mean. Lauren found the median. Lindsay found the mode.

a Who asked for the greatest raise in allowance?

b Why would you predict that one measure of center would be the highest?

SOLUTION

a Larry found the mean:

$$\frac{\text{sum}}{\text{number of items}} = \frac{420}{25} = \$16.80$$

Lauren found the median: There are 25 values. The middle value is the 13th value. The median is \$15.

Lindsay found the mode: \$10

Answer: Larry asked for the greatest increase in allowance.

b The single data value of \$100 is an outlier for this data set. It causes the sum, and therefore the mean, to be high. The mean is higher than the median or the mode.

If the data set is large, you may wish to use a graphing calculator to find the mean and median. While you cannot find the mode directly from the calculator, you can sort the data and count the occurrences of each number more easily.

Model Problems continue . . .

Model Problems *continued*

2. **MP 3, 4** A shoe factory employs 10 workers in a finishing department. Most of the employees have been hired recently. However, two employees have worked for the company since it opened forty years ago. The salaries of the employees are:

Alice	Barry	Carl	Don	Evan	Fran	Greg	Howie	Ike	Jake
\$12,000	\$14,000	\$15,000	\$15,000	\$15,000	\$16,000	\$17,000	\$18,000	\$80,000	\$80,000

Which measure of central tendency best describes the data?

SOLUTION

Most of the salaries are below \$20,000. However, Ike and Jake earn substantially more salary. This data has outliers to the right. The mean is much higher than the median. The median better represents the data in this situation.

Check: Mean $= \dfrac{\text{sum}}{\text{number of items}} = \dfrac{\$282{,}000}{10} = \$28{,}200$, which is not representative of a typical salary.

PRACTICE

1. What is the median of the set 80, 50, 67, 55, 70, 65, 75, 50?

A. 50
B. 64
C. 66
D. 67

2. The mean of a set of test scores is 83. If a score of 85 is added to the set and a new mean is calculated,

A. the new mean is greater than 83.
B. the new mean is less than 83.
C. the new mean is 83.
D. the effect on the new mean cannot be determined.

3. Which *must* be a value in the data set?

A. mean
B. median
C. mode
D. none of the above

4. Find the mean of these shoe sizes.

Size	Frequency
5	2
6	4
7	5
8	6
9	3

A. 7.0
B. 7.8
C. 7.2
D. 8.4

5. The average of A and B is 6. The average of X, Y, and Z is 16. What is the average of A, B, X, Y, and Z?

6. The average grade on a test taken by 20 students was 75. When one more student took the test after school, the class average became 76. What score did that student receive?

7. Find the mean, median, and mode of this data set:

$-2, 5, 10, -6, 7, 5, -2, 5, 10, -15, 14$

8. On New Year's Day in Watertown, the following temperatures were recorded. What is their average (mean)?

Time	°F
6 A.M.	−10
10 A.M.	2
2 P.M.	8
6 P.M.	4

9. The average of four different positive integers is 9. What is the greatest value for one of the integers?

Practice Problems continue . . .

10. Five students took a makeup quiz for Mrs. Hald. Three students picked up their papers after school. Their grades were 75, 73, and 86. Mrs. Hald told them that the average of the five grades was 80. What was the average of the other two scores?

11. If $j > 0$, what is the average of $2j$, $4j - 3$, and 6?

12. Create a data set of seven integers in which the median is greater than the mode.

13. The average and the median of three fractions are each $\frac{1}{3}$. The largest fraction is $\frac{1}{2}$. What is the smallest fraction?

14. MP 3 Jon wants to convince his parents to give him a raise in his allowance. It was much lower than the allowances of his six best friends. These amounts are similar, except for Julia's allowance. She receives twice as much as each of his other friends. Jon told his parents the mean of the allowances. His father said he wanted to know the median. Explain why.

Exercises 15–17: Use the following frequency table.

Interval	Frequency
501–600	10
401–500	18
301–400	12
201–300	20
101–200	5

15. Find the modal interval.

16. Find the interval containing the median.

17. Why is it impossible to find the interval containing the mean? Find the least and greatest possible values of the mean.

18. If the mean is greater than the median, which direction is the data most likely to be skewed?

Exercises 19–20: The dot plot below shows the number of students at a local school interested in various after-school activities.

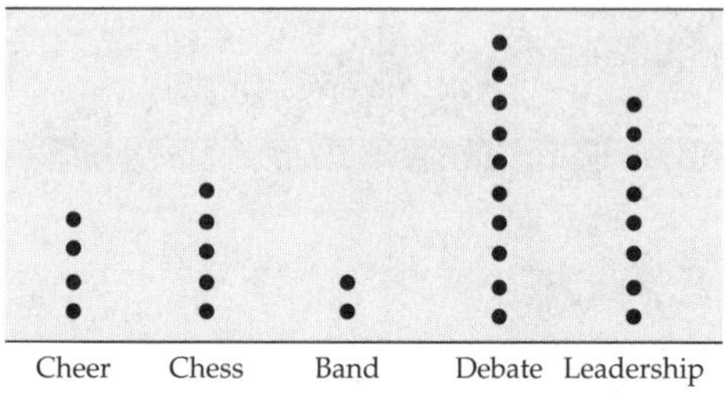

19. What is the dot plot telling us about students' preferences for after-school activities?

20. Why would the data shown here be important?

21. Create an original ten-item data set that has the same value mean and median.

LESSON 10.3

10.3 Single-Count Statistics with Dispersion

Interquartile Range and the Five-Number Summary

Recall that the median of a data set divides the set into two equal parts – that is, two parts with the same number of members. Quartiles are the values that separate the data into four parts, each containing one-fourth, or 25%, of the members.

> **The IQR describes the variability of the data.**

The range of a data set is the difference between the largest and smallest value. Often, we are interested in the **interquartile range (IQR)**. The IQR is the 1st Quartile subtracted from the 3rd Quartile.

For example:

53, 54, 55, 55, 56, 58, 59, 59, 59, 59, 60, 61, 61, 63, 64, 65, 75, 85, 95, 95

| 57 | 59.5 | 64.5 |

first quartile median third quartile

second quartile

- The first or lower quartile is the center of the lower half.
- The second quartile is the median.
- The third or upper quartile is the center of the upper half.
- The interquartile range is the difference between the third quartile and the first quartile. In this example, the interquartile range = 64.5 − 57 = 7.5.

To Calculate the Five-Number Summary on a Graphing Calculator
- Enter the data into the calculator as List 1.
- Press \boxed{STAT} $\boxed{\triangleright}$ to CALC, and $\boxed{1}$: 1-Var Stats.
- The screen shows 1-Var Stats and a blinking cursor.
- Unless you are not using L_1, arrow down to Calculate and press \boxed{ENTER}.
- Arrow down to see the five-number summary, the minimum value, first quartile value, median value, third quartile value, and maximum value, displayed as minX, Q_1, Med, Q_3, maxX.

> The quartiles can be found on the graphing calculator.

> The five-number summary is an excellent way to describe variation for skewed data.

MODEL PROBLEM

MP 5 Find the five-number summary for the following data values:

42, 15, 25, 30, 42, 75, 80, 85, 65, 25, 19, 72, 77, 25

SOLUTION

Step 1. Enter the values as List 1. Press \boxed{STAT} $\boxed{\triangleright}$ to CALC and $\boxed{1}$: 1-Var Stats.

```
EDIT CALC TESTS
1:1-Var Stats
2:2-Var Stats
3:Med-Med
4:LinReg(ax+b)
5:QuadReg
6:CubicReg
7↓QuartReg
```

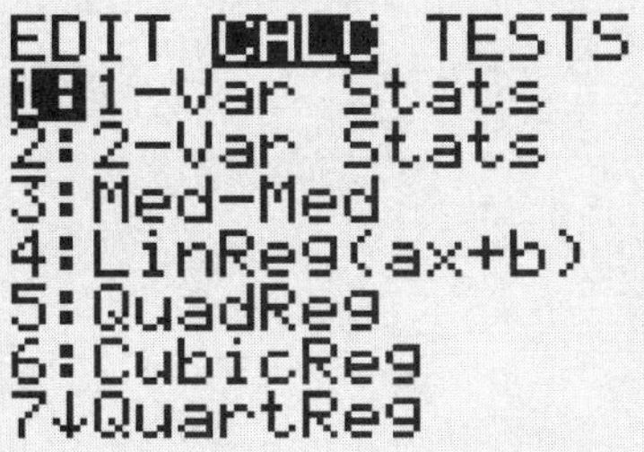

Step 2. The screen shows 1-Var Stats. Arrow down to Calculate and press \boxed{ENTER}. Arrow down to see the five-number summary.

```
       1-Var Stats
↑n=14
 minX=15
 Q₁=25
 Med=42
 Q₃=75
 maxX=85
```

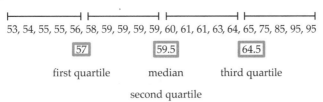

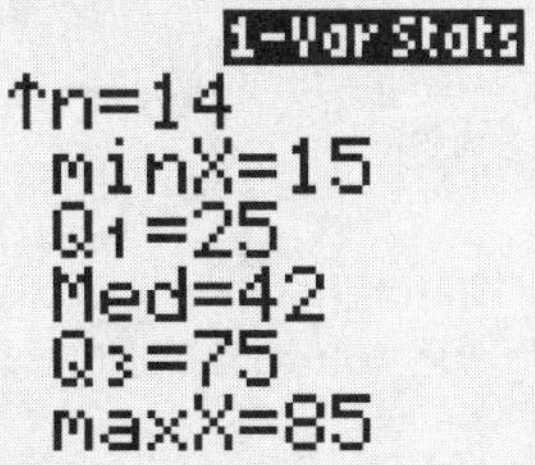

Answer: The five-number summary is minX = 15, Q_1 = 25, Med = 42, Q_3 = 75, and maxX = 85.

Box-and-Whisker Plots

Box-and-whisker plots are used to show the distribution of data. They describe data using quartiles, the highest and lowest values (the extreme values) in the data, the median of the data, and how close or far values are from the median. Box-and-whisker plots show how the data for each set are distributed and what the extreme values are.

> Box-and-whisker plots are useful for comparing two or more data sets.

To Construct a Box-and-Whisker Plot

- Draw a number line to include the lowest value and the highest value in the data set.
- Above the number line, mark the quartiles and the extreme values.
- Draw a box above the number line, with vertical sides passing through the lower and upper quartiles. Draw a vertical line in the box through the median (second quartile).
- Draw the "whiskers," horizontal lines extending from the vertical sides of the rectangle to the extreme values.

> In a box-and-whisker plot, outliers are data that fall more than 1.5 times the interquartile range from the quartiles. Do not extend whiskers to any outliers.

MODEL PROBLEMS

1. Draw a box-and-whisker plot for these data: 20 27 28 29 30 31 33 33 37 39 55

SOLUTION

Step 1. Draw the box.

The median is 31. The lower quartile is 28. The upper quartile is 37. Plot those values above a number line and draw the rectangle.

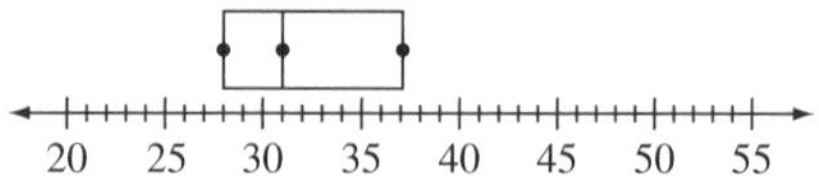

Step 2. Draw the whiskers.

The interquartile range is $37 - 28 = 9$. Data more than $1.5(9) = 13.5$ from the quartiles are outliers.

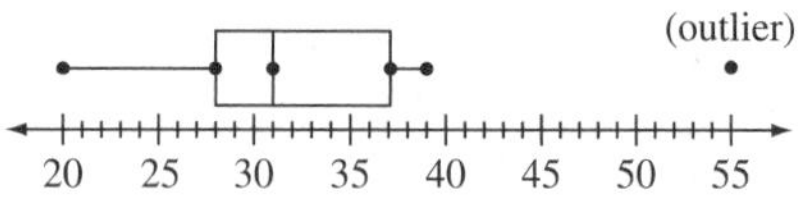

Left whisker check for outliers:

$28 - 13.5 = 14.5$

No data are smaller than 14.5, so there are no low outliers.

The left whisker will extend from the box to 20.

Right whisker for outliers:

$37 + 13.5 = 50.5$

One value, 55, is more than 50.5. The right whisker will therefore extend only to the next highest value, 39.

Model Problems continue . . .

Model Problems *continued*

2. **MP 3, 4** We show the basketball scores of two players, Deming and Botero.

Deming	12	14	15	17	20	22	24	24	24	28
Botero	10	15	17	17	20	21	22	22	25	31

a Draw box-and-whisker plots for the two sets of data.
b Compare and contrast the medians and distributions.

SOLUTION

a

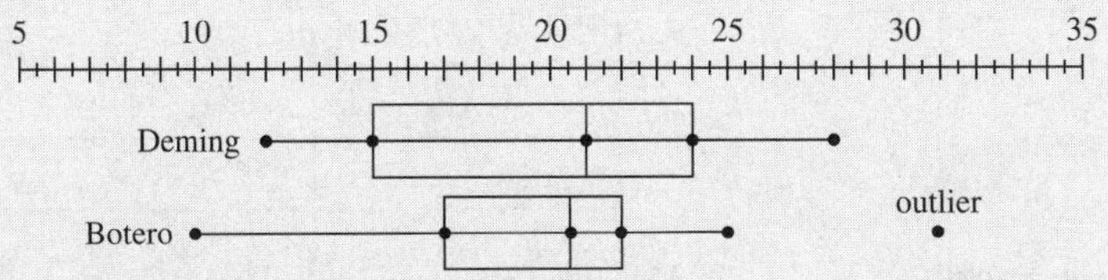

Box-and-whisker plots can also be constructed with a graphing calculator.

b The two players have approximately the same second quartiles, or medians. However, Deming's box is much wider than Botero's. The middle values have a much greater spread from the median. Botero's lower whisker extends farther because his minimum value is relatively far away from his lower quartile.

PRACTICE

1. Identify the first quartile for the following data set.

32, 24, 38, 26, 38, 36, 37, 39, 23, 40, 21, 31

A. 21
B. 25
C. 32
D. 34

2. The interquartile range of a data set is 18. The first quartile is 52. Which value could be the median?

A. 25
B. 34
C. 61
D. 97

3. This is a box-and-whisker plot for 60 test scores.

The upper quartile is

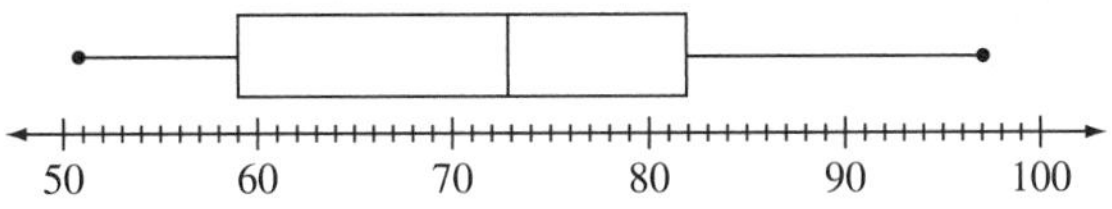

A. 59
B. 73
C. 82
D. 97

4. Find the interquartile range for this set of children's heights (in centimeters).

147, 130, 160, 150, 152, 120, 121, 125, 128, 121, 140, 142, 134, 126

A. 7
B. 22
C. 33
D. 40

5. These box-and-whisker plots show test scores for two classes.

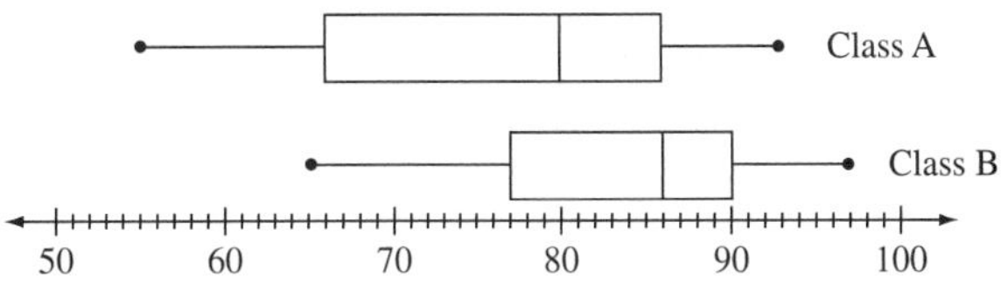

Which statement is *false*?

A. The interquartile range is greater for class A than for class B.
B. The second quartile is higher for class B than for class A.
C. The lowest score was in class A.
D. Class A did better than class B.

Practice Problems continue . . .

Exercises 6–7: Use this data set for the following questions: 60, 62, 62, 64, 68, 69, 71, 72, 74, 76, 78, 81, 83, 87

6. Find the five-number summary.

7. Construct a box-and-whisker plot.

Exercises 8–12: Use this data set for the following questions: 30, 67, 67, 68, 68, 69, 71, 71, 71, 72, 73, 74, 74, 75, 80

8. Find the five-number summary.

9. Construct a box-and-whisker plot.

10. In a box-and-whisker plot, what percentage of the scores are represented by the box?

11. In a box-and-whisker plot, what percentage of the scores are represented by each whisker?

12. In a box-and-whisker plot, what characteristic of the data would position the median in the middle of the box?

13. MP 2, 3 Is it possible to have a box-and-whisker plot with only one whisker? Explain your answer.

14. MP 3 Two box-and-whisker plots for the same number of data points have the same extremes and the same median. However, the box is twice as long for the first plot as for the second. What differences would you expect to find if you compared the data?

15. A class decided to compare a supermarket-brand chocolate chip cookie with a famous name brand. The students broke apart nine cookies of each brand and recorded the number of chips. Make a box-and-whisker plot for each brand and compare the data, including quartiles, interquartile ranges, and the lengths of the whiskers.

Supermarket Brand	Name Brand
4	7
4	7
5	8
5	9
6	9
7	9
10	10
12	10
18	11

16. MP 3, 4, 5 A small data set with similar values is changed by the addition of one outlier. Andrea says that the median would be affected more than the mean. Maryrose says that the mean would be affected more than the median. Who is correct? Explain why.

17. Sketch a box-and-whisker plot for a data set that is skewed left.

Sample Variance and Standard Deviation

The mean is one measure of where the center of some data lies. A measure called the **standard deviation** provides another way to summarize information about a data set. The greater the standard deviation, the greater the spread of data values from the mean.

For example, the mean of high temperatures for the four seasons is the same in Rio de Janeiro as in Taipei: 26°C. However, the data reveals that temperatures vary more in Taipei than they do in Rio.

Since two different data sets can have the same mean, it is important to have another way to describe the data.

City	Spring	Summer	Autumn	Winter
Rio de Janeiro (Brazil)	25	29	26	24
Taipei (Taiwan)	25	33	27	19

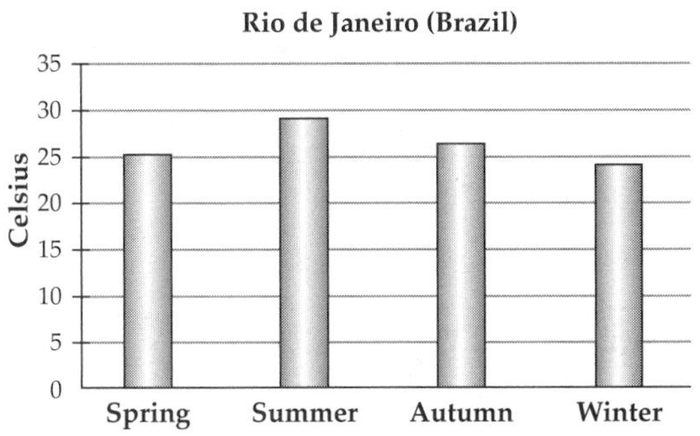

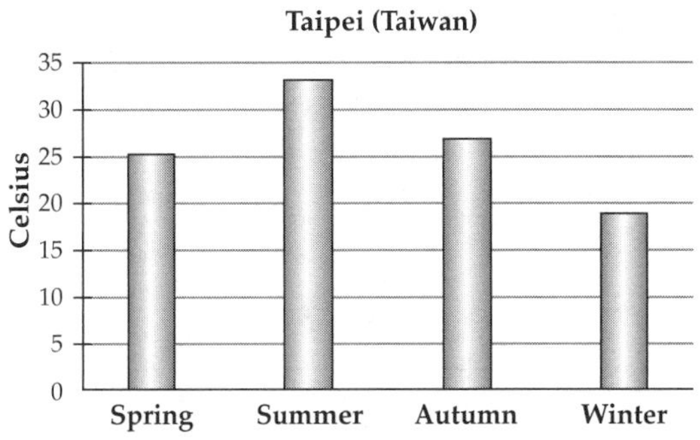

In order to measure the variability for the temperatures in Taipei, we will calculate the standard deviation, a measure based upon the distance of each value from the mean.

The formula for sample standard deviation is $s = \sqrt{\dfrac{(x_1 - \bar{x})^2 + (x_2 - \bar{x})^2 + \ldots + (x_n - \bar{x})^2}{n - 1}}$,
where s is the standard deviation, $x_1, x_2, \ldots, x_n$ are the data values, $\bar{x}$ is the mean, and n is the number of data values.

Step 1. Find the mean.	$\dfrac{25 + 33 + 27 + 19}{4} = 26$			
Step 2. Find the deviations by subtracting the mean from each value of the data.	$25 - 26 = -1$	$33 - 26 = 7$	$27 - 26 = 1$	$19 - 26 = -7$
Step 3. Square the deviations.	1	49	1	49
Step 4. Find the sum of the squared deviations.	$1 + 49 + 1 + 49 = 100$			
Step 5. Divide the sum of the squared deviations by 1 less than the number of data items.	In this example, $n - 1 = 4 - 1 = 3$. $\dfrac{100}{3} = 33.\overline{3}$ This value is called the *variance*.			
Step 6. The standard deviation is the square root of the variance.	Round to the nearest hundredth, $\sqrt{33.\overline{3}} = 5.77$			
We say that the standard deviation of temperature from the mean temperature is 5.77 °Celsius.				

MODEL PROBLEMS

1. What is the standard deviation of the seasonal temperatures in Rio? How does the standard deviation of the seasonal temperatures in Rio compare to the standard deviation of temperatures in Taipei?

City	Spring	Summer	Autumn	Winter
Rio de Janeiro (Brazil)	25	29	26	24
Taipei (Taiwan)	25	33	27	19

SOLUTION

$$\overline{x} = \frac{25 + 29 + 26 + 24}{4} = 26$$

x_n	$\overline{x}$	$x_n - \overline{x}$	$(x_n - \overline{x})^2$
25	26	−1	1
29	26	3	9
26	26	0	0
24	26	−2	4

$$s^2 = \frac{\text{total}}{n - 1} = \frac{1 + 9 + 0 + 4}{4 - 1} = \frac{14}{3}$$

$$s = \sqrt{\frac{14}{3}} \approx 2.16$$

The standard deviation for temperatures in Rio is approximately 2.16 °Celsius, while the standard deviation for temperature in Taipei is 5.77 °Celsius.

2. **MP 2, 3, 4** A sample of the cookie sales for a Scout troop in a rural area was used to plan the number of cases to order in advance. Five Scouts reported that last year, their sales were 20, 20, 30, 25, and 30 cases. A similar sample was conducted for a Scout troop in an urban area. The data collected for five Scouts was 49, 11, 0, 15, and 50 cases.

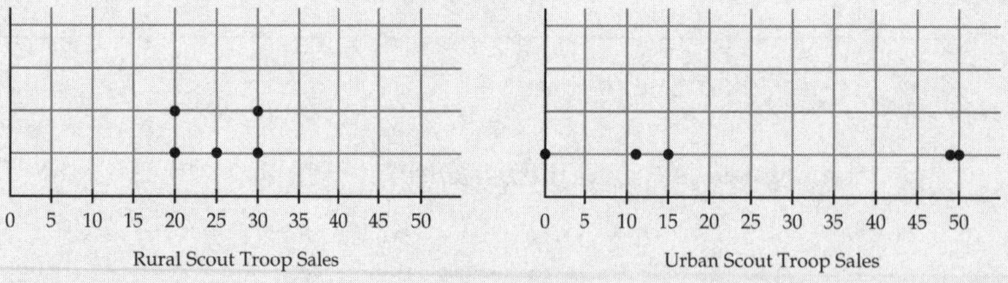

a Estimate which troop will have the greatest standard deviation.

b Calculate the standard deviation for each troop's data.

c Determine if your estimation was correct.

Model Problems continue . . .

SOLUTION

a The standard deviation for the urban troop should be greater because the values are spread farther from the mean than the rural troop.

b $\bar{x} = \dfrac{20 + 20 + 30 + 25 + 30}{5} = 25$

Rural troop:

x_n	$\bar{x}$	$x_n - \bar{x}$	$(x_n - \bar{x})^2$
20	25	−5	25
20	25	−5	25
30	25	5	25
25	25	0	0
30	25	5	25
		total	100

$s^2 = \dfrac{\text{total}}{n - 1} = \dfrac{100}{4} = 25$

$s = \sqrt{25} = 5$

Urban troop:

$\bar{x} = \dfrac{49 + 11 + 0 + 15 + 50}{5} = 25$

x_n	$\bar{x}$	$x_n - \bar{x}$	$(x_n - \bar{x})^2$
49	25	24	576
11	25	−14	196
0	25	−25	625
15	25	−10	100
50	25	25	625
		total	2122

$s^2 = \dfrac{\text{total}}{n - 1} = \dfrac{2122}{4} = 530.5$

$s = \sqrt{530.5} \approx 23.03$

c The prediction was correct. The data for the urban troop was more spread out. The standard deviation for the rural troop was 5, and the standard deviation for the urban troop was 23.03.

To Calculate Standard Deviation Using a Graphing Calculator

- Enter the data into the calculator as L_1 (List 1).
- Press [STAT] [▸] to CALC, and [1]: 1-Var Stats.
- The screen shows 1-Var Stats and a blinking cursor.
- Unless you are not using L_1, arrow down to Calculate and press [ENTER].
- Arrow down to see S_x.

This is the same procedure as finding the five-number summary on a graphing calculator.

MODEL PROBLEM

MP 4, 5 A specialty baby clothing company monitored the number of embroidered blankets made by each employee in one month. The results were:

14 15 11 11 8 18 21 16 16 12 19 25

Analyze this data using interquartile range and standard deviation. Which is a better measure of variability? Which gives more useful information?

SOLUTION

Use the graphing calculator to get results.
Enter the data as a list and use 1–Var Stats:

```
1-Var Stats
↑n=12
 minX=8
 Q1=11.5
 Med=15.5
 Q3=18.5
 maxX=25
```

```
1-Var Stats
x̄=15.5
Σx=186
Σx²=3134
Sx=4.776838057
σx=4.573474245
↓n=12
```

From the five-number summary, we know the median is 15.5. We know the IQR is 7 (18.5 – 11.5). The median and the mean are the same value. The standard deviation is a more useful measure of variation in this situation since the mean and median are the same value.

PRACTICE

1. Which comparison is true?

A. variance > standard deviation
B. standard deviation > variance
C. standard deviation > range
D. It depends on the data.

2. Which is always correct?

A. The variance and standard deviation both have the same unit measure as the data.
B. The variance has the same unit measure as the data.
C. The standard deviation has the same unit measure as the data.
D. Neither the variance nor the standard deviation has the same unit measure as the data.

Practice Problems continue . . .

Exercises 3–4: The two data sets listed below are monthly fund-raising totals in dollars for two clubs last year. Find the mean, the range, and the sample standard deviation to the nearest integer for each data set.

3. 25, 40, 50, 80, 78, 70, 45, 75, 95, 42

4. 62, 80, 11, 66, 40, 68, 81, 79, 48, 65

5. Can different lists have the same measures of dispersion?

6. The weights of the students in Mr. Collier's Book Club were used as a sample to describe the weights of students in their high school.

Male weights: 112, 120, 135, 140, 160, 150, 155, 170

Female weights: 95, 100, 105, 105, 115, 115, 120, 120, 130, 125

a Find the mean, the sample standard deviation, and the range, each to the nearest tenth, of the male weights.

b A new male student weighing 225 pounds joined the club. Find the new mean, standard deviation, and range to the nearest tenth.

c With the new student included in the data, which measure of variability gives the most information in this situation?

d Observing the data, do you believe that the standard deviation is greater for male students or for female students? Explain your reasoning. Check your answer.

MP 2, 3 Exercises 7–8: Three data sets are shown in the dot plots below. Answer the questions without performing numeric calculations.

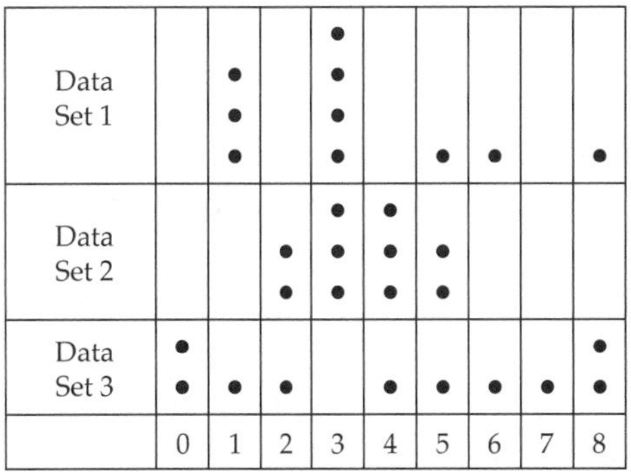

7. Which data set appears to have the smallest standard deviation? Explain your choice.

8. Which data set appears to have the largest standard deviation? Explain your choice.

MP 2 Exercises 9–10: Maryrose rolled a six-sided die 4 times. Each time, she rolled a three (3). Without calculation:

9. What was the mean value she rolled?

10. What was the standard deviation for the rolls?

LESSON 10.4

10.4 Two-Valued Statistics for Linear Behavior

Scatter Plots

A **scatter plot** relates two sets of data on a graph. Both the vertical and horizontal axes show numeric data amounts.

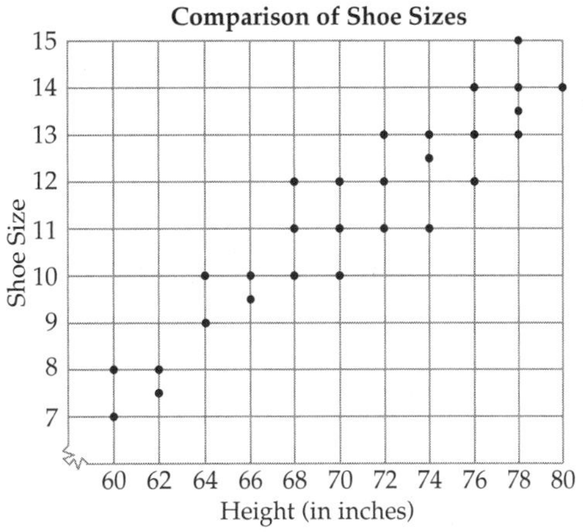

The scatter plot shows heights and shoe sizes for a group of males.

To Construct a Scatter Plot

- Construct and label both axes, using reasonable scales for the values. (Use a "break" symbol, if necessary.)
- Plot the data points.
- Give the scatter plot a title.

To Construct a Scatter Plot on a Graphing Calculator

- Enter the data values for the independent variable (x) in L_1.
- Enter the data values for the dependent variable (y) in L_2.
- Check that there is the same number of values in both lists.
- Press [2nd] [Y=].
- Press [1]. The cursor should be over On. Press [ENTER] to turn STAT PLOT 1 on.
- Using the arrows and cursor, make sure the first graph type is selected, L_1 and L_2 are the lists to be graphed (unless your data is in other lists), and the mark is □.
- Adjust the window so all the values will appear on the graph. The best window is usually achieved by pressing [ZOOM] and selecting [9]: ZoomStat.

Linear Regression

Regression is a process for finding an equation that matches the data. Regression graphs are representations of data.

Data that appear to have a linear correlation can be approximated by a **line of best fit.**

- The line of best fit will have a slope and y-intercept that help us to predict changes in the *dependent variable*, y-values, from changes in the *independent variable*, x-values.
- The slope tells us how much the y-value of the line of best fit changes with a one-unit change in the x-value.
- The sign of the slope tells us whether y gets larger or smaller as x gets larger. The slope of the line will depend on whether the correlation is positive or negative.
- The y-intercept helps us to understand the predicted value of y when x is zero.

Types of correlation include:

(1) Positive linear correlation
The plotted points appear to cluster around a straight line. The line has a positive slope – the two sets of data increase together. This graph is an example of positive linear **correlation**. The two sets of data generally increase together.

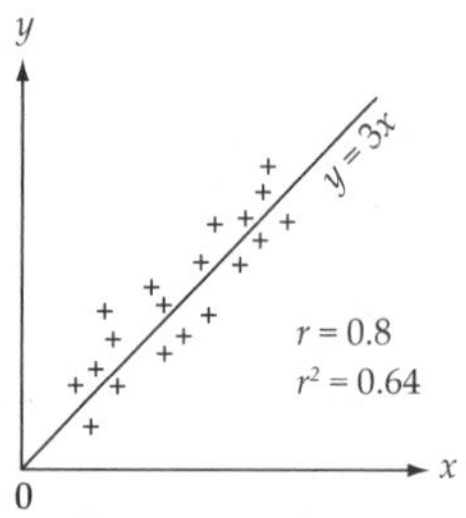

Positive correlation

(2) Negative linear correlation
Negative linear correlation is demonstrated by data that clusters around a line with a negative slope.

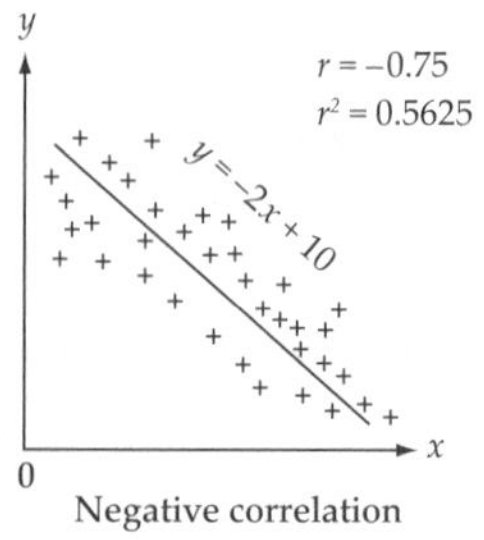

Negative correlation

(3) No correlation
Sometimes, there is no obvious relationship between the data sets. In such cases, we say there is no correlation.

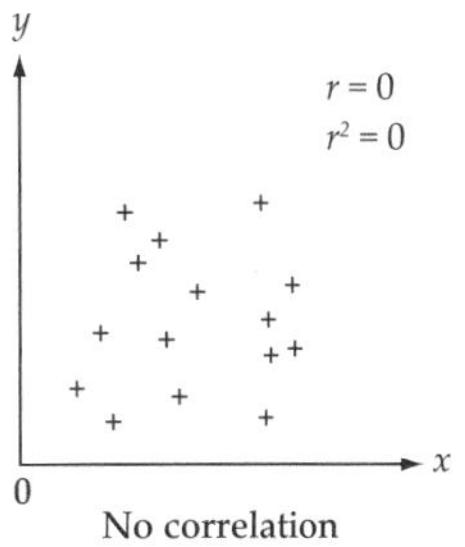

No correlation

The value of r is the **correlation coefficient**, where $-1 \leq r \leq 1$.

- If r is positive, the correlation is positive. The slope of the line of best fit is positive.
- If r is negative, the correlation is negative. The slope of the line of best fit is negative.
- The closer $|r|$ is to 1, the better the data fits the line.
- If r is zero, there is no correlation.

The correlation coefficient indicates the type and strength of the correlation.

The strength of the correlation depends on $|r|$.

- Strong positive or strong negative correlation: $|r| \geq 0.8$
- Moderate positive or moderate negative correlation: $0.5 \leq |r| < 0.8$
- Weak correlation: $|r| < 0.5$

The value of r^2 (or R^2) is the **coefficient of determination**, where $0 \leq r^2 \leq 1$.

- The coefficient of determination reveals the percent change in the dependent variable due to the independent variable. It is the square of the correlation coefficient.
- The closer r^2 is to 1, the better the data fits the line.
- Positive or negative correlation is not indicated by the coefficient of determination.

The coefficient of determination can be represented by r^2 or R^2.

To Find the Correlation Coefficient and Coefficient of Determination Using a Graphing Calculator

- Turn the calculator Diagnostics On.
- Press [2nd] [0] to get into the CATALOG menu.
- Press [▼] to DiagnosticsOn.
- Press [ENTER] and then press [ENTER] again.

- Enter the data into the calculator as two lists.

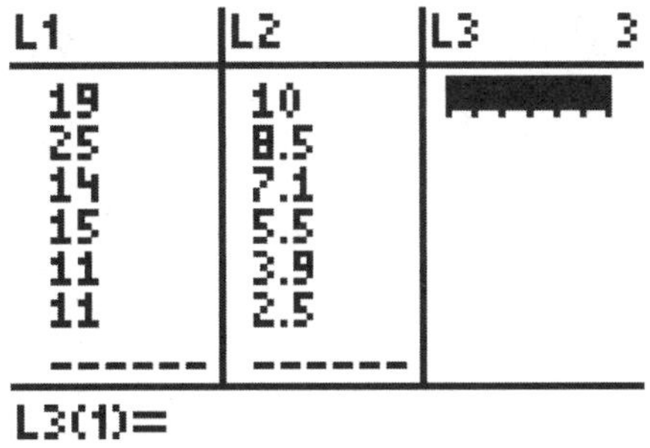

L1 L2 L3 3
19 10
25 8.5
14 7.1
15 5.5
11 3.9
11 2.5
L3(1)=

- Press [STAT] [▶] [CALC] and select [4]: LinReg(ax+ b).

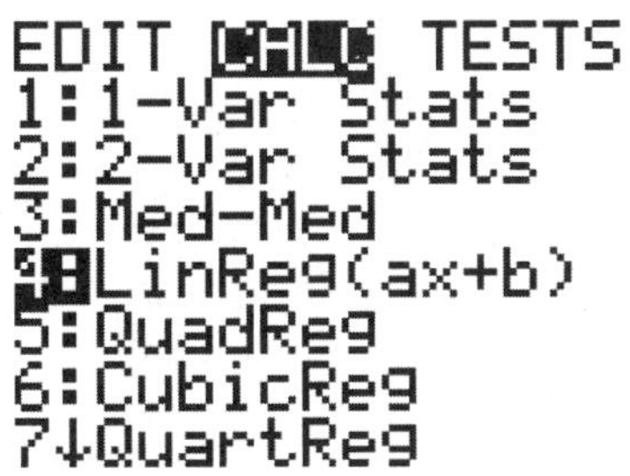

- A screen with the header LinReg(ax+ b) appears.

- Assuming you are using L_1 and L_2, arrow down to Store RegEQ, press [ALPHA] [F4], and choose Y_1 to represent the line of best fit.

- Arrow down to Calculate and press [ENTER].

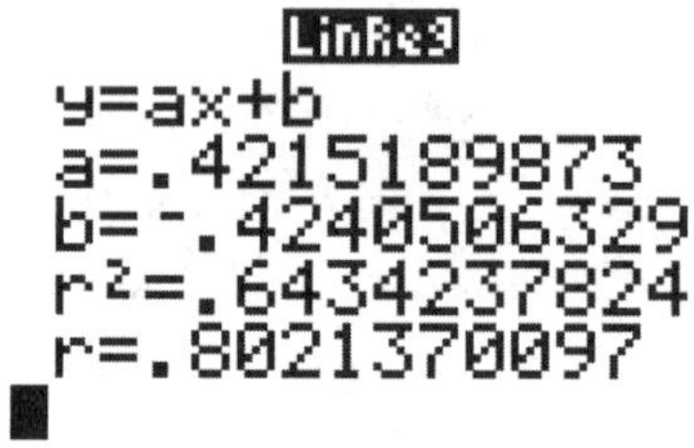

The line of best fit is displayed as $y = ax + b$.

- The graph of the function, now assigned to Y_1, is available.

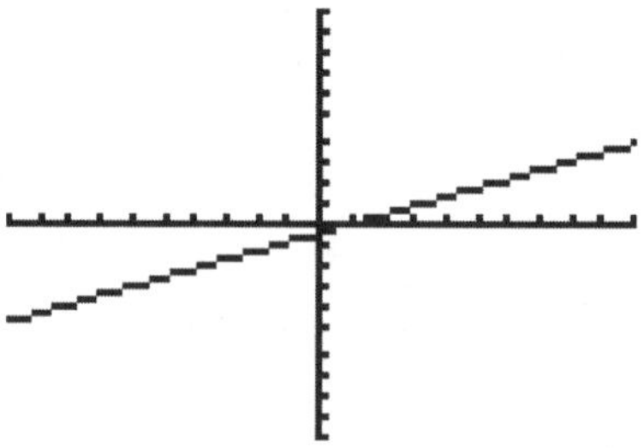

Residuals and Residual Plots

The distance between the predicted location of a point on a line, and the distance from that line to an actual data point, is called a **residual**. The line of best fit is found by using the method of least squares. For each line and each point on that line, the residual is squared.

The line that has the least sum of the squares is the line of best fit, or regression line.

$$\text{residual} = \text{actual value} - \text{predicted value}$$
$$e = y - \hat{y}$$

To Plot the Residuals Using STAT PLOT 2

- Make sure all other plots are turned off.
- Press [2nd] [Y=] to get to STAT PLOTS.
- Press [▼] [ENTER] [ENTER] to STAT PLOT 2, turn it on, and choose scatter plot.
- For the Xlist, (assuming the x's are in L_1), press [2nd] [1] [ENTER].
- For the Ylist, press [2nd] [STAT], cursor up to RESID, [ENTER] [ENTER].
- View with [ZOOM] [9].

We can plot the residuals of regression lines as dependent variables against the observed x-data values.

MODEL PROBLEMS

1. **MP 5** Copy the following data into L_1 and L_2. Make a scatter plot from the data. Looking at the scatter plot, describe the correlation, if any. Using the calculator, find the line of best fit. Find the value of r. Compare the correlation results to your estimate. Graph the line of best fit along with the scatter plot. Predict the L_2 value when L_1 is 210.

L_1	52	70	100	117	120	148	162	169	172	234	252	280
L_2	22	23	25	27	28	29	30	31	32	33	34	35

SOLUTION

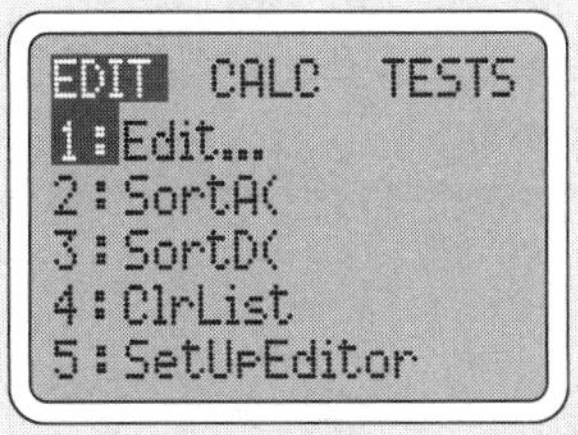

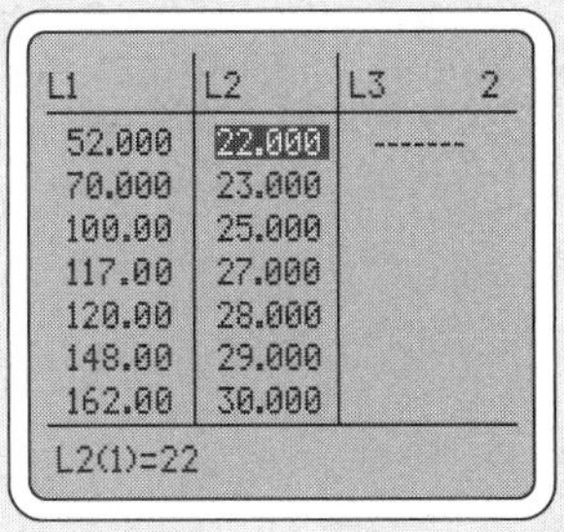

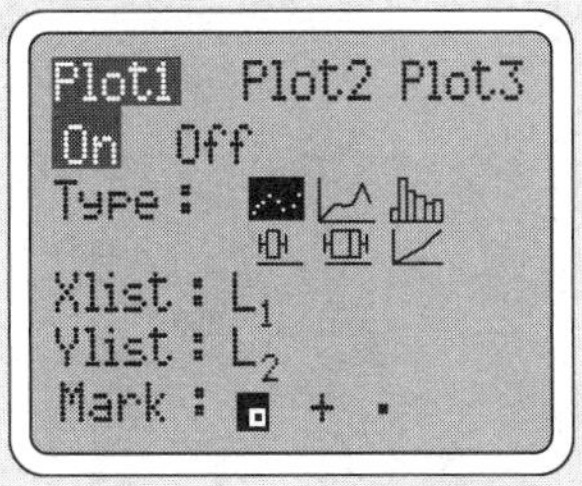

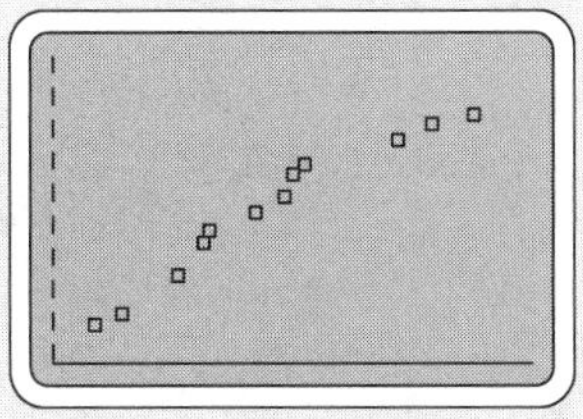

The points appear to have a strong positive correlation. Use the calculator to find the line of best fit and the correlation coefficient.

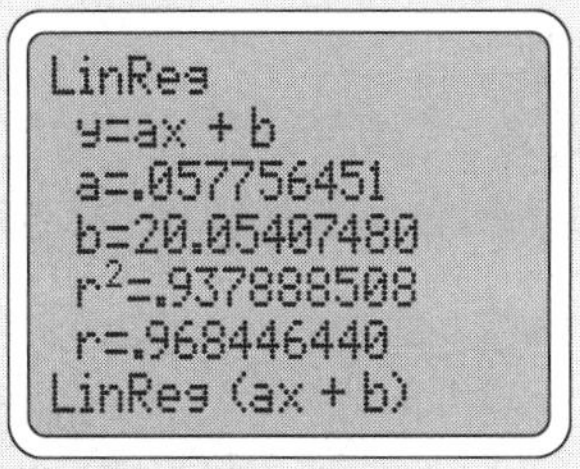

If you round your a and b values to the nearest hundredth and substitute them into the standard linear equation, the equation for the line of best fit is $y = 0.06x + 20.05$. To graph the line of best fit, indicate the lists and the Y subscript for the line.

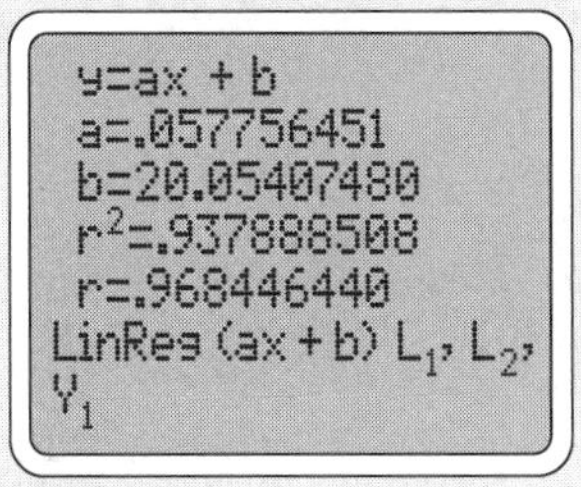

The graph will show that the scatter plot points are close to the line. The value of r shown above, 0.968446440, verifies that there is a strong positive correlation between the two lists.

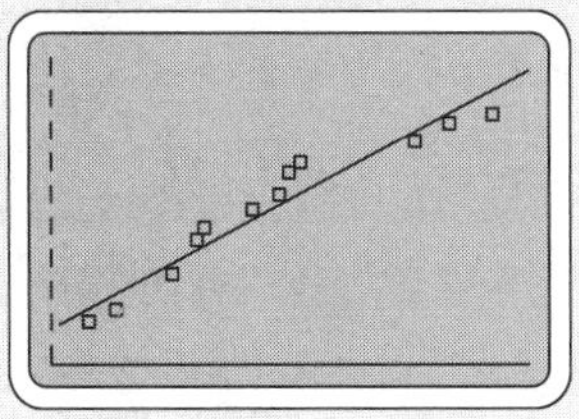

To find the value of L_2 when L_1 is 210, simply plug 210 into the equation of the line of best fit we found above:

$y = 0.06x + 20.05$

$y = 0.06(210) + 20.05$

$y = 32.65$

$y \approx 33$

Model Problems continue . . .

2. **MP 5** Plot the residuals for the regression line in Model Problem 1.

SOLUTION

Turn STAT PLOT 2 on.

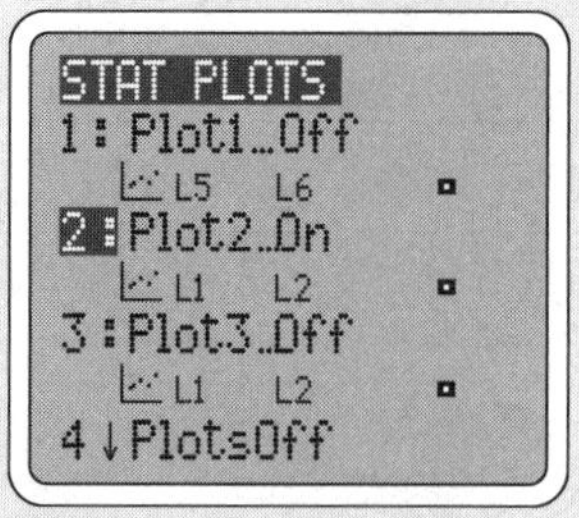

If the residuals are fairly evenly distributed above and below the *x*-axis and show no particular pattern or trend, you were probably right to choose linear regression. But if there is a trend, your data is probably non-linear.

Choose scatter plot.

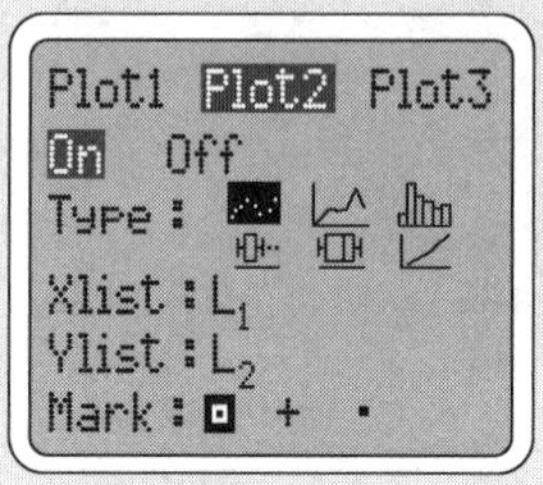

Choose L_1 for the Xlist.

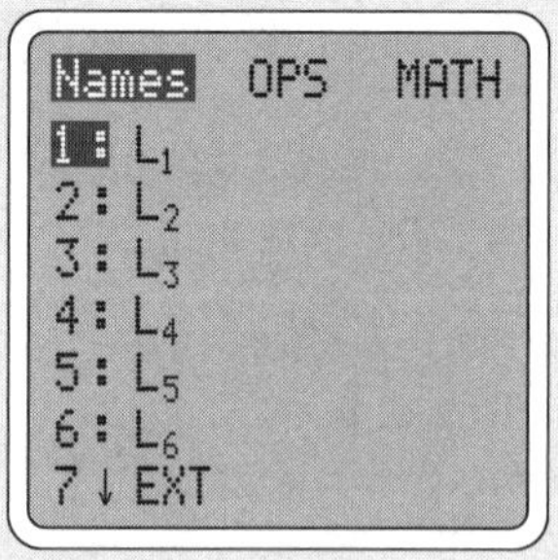

Choose RESID for the Ylist.

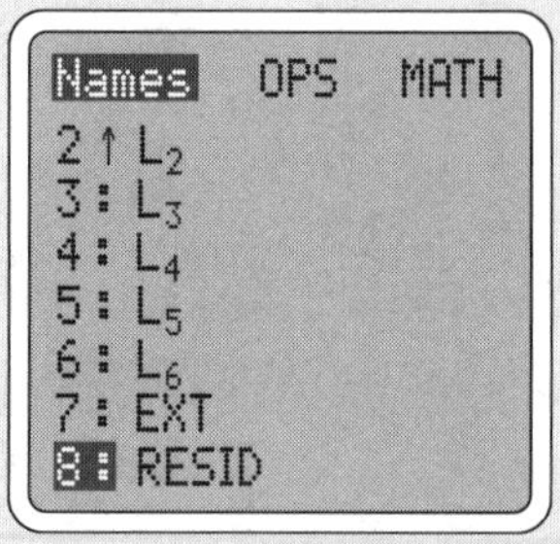

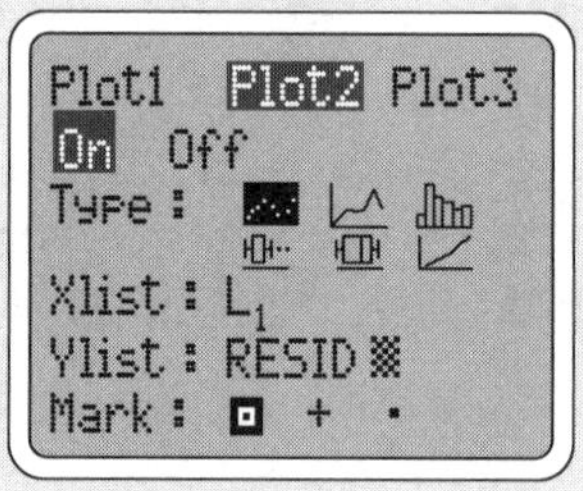

View with ZOOM 9.

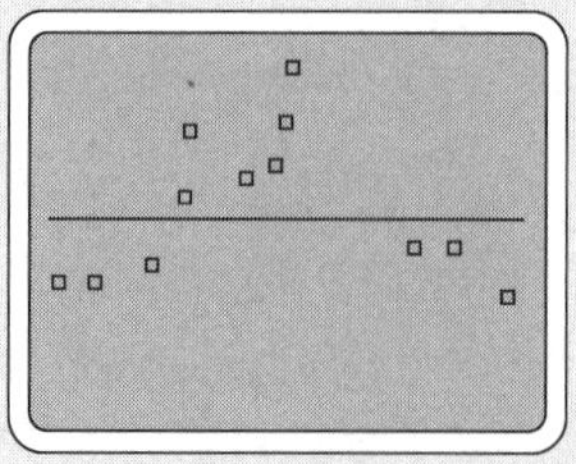

Note that the residual plot has no trend. This reinforces our decision that the data is linear.

Common Regression Analysis Errors

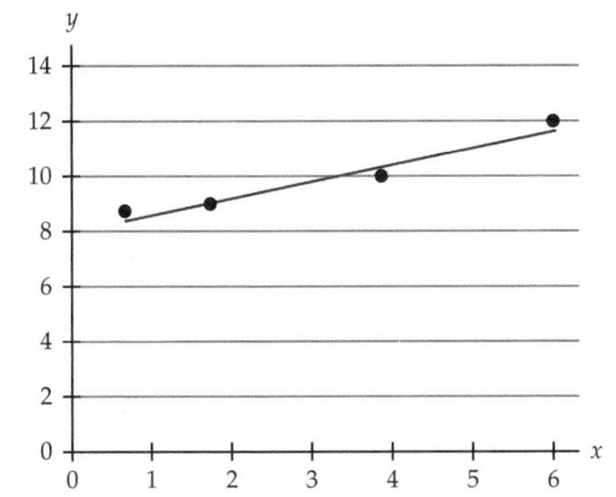	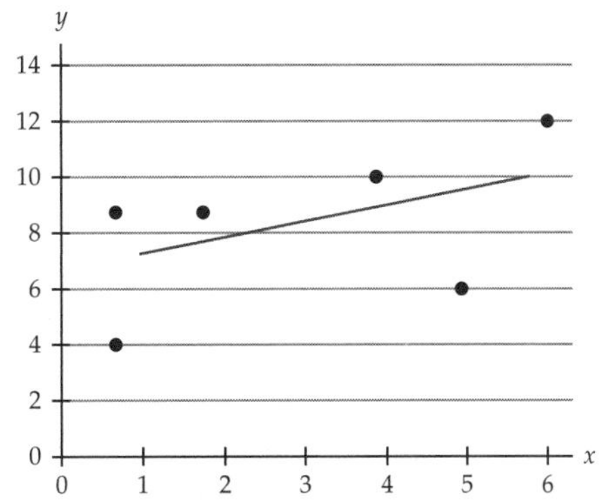
We show two graphs. The graph on the left has four data points. It has an *r* of 0.96 out of a possible 1. That is high. We do not have enough data.	We added two points, which did not seem far off the line to our eye, to the graph on the left to make the graph on the right. The *r* fell to 0.47, which is below the standard to have statistical meaning.

For a simple regression analysis in a student project, 25 to 30 pieces of data would likely be a good starting point.

Another pitfall in statistics in general, including regression analysis, is a *bias* in data.

- For example, if you asked only the girls in your school what their favorite television show is and then said that show was "your high school's favorite show," you have used biased data. You should have surveyed both girls and boys (unless you go to an all-girls school).

A **bias** is a systemic factor in the data that makes a conclusion wrong.

Extrapolation is making a prediction of a *y*-value using an *x*-value outside the range of the sample data.

- For example, if a positive correlation was found between hours of studying and lines of poetry memorized, the line of best fit would probably fail to be an appropriate model for additional lines of poetry memorized after several hours of study.

In cases where we see strong correlation, we sometimes assume that the *x*-values, or independent variables, cause the *y*-values, or dependent variables. Just because two variables are strongly correlated, we cannot assume that one causes the other. A correlation may be a mere coincidence, or the values of both variables might be caused by the values of a third variable that is unknown to us.

- For example, if we find a high correlation between sales of a particular product and arrests for a particular crime, we cannot say that one causes the other.
- However, if we find that the frequency of a parent taking a child to the library is strongly correlated to the child's interest in books, we may be correct in assuming the frequency of library visits is caused by a child's interest in books.

Correlation does not always mean causation.

PRACTICE

Exercises 1–4:

a Copy the data shown into L_1 and L_2 and graph a scatter plot from the data.
b Looking at the scatter plot, describe the correlation, if any.
c Find the linear regression formula using your calculator. Round answers to the nearest tenth.
d Using the calculator values for the slope and y-intercept, describe the meaning of the slope and y-intercept in the context of the problem.
e Find the actual value of r.
f Graph the line of best fit along with the scatter plot.
g Graph the residual plot.

1. In a local community college, freshmen mathematics marks were compared to physics marks, as shown in the table below. Copy the mathematics marks into L_1 and the physics marks into L_2.

Student Number	1	2	3	4	5	6	7	8	9	10	11	12	13	14	15	16	17	18	19	20
Mathematics Marks	45	67	93	45	56	67	68	34	54	89	59	60	43	90	41	30	56	76	89	65
Physics Marks	56	69	89	39	52	61	69	43	59	94	60	52	41	84	41	39	60	73	92	62

2. At a family barbecue, the following amounts of burgers and soda were consumed. Copy the burger amounts into L_1 and the soda amounts into L_2.

	Burgers	**Cans of Soda**
Uncle Eric	5	8
Uncle Andrew	4	10
Aunt Wendy	3	4
Cousin Caryn	2	6
Aunt Courtney	1	2

3. A quiz was scaled from 0 to 6 points. The school psychologist measured the test anxiety of five students preparing for the test and recorded their test results. Copy the test anxiety scores into L_1 and the quiz scores into L_2.

	Anxiety Score	**Quiz Score**
Student 1	1	1
Student 2	2	4
Student 3	3	3
Student 4	4	4
Student 5	5	1

4. Student IQ scores were measured against their creativity scores. Copy the IQ scores into L_1 and the creativity scores into L_2.

	IQ Score	**Creativity Score**
Student 1	140	130
Student 2	130	125
Student 3	130	140
Student 4	125	125
Student 5	110	115

5. It has been shown that shoe size is highly correlated to reading level. Do you believe large shoe size is a cause of reading proficiency? Explain your answer.

6. Among the coastal towns in a southern state, it was found that family size was negatively correlated to plans to attend a four-year college. Do you believe family size is a cause of decisions about college?

Practice Problems continue . . .

7. **MP 3, 4, 5** The following study compares the amount of soda spending to candy spending for a small group of people in one week.

Soda Spending	Candy Spending
\$4.03	\$6.47
\$3.76	\$6.13
\$3.77	\$6.19
\$3.34	\$4.89
\$3.47	\$5.63
\$2.92	\$4.52
\$3.20	\$5.89
\$2.71	\$4.79
\$3.53	\$5.27
\$4.51	\$6.08
\$4.56	\$4.02

a Create a scatter plot that represents the data.
b Choose the best description of the data.
c What is the correlation coefficient?
d Predict how much one person spent on candy if he spent \$2.45 on soda.

8. A comparison of high school student populations (in thousands) and the dollar sales of pizza (in thousands) at ten schools is shown below.

Number of Students	Pizza Sales
2	58
6	105
8	88
8	118
12	117
16	137
20	157
20	169
22	149
26	202

a Create a scatter plot that represents these data.
b Determine the line of best fit for the given data.
c What is the correlation coefficient?
d Predict approximately how many pizza sales would occur if the population of a high school was 10,000.

9. **MP 3, 4, 5** The heights and weights of several people waiting to board a bus in Trafalgar Square were recorded. Copy the heights (meters) into L_1 and the weights (kilograms) into L_2.

Height (m)	1.63	1.65	1.69	1.73	1.81	1.83	1.83	1.88
Weight (kg)	57	53	62	69	70	78	83	80

a Create a scatter plot that represents these data.
b Determine the line of best fit for the given data.
c What is the correlation coefficient?
d Graph a residual plot for the line of regression.
e Predict the weight of a person whose height is 1.75 meters.
f Would it be reasonable to use this chart to predict weights of toddlers?

10. In recent years, physicians have used the so-called diving reflex to reduce abnormally rapid heartbeats in humans by submerging the patient's face in cold water while the breath is held. A research physician conducted an experiment to investigate the effects of various cold temperatures on the pulse rates of ten small children. The results are presented below. Create a scatter plot and determine and graph the line of best fit. What is the correlation coefficient?

Child	Temperature of Water x °F	Reduction in Pulse y beats/minute
1	68	2
2	65	5
3	70	1
4	62	10
5	60	9
6	55	13
7	58	10
8	65	3
9	69	4
10	63	6

Practice Problems continue . . .

11. A park ranger measured the diameter versus the height of trees in front of the Information Center. Create a scatter plot and determine and graph the line of best fit.

Diameter (ft)	Height (ft)
2.1	40
1.7	37
1.1	35
1.5	36
2.7	42

12. The table shows the amount of study time, in hours, students spend before a test and the test grade. Create a scatter plot and determine and graph the line of best fit.

Study Time (in hours)	Test Grade (in percent)
10	90
5	80
4	72
12	94
3	68
6	87

LESSON 10.5

10.5 Two-Valued Statistics for Non-Linear Behavior

Data may have a correlation that is not linear. For instance, in the graph on the right, the data has the shape of a curve.

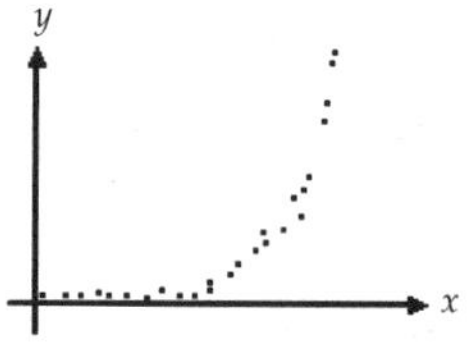

MODEL PROBLEMS

1. MP 1, 4, 5 The approximate population growth of a town as a function of time starting at year 0 is shown in the table. Determine the function that best matches the data.

Year	Population
0	20,000
3	21,280
6	22,500
9	23,870
12	25,400
15	26,920
18	28,570

SOLUTION

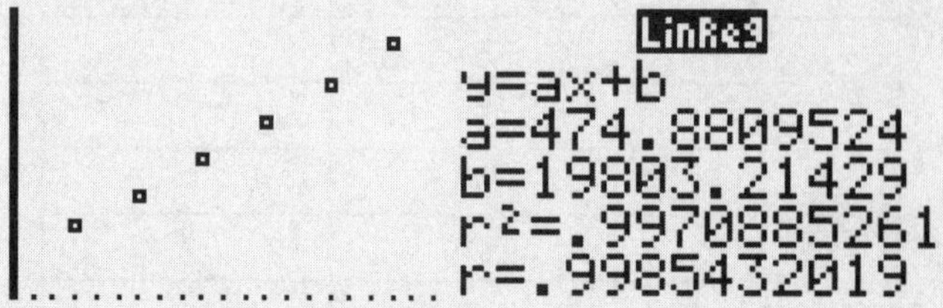

Create a scatter plot using the data in the table. The scatter plot looks somewhat linear. The linear regression procedure tells us we have a high r score.

Plot the residuals. View with [ZOOM] [9].

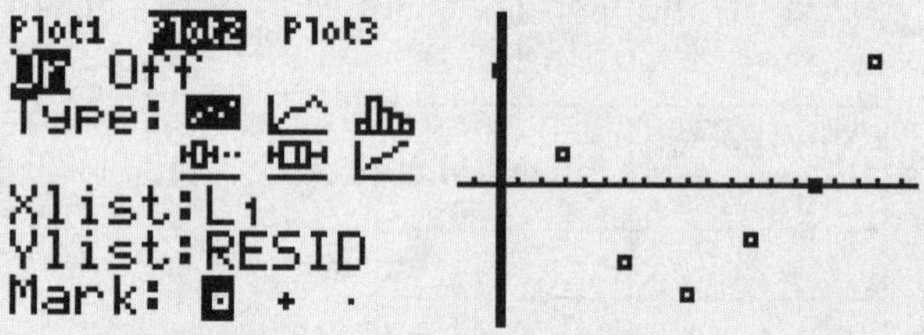

The residuals have a pattern. We should try another function shape.

We will try exponential regression.

Press [STAT] [▸] to CALC and [0]: ExpReg [2nd] [1] [,] [2nd] [2] [▸] [ENTER].

The function the calculator will give us has the form $y = a(b^x)$. Our exponential regression screen shows us that $|r|$ is very close to one. We determine the best fit is exponential.

Answer: $y = 20{,}010.012(1.020)^x$ (values rounded to the nearest thousandth)

Model Problems continue . . .

Model Problems *continued*

2. **MP 1, 3, 4, 5** Students in a physics lab used data collection software and collected the following values related to a ball thrown straight up. Determine the function that best matches the data.

Time (seconds)	0	1	2	3	4	5	6
Height (meters)	0.3	1.3	1.7	1.9	2.0	1.7	0.9

SOLUTION

The scatter plot looks like a parabola. We will limit our exploration to a quadratic curve of best fit.

The calculator will give us a function that has the form $y = ax^2 + bx + c$. Our quadratic regression screen shows us that R^2 is very close to one. We expect this since the data was collected in a controlled setting.

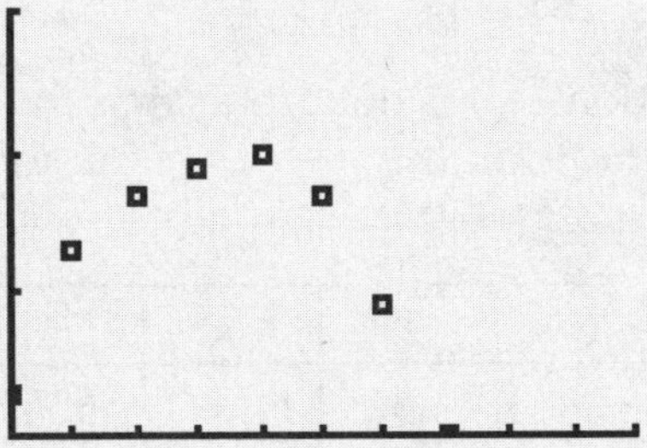

The scatter plot and the regression curve match very closely.

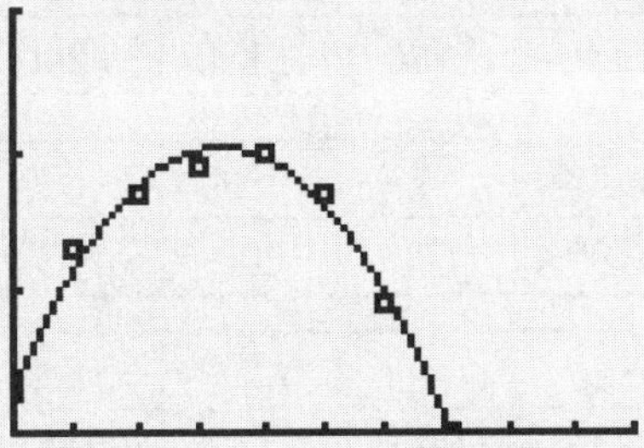

Answer: $y = -0.151x^2 + 1.011x + 0.333$

PRACTICE

Exercises 1–4: Given the scatter plot, select the equation that shows the best fit to the data.

1.

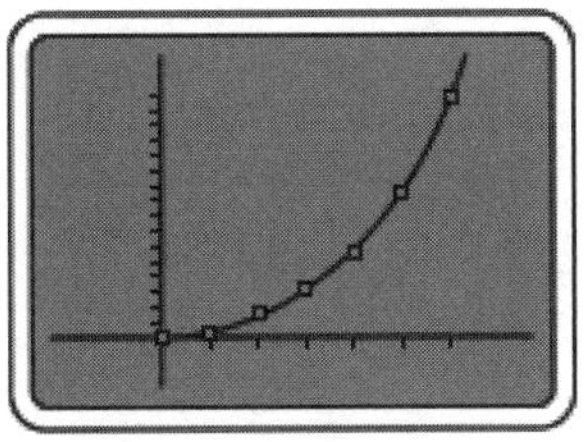

A. $y = 6x + 5$
B. $y = -6x^2$
C. $y = 1.6^x - 1$
D. $y = 1.6^x$

2.

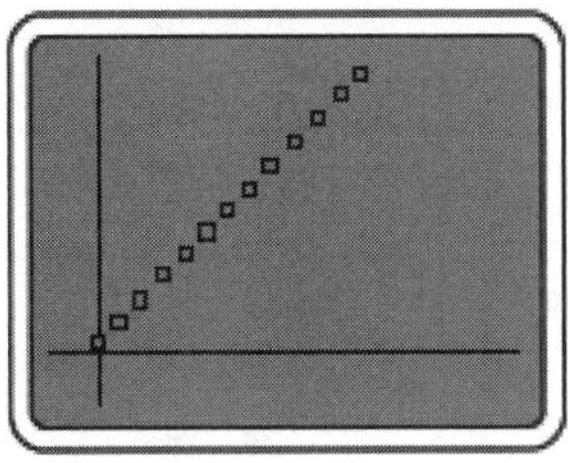

A. $y = 3x$
B. $y = -3x^2$
C. $y = 3(1.05)^x$
D. $y = -3x$

Practice Problems continue . . .

3.

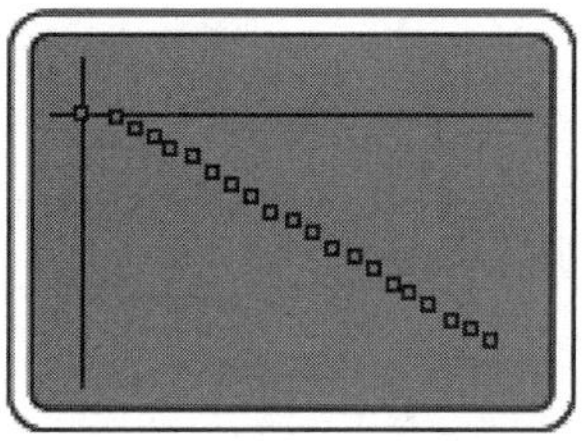

A. $y = 3x$
B. $y = -3x^2 - 2x + 5$
C. $y = 3(1.05)^{-x}$
D. $y = -3x + 20$

4.

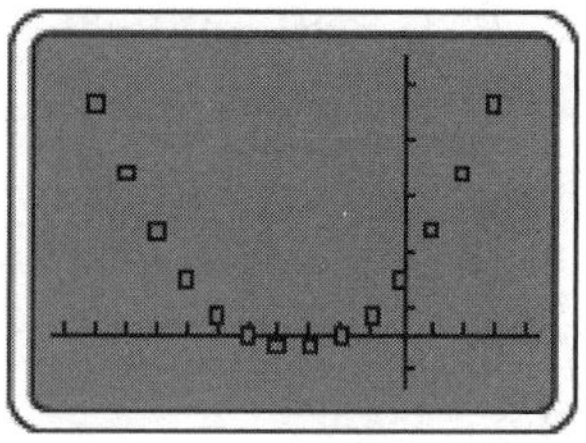

A. $y = x^2 + 7x + 10$
B. $y = -x + 10$
C. $y = 5x + 10$
D. $y = -x^2 - 7x + 10$

Exercises 5–12: The data shown in the tables below are not linear.

a Determine if the data fits either a quadratic or an exponential function best by comparing R^2 values. Find the function.
b If it is exponential, find the coefficient of correlation. If it is quadratic, find the coefficient of determination. (Round the values to the nearest hundredth.)
c Explain why the curve fits the data well or why it does not.

5.

x	1	2	3	4	5	6	7	8	9	10
y	500	1	1,525	2,675	4,675	8,200	14,325	14,000	15,775	21,975

6.

x	0	1	2	3	4	5	6	7	8	9	10
y	60	20	0	−40	−80	−150	−240	−320	−420	−500	−630

7.

x	0	1	2	3	4	5	6	7	8
y	0	35	60	100	130	200	275	425	500

8.

x	2	3	4	5	6	7	8	9	10
y	0	175	300	525	950	1,600	2,000	2,950	4,000

9.

x	0	1	2	3	4	5	6	7
y	200	225	270	305	340	390	425	650

10.

x	0	1	2	3	4	5	6	7	8
y	450	442	500	970	204	200	100	78	80

11.

x	1	2	3	4	5	6	7	8	9
y	1	2	5	8	14	18	26	34	43

12.

x	1	2	3	4	5	6	7	8
y	7	12	13	17	21	28	37	50

LESSON 10.6

10.6 Analyzing Bivariate Categorical Data

Bivariate data shows the relationship between two variables. Bivariate categorical data results from collecting data on two categorical variables.

Two-Way Relative Frequency Tables and Conditional Relative Frequency

The **two-way frequency table** shows the results of a survey about elective subject preferences given to 93 students.

	Tech	Art	Music	Total
Males	7	18	20	45
Females	6	22	20	48
Total	13	40	40	93

- Sums in the total column (totals on the right) and sums in the total row (totals on the bottom) are called **marginal frequencies**.
- Entries in the body of the table are called **joint frequencies**.

> Two-way frequency tables are also called *contingency tables*.

Looking at the *marginal frequencies* for art and music, we might be tempted to say that these electives are equally popular. However, the *joint frequencies* tell us that more females prefer art and that males and females equally prefer music.

- A **conditional relative frequency** compares a joint frequency to a marginal frequency. For each joint frequency, there are two conditional relative frequencies: one comparing the joint frequency to the marginal frequency for the row, and the other comparing the joint frequency to the marginal frequency for the column.
  (1) If we analyze the columns in the two-way frequency table, the *conditional relative frequency* of art students being female is $\frac{22}{40}$, or 0.55. This conditional relative frequency shows that 55% of art students are females.
  (2) If we analyze the rows in the two-way frequency table, the *conditional relative frequency* of females selecting art as a favorite elective course is $\frac{22}{48}$, or 0.46. This shows us that 46% of girls chose art.

> In the example two-way frequency table, the conditions of interest in the rows are gender (male or female) and in the columns are electives (tech, art, and music).

The table below is a **relative frequency table**.

	Tech	Art	Music	Total
Males	0.075	0.19	0.215	0.48
Females	0.065	0.24	0.215	0.52
Total	0.14	0.43	0.43	1

- **Joint relative frequency** is the ratio of the number of observations of the joint frequency to the total number of observations. They are the **conditional frequencies** in the body of a relative frequency table. The sum of all the joint relative frequencies is 1.
- In a relative frequency table, an entry in a row or column marked "Total" is called a **marginal relative frequency**. Each such entry is the ratio of the marginal frequency to the total number of observations. The sum of the marginal relative frequencies in a row or column is 1.

Association in Categorical Data

Association is noted when one categorical variable is dependent upon another.

- For example, since the conditional relative frequency of electives selected by females is different than the selection of electives by males, then gender and electives are associated. This means that knowing the gender of a student tells us something about their likely preferences.

- If the conditional relative frequencies are very similar or the same, there is not an association between the quantities. Look at the preferences for music; we do not find an association between gender and selection of music.

The chart below indicates a strong association between dwelling style and tendency to like yogurt. Likely, this data is the result of a particular limited collection of data. We would not be willing to say that, in general, people who like yogurt are more likely to live in single-family homes.

	Likes Yogurt	Does Not Like Yogurt	Total
Single-family homes	89	26	115
Multi-family homes	34	81	115
Total	123	107	230

When we look at categorical data summaries, we must be careful not to assume one category causes the other, even if there appears to be association between the variables.

MODEL PROBLEM

MP 1, 3, 4, 5 Teddy surveyed students in his high school to see if they were for or against purchasing water filtration systems for the school water fountains. The two-way frequency table to the right shows the results of his survey.

	For	Against	Total
Males	60	50	110
Females	75	55	130
Total	135	105	240

a Identify and describe the marginal frequencies.

b Identify and describe the joint frequencies by column.

c Identify and describe the joint frequencies by row.

d What inferences did you make using the joint frequencies that were not evident using the marginal frequencies?

e Display the results of this survey using a two-way relative frequency table. Round cell entries to the nearest hundredth.

f Find the conditional relative frequency of females choosing the filtration system and the conditional relative frequency of males choosing the filtration system.

g Are gender and opinion about the filtration system associated?

SOLUTION

a The marginal frequencies in the total column indicate that 110 males and 130 females responded to the survey. There was not a big difference in participation by gender. The marginal frequencies in the total row indicate that 135 students favor the water filtration system and 105 students oppose the system. More students favor the system than oppose it.

b The first column shows us that 60 males and 75 females are in favor of the system. The second column shows us that 50 males and 55 females are against the system.

c The first row tells us that 60 males are for the system and 50 are against it. The second row tells us that 75 females are for the system and 55 are against it.

d Both genders have a similar opinion about the project.

e

	For	Against	Total
Males	0.25	0.21	0.46
Females	0.31	0.23	0.54
Total	0.56	0.44	1.00

f females: $\frac{75}{130}$, or approximately 0.58

males: $\frac{60}{110}$, or approximately 0.55

g The majority of both genders favor the system. The difference in conditional relative frequencies is very small. We cannot say gender and preference are associated.

PRACTICE

Exercises 1–4: Refer to the two-way frequency table below, showing sport preferences for surveyed high school students and middle school students.

	Soccer	Tennis	Basketball	Football	Total
High School Students	30	30	20	40	120
Middle School Students	20	20	20	20	80
Total	50	50	40	60	200

1. What two categories are represented in the table?

2. Could the results of the survey have been represented if the row and column categories were reversed?

3. Create a two-way relative frequency table for the data.

4. Find the conditional relative frequency of high school students preferring tennis. Are school level and sport preference associated?

Exercises 5–7: Answer the questions, using the table below.

	Rocky Road	Caramel Crunch	Macho Mocha	Strawberry Swirl	Chunky Chocolate	Total
Adults	12	8	12		12	
Children		2		1		
Total	30		12	4	30	

5. Gerry conducted a survey to determine favorite ice cream flavors by visiting the neighborhood ice cream shop. Unfortunately, one customer dripped his ice cream on the results. Fill in the missing data values.

6. Which missing cells represent joint frequencies? Which missing cells represent marginal frequencies?

7. Find the conditional relative frequency of children preferring Chunky Chocolate.

MP 3, 4 Exercises 8–11:

People parking on Main Street were asked about the number of hours to be permitted using Main Street parking meters. The people surveyed were asked to describe themselves as shoppers or "other" and were asked to choose from one hour, two hours, or 4 hours. The data collected showed the following numbers of responses:

Shoppers and one hour: 20 Shoppers and two hours: 40 Shoppers and four hours: 20

"Other" and one hour: 20 "Other" and two hours: 10 "Other" and four hours: 50

8. Create a two-way frequency table for the data.

9. Create a two-way relative frequency table for the data.

10. Find the conditional relative frequency of shoppers preferring a 2-hour shopping limit.

11. What conclusions might you draw about who the "other" responders are from the data results? Is there an association between parking time preference and reason for parking?

Practice Problems continue . . .

MP 3, 4 Exercises 12–14: Use the table below to answer the following questions.

David gathered data on 100 students describing their preference for a fund-raiser. He read the results to Dana, so she could make a chart. Dana could not hear everything David said. She entered the results she could hear clearly:

	Food Kitchen	Nursing Home	Day Care Center	Total
Males	30	5		40
Females	10		20	60
Total	40			100

12. Fill in the unknown cells.

13. Create a two-way relative frequency table for the data.

14. Find the conditional relative frequency of males choosing the nursing home.

15. Suppose a study of fruit preference and outside reading habits showed that the responders who like apples are likely to read more than 2 books every month and the responders who like bananas are likely to read 2 books every week. Would we say there is a association between fruit preference and reading habits?

16. Suppose a study of hours of sleep and ability to focus on tasks showed that people who sleep less than 5 hours each night are less likely to be able to focus on tasks. Would we say there is a association between hours of sleep and ability to focus on tasks?

CHAPTER 10 REVIEW

Exercises 1–2: Used toys are collected by Mr. Crisci's class. The results are shown in the table.

Toys Collected by Mr. Crisci's Class					
Arjun	3	Jaclyn	2	Steven	0
Brittany	3	Laura	0	Teddy	2
Eric	1	Marra	2	Thomas	3
Fran	10	Pat	1	Vance	4
Greg	0	Rob	2	Wanda	2
Harry	10	Rita	2	William	1
Jacob	5	Sammi	10	Zachary	3

1. Construct a dot plot for the data. Without calculating, determine which will be larger, the mean or the median. Explain your reasoning.

2. Which measure of central tendency is best to describe the data? Explain your reasoning.

Chapter Review continues . . .

3. In Mrs. Bourne's class, the median number of books read last summer was 8 and the mean number of books read was 12. Which of the following must be true?

A. 50% of the students read 8 books
B. 50% of the students read 12 books
C. At least one student read more than 12 books
D. Most students read 8 books

Exercises 4–8: Use the following test grades of 20 students to complete each exercise:

100, 100, 90, 95, 97, 92, 100, 100, 90, 83, 87, 93, 95, 92, 81, 95, 96, 95, 100, 88

4. Construct a frequency table for the data, using intervals of 5.

5. Construct a dot plot for the data.

6. Use the graphs constructed to describe the shape of the data.

7. Which is larger, the mean or the median?

8. Which measure of central tendancy is better for this data?

Exercises 9–10: Use the following frequency table.

Grade Interval	Frequency
91–100	8
81–90	16
71–80	14
61–70	6
51–60	0
41–50	0
31–40	1
21–30	2

9. Find the modal interval.

10. Find the interval containing the median.

11. Create data and a dot plot with at least 7 data values for which the mean = the median = the mode.

12. Create data and a dot plot with at least 7 data values for which the mean = the median < the mode.

13. A class average on a 40-question science test was 28.5. The 19 girls in the class scored 539 points. How many points did the 11 boys score?

Exercises 14–15: Use the table below.

Interval	Frequency	Cumulative Frequency
91–100	6	40
81–90	12	
71–80	8	
61–70	8	14
51–60	6	6

14. Complete the table.

15. Find the interval containing the median.

16. On the axis below, arrange entries for 8 students' logs of community service, each between zero hours and 10 hours so the data shows a standard deviation that is the largest possible value it could be.

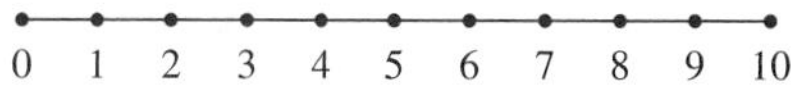

17. On the axis below, arrange entries for 8 students' logs of community service, each between zero hours and 10 hours so the data shows a standard deviation that is the smallest possible value it could be. There are many correct answers to this problem.

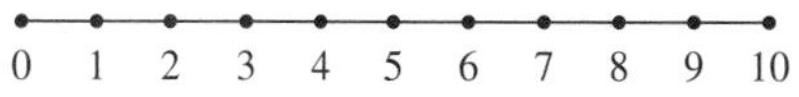

Exercises 18–19: Use the following data set.

51, 75, 75, 77, 81, 82, 84, 86, 87, 90, 91, 92, 96, 99, 100

18. Find the quartiles and interquartile range.

19. Construct a box-and-whisker plot.

20. The frequency table of January extra-help sessions given by a sample of 20 teachers is shown below.

Number of January Extra-Help Sessions	Frequency
16	2
12	10
10	6
4	2

Find the standard deviation for these data.

Chapter Review continues . . .

MP 3, 4 Exercises 21–24: Students observed the growth of a plant for the first week that sprouts were noticed. They recorded their observations on the chart below.

Day	Height (cm)
1	1.40
2	2.55
3	3.80
4	5.00
5	6.25
6	7.45
7	8.60

21. Make a scatter plot of the data.

22. Select a curve which best fits the data.

23. Write the formula for the curve, find r^2, find r (unless the curve is quadratic), and plot the residuals. Use this information to discuss the goodness of fit for the curve selected.

24. Can we extrapolate the regression curve to predict the height of the plant after a month?

Exercises 25–27: Dominoes were placed in a bag. The contents were spilled onto a table. The dominoes landing facedown were removed. The remaining dominoes were put back in the bag. The process was repeated again and again. The number of dominoes remaining after each spill was recorded:

Spill Number	Dominoes Remaining
1	66
2	34
3	16
4	8
5	5
6	2
7	1
8	0

25. Make a scatter plot of the data.

26. Select which type of curve best fits the data.

27. Write the formula for the curve and discuss its goodness of fit.

Exercises 28–30: A large basin with a drain on the bottom was filled with water to a depth of 22 centimeters. The drain was opened for 15 seconds and the depth was remeasured. This process was continued for $1\frac{1}{2}$ minutes. The following data was collected.

Time (seconds)	Depth (centimeters)
0	22
15	18
30	14
45	11
60	6
75	4
90	2

28. Make a scatter plot of the data.

29. Select which curve best fits the data.

30. Write the formula for the curve and discuss its goodness of fit.

MP 2, 4 Exercises 31–33:

Alana gathered data on 50 students describing their favorite holiday. Fill in the missing values on her two-way frequency table.

	Thanks-giving	Valentine's Day	Memorial Day	Total
Males	15		5	30
Females	10			
Total		15	10	50

31. Fill in the unknown cells.

32. Create a two-way relative frequency table for the data.

33. Find the conditional relative frequency of females choosing Valentine's Day.

34. **MP 3** A recent study indicates that there is a positive correlation between women's skirt lengths and the composite value of stocks on the New York Stock Exchange. How would you respond to this indication?

35. **MP 2, 3** If z is added to each data value in a set of data, what would be the changes to the mean and standard deviation?

36. **MP 2, 3** If each data value is multiplied by a constant k, where $k > 0$, what would be the values of the new mean and the new standard deviation?

Cumulative Review for Chapters 1–10

1. Rob purchased a signed baseball for \$125. He expects the value of the baseball to double every two years. When will the baseball reach a value of \$32,000?

A. 4 years

B. 8 years

C. 16 years

D. 32 years

2. Consider a sequence that follows a "minus 3" pattern: 60, 57, 54,.…Write an explicit formula for the sequence.

A. $A(n) = 60 - 3(n + 1)$

B. $A(n) = 60 + 3n$

C. $A(n) = 60 - 3(n - 1)$

D. $A(n) = 60 - 3n$

3. If $3, j, k, \frac{-1}{9}$ forms a geometric sequence, find the values of j and k.

A. $j = 1, k = -\frac{1}{3}$

B. $j = -1, k = \frac{1}{3}$

C. $j = -1, k = -\frac{1}{3}$

D. $j = 1, k = \frac{1}{3}$

4. A college student needs at least \$575 to go away for the weekend. He has \$355. He is babysitting at \$20 per hour to raise the rest of the money. Which of the following inequalities will help him find the number of hours he must babysit?

A. $20h + 355 \geq 575$

B. $20h + 575 \geq 355$

C. $20h + 355 < 575$

D. $20h + 575 < 355$

5. A diagram in a science book was 8 inches long and 4 inches wide. The lab group increased the length and the width by 125% for their report. What is the area of the diagram in their report?

A. 15 in^2

B. 40 in^2

C. 50 in^2

D. 64 in^2

6. Josh has the opportunity to invest \$1000 earned at a summer camp. His money will grow at the rate of 10% compounded annually. He has a better opportunity to invest once he has \$1500. After how many years will he be able to change his investment plan?

A. 8 years

B. 7 years

C. 6 years

D. 5 years

7. How many points do the graphs of $y = x^3$ and $y = \sqrt[3]{x}$ have in common?

A. 3

B. 2

C. 1

D. none

8. Which of the following statements are true?

A. When the sum of the residuals is greater than zero, the data set is non-linear.

B. A random pattern on residuals supports a linear model.

C. A random pattern on residuals supports an exponential model.

D. A random pattern on residuals supports a quadratic model.

9. When data is skewed to the right,

A. The majority of the data is to the right and the mean is larger than the median.
B. The majority of the data is to the right and the mean is smaller than the median.
C. The majority of the data is to the left and the mean is larger than the median.
D. The majority of the data is to the left and the mean is smaller than the median.

10. Kevin collected money for a charity read-a-thon at school. His father gave him \$10 for signing up and \$3 for every book he read. Altogether, his father gave him \$70. How many books did Kevin read?

11. **MP 2** A triangular number counts the number of objects that can form an equilateral triangle, such as the shapes below.

Draw the next two shapes in this pattern. How many dots are in each shape?

12. Write a recursive and an explicit formula for the sequence 2, 20, 200, 2000.

13. **MP 1, 4** Sean has \$500 to invest for 5 years. Would he have more in his account at the end of 5 years if he invested in a fund providing 6% interest compounded monthly or one providing 4% compounded annually?

14. **MP 4, 7** Every year since 2010, the population of North Side Elementary School has decreased by 10%. What type of function does this change model?

15. **MP 5** Given $g(x) = |x - 4| + 1$, describe how to get the graph of $g(x)$ from the parent graph $f(x) = |x|$ using transformations.

16. Find the vertex for $y = (x + 4)^2 + 1$.

17. **MP 2** Jack had four times as many videos as Jill. After Jack gave 60 to his cousin and Jill lost 6, they both had the same number of videos. How many videos did they each have originally?

18. The graph of a parent function $f(x)$ has been translated 2 units to the left, vertically stretched by a factor of 2, and moved down 5 units. Write the formula for $g(x)$, the transformed graph.

19. **MP 1, 7** Describe the transformation of the quadratic parent function $f(x) = x^2$ that results in the function $g(x) = 3x^2 + 12x + 11$.

20. **MP 3** The quadratic projectile formula has no t term if the ball is dropped rather than tossed straight up. Explain why.

21. Write a quadratic function from the following table of points on the graph:

x	0	5	10	15
y	4	89	324	709

MP 1, 4, 7, 8 Exercises 22–24: An arrow is shot into the air. A function representing the relationship between the number of seconds it is in the air, t, and the height of the arrow in meters, h, is given by: $h(t) = -5.4t^2 + 32.4t + 3.5$

22. Complete the square for this function.

23. What is the maximum height for the arrow?

24. How many seconds will it take the arrow to reach its maximum height?

25. The number of hours of weekly studying for 10 students is shown below. Create a dot plot and determine a good measure of central tendency.

Student	Hours of Studying
1	10
2	8
3	6
4	8
5	5
6	8
7	6
8	10
9	8
10	8

26. MP 2 Andrea did a study about the effects of shoe size on the number of DVDs her classmates owned. Based on the graph of her data, she found that there was a negative correlation between shoe size and number of DVDs. She concluded that "having small feet makes a person likely to own lots of DVDs." Do you agree with Andrea's conclusion?

27. Data was recorded showing the height of a burning candle. Express the candle's height as a function of time.

Time (hours)	Height (inches)
0	10
1	8.5
2	7.1
3	5.5
4	3.9
5	2.5

28. MP 3 Suppose time (in minutes) to run 10 laps around the track was recorded for 50 runners, ages 15 to 50, and the following regression line resulted from the recorded times.

$$y = \frac{x}{3} + 5.5$$

Interpret the meaning in context for the slope of this function.

29. MP 3 Teachers and students were surveyed on their scheduling preferences for mid-term week. They were given two options:

(1) If the teacher or student does not have an exam to proctor or sit for, they are not required to attend school.

(2) If the teacher or student does not have an exam to proctor or sit for, they are required to facilitate or attend an extra-help session.

The following two-way frequency table shows the results of the survey.

	No school if no exam	Required extra help if no exam	Total
Teachers	20	40	60
Students	380	60	440
Total	400	100	560

Are school role and scheduling preference associated? Explain your answer.

Digital Activities

Digital activities are available online at **www.amscomath.com**.

LESSONS

1.1 Writing and Translating Algebraic Expressions

In this activity, practice your skills by writing equations and moving between equations and words.

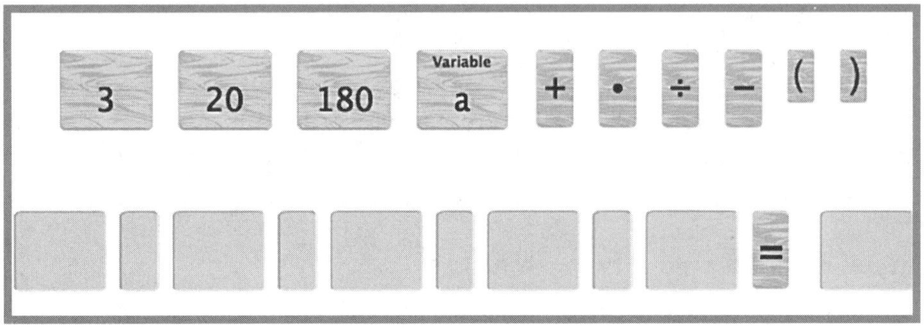

Go to **www.amscomath.com** to use the activities.

1.3 Simple Algebraic Inequalities

In this activity, practice translating word problems into inequalities with numbers and symbols.

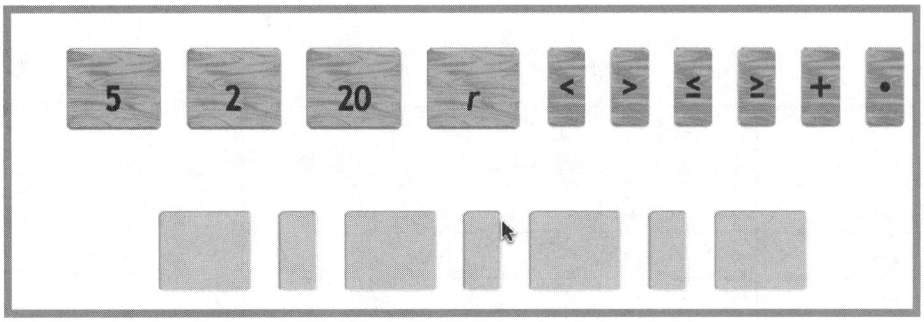

1.6 Exponents

In this activity, practice the order of operations.

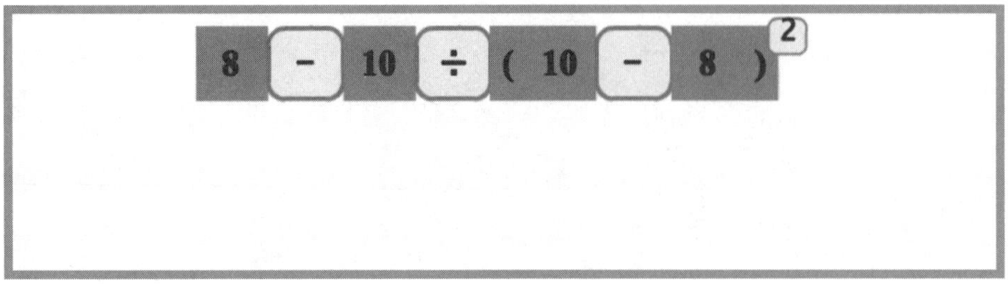

2.5 Solving Inequalities

In this activity, match the graph on top by changing the inequality symbol and the number in the controls.

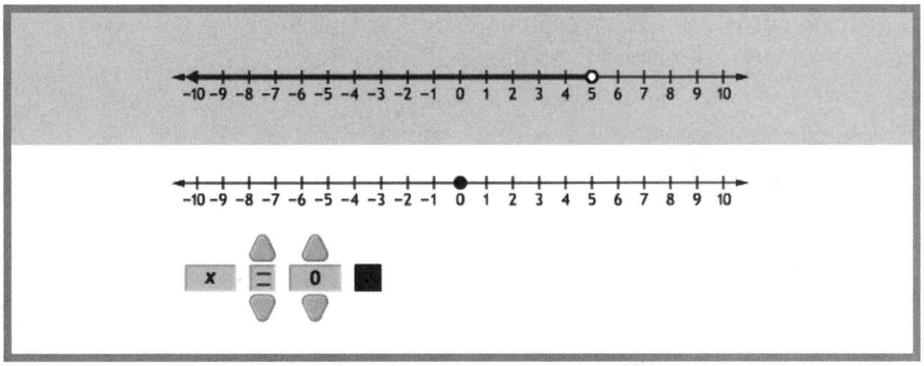

In this activity, solve inequalities to see the juggler juggle.

3.1 Graphing Linear Equations

In this activity, practice graphing lines by plotting solutions to equations.

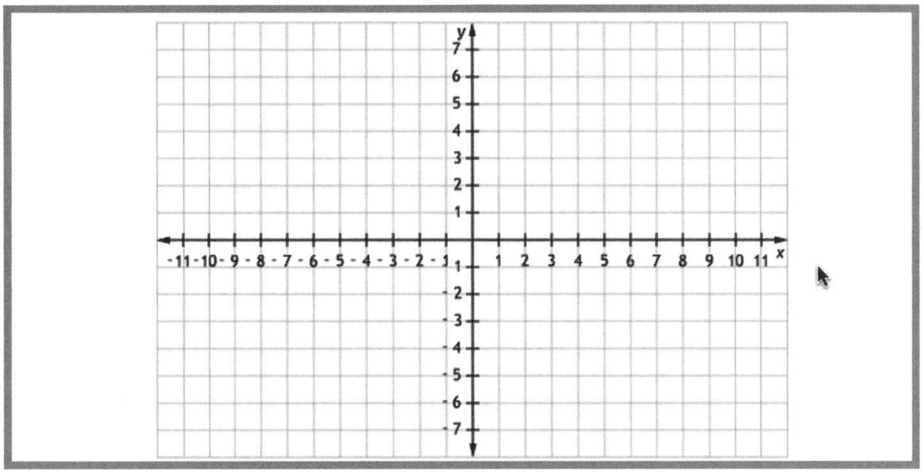

Go to **www.amscomath.com** to use the activities.

3.4 Graphing and Writing Linear Equations Using the Slope-Intercept and Point-Slope Forms

We show one of two similar activities. In these activities, you have to escape through the door in the lower right-hand corner. You can graph lines by setting the slope and y-intercept in the equation below. The dashed lines provide a path the character can follow to the door.

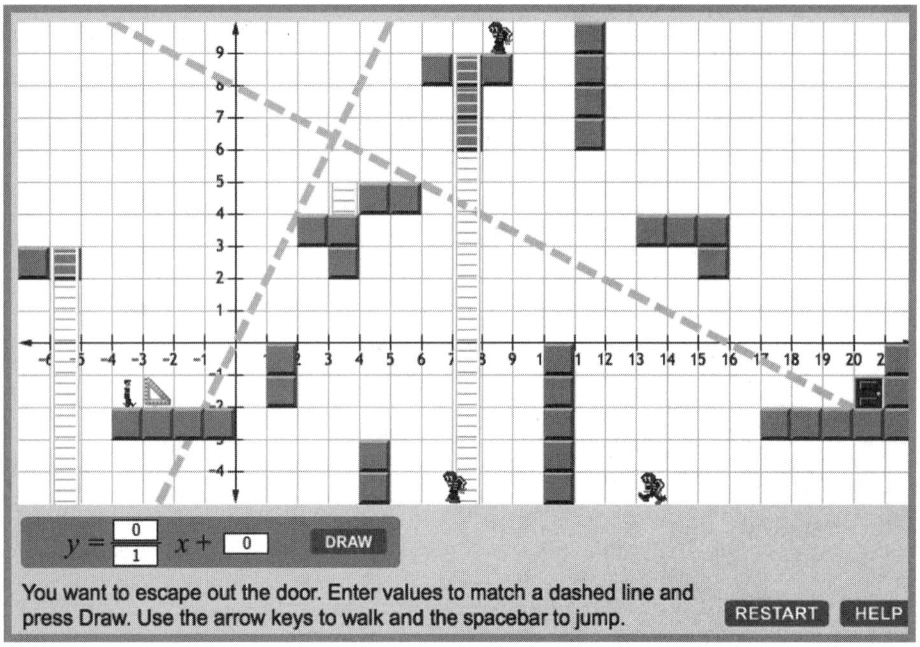
DRAW
You want to escape out the door. Enter values to match a dashed line and press Draw. Use the arrow keys to walk and the spacebar to jump.
RESTART
HELP

In this activity, practice graphing a line using the y-intercept.

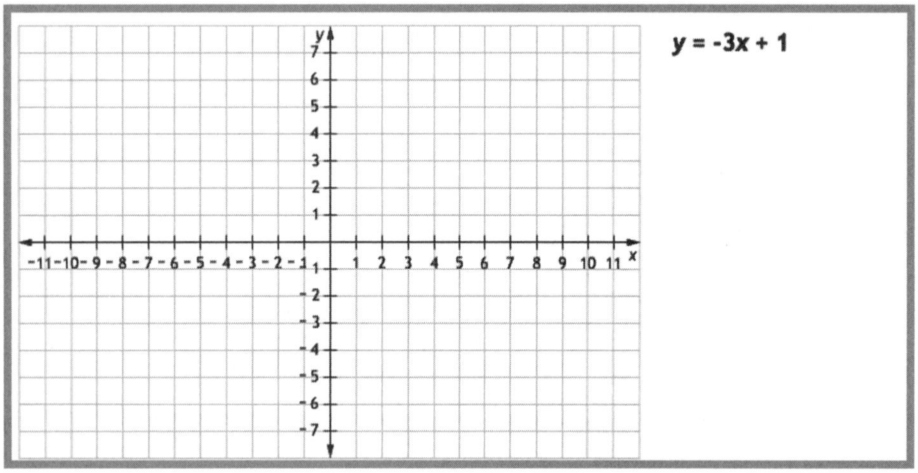
y = -3x + 1

Go to **www.amscomath.com** to use the activities.

In this activity, graph linear equations by plotting the *x*- and *y*-intercepts.

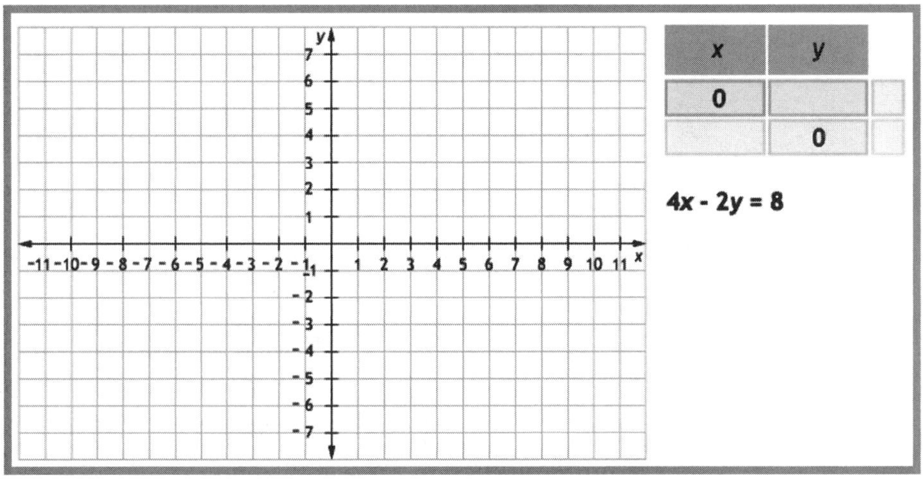

Go to **www.amscomath.com** to use the activities.

3.8 Modeling with Linear Functions

In these activities, you are given a situation and need to analyze function graphs to arrive at conclusions.

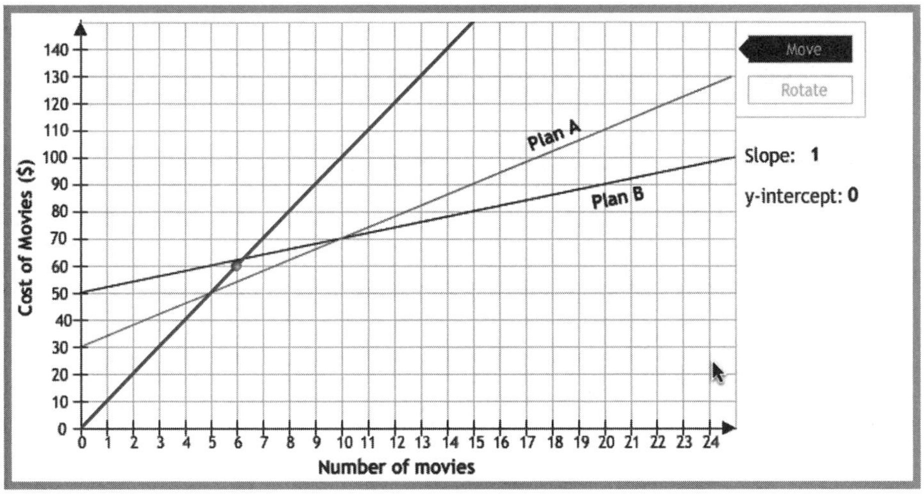

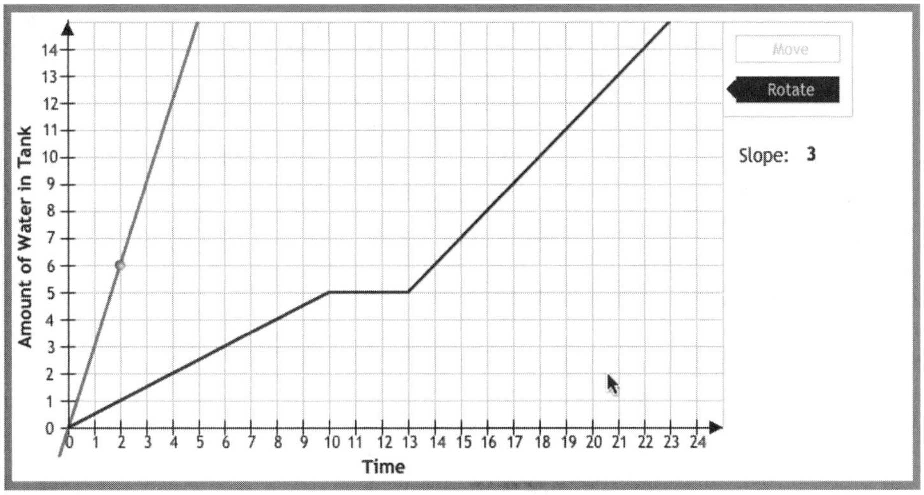

4.1 Graphing Linear Inequalities

In this activity, practice graphing linear inequalities that you are given.

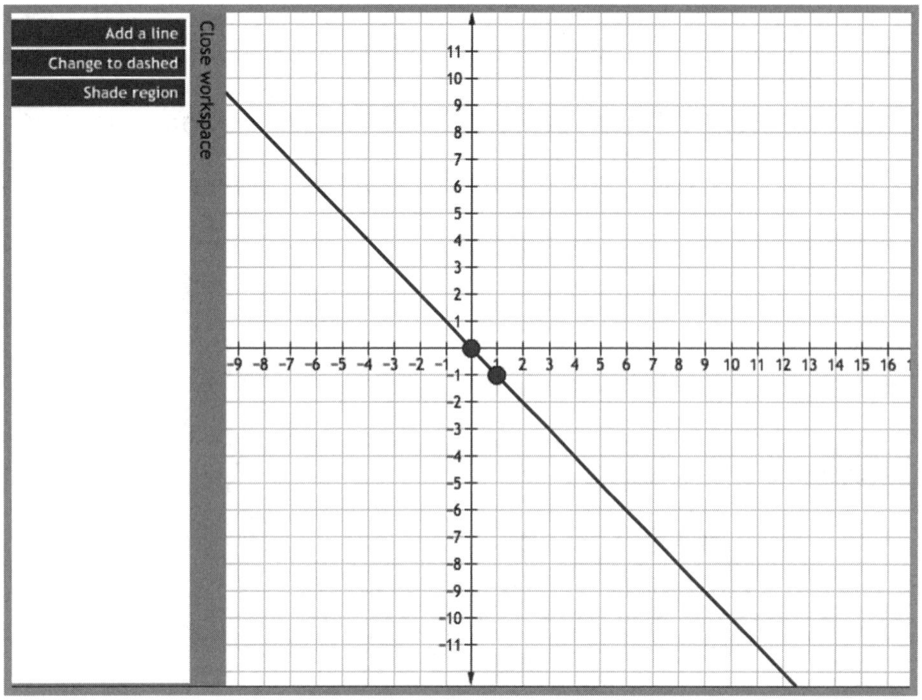

Go to **www.amscomath.com** to use the activities.

4.2 Absolute Value Inequalities and Graphing on the Number Line

In this activity, match the graph on top by determining the correct conjunction.

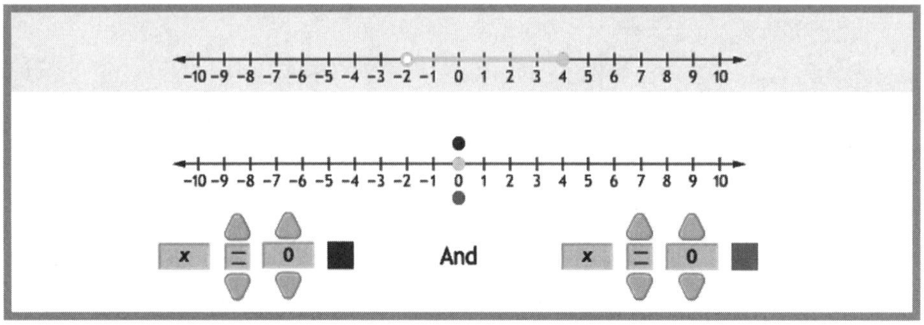

In this activity, match the graph on top by determining the correct disjunction.

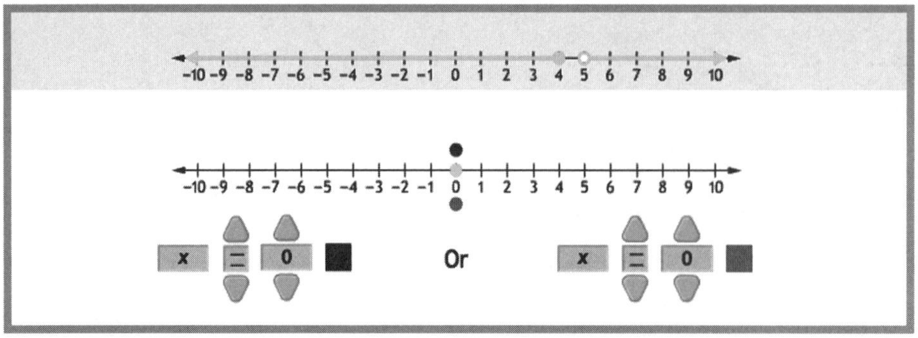

In this activity, graph conjunctions and disjunctions using a number line.

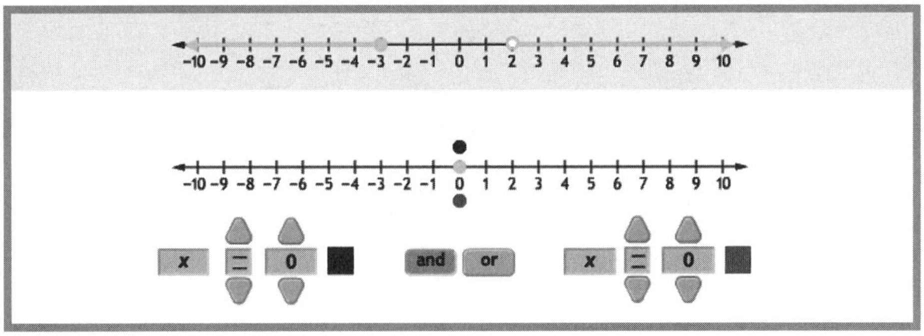

4.4 Graphing Absolute Value Functions

In this activity, experiment with adding a constant to the input of an absolute value parent function.

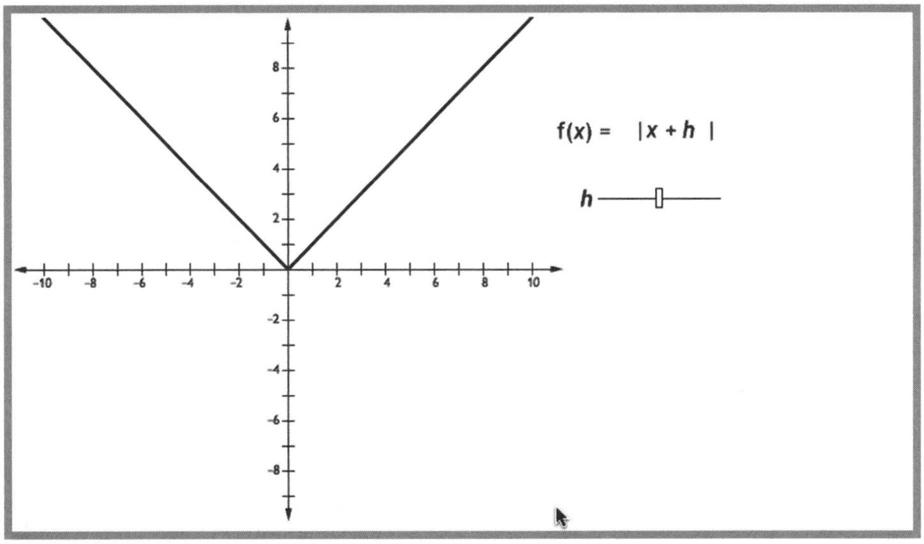

5.1 Solving Systems of Linear Equations by Graphing

In this activity, solve several systems of equations by graphing. To graph a line, drag both of the dots on one of the lines shown to points on the line you are graphing.

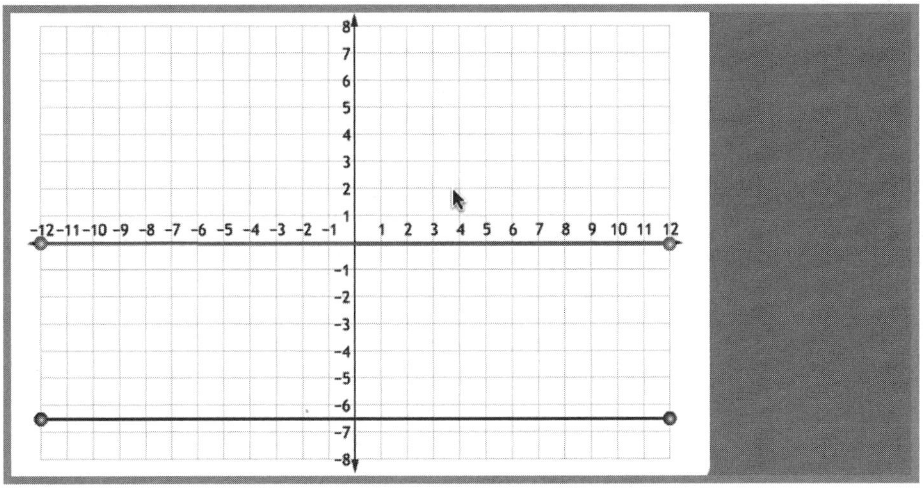

Go to **www.amscomath.com** to use the activities.

5.4 Solving Systems of Linear Inequalities by Graphing

In this activity, follow the prompts to graph the system of inequalities. The activity will graph the first line for you, but you need to choose whether the line is dashed or solid. Then, you click on the region of the graph where the inequality is true. Do the same for the second inequality. Then, click the region where both inequalities are true.

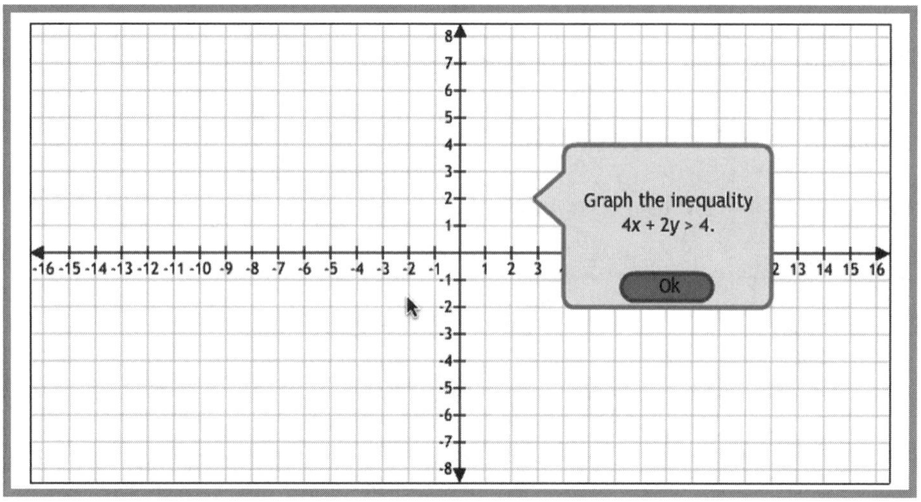

In this activity, solve several systems of inequalities.

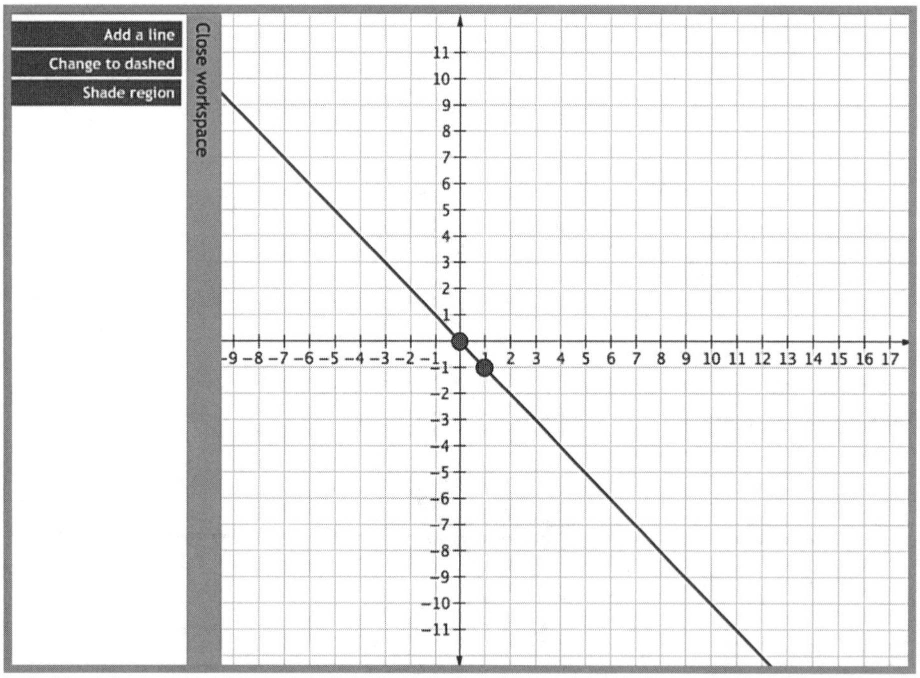

To solve a system of inequalities, graph each inequality and find the region where the solutions overlap.

6.1 Adding and Subtracting Polynomials

In this activity, practice simplifying expressions by combining like terms.

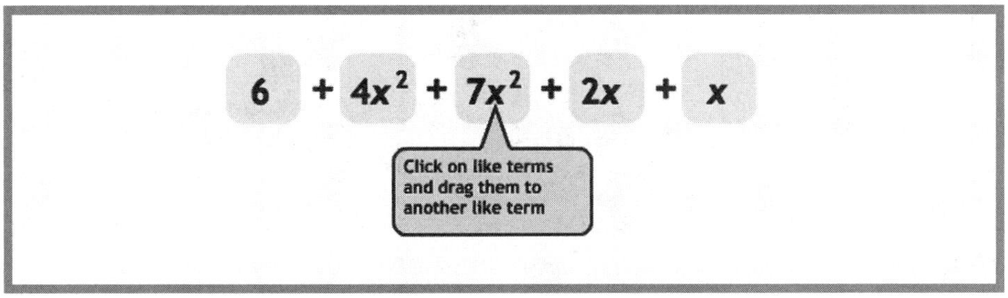

Go to **www.amscomath.com** to use the activities.

6.4 Multiplying a Polynomial by a Polynomial

In this activity, practice multiplying binomials using FOIL.

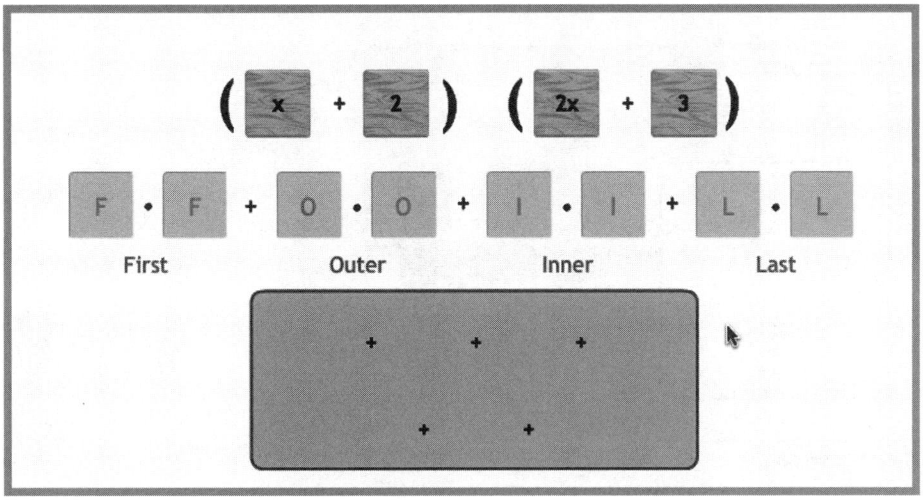

7.3 Factoring Trinomials

We show one of two similar activities below. In these activities, use the box method to factor trinomials.

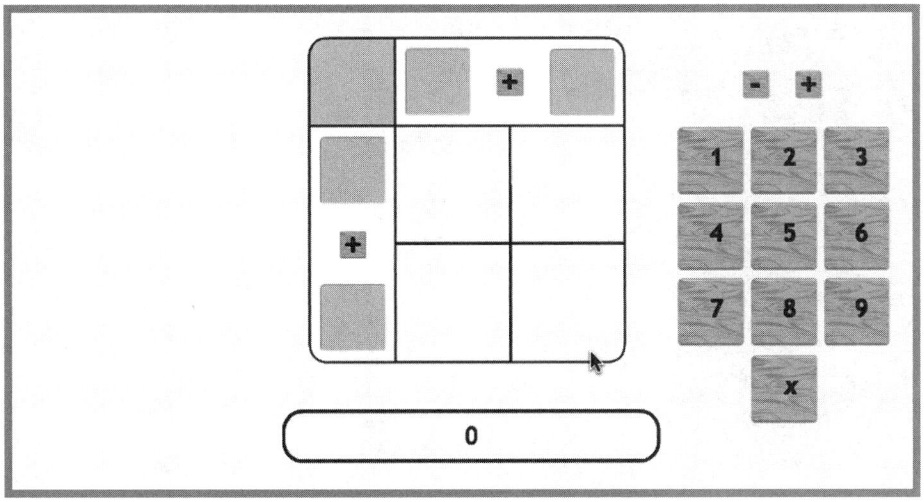

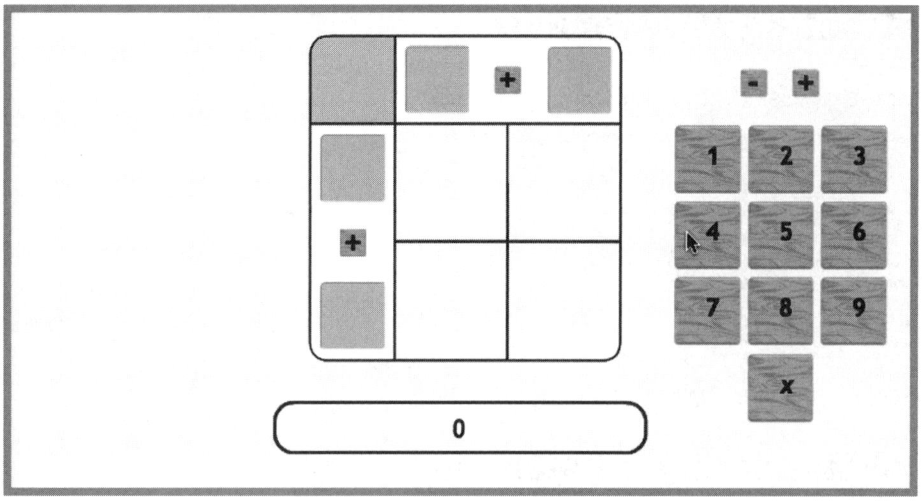

Go to **www.amscomath.com** to use the activities.

In this activity, use the box method to factor trinomials where a ≠ 1.

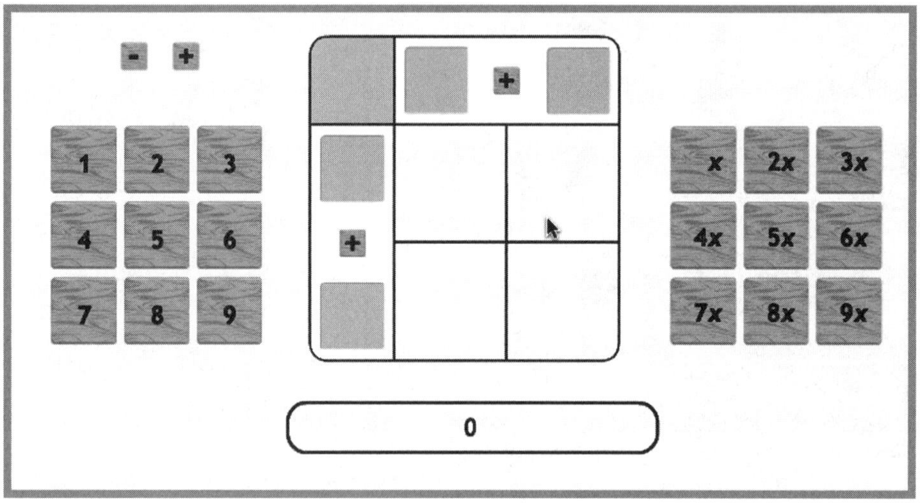

In this activity, factor trinomials to make the juggler juggle.

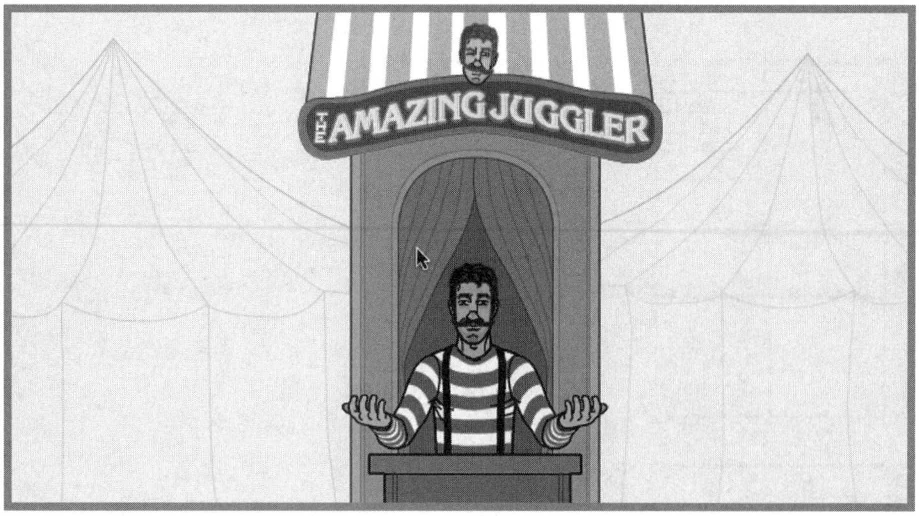

8.5 Graphing Quadratic Functions

In this activity, locate the vertex and four other points on the parabola. We give you the *x*-coordinates of the points to plot and you calculate the matching *y*-coordinate.

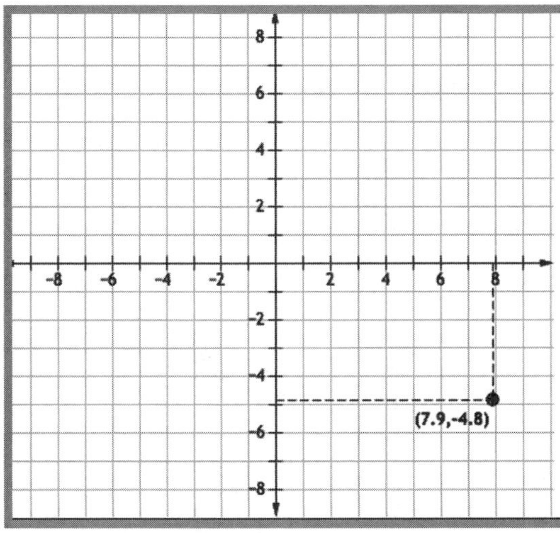

$f(x) = 1.5x^2$

	x	$f(x)$
Vertex	0	
Point 1	1	
Point 2	2	
Point 3	-1	
Point 4	-2	

8.6 Quadratic Functions in Vertex Form

In this activity, locate the vertex of a parabola using the vertex form of a parabola.

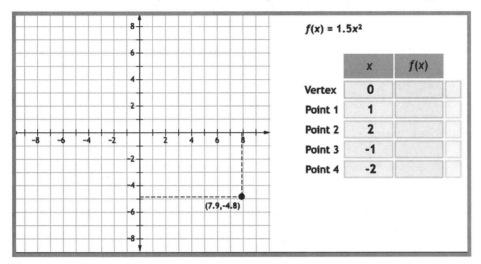

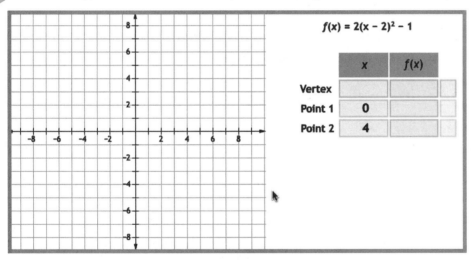

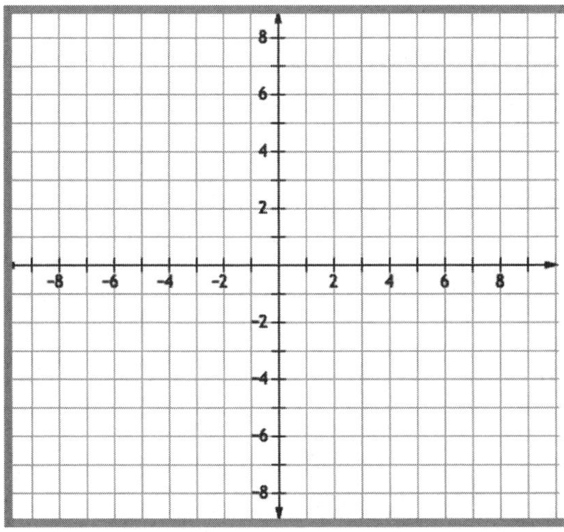

$f(x) = 2(x - 2)^2 - 1$

	x	$f(x)$
Vertex		
Point 1	0	
Point 2	4	

Go to **www.amscomath.com** to use the activities.

8.7 Transformations of Quadratic Functions

In this activity, practice translating quadratic functions horizontally.

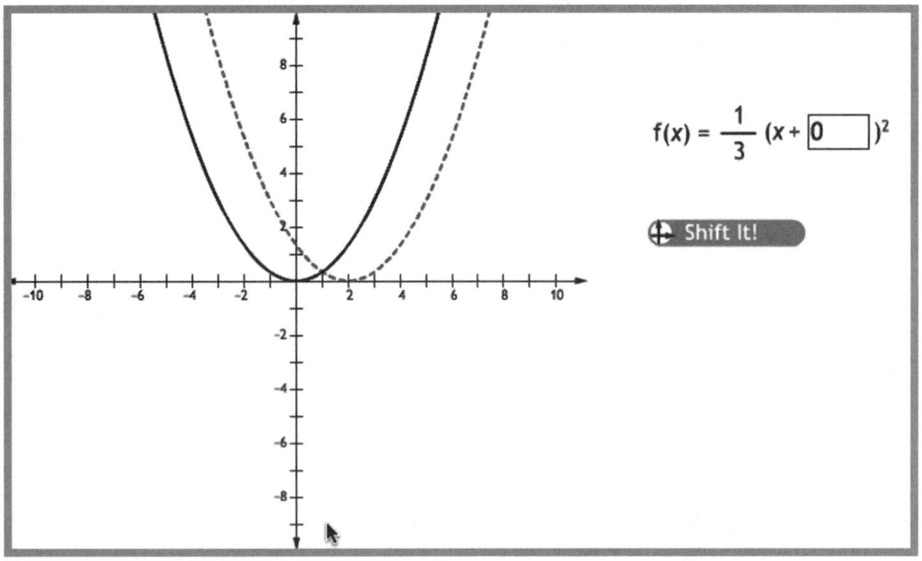

In this activity, practice translating quadratic functions vertically.

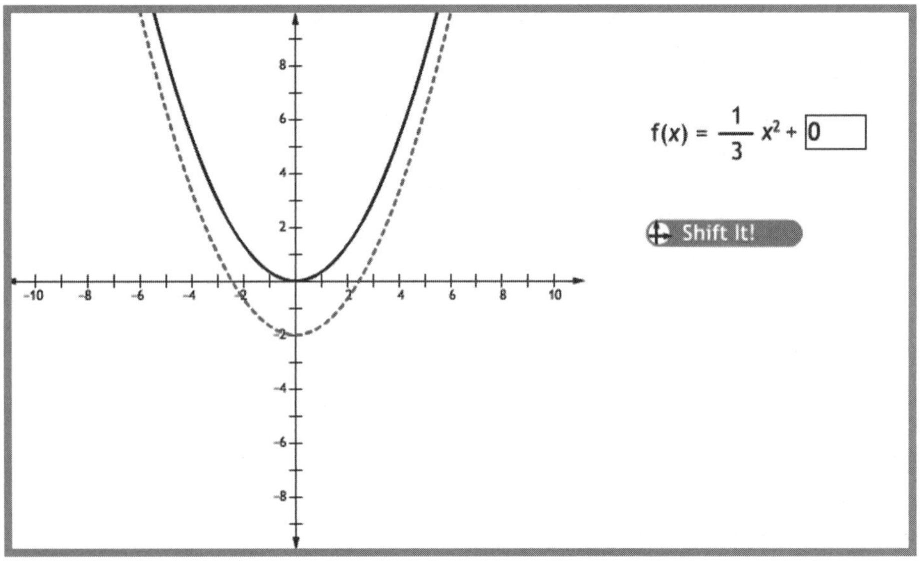

Go to **www.amscomath.com** to use the activities.

In this activity, translate functions up, down, left, and right to match parent functions.

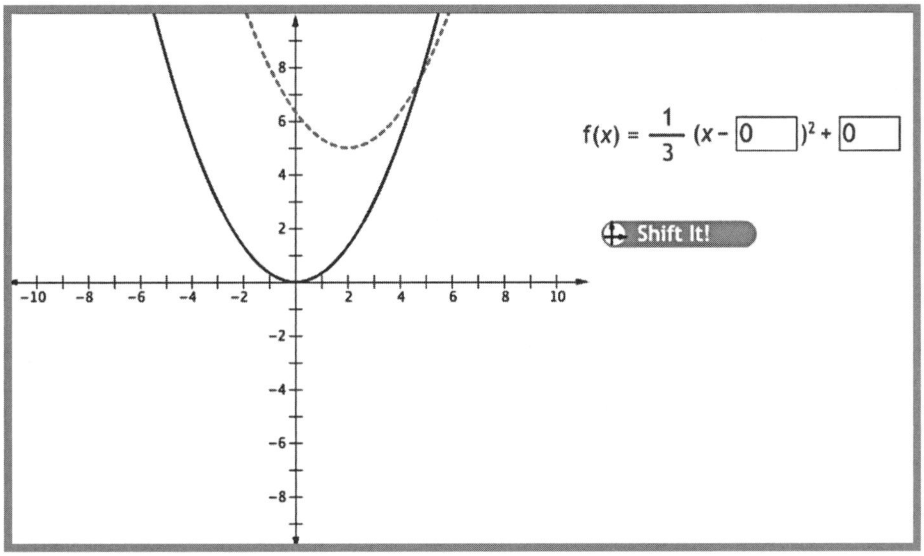

The graph is translated up or down depending on the value added to the output. It is translated left or right depending on the value added to the input.

8.11 Graphing Cubic and Root Functions

In this activity, experiment with translating square root graphs.

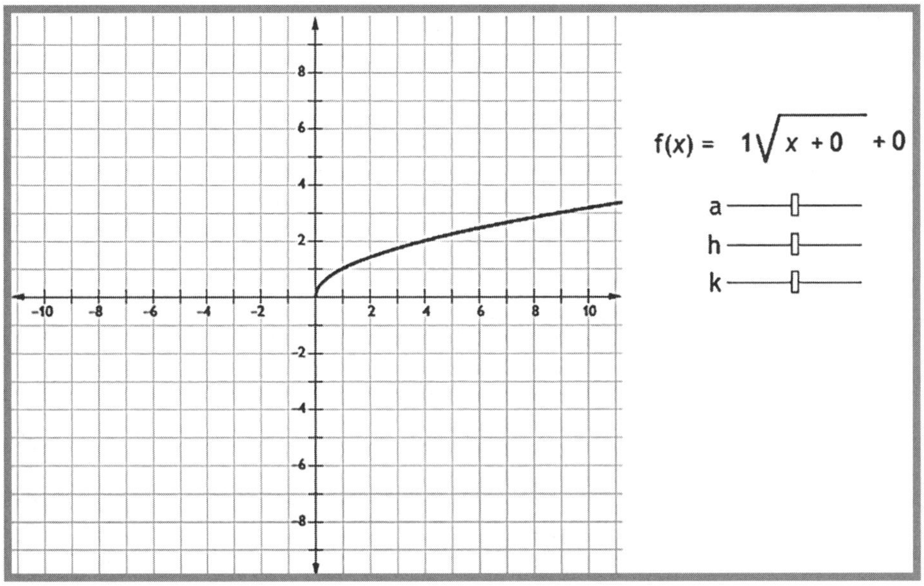

9.2 Graphing Exponential Functions

In this activity, graph an exponential function by plotting points.

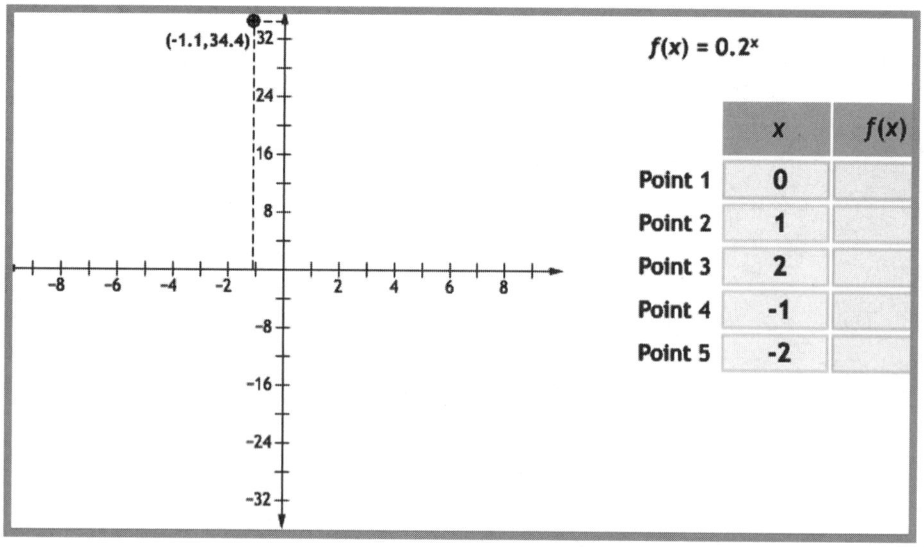

In this activity, translate an exponential function.

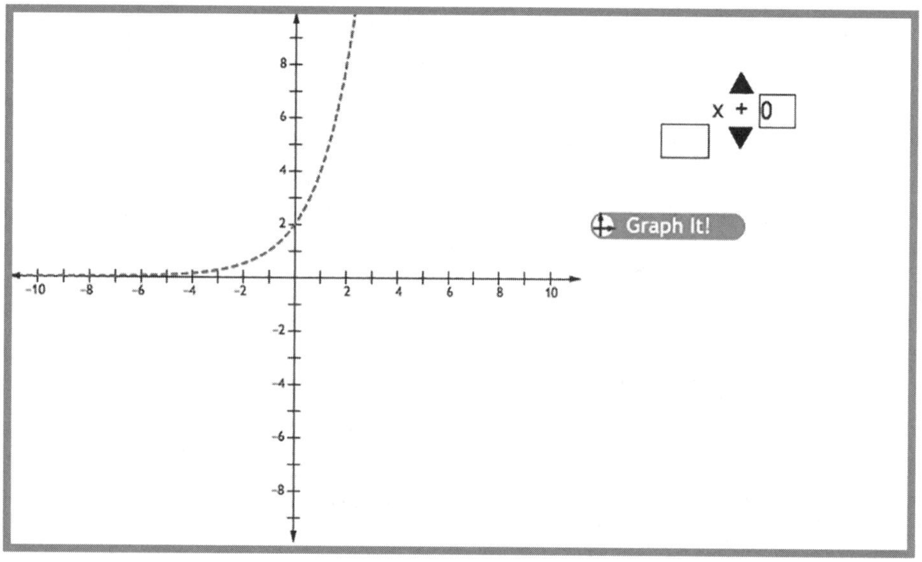

Go to **www.amscomath.com** to use the activities.

9.4 Sequences and Arithmetic Sequences

We show one of two similar activities below. In these activities, you help a frog locate his (mathematically oriented) flies using your knowledge of arithmetic sequences.

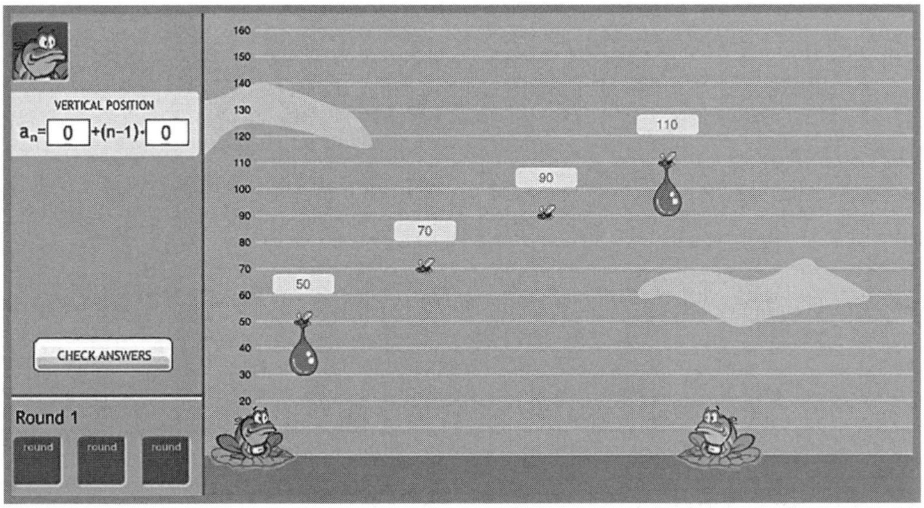

We show one of three similar activities below. In these activities, enter values for the formulas for the odd rows of the pattern as well as the even rows.

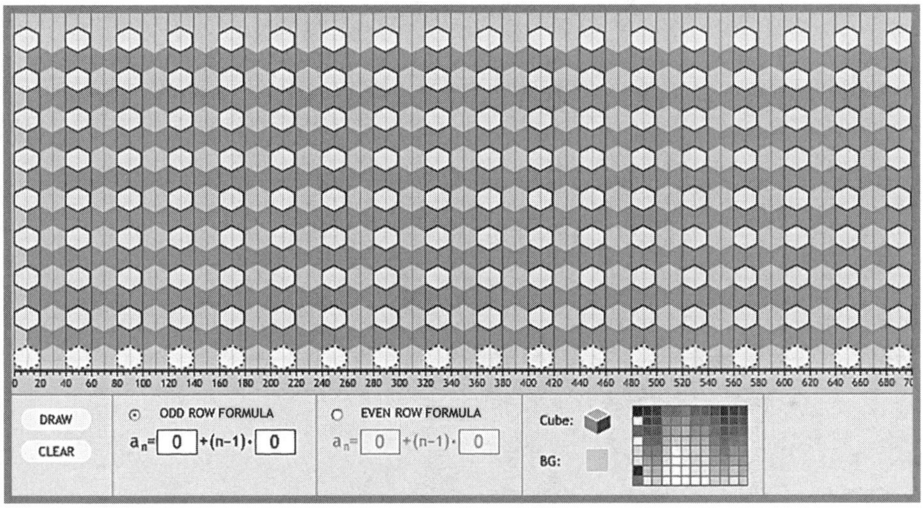

9.5 Geometric Sequences

We show one of two similar activities below. In these activities, you help a frog locate his (mathematically oriented) flies using your knowledge of geometric sequences.

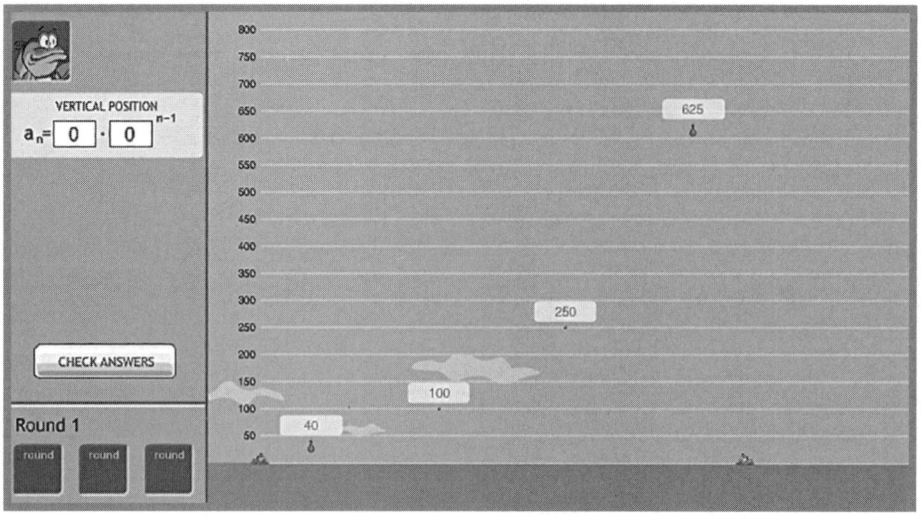

We show one of two similar activities below. In these activities, you are asked to state formulas for both the horizontal and vertical locations of the shape in order to create art.

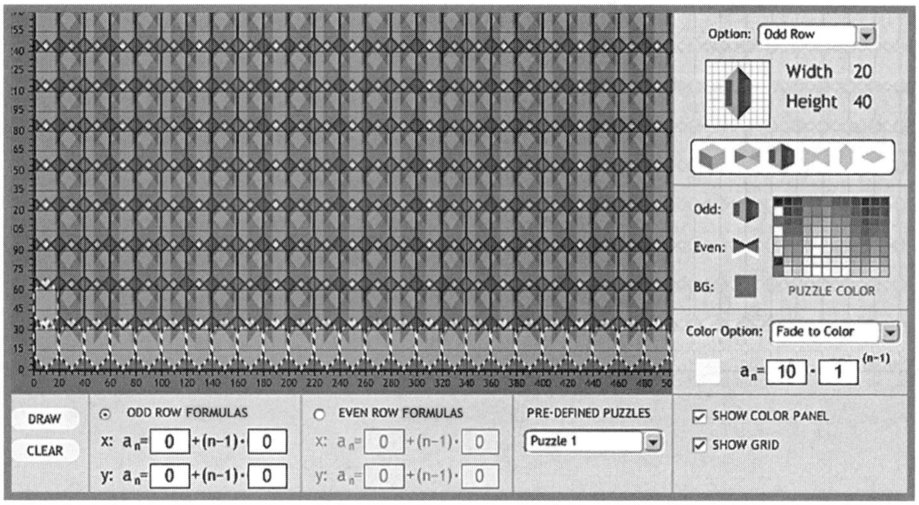

Go to **www.amscomath.com** to use the activities.

10.4 Two-Valued Statistics for Linear Behavior

In this activity, draw a trend line for the data shown.

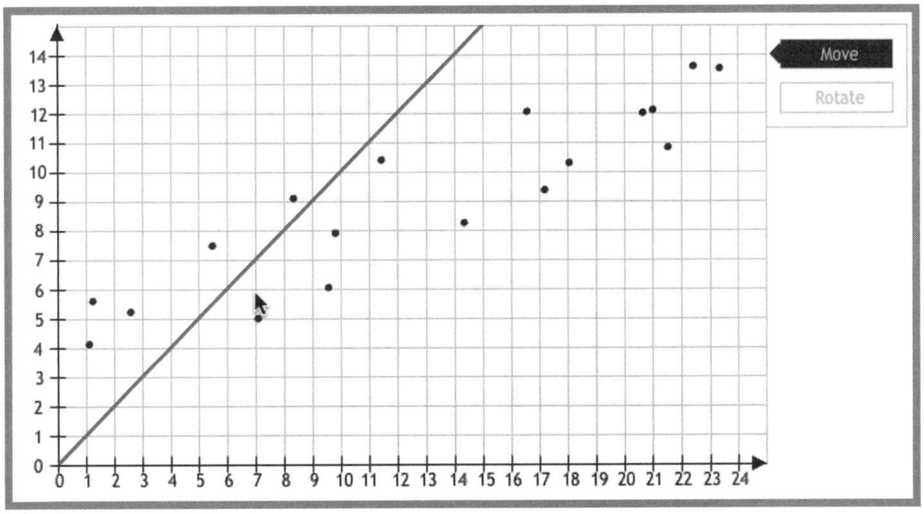

In this activity, collect data for a dropped cannonball on how much time passed after it was dropped and its speed after falling for that length of time.

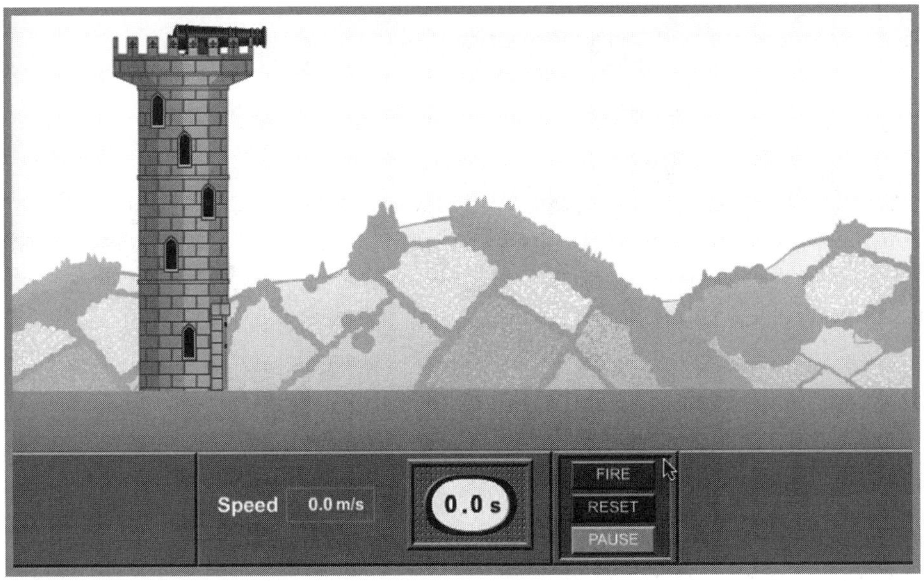

In this activity, plot and analyze your cannonball data.

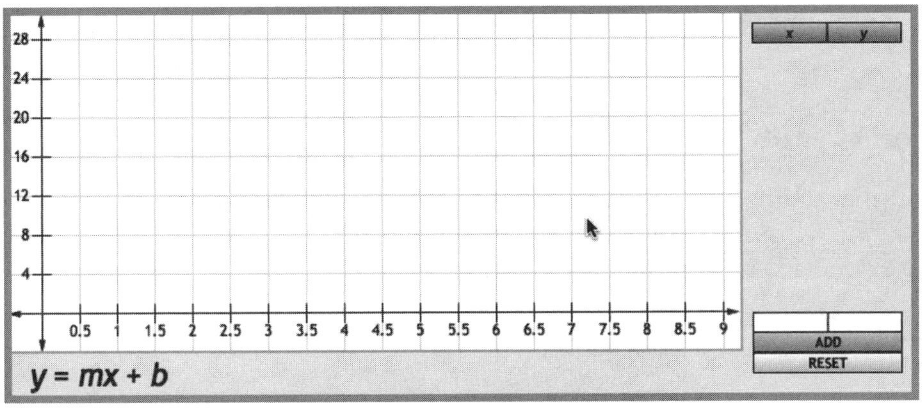

Appendix

Using Your Graphing Calculator

Graphing calculators vary widely in format and capability. As their name implies, these calculators can graph equations and draw bar charts, scatter plots, and other statistical graphs. They have several rows of function keys like scientific calculators, but many of their special functions can be accessed only by selecting menu choices on the display screen. For example, to change from radians to degrees, you will need to press MODE to access a menu. Then you can highlight the word *Degree* (if it is not already highlighted) and press ENTER.

Calculators vary widely in the location of function keys and menu choices. We will show general guidelines for the procedures you are most likely to use, but there are many more powerful operations open to you. Take the time to explore your calculator's menus and find the functions *you* will need the most.

One important difference you should notice is that the graphing calculator does not have an equals = key. Instead, it has ENTER. Other types of calculators perform some operations as you go along. However, a graphing calculator does not calculate anything until you press ENTER. It then follows the rules for order of operations to find the answer. One nice feature is that the operation you put in is generally still visible on the screen above the answer that comes out. Then if you don't get the answer you expected, you can see what you entered to determine if you made an error.

Some other differences: it may not be necessary to press × in order to do multiplication. Some calculators let you type the same way you would write an expression. *Example*: 3(5 + 2) or 6 TAN 30 could be entered exactly as just shown, without having to insert a times sign. Also, the graphing calculator does not have an x^y key. Instead it has a ∧ key. To use this key, enter the base, press ∧, enter the exponent, and then press ENTER.

Note: Some graphing calculators can also solve linear and quadratic equations, draw lines of best fit, calculate with matrices, and perform various other high-level mathematical calculations. Since the procedures for such activities are not consistent from one calculator model to the next, we will not cover them here. You will need to experiment with your calculator, ask your teacher, or consult the calculator's manual.

▲ ▼ ◀ ▶ Moving the Cursor

These four arrow keys allow you to move around in equations, menus, and graphs.

WINDOW Defining the Screen Layout

This key lets you access a menu that defines the area of a graph. The horizontal axis will extend from *Xmin* to *Xmax* with markings at an interval equal to *Xscl*. Similarly, the vertical axis will extend from *Ymin* to *Ymax* with markings at an interval of *Yscl*.

Graphing Equations

[y=] This key lets you enter equations to be graphed. It is sometimes possible to enter more than one equation. The equation should be solved for y in terms of x (which must be entered with the special variable key [X, T, θ, n]). Use [CLEAR] to erase equations you no longer need.

To see a table of values for the equation(s) you enter in the [y=] screen, press [TABLE]. To change the increment by which the x-value changes, or to enter the values individually, press [TBLSET] and adjust the settings as you wish.

[GRAPH] This key allows you to see the graph defined by the [WINDOW] menu with the equations from [y=] graphed on it. To find the coordinates of specific points on the graph, such as x-intercepts, press [TRACE] and use the arrows to move the cursor to the point of interest. You may also be able to enter x-values with the keypad.

You can alter the type of line drawn on a graph or add shading to a graph by choosing one of several options. In the [y=] screen, press the left arrow key until the cursor is on the diagonal slash to the left of the Y for the equation whose graph you wish to alter. Press [ENTER] several times to see the various options for shading and line weight and style. When you have chosen the one you want, press [GRAPH] to see the result.

Graphing Data

[STAT] Pressing this key allows you to access statistical data. Choosing EDIT allows you to enter lists of data you wish to graph. Choosing CALC allows you to calculate values (like the median of your data, $\bar{x}$) or find equations to approximate your data (like the linear regression and median-median lines of best fit).

[STAT PLOT] Pressing this key allows you to select and turn on different types of graphs of your data: broken-line graphs, histograms, scatter plots, and box-and-whisker plots are among the choices.

Depending on which graph you choose, options such as Xlist, Ylist, and Mark may appear to allow you to tell the calculator where the lists of data are stored (e.g., L_1), and what type of point you would like the graph to display. Once you have entered this information, press [GRAPH] to see the display. You can use [TRACE] and the arrow keys to identify points on the graph.

Note: The [WINDOW] menu also controls the appearance of statistical graphs. The *Xscl* value controls the range of values for each bar in the histogram.

INTERSECT is an operation found under the CALC menu. This operation finds the coordinates of a point at which two or more functions intersect. Make sure that the cursor is on the graph of the first function by pressing [ENTER]. Press the up and down arrow keys to move the cursor closer to the point of intersection on the first function. Then press [ENTER] to select the second function and press the up and down arrow keys to move the cursor closer to the point of intersection. Press [ENTER]. The location you found will be displayed as Guess? on the bottom of the screen. Press [ENTER] again. The coordinates of the intersection will be displayed and the cursor will be moved to the intersection.

ZERO is another operation found under the CALC menu. This operation finds the root of the function where it crosses the x-axis. Using the left and right arrow keys, select one point on either side of the root you wish to find. Press [ENTER] to record the left bound. Move the left and right arrows again to record the right bound and press [ENTER] again. The coordinates of the function where it intersects the x-axis are displayed.

Glossary

absolute value (p. 150) Distance from the origin. It must be 0 or positive.

accuracy (p. 37) How close a measurement is to the actual value.

addition property of equality (p. 46) Adding the same number to both sides of an equation produces an equivalent equation.

addition property of inequality (p. 74) Adding the same number to each side of an inequality results in an equivalent inequality.

additive identity (p. 17) Zero, because adding 0 to a number does not change the number.

additive inverse (p. 17) A number's opposite, which is the negative of the number. When you add a number to its additive inverse, the result is 0.

algebraic equation (p. 6) Two algebraic expressions joined by an equality sign.

algebraic expression (p. 6) A mathematical expression with a variable, such as x or $x - 5$.

algebraic inequality (p. 6) Two algebraic expressions joined by any one of the inequality signs $<$, $>$, $\leq$, and $\geq$.

arithmetic sequence (p. 342) A sequence in which each term equals the sum of the previous term and a constant called the "common difference."

associative property (p. 17) Property of the addition and multiplication operations that allows moving the parentheses so that different terms are grouped together, but does not affect the resulting sum or product. For example, $5 + (7 + 2) = (5 + 7) + 2$ or $5 \bullet (7 \bullet 2) = (5 \bullet 7) \bullet 2$.

associative property of addition (p. 46) Property of the addition operation that allows moving the parentheses so that different terms are grouped together, but does not affect the resulting sum. For example, $5 + (7 + 2) = (5 + 7) + 2$.

associative property of multiplication (p. 48) Property of the multiplication operation that allows moving the parentheses so that different terms are grouped together, but does not change the resulting product. For example, $5 \bullet (7 \bullet 2) = (5 \bullet 7) \bullet 2$.

association (p. 393) Association is when one categorical variable is dependent upon another.

asymptote (p. 325) An asymptote is a line that the graph of a function continuously approaches but never touches.

axis of symmetry (p. 163) A line that divides a figure into two symmetric halves, such as the line that passes through the vertex of a parabola about which the parabola is symmetric.

base (p. 21) In an exponential expression, the base is the number raised to an exponent. In the expression 7^5, 7 is the base.

bias (p. 387) In a survey, bias refers to a tendency for a sample to misrepresent a population.

binomial (p. 212) A polynomial with two terms.

boundary line (p. 145) In the graph of an inequality on a grid, a line that defines the solution set of the inequality.

box-and-whisker plot (p. 374) A way to show distribution of data that gives a visual representation of the extremes, the median, and how close or far values are from the median.

box method (p. 223) A method to multiply polynomials by making a table of the products and listing the areas of the rectangles.

closed (p. 19) A set of numbers is closed under a mathematical operation if, when that operation is performed on any two or more numbers in that set, the result is also a number in the set. For example, the set of whole numbers is closed under addition, because adding any two whole numbers will always yield a whole number.

coefficient (p. 5) A number that multiplies a variable, like the 2 in $2h$.

coefficient of determination (p. 383) When creating an algebraic model to fit data, the coefficient of determination, r^2, provides a measure of how well the model fits the data. The value of r^2 varies from zero to one. The closer it is to one, the better the model fits the data.

common difference (p. 342) The constant number added to each term of an arithmetic sequence to get the next term.

common ratio (p. 348) The constant number that multiplies each term of a geometric sequence to get the next term.

commutative property (p. 17) The order of terms does not affect the sum or product. For example, $3 + 5 = 5 + 3$ and $3 \bullet 5 = 5 \bullet 3$.

commutative property of addition (p. 46) The order of terms in addition does not matter. For example, $6 + 2 = 2 + 6$.

commutative property of multiplication (p. 48) The order of factors in multiplication does not matter. For example, $6 \bullet 2 = 2 \bullet 6$.

comparison property of numbers (p. 74) For all real numbers a and b, exactly one of the following statements is true: $a < b$, $a = b$, or $a > b$.

completing the square (p. 273) A technique for solving quadratic equations; to complete the square means to add a constant to a binomial to create a perfect square.

compound inequality (p. 73) A conjunction or disjunction that combines two or more inequalities.

conditional equation (p. 46) An equation that is true only for some values of the variable or variables. For example, $3x = 12$ is a conditional equation because it is only true when $x = 4$.

conditional frequency (p. 393) An entry in a relative frequency table. It is the ratio of a joint frequency to the total number of observations.

conditional relative frequency (p. 393) The ratio of a joint frequency to a marginal frequency in its row or column in a joint frequency table.

conjunction (p. 150) A statement created by combining two statements with the word "and."

consistent systems (p. 186) Systems of equations with one or more solutions are said to be consistent.

constant (p. 5) Numerical value that does not change. For example, 5, 4.2, and π are constants.

constant function (p. 93) A function with the same output for all input values.

constant of variation (p. 95) The ratio between two variables that are directly related. For example, in the relation $y = kx$, the constant of variation is k.

contradiction (p. 46) An equation that when solved results in a false statement, such as $1 = 0$.

correlation (p. 393) Correlation is a mathematical relationship between two variables. In statistical analysis, correlation is necessary but not sufficient to determine causation.

correlation coefficient (p. 383) The correlation coefficient is represented by r and indicates the strength of the correlation.

cross multiplication (p. 65) Multiplying each numerator on both sides of an equation by the denominator of the other side.

cube root (p. 26) A number that when cubed, or multiplied by itself three times, equals a given number.

cube root function (p. 313) A function that can be written in the form $f(x) = \sqrt[3]{x}$.

cubic equation (p. 265) A cubic equation is a third-degree polynomial equation, such as $ax^3 + bx^2 + cx + d = 0$, where a, b, c, and d are real numbers and $a \neq 0$.

dependent axis (p. 129) The axis upon which the values of the dependent variable are displayed, most commonly the y-axis.

dependent systems (p. 186) Systems of linear equations with an infinite number of solutions in common are said to be dependent.

dependent variable (p. 129) In a function, the dependent variable represents the effect, or output, caused by the value of the independent variable, or input.

difference of two squares (p. 226) A term used to describe a polynomial in which one perfect square is subtracted from another. For example, $x^2 - 4$.

direct variation (p. 95) A relationship between two variables that can be stated as a function of the form $y = kx$, where x and y are the variables and k is the constant of variation.

discriminant (p. 293) In the quadratic formula, the expression $b^2 - 4ac$ is the discriminant. The discriminant determines the number of real solutions to the quadratic equation. If the discriminant is positive, the equation has two different real solutions; if it equals zero, the equation has two identical real solutions (which can be thought of as a single solution); and if it is negative, the equation has no real solutions.

disjunction (p. 150) A statement created by combining two statements with the word "or."

distributive property (p. 17) The product of a factor and a sum (or difference) of terms (in parentheses) equals the sum (or corresponding difference) of the individual products of the factor with each term. For example, $3 \bullet (2 + 5) = 3 \bullet 2 + 3 \bullet 5$.

distributive property of multiplication over addition (p. 48) For all a, b, and c, $a\,(b + c) = ab + ac$.

distributive property of multiplication over subtraction (p. 48) For all a, b, and c, $a(b - c) = ab - ac$.

division property of equality (p. 48) Dividing by the same number on each side of an equation results in an equivalent equation.

division property of inequality (p. 74) Dividing both sides of an inequality by the same positive number results in an equivalent inequality. When both sides of an inequality are divided by a negative number, the inequality sign is reversed to create an equivalent inequality.

domain (p. 121) The domain of a function is the set of inputs.

dot plot (p. 366) A way to represent the frequencies of a small number of events, with dots stacked in designated categories.

double root (p. 262) Two identical solutions to a quadratic equation.

elimination method (p. 194) The process of adding or subtracting one equation to another in order to eliminate one or more variables and solve a system of equations.

end behavior (p. 163) The behavior of a function as x approaches positive infinity or negative infinity.

equation (p. 45) Two algebraic expressions joined by an equality sign.

evaluate (p. 13) To replace the variable, or variables, in an algebraic expression with a number, or numbers, and perform the indicated mathematical operations.

explicit (p. 341) The explicit definition of a sequence involves the first term in the sequence, and allows for calculation of any other term in the sequence.

explicit formula (p. 344) The formula for a sequence simplified from the general rule.

exponent (p. 21) In an exponential expression, the exponent tells how many copies of the base are multiplied together. In the expression, 7^5, 5 is the exponent.

exponential decay (p. 325) A decreasing exponential function. The graph of an exponential function with a base smaller than one.

exponential decay model (p. 335) The exponential decay model calculates exponential decay, $A = a(1 - r)^t$.

exponential function (p. 324) A function that contains a variable as an exponent.

exponential growth (p. 325) The graph of an exponential function with a base greater than 1.

exponential growth model (p. 335) The exponential growth model calculates exponential growth, $A = a(1 + r)^t$.

extrapolate (p. 387) Draw conclusions about data beyond the available data.

factor (p. 5) Factors are the numbers or expressions that when multiplied together yield a given product.

factoring (p. 241) The process of writing an equivalent expression that shows the factors of the original product.

factoring by grouping (p. 251) Grouping terms of a polynomial that can be factored so that those groups then have a common factor.

factoring completely (p. 245, p. 253) The process of factoring until all of the factors in the expression are prime – that is, the factors cannot be factored again.

FOIL method (p. 223) A way to multiply two binomials; stands for First, Outer, Inner, Last.

formula (p. 9) An equation that describes a relationship between two or more variables.

frequency (p. 365) How often something occurs.

general rule (p. 344) By knowing the first term of a sequence and the pattern of the sequence, any term can be calculated using the general rule.

geometric sequence (p. 348) A sequence in which each term equals the product of the previous term and a constant number called the "common ratio."

greatest common factor (p. 241) In a polynomial, the factor that is common to each term and has the greatest possible coefficient and the greatest possible power of each variable.

greatest integer function (p. 159) A step function $f(x) = [x]$, where $[x]$ designates the greatest integer not greater than x. For example, $f(2.9) = [2.9] = 2$.

greatest possible error (p. 37) For a given measurement the greatest possible error is equal to $\frac{1}{2}$ of the unit of measure. For example, if measuring something to the nearest 1 inch, the greatest possible error of measurement is $\frac{1}{2}$ inch.

grouping symbols (p. 13) Operations within grouping symbols must be done first in order of operations. Some examples of grouping symbols are parentheses, brackets, and a fraction bar.

half plane (p. 145) Half planes designate the halves of the coordinate plane above and below a given line, $y = mx + b$. For the half plane above the line, $y > mx + b$, and for the half plane below the line y, $< mx + b$.

histogram (p. 366) A graphical representation of the distribution of data using bars to represent frequency.

horizontal translation (p. 165) The horizontal shift of the graph of a function brought about by the insertion of a constant h. For example, the graph of $y = x^2$ is shifted to the right h units by writing $y = (x - h)^2$.

identity (p. 46) An equation for which the solution is the set of all real numbers. For example, $2x + 2x = 4x$.

identity function (p. 98) An identity function is a function whose output equals its input for all values of its input: $f(x) = x$.

incomplete quadratic equation (p. 267) An incomplete quadratic equation is a quadratic equation in which $b = 0$ or $c = 0$, or both $b = 0$ and $c = 0$.

independent axis (p. 129) The axis upon which the values of the independent variable are displayed, most commonly the x-axis.

independent variable (p. 129) In a function, the input variable that determines the value of the dependent variable, or output.

index (p. 26) When taking the nth root of a given number, b, n is called the index. For example, when taking the cube root of a number x, denoted $\sqrt[3]{x}$, the index is 3.

inequality (p. 72) Two expressions joined with a sign of inequality.

integer (p. 15) A whole number, such as 6, 0, −31.

intercept (p. 90) The point at which the graph of a function crosses a coordinate axis.

interquartile range (p. 372) The difference between the third and first quartiles.

intersection (p. 185) The intersection of two sets is the set of all elements that are common to both sets.

interval of measure (p. 37) The range of values described by a given measurement result, plus and minus the greatest possible error of measurement.

irrational number (p. 26) A number that cannot be written as a fraction made up of two integers or as a terminating or repeating decimal.

isolating the variable (p. 46) Performing mathematical operations on an algebraic equation in order to get the variable by itself on one side of the equation.

joint frequency (p. 393) The value in a cell of a two-way table that matches two category descriptions.

joint relative frequency (p. 393) The ratio of the number of observations of a joint frequency to the total number of observations in a frequency table.

least common denominator (p. 56) The smallest integer that allows two or more fractions to have the same denominator.

like terms (p. 53) Algebraic terms that have the same variable, or variables, with those variables of the same degree.

linear (p. 45) An equation whose graph is a line.

linear function (p. 98) A function of degree one whose graph is a non-vertical line.

line of best fit (p. 382) The best possible trend line for a set of data.

literal equation (p. 59) An algebraic equation involving only variables.

marginal frequency (p. 393) The total in a row or column in a two-way table.

marginal relative frequency (p. 393) The ratio of a marginal frequency to the total number of observations.

mean (p. 370) Also called "average," the mean of a set of values is the sum of the values divided by their count.

median (p. 370) In a set of values arranged from least to greatest, the median is the middle value.

mode (p. 370) In a set of values, the mode is the value (or values) that appears most frequently.

monomial (p. 211) A real number, a power of a variable, or a product of a real number and powers of variables.

multiplication property of equality (p. 48) Multiplying each side of an equation by the same number results in an equivalent equation.

multiplication property of inequality (p. 74) Multiplying both sides of an inequality by the same positive number results in an equivalent inequality. When both sides of an inequality are multiplied by the same negative number, the inequality sign is reversed to create an equivalent inequality.

multiplicative identity (p. 48) The multiplicative identity is 1, because if you multiply a number by 1, it stays the same.

multiplicative inverse (p. 18) The multiplicative inverse of a number, also called the "reciprocal," is 1 divided by the number.

order of operations (p. 13) The order in which mathematical operations must be performed in an algebraic expression. For example, multiplication is done before addition.

outlier (p. 368) A data point far from a trend line.

parallel (p. 93) Lines that have the same slope, so they never intersect.

parent function (p. 164) The most basic function in a family of functions.

perfect square (p. 26) The square of a rational number or polynomial.

perfect square trinomial (p. 226) The product of two identical binomials.

perpendicular (p. 107) Two lines that intersect at a right angle (90°) are called "perpendicular lines."

piecewise function (p. 154) A function that is defined by different expressions on different parts of the domain.

point-slope form (p. 113) The form of linear equation written $y - y_1 = m(x - x_1)$, where $(x_1 - y_1)$ is a point on the line and m is the slope of the line.

polynomial (p. 212) An expression made up of the sum (or difference) of more than one monomial.

power (p. 21) An algebraic expression with a base and an exponent. For example, 7^5 is a power.

precision (p. 38) How exact and reproducible a measurement can be.

principal square root (p. 25) The positive square root of a number.

properties of arithmetic operations (p. 17) The commutative property of multiplication and the associative property of addition are examples of properties of arithmetic operations.

properties of equality (p. 46) Properties including the multiplication and division properties of equality, used to solve equations.

proportion (p. 65) An equation stating two ratios are equal.

quadratic equation (p. 259) An equation that can be written with a quadratic trinomial on one side and zero on the other side.

quadratic formula (p. 290) A formula for solving quadratic equations: $x = \dfrac{-b \pm \sqrt{b^2 - 4ac}}{2a}$.

quadratic function (p. 280) A function that can be written in the form $f(x) = ax^2 + bx + c$.

quadratic trinomial (p. 247) A polynomial in one variable with three terms: a second-degree term (containing the square of the variable), a first-degree term, and a constant. For example, $5x^2 + 2x - 3$.

radical sign (p. 25) The sign that designates a root, or radical. For example, in the expression $\sqrt{n}$, n is the radicand and $\sqrt{}$ is the radical sign.

radicand (p. 25) The expression under a radical sign. For example, in the expression $\sqrt{n}$, n is the radicand and $\sqrt{}$ is the radical sign.

range (p. 121) Range is the set of output values of a function.

rate (p. 62) A ratio that compares the change in one quantity to the change in another. The denominator is usually one. For example, 55 miles per hour is a rate that can be expressed as the ratio $\dfrac{\text{55 miles}}{\text{1 hour}}$.

rate of change (p. 101) A relationship between two quantities that describes how much one quantity changes with respect to the other.

ratio (p. 62) A quotient that compares two quantities, with the first quantity being divided by the second.

rational number (p. 26) A number that can be written as a fraction, or ratio, of two integers when the denominator is not zero. For example, $\dfrac{3}{4}$.

reciprocal property (p. 18) The property that the product of any number and its multiplicative inverse, or reciprocal, is 1.

recursive (p. 341) The recursive definition of a sequence states the value of the first term of the sequence and gives a prescription for calculating any other term from the value of its preceding term.

reflection (p. 164) Flipping the graph of a function across a line, called the "reflection axis." Also, the result of such flipping.

regression (p. 382) The process of finding an equation that matches a data set.

relative frequency table (p. 393) The table that displays the percent of frequencies in each condition.

residual (p. 384) The distance from the predicted location of a point on a line to an actual data point.

root (p. 45) The value of a variable that makes an equation true is a root of the equation.

scatter plot (p. 381) A graphical representation of data in which data points are plotted in order to determine if there is a correlation between variables.

scientific notation (p. 32) An efficient way to write very large and very small numbers, with a leading value (between 1 and 10) multiplied by a power of 10.

sequence (p. 341) An ordered list of objects, such as the notes in a song or the terms in an arithmetic sequence.

significant digits (p. 35) The number of reliably known digits in a number.

slope (p. 101) How flat or steep a line is. Slope is a number calculated by dividing the rise—the vertical change between any two points on the line—by the run—the horizontal change between the same two points.

slope-intercept form (p. 111) The form of linear equation written $y = mx + b$, where m is the slope and b is the y-intercept.

solution (p. 45) All the values of the variable or variables that make two sides of an equation equal.

solution of a system (p. 185) All the values of the variable or variables that make a system of equations true.

special product (p. 241) Some expressions, such as the difference of squares and the square of a binomial, are products of binomials that follow a pattern and are referred to as "special products."

square (p. 21) A number raised to the second power, or multiplied by itself.

square of a binomial (p. 226) The product of a binomial and itself; two special formulas can be used to evaluate the square of a binomial. They are $(a + b)^2 = a^2 + 2ab + b^2$ and $(a - b)^2 = a^2 - 2ab + b^2$.

square root (p. 25) A number that when squared equals a given number, denoted with the radical sign $\sqrt{\ }$. For example, $\sqrt{4} = 2$ because $2 \bullet 2 = 2^2 = 4$.

square root function (p. 312) A function that can be written in the form $f(x) = \sqrt{x}$.

standard deviation (p. 376) When analyzing data, standard deviation supplies a measure of how spread out, or close together, values are compared to the mean. It is determined by the formula

$$s = \sqrt{\frac{(x_1 - \overline{x})^2 + (x_2 - \overline{x})^2 + \ldots + (x_n - \overline{x})^2}{n - 1}}$$

where s is the standard deviation, $x_1, \ldots, x_n$ are the values, and $\overline{x}$ is their mean.

standard form of a polynomial (p. 212) The standard form of a polynomial is written with its terms in descending order, with no like terms.

standard form of a quadratic equation (p. 259) The standard form of a quadratic equation is $ax^2 + bx + c = 0$, where a, b, and c are real numbers and $a \neq 0$.

step function (p. 159) A type of piecewise function that appears to step from one change to the next. The greatest integer function $y = [x]$ is an example of a step function.

substitution method (p. 190) Replacing a variable in one equation with an expression for that variable obtained from another equation, when solving a system of equations.

substitution principle (p. 46) A principle that states that an algebraic expression can be replaced by an equivalent algebraic expression.

subtraction property of equality (p. 46) Subtracting the same number from each side of an equality results in an equivalent equality.

subtraction property of inequality (p. 74) Subtracting the same number from each side of an inequality results in an equivalent inequality.

sum and product rule (p. 247) When factoring special quadratic trinomials, of the form $x^2 + bx + c$, the sum of the factors of c must equal b.

term (p. 5) A product of a number and powers of variables in an expression or equation. For example, in the equation $2a^3c + 5 = 2b$, the terms are $2a^3c$, 5, and $2b$.

transformation (p. 164) A transformation changes the location, orientation, size, proportions, or other geometric properties of a figure or graph.

transitive property of equality (p. 46) Property that states that when two expressions are each equal to a third, they must be equal to each other. For example, if $a = b$, and $b = c$, then $a = c$.

transitive property of inequality (p. 74) Property that states that for all numbers a, b, and c, if $a < b$ and $b < c$, then $a < c$, and similarly, if $a > b$ and $b > c$, then $a > c$.

trinomial (p. 212) A polynomial with three terms.

two-way frequency table (p. 393) A two-way table has categories for its columns and rows and shows the count of how many fit into each cell.

vertex (p. 163) The point at which the graph of a parabola changes direction. The vertex is the highest or lowest point on the graph of a parabola.

vertex form of a quadratic function (p. 285) The equation for a parabola in the form, $y = a(x - h)^2 + k$, where the point (h, k) is the vertex.

vertical shrinking (p. 164) The vertical flattening of a function by multiplying the function by a value a, where $0 < a < 1$. For example, $y = 0.5x^2$ is shrunk vertically relative to $y = x^2$.

vertical stretching (p. 164) The vertical elongation of a function by multiplying the function by a value $a > 1$. For example, $y = 2x^2$ is stretched vertically relative to $y = x^2$.

vertical translation (p. 164) The vertical shifting of the graph of a function, brought about by the insertion of a constant k. For example, the graph of $y = x^2$ is shifted up k units by writing $y = (x)^2 + k$.

***x*-intercept** (p. 90) The point at which the graph of a function crosses the x-axis. The value of y is zero at the x-intercept.

***y*-intercept** (p. 90) The point at which the graph of a function crosses the y-axis. The value of x is zero at the y-intercept.

zero product property (p. 18) Property that states that if the product of two real numbers is zero, at least one of the numbers must be zero.

Index

D

E

F

G

H

I

J

L

M

N

O

R

S

T

ALGEBRA I (COMMON CORE) January 2015

Part I

Answer all 24 questions in this part. Each correct answer will receive 2 credits. No partial credit will be allowed. For each statement or question, choose the word or expression that, of those given, best completes the statement or answers the question. Record your answers on your separate answer sheet. [48]

Use this space for computations.

1 The owner of a small computer repair business has one employee, who is paid an hourly rate of \$22. The owner estimates his weekly profit using the function $P(x) = 8600 - 22x$. In this function, x represents the number of

(1) computers repaired per week

(2) hours worked per week

(3) customers served per week

(4) days worked per week

2 Peyton is a sprinter who can run the 40-yard dash in 4.5 seconds. He converts his speed into miles per hour, as shown below.

$$\frac{40\text{ yd}}{4.5\text{ sec}} \bullet \frac{3\text{ ft}}{1\text{ yd}} \bullet \frac{5280\text{ ft}}{1\text{ mi}} \bullet \frac{60\text{ sec}}{1\text{ min}} \bullet \frac{60\text{ min}}{1\text{ hr}}$$

Which ratio is *incorrectly* written to convert his speed?

(1) $\frac{3\text{ ft}}{1\text{ yd}}$

(2) $\frac{5280\text{ ft}}{1\text{ mi}}$

(3) $\frac{60\text{ sec}}{1\text{ min}}$

(4) $\frac{60\text{ min}}{1\text{ hr}}$

3 Which equation has the same solutions as $2x^2 + x - 3 = 0$?

(1) $(2x - 1)(x + 3) = 0$

(2) $(2x + 1)(x - 3) = 0$

(3) $(2x - 3)(x + 1) = 0$

(4) $(2x + 3)(x - 1) = 0$

Use this space for computations.

4 Krystal was given \$3000 when she turned 2 years old. Her parents invested it at a 2% interest rate compounded annually. No deposits or withdrawals were made. Which expression can be used to determine how much money Krystal had in the account when she turned 18?

(1) $3000(1 + 0.02)^{16}$
(2) $3000(1 - 0.02)^{16}$
(3) $3000(1 + 0.02)^{18}$
(4) $3000(1 - 0.02)^{18}$

5 Which table of values represents a linear relationship?

x	f(x)
−1	−3
0	−2
1	1
2	6
3	13

(1)

x	f(x)
−1	−3
0	−1
1	1
2	3
3	5

(3)

x	f(x)
−1	$\frac{1}{2}$
0	1
1	2
2	4
3	8

(2)

x	f(x)
−1	−1
0	0
1	1
2	8
3	27

(4)

6 Which domain would be the most appropriate set to use for a function that predicts the number of household online-devices in terms of the number of people in the household?

(1) integers
(2) whole numbers
(3) irrational numbers
(4) rational numbers

Use this space for computations.

7 The inequality $7 - \frac{2}{3}x < x - 8$ is equivalent to

(1) $x > 9$ (3) $x < 9$

(2) $x > -\frac{3}{5}$ (4) $x < -\frac{3}{5}$

8 The value in dollars, $v(x)$, of a certain car after x years is represented by the equation $v(x) = 25{,}000(0.86)^x$. To the *nearest dollar*, how much more is the car worth after 2 years than after 3 years?

(1) 2589 (3) 15,901

(2) 6510 (4) 18,490

9 Which function has the same y-intercept as the graph below?

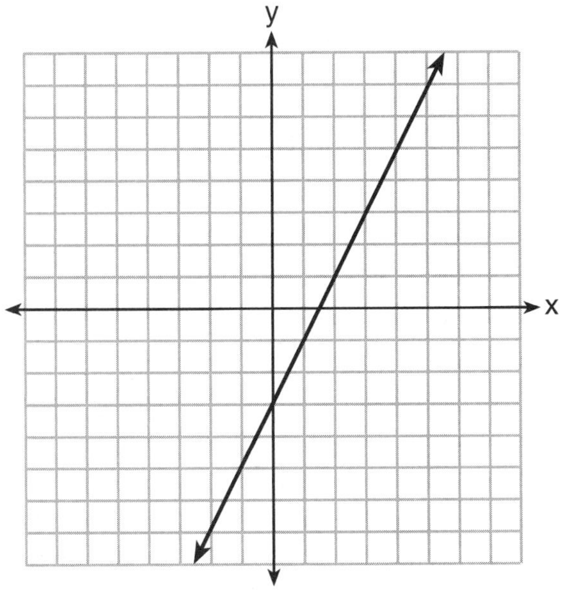

(1) $y = \frac{12 - 6x}{4}$ (3) $6y + x = 18$

(2) $27 + 3y = 6x$ (4) $y + 3 = 6x$

Use this space for computations.

10 Fred is given a rectangular piece of paper. If the length of Fred's piece of paper is represented by $2x - 6$ and the width is represented by $3x - 5$, then the paper has a total area represented by

(1) $5x - 11$
(2) $6x^2 - 28x + 30$
(3) $10x - 22$
(4) $6x^2 - 6x - 11$

11 The graph of a linear equation contains the points (3,11) and (−2,1). Which point also lies on the graph?

(1) (2,1)
(2) (2,4)
(3) (2,6)
(4) (2,9)

12 How does the graph of $f(x) = 3(x - 2)^2 + 1$ compare to the graph of $g(x) = x^2$?

(1) The graph of $f(x)$ is wider than the graph of $g(x)$, and its vertex is moved to the left 2 units and up 1 unit.
(2) The graph of $f(x)$ is narrower than the graph of $g(x)$, and its vertex is moved to the right 2 units and up 1 unit.
(3) The graph of $f(x)$ is narrower than the graph of $g(x)$, and its vertex is moved to the left 2 units and up 1 unit.
(4) The graph of $f(x)$ is wider than the graph of $g(x)$, and its vertex is moved to the right 2 units and up 1 unit.

13 Connor wants to attend the town carnival. The price of admission to the carnival is \$4.50, and each ride costs an additional 79 cents. If he can spend at most \$16.00 at the carnival, which inequality can be used to solve for r, the number of rides Connor can go on, and what is the maximum number of rides he can go on?

(1) $0.79 + 4.50r \leq 16.00$; 3 rides
(2) $0.79 + 4.50r \leq 16.00$; 4 rides
(3) $4.50 + 0.79r \leq 16.00$; 14 rides
(4) $4.50 + 0.79r \leq 16.00$; 15 rides

Use this space for computations.

14 Corinne is planning a beach vacation in July and is analyzing the daily high temperatures for her potential destination. She would like to choose a destination with a high median temperature and a small interquartile range. She constructed box plots shown in the diagram below.

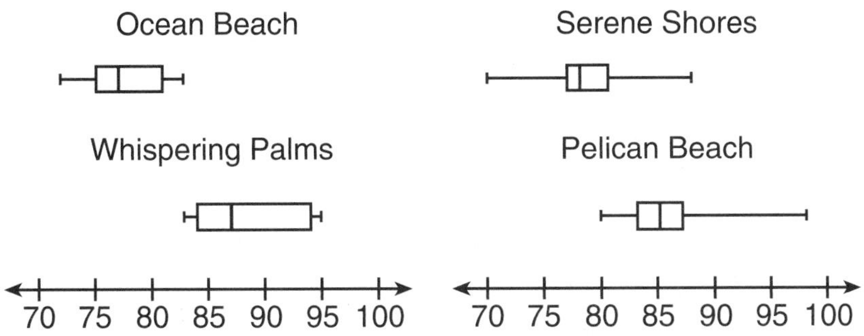

Which destination has a median temperature above 80 degrees and the smallest interquartile range?

(1) Ocean Beach
(2) Whispering Palms
(3) Serene Shores
(4) Pelican Beach

15 Some banks charge a fee on savings accounts that are left inactive for an extended period of time. The equation $y = 5000(0.98)^x$ represents the value, y, of one account that was left inactive for a period of x years.

What is the y-intercept of this equation and what does it represent?

(1) 0.98, the percent of money in the account initially
(2) 0.98, the percent of money in the account after x years
(3) 5000, the amount of money in the account initially
(4) 5000, the amount of money in the account after x years

Use this space for computations.

16 The equation for the volume of a cylinder is $V = \pi r^2 h$. The positive value of r, in terms of h and V, is

(1) $r = \sqrt{\frac{V}{\pi h}}$

(2) $r = \sqrt{V\pi h}$

(3) $r = 2V\pi h$

(4) $r = \frac{V}{2\pi}$

17 Which equation has the same solutions as $x^2 + 6x - 7 = 0$?

(1) $(x + 3)^2 = 2$

(2) $(x - 3)^2 = 2$

(3) $(x - 3)^2 = 16$

(4) $(x + 3)^2 = 16$

18 Two functions, $y = |x - 3|$ and $3x + 3y = 27$, are graphed on the same set of axes. Which statement is true about the solution to the system of equations?

(1) (3,0) is the solution to the system because it satisfies the equation $y = |x - 3|$.

(2) (9,0) is the solution to the system because it satisfies the equation $3x + 3y = 27$.

(3) (6,3) is the solution to the system because it satisfies both equations.

(4) (3,0), (9,0), and (6,3) are the solutions to the system of equations because they all satisfy at least one of the equations.

Use this space for computations.

19 Miriam and Jessica are growing bacteria in a laboratory. Miriam uses the growth function $f(t) = n^{2t}$ while Jessica uses the function $g(t) = n^{4t}$, where n represents the initial number of bacteria and t is the time, in hours. If Miriam starts with 16 bacteria, how many bacteria should Jessica start with to achieve the same growth over time?

(1) 32 (3) 8

(2) 16 (4) 4

20 If a sequence is defined recursively by $f(0) = 2$ and $f(n + 1) = -2f(n) + 3$ for $n \geq 0$, then $f(2)$ is equal to

(1) 1 (3) 5

(2) -11 (4) 17

21 An astronaut drops a rock off the edge of a cliff on the Moon. The distance, $d(t)$, in meters, the rock travels after t seconds can be modeled by the function $d(t) = 0.8t^2$. What is the average speed, in meters per second, of the rock between 5 and 10 seconds after it was dropped?

(1) 12 (3) 60

(2) 20 (4) 80

22 When factored completely, the expression $p^4 - 81$ is equivalent to

(1) $(p^2 + 9)(p^2 - 9)$

(2) $(p^2 - 9)(p^2 - 9)$

(3) $(p^2 + 9)(p + 3)(p - 3)$

(4) $(p + 3)(p - 3)(p + 3)(p - 3)$

Use this space for computations.

23 In 2013, the United States Postal Service charged \$0.46 to mail a letter weighing up to 1 oz. and \$0.20 per ounce for each additional ounce. Which function would determine the cost, in dollars, $c(z)$, of mailing a letter weighing z ounces where z is an integer greater than 1?

(1) $c(z) = 0.46z + 0.20$

(2) $c(z) = 0.20z + 0.46$

(3) $c(z) = 0.46(z - 1) + 0.20$

(4) $c(z) = 0.20(z - 1) + 0.46$

24 A polynomial function contains the factors x, $x - 2$, and $x + 5$. Which graph(s) below could represent the graph of this function?

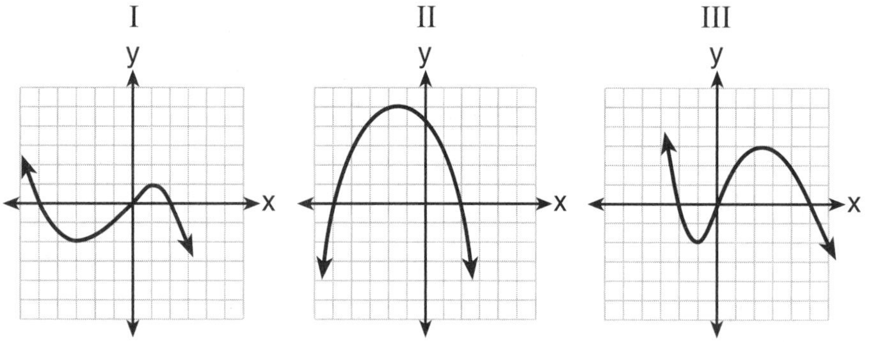

(1) I, only

(2) II, only

(3) I and III

(4) I, II, and III

Part II

Answer all 8 questions in this part. Each correct answer will receive 2 credits. Clearly indicate the necessary steps, including appropriate formula substitutions, diagrams, graphs, charts, etc. For all questions in this part, a correct numerical answer with no work shown will receive only 1 credit. All answers should be written in pen, except for graphs and drawings, which should be done in pencil. [16]

25 Ms. Fox asked her class "Is the sum of 4.2 and $\sqrt{2}$ rational or irrational?" Patrick answered that the sum would be irrational.

State whether Patrick is correct or incorrect. Justify your reasoning.

26 The school newspaper surveyed the student body for an article about club membership. The table below shows the number of students in each grade level who belong to one or more clubs.

	1 Club	2 Clubs	3 or More Clubs
9th	90	33	12
10th	125	12	15
11th	87	22	18
12th	75	27	23

If there are 180 students in ninth grade, what percentage of the ninth grade students belong to more than one club?

27 A function is shown in the table below.

x	f(x)
–4	2
–1	–4
0	–2
3	16

If included in the table, which ordered pair, $(-4,1)$ or $(1,-4)$, would result in a relation that is no longer a function? Explain your answer.

28 Subtract $5x^2 + 2x - 11$ from $3x^2 + 8x - 7$. Express the result as a trinomial.

29 Solve the equation $4x^2 - 12x = 7$ algebraically for x.

30 Graph the following function on the set of axes below.

$$f(x) = \begin{cases} |x|, & -3 \le x < 1 \\ 4, & 1 \le x \le 8 \end{cases}$$

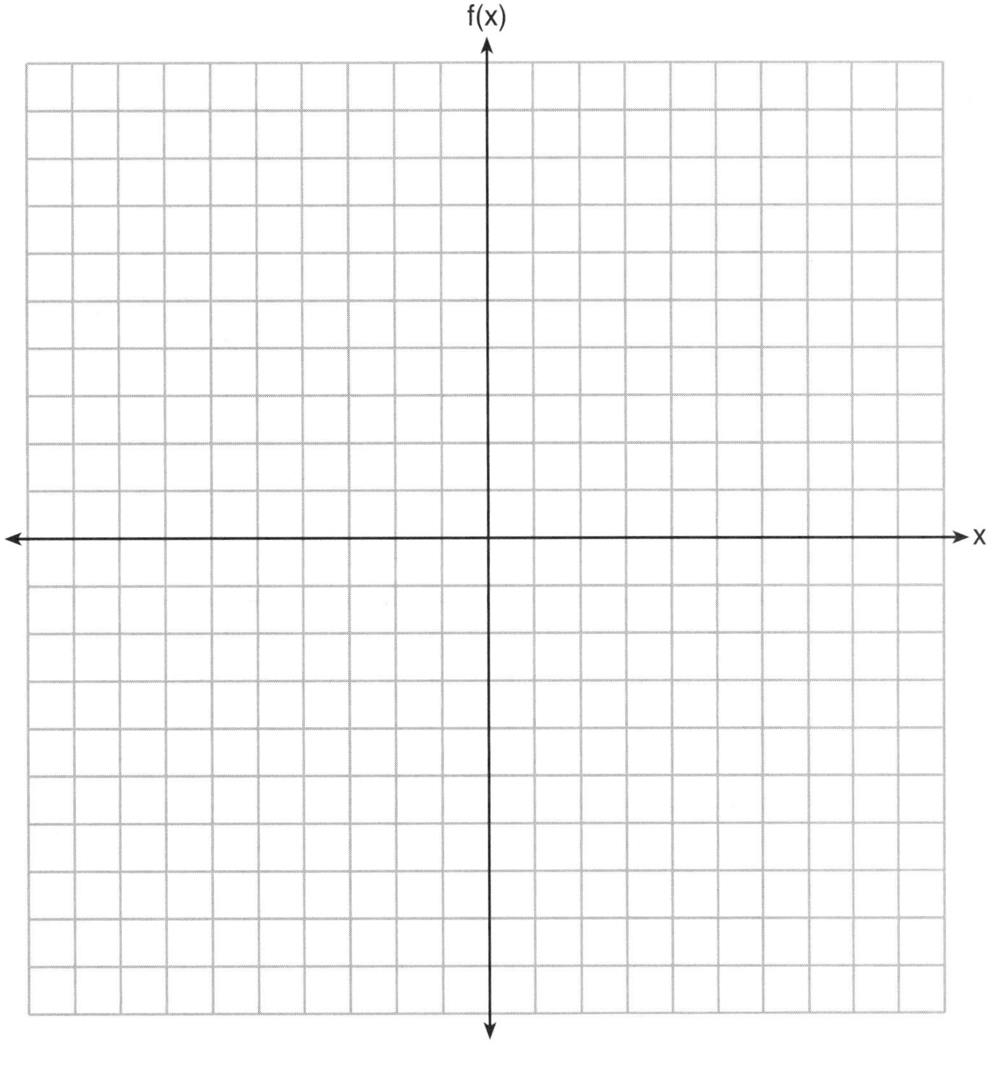

31 A gardener is planting two types of trees:

Type *A* is three feet tall and grows at a rate of 15 inches per year.

Type *B* is four feet tall and grows at a rate of 10 inches per year.

Algebraically determine exactly how many years it will take for these trees to be the same height.

32 Write an exponential equation for the graph shown below.

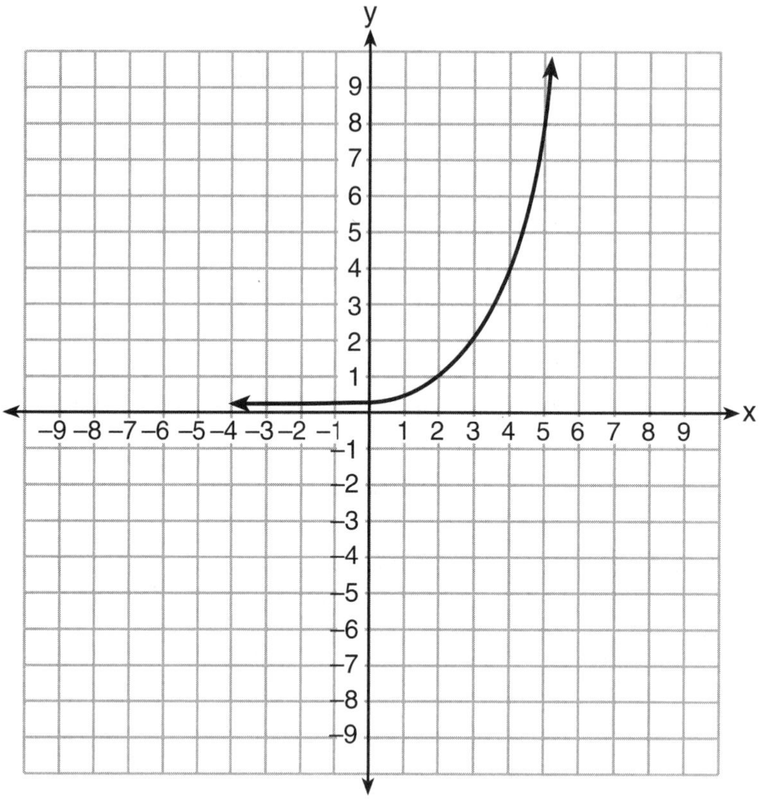

Explain how you determined the equation.

Part III

Answer all 4 questions in this part. Each correct answer will receive 4 credits. Clearly indicate the necessary steps, including appropriate formula substitutions, diagrams, graphs, charts, etc. For all questions in this part, a correct numerical answer with no work shown will receive only 1 credit. All answers should be written in pen, except for graphs and drawings, which should be done in pencil. [16]

33 Jacob and Zachary go to the movie theater and purchase refreshments for their friends. Jacob spends a total of \$18.25 on two bags of popcorn and three drinks. Zachary spends a total of \$27.50 for four bags of popcorn and two drinks.

Write a system of equations that can be used to find the price of one bag of popcorn and the price of one drink.

Using these equations, determine and state the price of a bag of popcorn and the price of a drink, to the *nearest cent*.

34 The graph of an inequality is shown below.

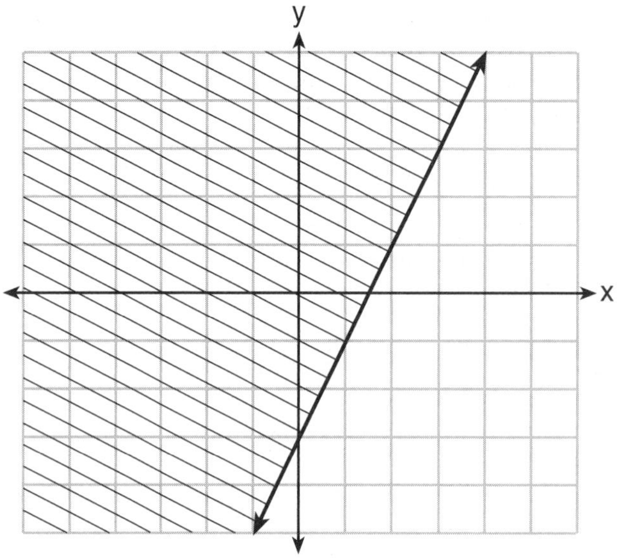

a) Write the inequality represented by the graph.

b) On the same set of axes, graph the inequality $x + 2y < 4$.

c) The two inequalities graphed on the set of axes form a system. Oscar thinks that the point (2,1) is in the solution set for this system of inequalities. Determine and state whether you agree with Oscar. Explain your reasoning.

35 A nutritionist collected information about different brands of beef hot dogs. She made a table showing the number of Calories and the amount of sodium in each hot dog.

Calories per Beef Hot Dog	Milligrams of Sodium per Beef Hot Dog
186	495
181	477
176	425
149	322
184	482
190	587
158	370
139	322

a) Write the correlation coefficient for the line of best fit. Round your answer to the *nearest hundredth.*

b) Explain what the correlation coefficient suggests in the context of this problem.

36 a) Given the function $f(x) = -x^2 + 8x + 9$, state whether the vertex represents a maximum or minimum point for the function. Explain your answer.

b) Rewrite $f(x)$ in vertex form by completing the square.

Part IV

Answer the question in this part. A correct answer will receive 6 credits. Clearly indicate the necessary steps, including appropriate formula substitutions, diagrams, graphs, charts, etc. A correct numerical answer with no work shown will receive only 1 credit. All answers should be written in pen, except for graphs and drawings, which should be written in pencil. [6]

37 New Clarendon Park is undergoing renovations to its gardens. One garden that was originally a square is being adjusted so that one side is doubled in length, while the other side is decreased by three meters.

The new rectangular garden will have an area that is 25% more than the original square garden. Write an equation that could be used to determine the length of a side of the original square garden.

Explain how your equation models the situation.

Determine the area, in square meters, of the new rectangular garden.

ALGEBRA I (COMMON CORE) June 2015

Part I

Answer all 24 questions in this part. Each correct answer will receive 2 credits. No partial credit will be allowed. Utilize the information provided for each question to determine your answer. Note that diagrams are not necessarily drawn to scale. For each statement or question, choose the word or expression that, of those given, best completes the statement or answers the question. Record your answers on your separate answer sheet. [48]

Use this space for computations.

1 The cost of airing a commercial on television is modeled by the function $C(n) = 110n + 900$, where n is the number of times the commercial is aired. Based on this model, which statement is true?

(1) The commercial costs \$0 to produce and \$110 per airing up to \$900.

(2) The commercial costs \$110 to produce and \$900 each time it is aired.

(3) The commercial costs \$900 to produce and \$110 each time it is aired.

(4) The commercial costs \$1010 to produce and can air an unlimited number of times.

2 The graph below represents a jogger's speed during her 20-minute jog around her neighborhood.

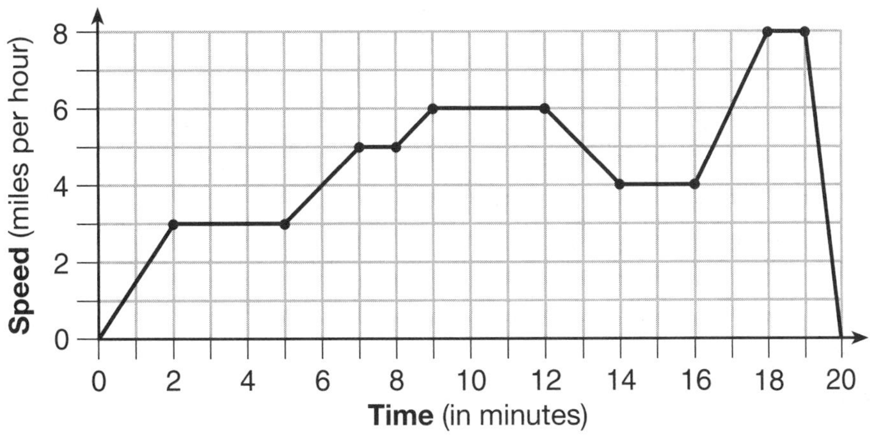

Which statement best describes what the jogger was doing during the 9–12 minute interval of her jog?

(1) She was standing still.

(2) She was increasing her speed.

(3) She was decreasing her speed.

(4) She was jogging at a constant rate.

Use this space for computations.

3 If the area of a rectangle is expressed as $x^4 - 9y^2$, then the product of the length and the width of the rectangle could be expressed as

(1) $(x - 3y)(x + 3y)$

(2) $(x^2 - 3y)(x^2 + 3y)$

(3) $(x^2 - 3y)(x^2 - 3y)$

(4) $(x^4 + y)(x - 9y)$

4 Which table represents a function?

x	2	4	2	4
f(x)	3	5	7	9

(1)

x	0	−1	0	1
f(x)	0	1	−1	0

(2)

x	3	5	7	9
f(x)	2	4	2	4

(3)

x	0	1	−1	0
f(x)	0	−1	0	1

(4)

5 Which inequality is represented in the graph below?

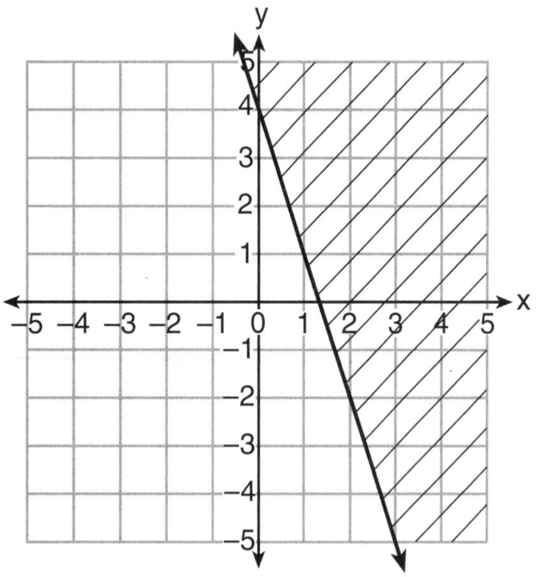

(1) $y \geq -3x + 4$

(2) $y \leq -3x + 4$

(3) $y \geq -4x - 3$

(4) $y \leq -4x - 3$

Use this space for computations.

6 Mo's farm stand sold a total of 165 pounds of apples and peaches. She sold apples for \$1.75 per pound and peaches for \$2.50 per pound. If she made \$337.50, how many pounds of peaches did she sell?

(1) 11 (3) 65

(2) 18 (4) 100

7 Morgan can start wrestling at age 5 in Division 1. He remains in that division until his next odd birthday when he is required to move up to the next division level. Which graph correctly represents this information?

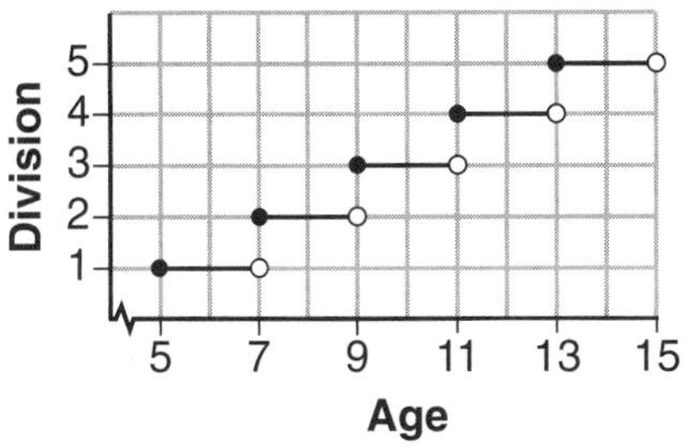

(1)

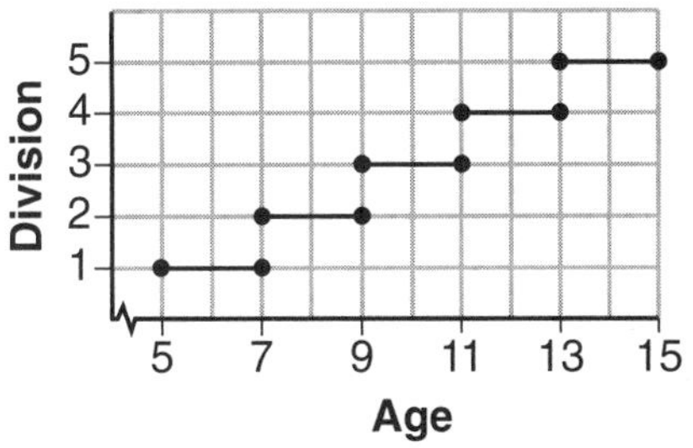

(3)

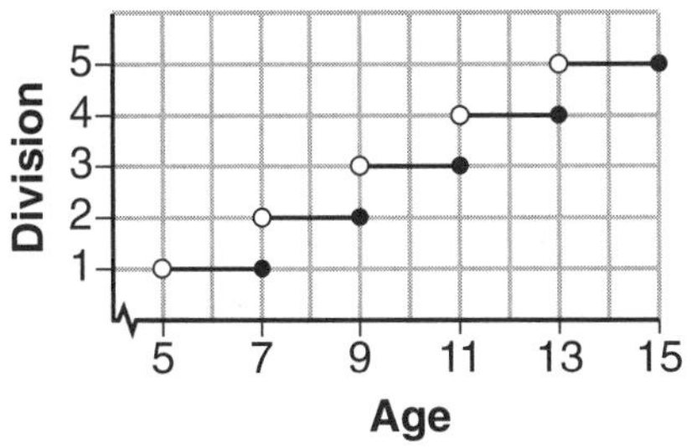

(2)

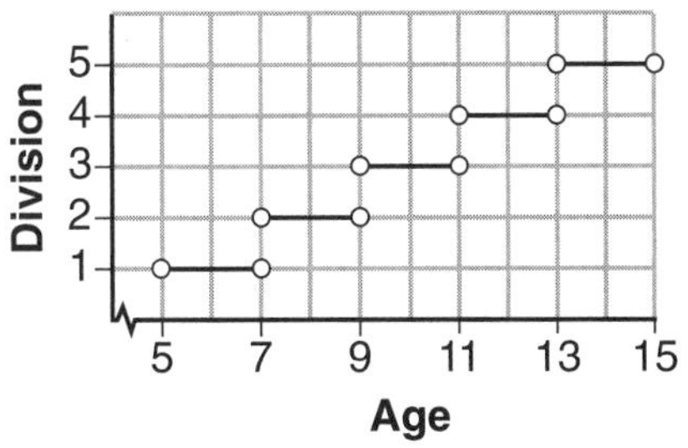

(4)

Use this space for computations.

8 Which statement is *not* always true?

(1) The sum of two rational numbers is rational.

(2) The product of two irrational numbers is rational.

(3) The sum of a rational number and an irrational number is irrational.

(4) The product of a nonzero rational number and an irrational number is irrational.

9 The graph of the function $f(x) = \sqrt{x + 4}$ is shown below.

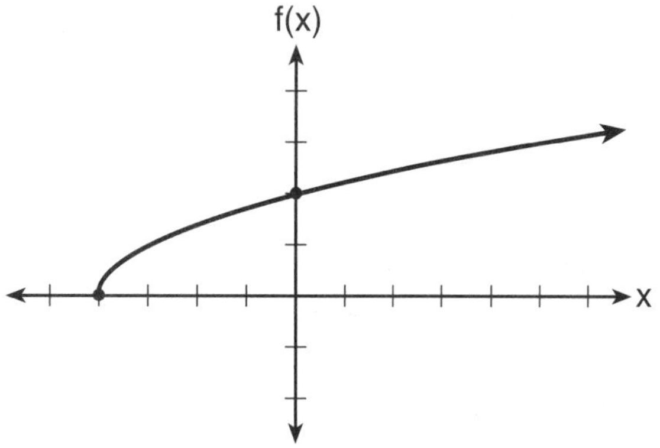

The domain of the function is

(1) $\{x | x > 0\}$

(2) $\{x | x \geq 0\}$

(3) $\{x | x > -4\}$

(4) $\{x | x \geq -4\}$

10 What are the zeros of the function $f(x) = x^2 - 13x - 30$?

(1) -10 and 3

(2) 10 and -3

(3) -15 and 2

(4) 15 and -2

Use this space for computations.

11 Joey enlarged a 3-inch by 5-inch photograph on a copy machine. He enlarged it four times. The table below shows the area of the photograph after each enlargement.

Enlargement	0	1	2	3	4
Area (square inches)	15	18.8	23.4	29.3	36.6

What is the average rate of change of the area from the original photograph to the fourth enlargement, to the *nearest tenth*?

(1) 4.3
(2) 4.5
(3) 5.4
(4) 6.0

12 Which equation(s) represent the graph below?

I $y = (x + 2)(x^2 - 4x - 12)$

II $y = (x - 3)(x^2 + x - 2)$

III $y = (x - 1)(x^2 - 5x - 6)$

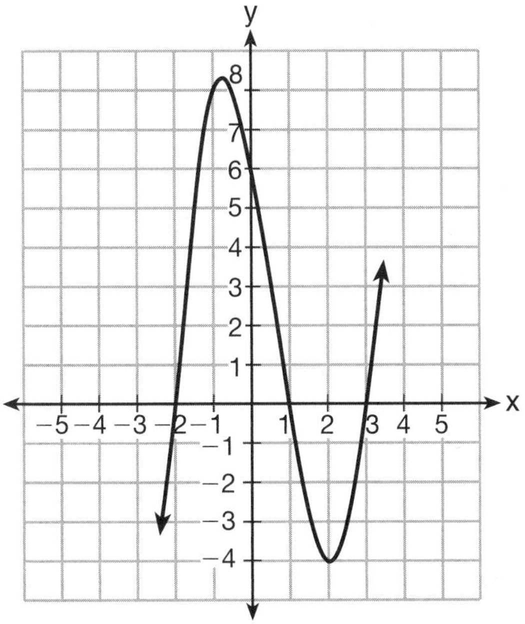

(1) I, only
(2) II, only
(3) I and II
(4) II and III

Use this space for computations.

13 A laboratory technician studied the population growth of a colony of bacteria. He recorded the number of bacteria every other day, as shown in the partial table below.

t (time, in days)	0	2	4
f(t) (bacteria)	25	15,625	9,765,625

Which function would accurately model the technician's data?

(1) $f(t) = 25^t$

(2) $f(t) = 25^{t+1}$

(3) $f(t) = 25t$

(4) $f(t) = 25(t + 1)$

14 Which quadratic function has the largest maximum?

$h(x) = (3 - x)(2 + x)$

(1)

$k(x) = -5x^2 - 12x + 4$

(3)

x	f(x)
−1	−3
0	5
1	9
2	9
3	5
4	−3

(2)

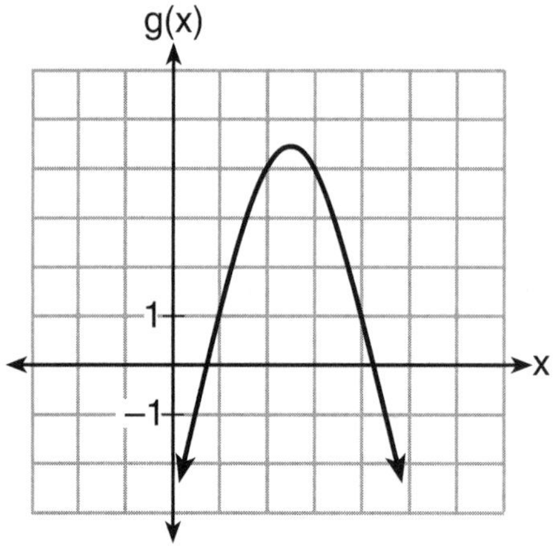

(4)

15 If $f(x) = 3^x$ and $g(x) = 2x + 5$, at which value of x is $f(x) < g(x)$?

(1) −1

(2) 2

(3) −3

(4) 4

Use this space for computations.

16 Beverly did a study this past spring using data she collected from a cafeteria. She recorded data weekly for ice cream sales and soda sales. Beverly found the line of best fit and the correlation coefficient, as shown in the diagram below.

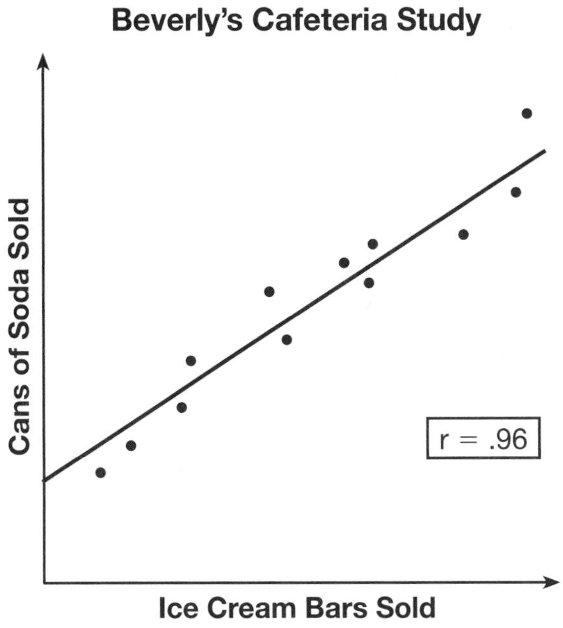

Given this information, which statement(s) can correctly be concluded?

I. Eating more ice cream causes a person to become thirsty.

II. Drinking more soda causes a person to become hungry.

III. There is a strong correlation between ice cream sales and soda sales.

(1) I, only
(2) III, only
(3) I and III
(4) II and III

17 The function $V(t) = 1350(1.017)^t$ represents the value $V(t)$, in dollars, of a comic book t years after its purchase. The yearly rate of appreciation of the comic book is

(1) 17%
(2) 1.7%
(3) 1.017%
(4) 0.017%

Use this space for computations.

18 When directed to solve a quadratic equation by completing the square, Sam arrived at the equation $\left(x - \frac{5}{2}\right)^2 = \frac{13}{4}$. Which equation could have been the original equation given to Sam?

(1) $x^2 + 5x + 7 = 0$
(2) $x^2 + 5x + 3 = 0$
(3) $x^2 - 5x + 7 = 0$
(4) $x^2 - 5x + 3 = 0$

19 The distance a free falling object has traveled can be modeled by the equation $d = \frac{1}{2}at^2$, where a is acceleration due to gravity and t is the amount of time the object has fallen. What is t in terms of a and d?

(1) $t = \sqrt{\frac{da}{2}}$
(2) $t = \sqrt{\frac{2d}{a}}$
(3) $t = \left(\frac{da}{d}\right)^2$
(4) $t = \left(\frac{2d}{a}\right)^2$

20 The table below shows the annual salaries for the 24 members of a professional sports team in terms of millions of dollars.

0.5	0.5	0.6	0.7	0.75	0.8
1.0	1.0	1.1	1.25	1.3	1.4
1.4	1.8	2.5	3.7	3.8	4
4.2	4.6	5.1	6	6.3	7.2

The team signs an additional player to a contract worth 10 million dollars per year. Which statement about the median and mean is true?

(1) Both will increase.
(2) Only the median will increase.
(3) Only the mean will increase.
(4) Neither will change.

Use this space for computations.

21 A student is asked to solve the equation $4(3x - 1)^2 - 17 = 83$. The student's solution to the problem starts as

$$4(3x - 1)^2 = 100$$
$$(3x - 1)^2 = 25$$

A correct next step in the solution of the problem is

(1) $3x - 1 = \pm 5$

(2) $3x - 1 = \pm 25$

(3) $9x^2 - 1 = 25$

(4) $9x^2 - 6x + 1 = 5$

22 A pattern of blocks is shown below.

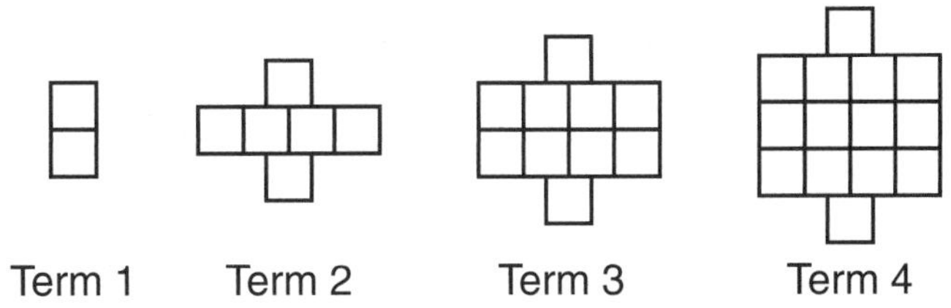

If the pattern of blocks continues, which formula(s) could be used to determine the number of blocks in the *n*th term?

I	II	III
$a_n = n + 4$	$a_1 = 2$ $a_n = a_{n-1} + 4$	$a_n = 4n - 2$

(1) I and II

(2) I and III

(3) II and III

(4) III, only

Use this space for computations.

23 What are the solutions to the equation $x^2 - 8x = 24$?

(1) $x = 4 \pm 2\sqrt{10}$
(2) $x = -4 \pm 2\sqrt{10}$
(3) $x = 4 \pm 2\sqrt{2}$
(4) $x = -4 \pm 2\sqrt{2}$

24 Natasha is planning a school celebration and wants to have live music and food for everyone who attends. She has found a band that will charge her \$750 and a caterer who will provide snacks and drinks for \$2.25 per person. If her goal is to keep the average cost per person between \$2.75 and \$3.25, how many people, p, must attend?

(1) $225 < p < 325$
(2) $325 < p < 750$
(3) $500 < p < 1000$
(4) $750 < p < 1500$

Part II

Answer all 8 questions in this part. Each correct answer will receive 2 credits. Clearly indicate the necessary steps, including appropriate formula substitutions, diagrams, graphs, charts, etc. Utilize the information provided for each question to determine your answer. Note that diagrams are not necessarily drawn to scale. For all questions in this part, a correct numerical answer with no work shown will receive only 1 credit. All answers should be written in pen, except for graphs and drawings, which should be done in pencil. [16]

25 Graph the function $y = |x - 3|$ on the set of axes below.

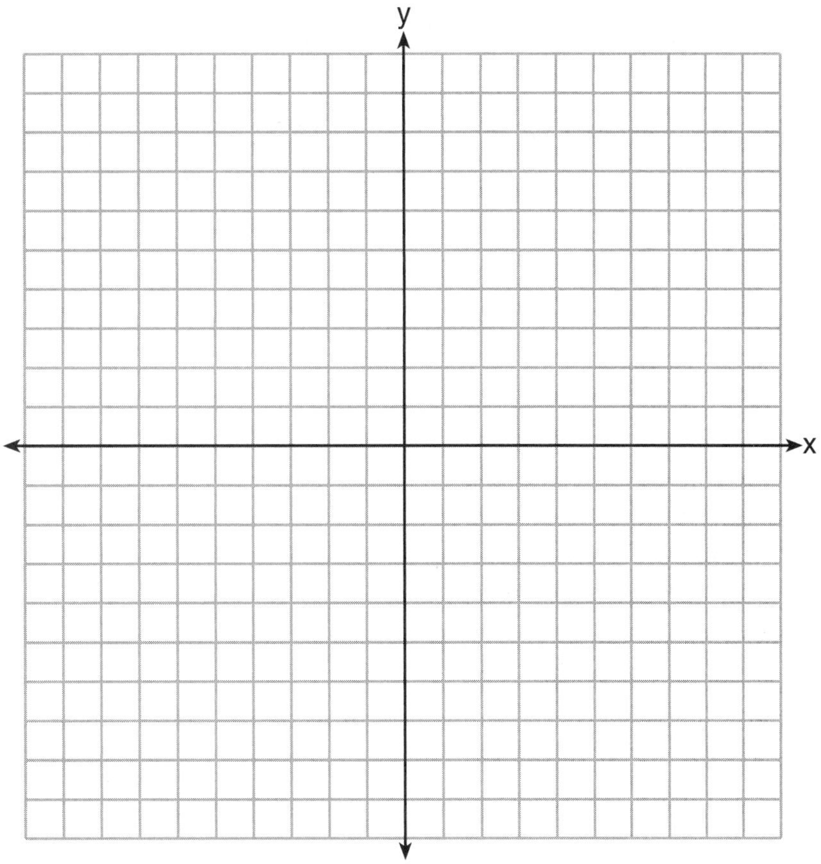

Explain how the graph of $y = |x - 3|$ has changed from the related graph $y = |x|$.

26 Alex is selling tickets to a school play. An adult ticket costs \$6.50 and a student ticket costs \$4.00. Alex sells x adult tickets and 12 student tickets. Write a function, $f(x)$, to represent how much money Alex collected from selling tickets.

27 John and Sarah are each saving money for a car. The total amount of money John will save is given by the function $f(x) = 60 + 5x$. The total amount of money Sarah will save is given by the function $g(x) = x^2 + 46$. After how many weeks, x, will they have the same amount of money saved? Explain how you arrived at your answer.

28 If the difference $(3x^2 - 2x + 5) - (x^2 + 3x - 2)$ is multiplied by $\frac{1}{2}x^2$, what is the result, written in standard form?

29 Dylan invested \$600 in a savings account at a 1.6% annual interest rate. He made no deposits or withdrawals on the account for 2 years. The interest was compounded annually. Find, to the *nearest cent*, the balance in the account after 2 years.

30 Determine the smallest integer that makes $-3x + 7 - 5x < 15$ true.

31 The residual plots from two different sets of bivariate data are graphed below.

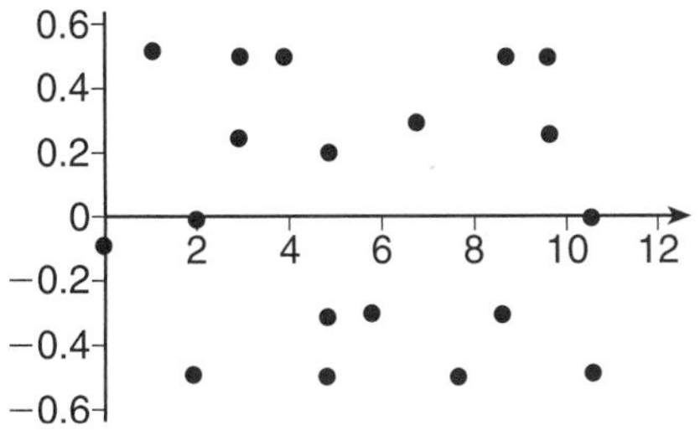

Graph A

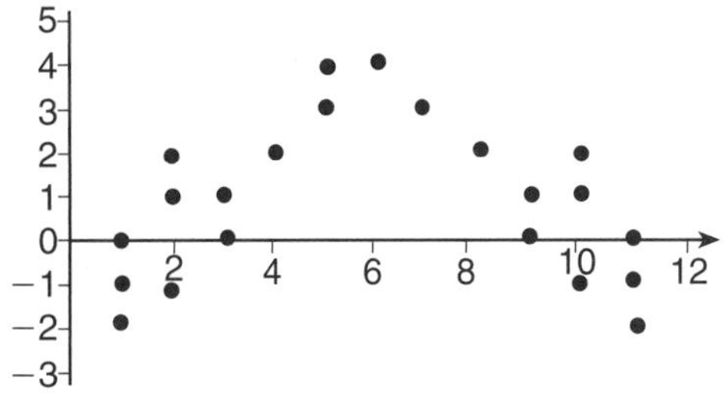

Graph B

Explain, using evidence from graph *A* and graph *B*, which graph indicates that the model for the data is a good fit.

32 A landscaper is creating a rectangular flower bed such that the width is half of the length. The area of the flower bed is 34 square feet. Write and solve an equation to determine the width of the flower bed, to the *nearest tenth of a foot*.

Part III

Answer all 4 questions in this part. Each correct answer will receive 4 credits. Clearly indicate the necessary steps, including appropriate formula substitutions, diagrams, graphs, charts, etc. Utilize the information provided for each question to determine your answer. Note that diagrams are not necessarily drawn to scale. For all questions in this part, a correct numerical answer with no work shown will receive only 1 credit. All answers should be written in pen, except for graphs and drawings, which should be done in pencil. [16]

33 Albert says that the two systems of equations shown below have the same solutions.

First System	Second System
$8x + 9y = 48$	$8x + 9y = 48$
$12x + 5y = 21$	$-8.5y = -51$

Determine and state whether you agree with Albert. Justify your answer.

34 The equation to determine the weekly earnings of an employee at The Hamburger Shack is given by $w(x)$, where x is the number of hours worked.

$$w(x) = \begin{cases} 10x, & 0 \leq x \leq 40 \\ 15(x - 40) + 400, & x > 40 \end{cases}$$

Determine the difference in salary, *in dollars*, for an employee who works 52 hours versus one who works 38 hours.

Determine the number of hours an employee must work in order to earn \$445. Explain how you arrived at this answer.

35 An on-line electronics store must sell at least \$2500 worth of printers and computers per day. Each printer costs \$50 and each computer costs \$500. The store can ship a maximum of 15 items per day.

On the set of axes below, graph a system of inequalities that models these constraints.

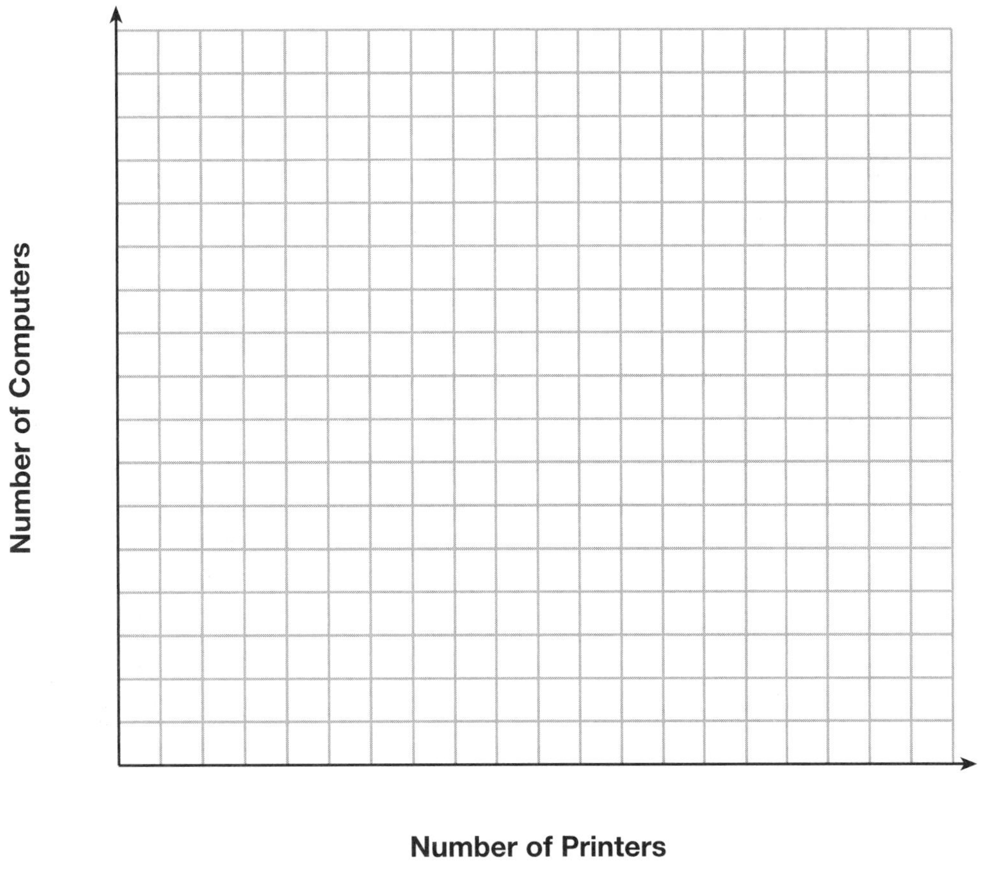

Determine a combination of printers and computers that would allow the electronics store to meet all of the constraints. Explain how you obtained your answer.

36 An application developer released a new app to be downloaded. The table below gives the number of downloads for the first four weeks after the launch of the app.

Number of Weeks	1	2	3	4
Number of Downloads	120	180	270	405

Write an exponential equation that models these data.

Use this model to predict how many downloads the developer would expect in the 26th week if this trend continues. Round your answer to the *nearest download*.

Would it be reasonable to use this model to predict the number of downloads past one year? Explain your reasoning.

Part IV

Answer the question in this part. A correct answer will receive 6 credits. Clearly indicate the necessary steps, including appropriate formula substitutions, diagrams, graphs, charts, etc. Utilize the information provided for each question to determine your answer. Note that diagrams are not necessarily drawn to scale. A correct numerical answer with no work shown will receive only 1 credit. All answers should be written in pen, except for graphs and drawings, which should be written in pencil. [6]

37 A football player attempts to kick a football over a goal post. The path of the football can be modeled by the function $h(x) = -\frac{1}{225}x^2 + \frac{2}{3}x$, where x is the horizontal distance from the kick, and $h(x)$ is the height of the football above the ground, when both are measured in feet.

On the set of axes below, graph the function $y = h(x)$ over the interval $0 \leq x \leq 150$.

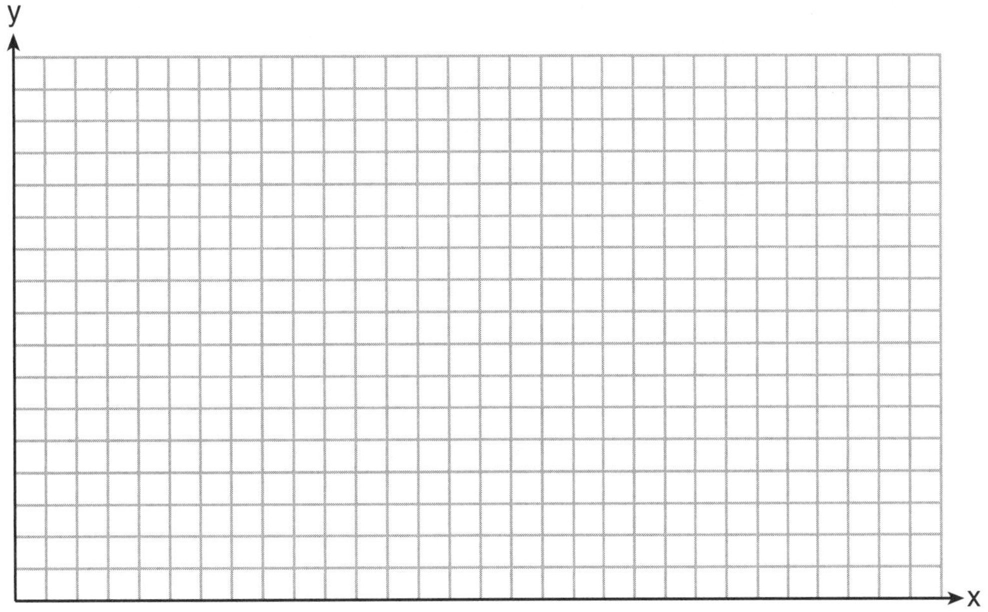

Determine the vertex of $y = h(x)$. Interpret the meaning of this vertex in the context of the problem.

The goal post is 10 feet high and 45 yards away from the kick. Will the ball be high enough to pass over the goal post? Justify your answer.

ALGEBRA I (COMMON CORE) March 2016

Part I

Answer all 24 questions in this part. Each correct answer will receive 2 credits. No partial credit will be allowed. Utilize the information provided for each question to determine your answer. Note that diagrams are not necessarily drawn to scale. For each statement or question, choose the word or expression that, of those given, best completes the statement or answers the question. Record your answers on your separate answer sheet. [48]

Use this space for computations.

1 In the function $f(x) = (x - 2)^2 + 4$, the minimum value occurs when x is

(1) -2 (3) -4

(2) 2 (4) 4

2 The graph below was created by an employee at a gas station.

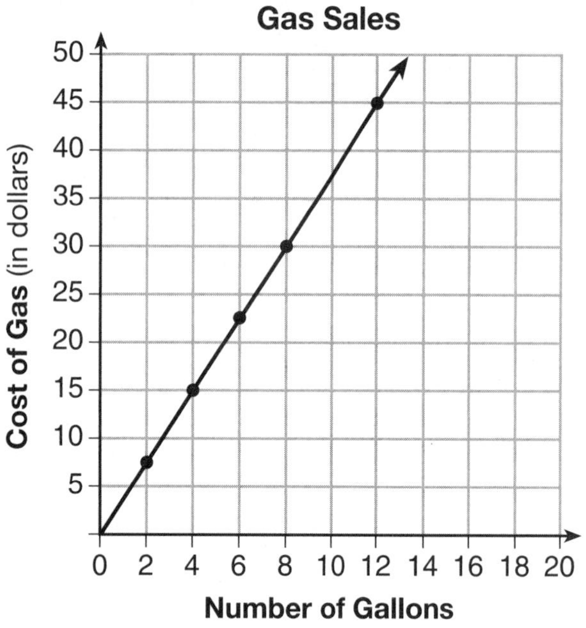

Which statement can be justified by using the graph?

(1) If 10 gallons of gas was purchased, \$35 was paid.

(2) For every gallon of gas purchased, \$3.75 was paid.

(3) For every 2 gallons of gas purchased, \$5.00 was paid.

(4) If zero gallons of gas were purchased, zero miles were driven.

Use this space for computations.

3 For a recently released movie, the function $y = 119.67(0.61)^x$ models the revenue earned, y, in millions of dollars each week, x, for several weeks after its release.

Based on the equation, how much more money, in millions of dollars, was earned in revenue for week 3 than for week 5?

(1) 37.27 (3) 17.06

(2) 27.16 (4) 10.11

4 Given the following expressions:

I. $-\frac{5}{8} + \frac{3}{5}$ III. $(\sqrt{5}) \cdot (\sqrt{5})$

II. $\frac{1}{2} + \sqrt{2}$ IV. $3 \cdot (\sqrt{49})$

Which expression(s) result in an irrational number?

(1) II, only (3) I, III, IV

(2) III, only (4) II, III, IV

5 Which inequality is represented by the graph below?

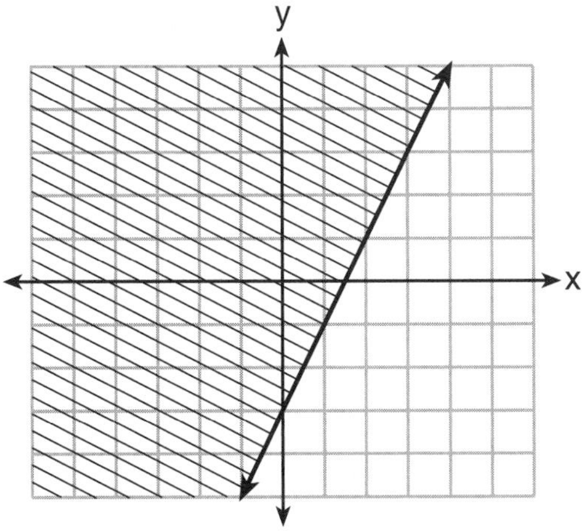

(1) $y \leq 2x - 3$ (3) $y \leq -3x + 2$

(2) $y \geq 2x - 3$ (4) $y \geq -3x + 2$

Use this space for computations.

6 Michael borrows money from his uncle, who is charging him simple interest using the formula $I = Prt$. To figure out what the interest rate, r, is, Michael rearranges the formula to find r. His new formula is r equals

(1) $\frac{I-P}{t}$ (3) $\frac{I}{Pt}$

(2) $\frac{P-I}{t}$ (4) $\frac{Pt}{I}$

7 Which equation is equivalent to $y - 34 = x(x - 12)$?

(1) $y = (x - 17)(x + 2)$ (3) $y = (x - 6)^2 + 2$

(2) $y = (x - 17)(x - 2)$ (4) $y = (x - 6)^2 - 2$

8 The equation $A = 1300(1.02)^7$ is being used to calculate the amount of money in a savings account. What does 1.02 represent in this equation?

(1) 0.02% decay (3) 2% decay

(2) 0.02% growth (4) 2% growth

9 The zeros of the function $f(x) = 2x^2 - 4x - 6$ are

(1) 3 and -1 (3) -3 and 1

(2) 3 and 1 (4) -3 and -1

10 When $(2x - 3)^2$ is subtracted from $5x^2$, the result is

(1) $x^2 - 12x - 9$ (3) $x^2 + 12x - 9$

(2) $x^2 - 12x + 9$ (4) $x^2 + 12x + 9$

Use this space for computations.

11 Joe has a rectangular patio that measures 10 feet by 12 feet. He wants to increase the area by 50% and plans to increase each dimension by equal lengths, x. Which equation could be used to determine x?

(1) $(10 + x)(12 + x) = 120$
(2) $(10 + x)(12 + x) = 180$
(3) $(15 + x)(18 + x) = 180$
(4) $(15)(18) = 120 + x^2$

12 When factored completely, $x^3 - 13x^2 - 30x$ is

(1) $x(x + 3)(x - 10)$
(2) $x(x - 3)(x - 10)$
(3) $x(x + 2)(x - 15)$
(4) $x(x - 2)(x + 15)$

13 The table below shows the cost of mailing a postcard in different years. During which time interval did the cost increase at the greatest average rate?

Year	1898	1971	1985	2006	2012
Cost (¢)	1	6	14	24	35

(1) 1898–1971
(2) 1971–1985
(3) 1985–2006
(4) 2006–2012

14 When solving the equation $x^2 - 8x - 7 = 0$ by completing the square, which equation is a step in the process?

(1) $(x - 4)^2 = 9$
(2) $(x - 4)^2 = 23$
(3) $(x - 8)^2 = 9$
(4) $(x - 8)^2 = 23$

15 A construction company uses the function $f(p)$, where p is the number of people working on a project, to model the amount of money it spends to complete a project. A reasonable domain for this function would be

(1) positive integers
(2) positive real numbers
(3) both positive and negative integers
(4) both positive and negative real numbers

Use this space for computations.

16 Which function is shown in the table below?

x	f(x)
–2	$\frac{1}{9}$
–1	$\frac{1}{3}$
0	1
1	3
2	9
3	27

(1) $f(x) = 3x$ (3) $f(x) = -x^3$

(2) $f(x) = x + 3$ (4) $f(x) = 3^x$

17 Given the functions $h(x) = \frac{1}{2}x + 3$ and $j(x) = |x|$, which value of x makes $h(x) = j(x)$?

(1) -2 (3) 3

(2) 2 (4) -6

18 Which recursively defined function represents the sequence 3, 7, 15, 31, …?

(1) $f(1) = 3,\ f(n + 1) = 2^{f(n)} + 3$

(2) $f(1) = 3,\ f(n + 1) = 2^{f(n)} - 1$

(3) $f(1) = 3,\ f(n + 1) = 2f(n) + 1$

(4) $f(1) = 3,\ f(n + 1) = 3f(n) - 2$

19 The range of the function defined as $y = 5^x$ is

(1) $y < 0$ (3) $y \leq 0$

(2) $y > 0$ (4) $y \geq 0$

Use this space for computations.

20 The graph of $y = f(x)$ is shown below.

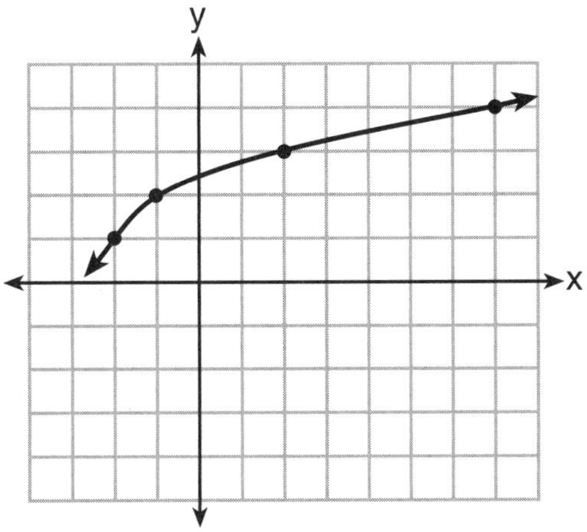

What is the graph of $y = f(x + 1) - 2$?

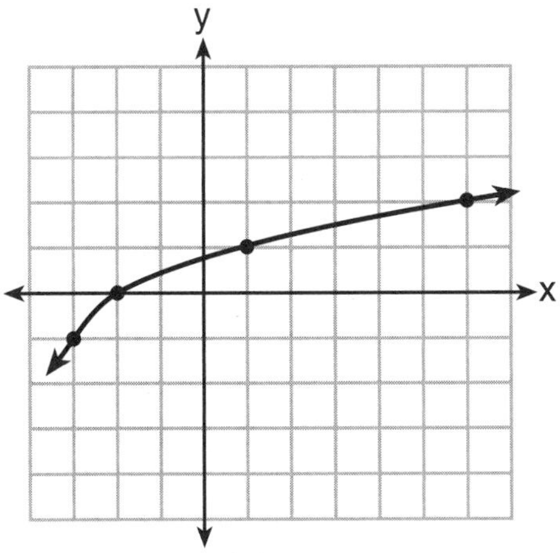

(1)

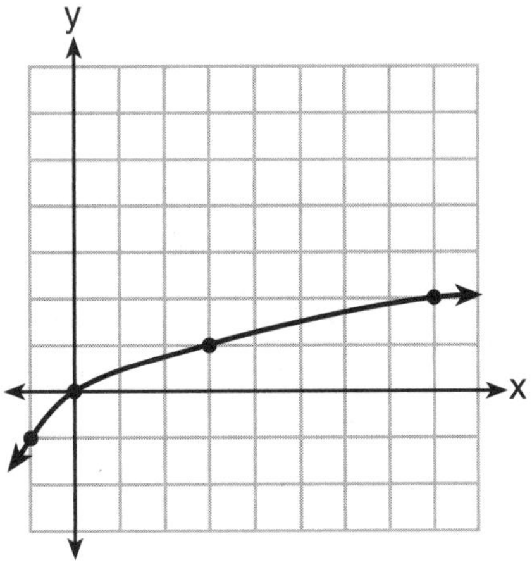

(3)

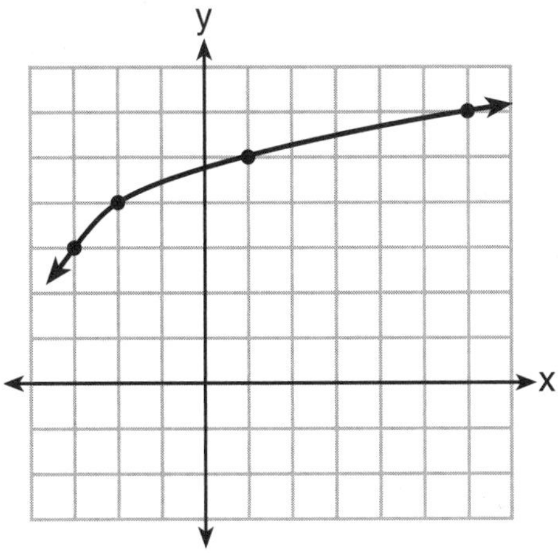

(2)

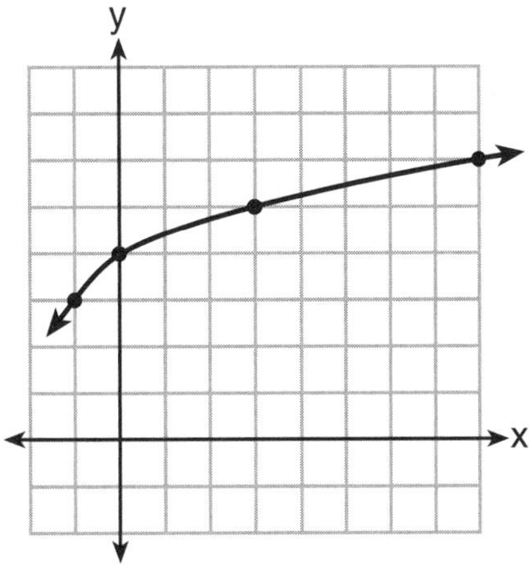

(4)

Use this space for computations.

21 Which pair of equations could *not* be used to solve the following equations for x and y?

$$4x + 2y = 22$$
$$-2x + 2y = -8$$

(1) $4x + 2y = 22$
$2x - 2y = 8$

(2) $4x + 2y = 22$
$-4x + 4y = -16$

(3) $12x + 6y = 66$
$6x - 6y = 24$

(4) $8x + 4y = 44$
$-8x + 8y = -8$

22 The graph representing a function is shown below.

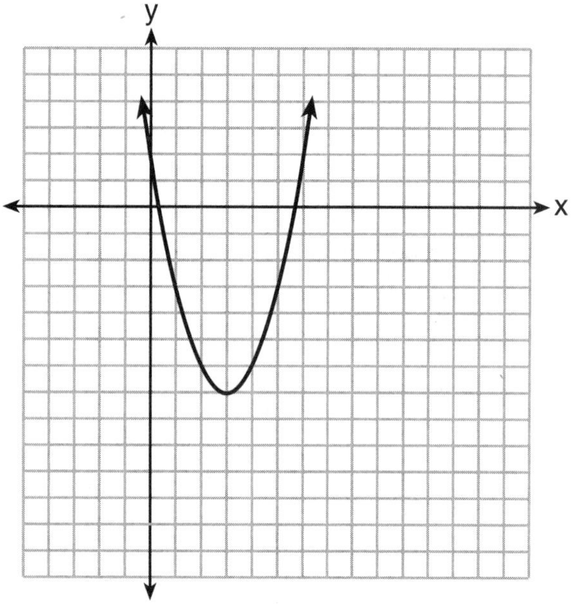

Which function has a minimum that is *less* than the one shown in the graph?

(1) $y = x^2 - 6x + 7$

(2) $y = |x + 3| - 6$

(3) $y = x^2 - 2x - 10$

(4) $y = |x - 8| + 2$

Use this space for computations.

23 Grisham is considering the three situations below.

I. For the first 28 days, a sunflower grows at a rate of 3.5 cm per day.

II. The value of a car depreciates at a rate of 15% per year after it is purchased.

III. The amount of bacteria in a culture triples every two days during an experiment.

Which of the statements describes a situation with an equal difference over an equal interval?

(1) I, only (3) I and III

(2) II, only (4) II and III

24 After performing analyses on a set of data, Jackie examined the scatter plot of the residual values for each analysis. Which scatter plot indicates the best linear fit for the data?

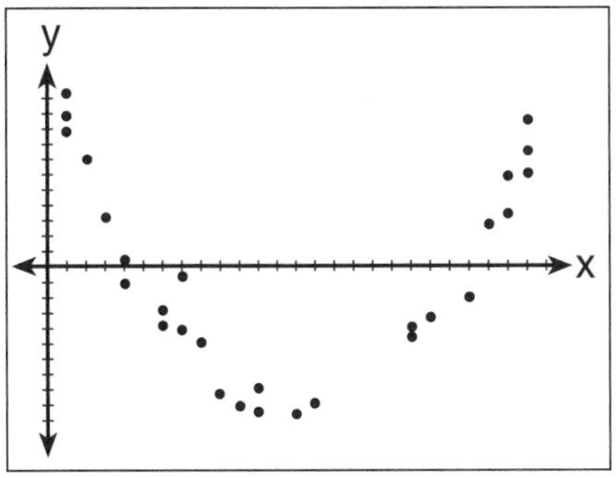

(1)

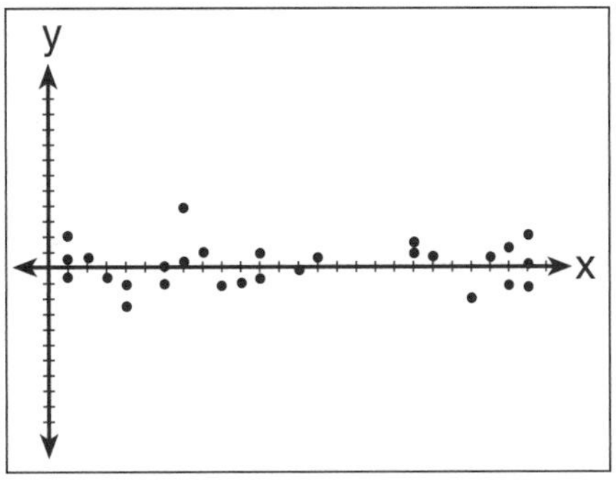

(3)

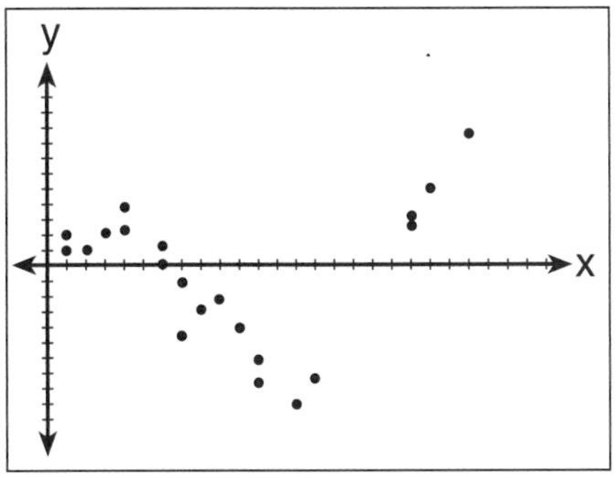

(2)

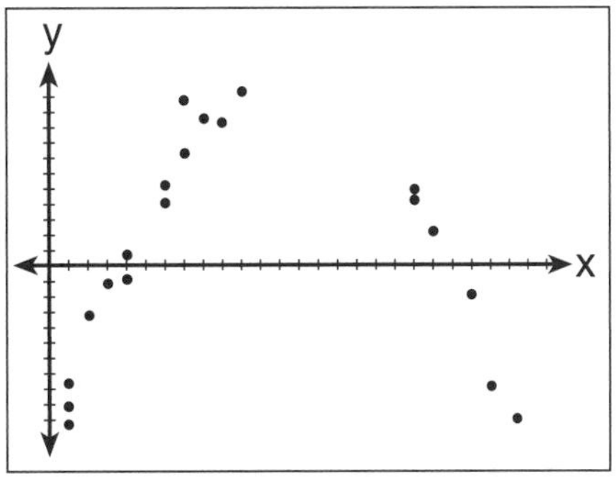

(4)

Part II

Answer all 8 questions in this part. Each correct answer will receive 2 credits. Clearly indicate the necessary steps, including appropriate formula substitutions, diagrams, graphs, charts, etc. Utilize the information provided for each question to determine your answer. Note that diagrams are not necessarily drawn to scale. For all questions in this part, a correct numerical answer with no work shown will receive only 1 credit. All answers should be written in pen, except for graphs and drawings, which should be done in pencil. [16]

25 The function, $t(x)$, is shown in the table below.

x	t(x)
–3	10
–1	7.5
1	5
3	2.5
5	0

Determine whether $t(x)$ is linear or exponential. Explain your answer.

26 Marcel claims that the graph below represents a function.

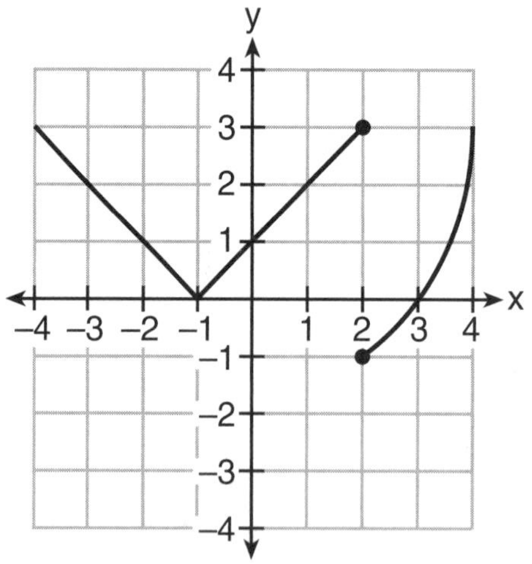

State whether Marcel is correct. Justify your answer.

27 Solve the equation for y.

$$(y - 3)^2 = 4y - 12$$

28 The graph below shows the variation in the average temperature of Earth's surface from 1950–2000, according to one source.

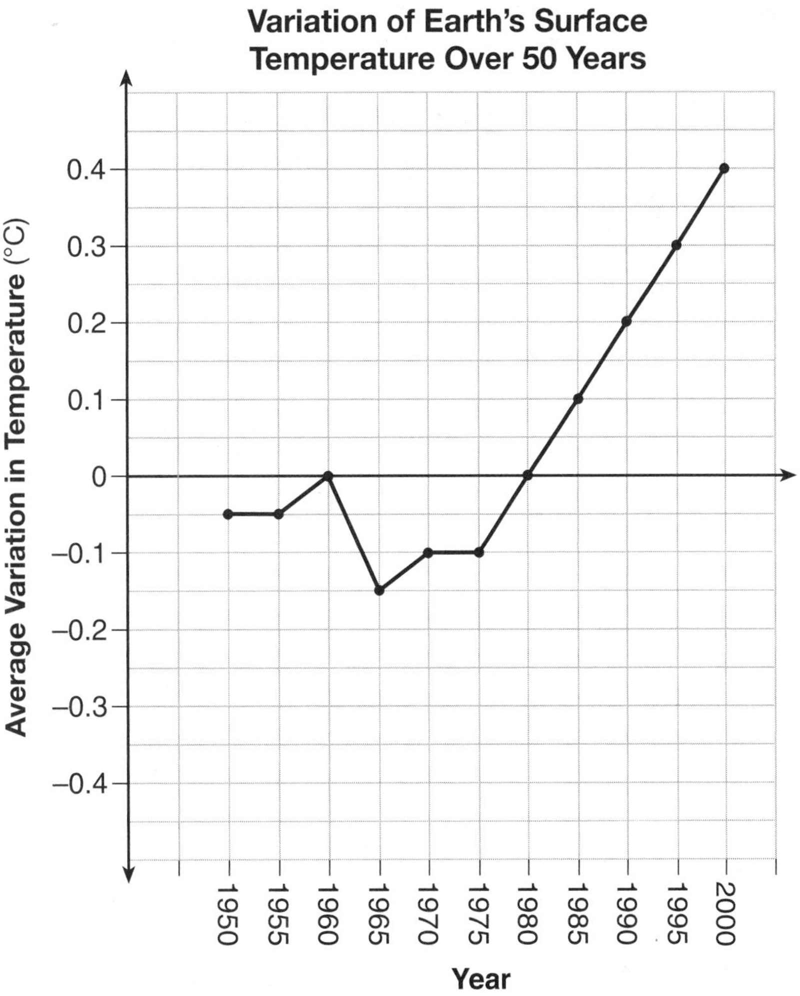

During which years did the temperature variation change the most per unit time? Explain how you determined your answer.

29 The cost of belonging to a gym can be modeled by $C(m) = 50m + 79.50$, where $C(m)$ is the total cost for m months of membership.

State the meaning of the slope and y-intercept of this function with respect to the costs associated with the gym membership.

30 A statistics class surveyed some students during one lunch period to obtain opinions about television programming preferences. The results of the survey are summarized in the table below.

Programming Preferences

	Comedy	Drama
Male	70	35
Female	48	42

Based on the sample, predict how many of the school's 351 males would prefer comedy. Justify your answer.

31 Given that $a > b$, solve for x in terms of a and b:

$$b(x - 3) \geq ax + 7b$$

32 Jacob and Jessica are studying the spread of dandelions. Jacob discovers that the growth over t weeks can be defined by the function $f(t) = (8) \bullet 2^t$. Jessica finds that the growth function over t weeks is $g(t) = 2^{t+3}$.

Calculate the number of dandelions that Jacob and Jessica will each have after 5 weeks.

Based on the growth from both functions, explain the relationship between $f(t)$ and $g(t)$.

Part III

Answer all 4 questions in this part. Each correct answer will receive 4 credits. Clearly indicate the necessary steps, including appropriate formula substitutions, diagrams, graphs, charts, etc. Utilize the information provided for each question to determine your answer. Note that diagrams are not necessarily drawn to scale. For all questions in this part, a correct numerical answer with no work shown will receive only 1 credit. All answers should be written in pen, except for graphs and drawings, which should be done in pencil. [16]

33 Let $h(t) = -16t^2 + 64t + 80$ represent the height of an object above the ground after t seconds. Determine the number of seconds it takes to achieve its maximum height. Justify your answer.

State the time interval, in seconds, during which the height of the object *decreases*. Explain your reasoning.

34 Fred's teacher gave the class the quadratic function $f(x) = 4x^2 + 16x + 9$.

a) State two different methods Fred could use to solve the equation $f(x) = 0$.

b) Using one of the methods stated in part a, solve $f(x) = 0$ for x, to the *nearest tenth*.

35 Erica, the manager at Stellarbeans, collected data on the daily high temperature and revenue from coffee sales. Data from nine days this past fall are shown in the table below.

	Day 1	Day 2	Day 3	Day 4	Day 5	Day 6	Day 7	Day 8	Day 9
High Temperature, t	54	50	62	67	70	58	52	46	48
Coffee Sales, f(t)	$2900	$3080	$2500	$2380	$2200	$2700	$3000	$3620	$3720

State the linear regression function, $f(t)$, that estimates the day's coffee sales with a high temperature of t. Round all values to the *nearest integer*.

State the correlation coefficient, r, of the data to the *nearest hundredth*. Does r indicate a strong linear relationship between the variables? Explain your reasoning.

36 A contractor has 48 meters of fencing that he is going to use as the perimeter of a rectangular garden. The length of one side of the garden is represented by x, and the area of the garden is 108 square meters.

Determine, algebraically, the dimensions of the garden in meters.

Part IV

Answer the question in this part. A correct answer will receive 6 credits. Clearly indicate the necessary steps, including appropriate formula substitutions, diagrams, graphs, charts, etc. Utilize the information provided to determine your answer. Note that diagrams are not necessarily drawn to scale. A correct numerical answer with no work shown will receive only 1 credit. All answers should be written in pen, except for graphs and drawings, which should be done in pencil. [6]

37 The Reel Good Cinema is conducting a mathematical study. In its theater, there are 200 seats. Adult tickets cost \$12.50 and child tickets cost \$6.25. The cinema's goal is to sell at least \$1500 worth of tickets for the theater.

Write a system of linear inequalities that can be used to find the possible combinations of adult tickets, x, and child tickets, y, that would satisfy the cinema's goal.

Graph the solution to this system of inequalities on the set of axes on the next page. Label the solution with an S.

Marta claims that selling 30 adult tickets and 80 child tickets will result in meeting the cinema's goal. Explain whether she is correct or incorrect, based on the graph drawn.

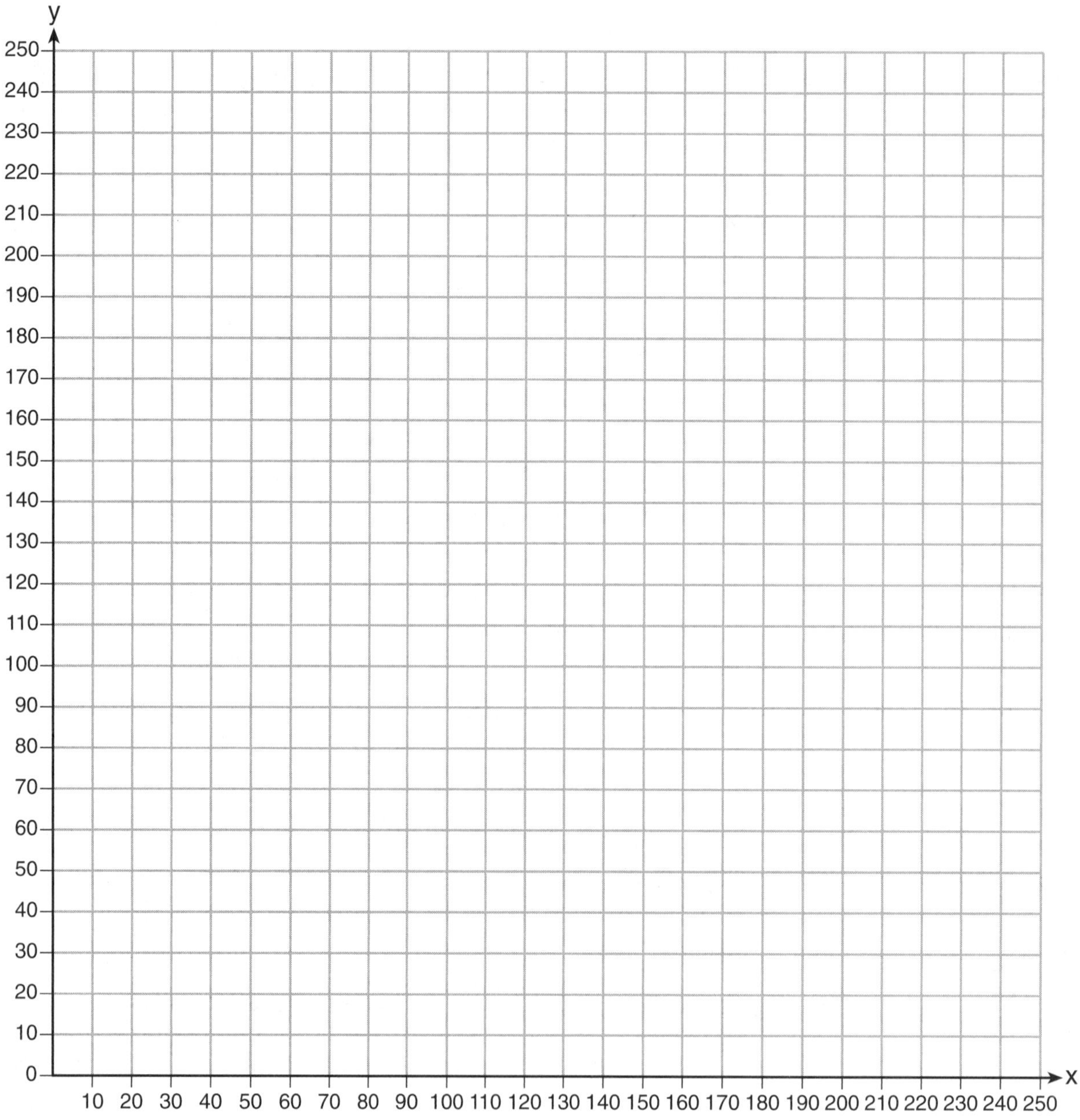
y
x
0
10
20
30
40
50
60
70
80
90
100
110
120
130
140
150
160
170
180
190
200
210
220
230
240
250

High School Math Reference Sheet

1 inch = 2.54 centimeters
1 meter = 39.37 inches
1 mile = 5280 feet
1 mile = 1760 yards
1 mile = 1.609 kilometers

1 kilometer = 0.62 mile
1 pound = 16 ounces
1 pound = 0.454 kilogram
1 kilogram = 2.2 pounds
1 ton = 2000 pounds

1 cup = 8 fluid ounces
1 pint = 2 cups
1 quart = 2 pints
1 gallon = 4 quarts
1 gallon = 3.785 liters
1 liter = 0.264 gallon
1 liter = 1000 cubic centimeters

Triangle	$A = \frac{1}{2}bh$
Parallelogram	$A = bh$
Circle	$A = \pi r^2$
Circle	$C = \pi d$ or $C = 2\pi r$
General Prisms	$V = Bh$
Cylinder	$V = \pi r^2 h$
Sphere	$V = \frac{4}{3}\pi r^3$
Cone	$V = \frac{1}{3}\pi r^2 h$
Pyramid	$V = \frac{1}{3}Bh$

Pythagorean Theorem	$a^2 + b^2 = c^2$
Quadratic Formula	$x = \frac{-b \pm \sqrt{b^2 - 4ac}}{2a}$
Arithmetic Sequence	$a_n = a_1 + (n - 1)d$
Geometric Sequence	$a_n = a_1 r^{n-1}$
Geometric Series	$S_n = \frac{a_1 - a_1 r^n}{1 - r}$ where $r \neq 1$
Radians	1 radian $= \frac{180}{\pi}$ degrees
Degrees	1 degree $= \frac{\pi}{180}$ radians
Exponential Growth/Decay	$A = A_0 e^{k(t - t_0)} + B_0$

Scrap Graph Paper — This sheet will *not* be scored.

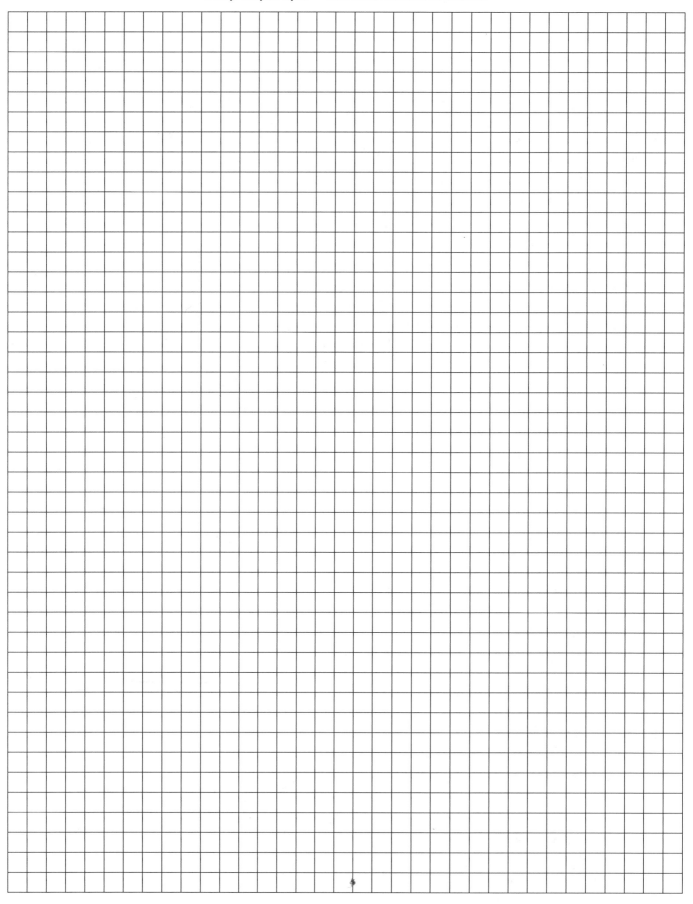

Scrap Graph Paper — This sheet will *not* be scored.

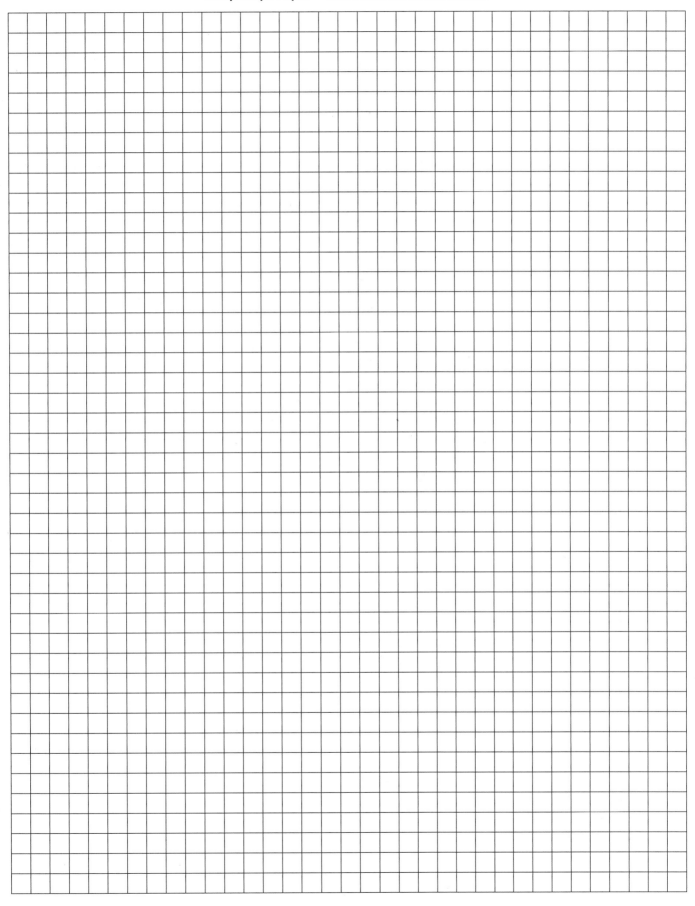